NP 136

OCEAN PASSAGES
FOR THE WORLD

THIRD EDITION
1973

PUBLISHED BY THE HYDROGRAPHER OF THE NAVY

A

Previous editions:

First published   1895

First edition   1923

Second edition   1950

Oh God be good to me,
    Thy sea is so wide and my ship is so small.
            Breton fisherman's prayer

Preface

The Third Edition of *Ocean Passages for the World* has been prepared by Commander H. L. Jenkins, O.B.E., D.S.C., Royal Navy, and contains the latest information received in the Hydrographic Department to the date given below. It supersedes the Second Edition (1950) and Supplement No. 2 (1960), which are cancelled.

Information on currents and ice has been supplied by the Meteorological Office, Bracknell.

The following sources of information, other than Hydrographic Department Publications and Ministry of Defence papers, have been consulted.

British: Marine Observer's Handbook, 9th Edition.

U.S.A.: United States Naval Oceanographic Office Pilot Charts.

Reports received from the Masters of a number of seagoing ships have been added to the extensive information on which previous editions were based, and have been embodied in the present edition.

G. P. D. HALL,
Rear Admiral,
Hydrographer of the Navy.

Hydrographic Department,
  Ministry of Defence,
  Taunton,
  Somerset, TA1 2DN

    9th November, 1973.

Contents

List of Charts and Diagrams

CHARTS

DIAGRAMS

Explanatory Notes

Ocean Passages for the World contains information, based on the latest material available in the Hydrographic Department, relating to the planning and conduct of ocean voyages. The ocean areas with which this book is concerned lie, mainly, outside the areas covered in detail by Admiralty Sailing Directions but, since many passages pass through some coastal areas, and since there is much oceanic information in Admiralty Sailing Directions, the latter should always be closely consulted.

Ocean Passages for the World is kept up to date by periodical supplements. In addition a small number of Notices to Mariners are published specially to correct Sailing Directions for important information which cannot await the next supplement. A list of such notices in force is published at the end of each month in the weekly edition of Admiralty Notices to Mariners. Those still in force at the end of the year are reprinted in the Annual Summary of Admiralty Notices to Mariners.

This volume should not be used without reference to the latest supplement and those Notices to Mariners published specially to correct Sailing Directions.

Reference to hydrographic and other publications.

The Mariner's Handbook gives general information affecting navigation and is complementary to this volume.

Admiralty List of Lights should be consulted for details of lights, light-vessels, lighthouse-buoys and fog-signals.

Admiralty List of Radio Signals should be consulted for information relating to coast and port radio stations, radio details of pilotage services, radiobeacons, and direction finding stations, meteorological services, and radio navigational aids.

Annual Summary of Admiralty Notices to Mariners contains, in addition to the temporary and preliminary notices, and notices affecting Sailing Directions only in force, a number of notices giving information of a permanent nature covering radio messages and navigational warnings, distress and rescue at sea, exercise areas, and areas dangerous due to mines.

The International Code of Signals should be consulted for details of distress and life-saving signals, international ice-breaker signals as well as international flag signals.

Remarks on subject matter.

Names are taken from the most authoritative source and are, where changes have taken place, the latest officially adopted. Since the charts used for passage planning may not be newly published or on the largest scale, recourse may be necessary, when identifying named objects, to Admiralty Sailing Directions which, with their supplements, record name changes.

Tidal information relating to the daily vertical movements of the water is not given; for this *Admiralty Tide Tables* should be consulted. Changes in water level of an abnormal nature are mentioned.

Units and terminology used in this volume are:

Latitude and Longitude given in brackets are approximate.

Bearings and directions are referred to the true compass and when given in degrees are reckoned clockwise from 000° (North) to 359°. The bearings of all objects, alignments and light sectors are given as seen from seaward. Courses always refer to the course made good.

Winds are described by the direction from which they blow.

Tidal streams and currents are described by the direction towards which they flow.

Distances are expressed in sea miles of 1852 metres.

Depths are given below chart datum, except where otherwise stated.

Elevations are given above the level of Mean High Water Springs or Mean Higher High Water, whichever is quoted in the Admiralty Tide Tables.

Heights of objects as distinct from their elevation, refer to the heights of the structures above the ground. A statement, 'a hill . . . metres high", is occasionally used when there could be no confusion, and in this case the reference is as for an elevation.

Metric units are used for all measurements of depths, heights and short distances.

Time is expressed in the four-figure notation beginning at midnight, and is given in local time unless otherwise stated. Details of local time kept will be found in *Admiralty List of Radio Signals*.

The following abbreviations are used:

N	—	North	S	—	South
N'ly	—	northerly	S'ly	—	southerly
N-bound	—	northbound	S-bound	—	southbound
N-going	—	northgoing	S-going	—	southgoing
E	—	East	W	—	West
E'ly	—	easterly	W'ly	—	westerly
E-bound	—	eastbound	W-bound	—	westbound
E-going	—	eastgoing	W-going	—	westgoing
Aux Y	—	Auxiliary Yacht.	mb	—	Millibar or millibars.
°C	—	Degrees Celsius.	M/F	—	Medium frequency.
D/F	—	Direction Finding.	MV	—	Motor Vessel.
fm	—	Fathoma or fathoms.	MY	—	Motor Yacht.
ft	—	Foot or feet	No.	—	Ordinal number.
MHWS	—	Mean High Water Springs.	RMS	—	Royal Mail Ship.
MLWS	—	Mean Low Water Springs.	RN	—	Royal Navy.
MHHW	—	Mean Higher High Water.	R/T	—	Radio telephone or radio telephony.
MLLW	—	Mean Lower Low Water.	SS	—	Steam ship.
HMS	—	Her Majesty's Ship.	UHF	—	Ultra high frequency.
kHz	—	Kilohertz.	VHF	—	Very high frequency.
m	—	Metre or metres.	W/T	—	Wireless telegraphy.

PART I

POWER VESSEL ROUTES

CONTENTS

CHAPTER 1

PLANNING A PASSAGE

CONTENTS

OCEAN CURRENTS

ICE

ELECTRONIC AIDS AND POSITION FIXING SYSTEMS

NOTES AND CAUTIONS

OCEAN PASSAGES FOR THE WORLD

1.01.   Ocean Passages for the World is written for use in planning deep-sea voyages. It contains notes on the weather and other factors affecting passages, directions for a number of recommended routes, and distance figures designed to help the planner to calculate his voyage time on these routes. It bears much the same relation to the Admiralty charts of the oceans as the Sailing Directions bear to the coastal charts. This book must be used in conjunction with the Admiralty charts and Sailing Directions; chapter 1 contains information applicable to all sea areas; the later chapters treat the individual oceans, chapters 2–8 for power vessels and chapters 9–11 for sailing vessels.

1.02.   Routeing charts, which are vital to passage planning, cover the ocean areas of the world and show, month by month, meteorological and ice conditions, ocean currents, load line zones, areas in which it is an offence to discharge persistent oils, and some recommended tracks and distances. Routeing charts are all drawn on a scale of 1:13,880,000 at the approximate mid-latitude, and are numbered 5124(1) to 5124(12) for North Atlantic Ocean 5125(1) to 5125(12) for South Atlantic Ocean, 5126(1) to 5126(12) for Indian Ocean, 5127(1) to 5127(12) for North Pacific Ocean, and 5128(1) to 5128(12) for South Pacific Ocean.

1.03.   Load Line Rules are published in 1968 No. 1053 *The Merchant Shipping Load Line Rules 1968.* They apply to all ships except ships of war, ships solely engaged in fishing, and pleasure yachts. See chart D6083 and Routeing Charts.

1.04.   Routes. The routes for power vessels recommended herein are intended mainly for vessels with sea-going speeds of up to 15 knots and moderate draught, but they should be considered by all ships, particularly in high latitudes where there is risk of encountering ice and heavy weather. The special requirements of ships drawing more than 12m are not covered. Only a selection from the immense variety of possible voyages is included; when planning voyages not described in the book, reference should be made to adjacent routes.

1.05.   Directions for each route embody all available experience from sea and, although conditions are never consistent, it is hoped that the advice given represents a good average.

GENERAL PLANNING

1.11.   The best track. The art of passage planning has been practised from time immemorial. The selection of the best track for an individual voyage demands skilled evaluation of all the factors controlling the voyage and modification of the shortest route accordingly.

In the past, most passage planning has been done with the aid of statistics on weather, currents, and climate which, together with the experience of previous voyages, have enabled the publication of suggested routes for a wide variety of passages. These statistic-based or "climatic" routes, usually depending on factors which can vary seasonally, serve the mariner's purpose up to a point, but they do not take into account short-term variations in the statistical pattern, which can be detected and even forecast by modern methods, and can therefore be incorporated in the plan or transmitted to the vessel at sea with great benefit to the immediate conduct of the voyage.

Each chapter of routes for power vessels contains a review, based on all available statistics and experience, of the usual climatic and other conditions affecting the area concerned. Having made a first study of the projected passage with the aid of the routes recommended as a result, the required route should be adjusted to meet such factors as urgency, risk of damage, and fuel consumption. In addition, the growing availability of shore-based routeing advice, together with forecasts of weather, currents, swell, and ice movements should be taken into account, see 1.61. A great deal of information is thus available to the shipmaster in most parts of the world, for application in aid of the successful prosecution of the voyage.

1.12. Terminal ports. Routes given in this book are indexed under the port of departure. If the actual passage to be undertaken is not covered, guidance can be obtained from adjacent routes.

1.13. Distances for the routes are between the indexed arrival and departure positions, to the nearest 10 miles for passages of more than 1000 miles and to the nearest 5 miles below that figure. The arrival and departure positions are usually pilot grounds or anchorages, as given in Admiralty Sailing Directions, and the duration of the voyage between pilots may be computed with the aid of the logarithmic scale (Diagram 1) The constituents of most of the distances have been computed on the "international spheroid" figure of the Earth, which has a compression of $\frac{1}{297.0}$ and a nautical mile of 1852 metres.

For distances not given in this book, see *Admiralty Distance Tables*, which uses the same data.

1.14. Charts and publications. The appropriate charts, Admiralty Sailing Directions, *Admiralty List of Lights* and *Admiralty List of Radio Signals* should be obtained by reference to the *Catalogue of Admiralty Charts and other Hydrographic Publications*. For charts embodied in this book, see page vi.

1.15. Great circle sailing. Broadly speaking, great circle sailing holds the advantage in distance over the rhumb line to the greatest extent in high latitudes and on E–W courses. Although the Earth is not perfectly spherical, and the "international spheroid" (1.13) has been used in the computation of the distances in this book, differences in distances and tracks taken out for the true sphere and the international spheroid are negligible for passage purposes. Great circle sections of the route may therefore be safely calculated by spherical trigonometry, or the *Tables of Computed Altitude and Azimuth* may be used for the purpose within the limits imposed by their primary function. Also, the great circle track may be plotted with the help of the Great Circle Diagram (chart 5029) or the gnomonic charts, but there is no graphic method of obtaining the distance.

When calculating the great circle track for passage purposes the two main requirements are the whole distance, for logistic planning, and the latitude in which a series of chosen meridians are crossed, for plotting the track, which will be steered by rhumb line between those meridians. This involves, firstly, the solution of the polar triangle contained by the terminal meridians and the track. The distance may be worked by the "haversine" formula, for which the data are the latitudes of the terminal positions and their difference of longitude. Calculation of the intermediate positions depends upon their longitude E or W of the vertex of the track, to find which it is necessary to know whether it lies between the terminal positions or on an extension E or W of the track. If the azimuth of either end is more than 90°, the vertex of the track will lie on the extension from that position. In cases where there is no doubt whether the azimuth is more or less than 90°, it may be worked by the "sine" formula, but in other cases the "$\frac{1}{2}$-log haversine" formula should be used.

1.16. Formulae for great circle sailing.

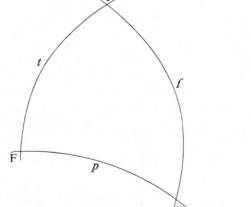

Spherical triangle

Diagram 2.

P = the Pole	p = great circle track
F = position "from"	f = 90° ± Lat. T*
T = position "to"	t = 90° ± Lat. F*

* The sign is determined by the name of the pole and the name of the latitude of the place. Same names subtract; opposite names, add.

In Diagram 2, the formulae are expressed as follows:

Haversine formula … $\text{hav}\,p = \text{hav}(t \sim f) + \sin f \sin t \, \text{hav} \angle P$.

Sine formula … $\sin \angle F = \dfrac{\sin \angle P \sin f}{\sin p}$ or $\sin \angle T = \dfrac{\sin \angle P \sin t}{\sin p}$.

½-Log haversine formula (in logarithmic form) …
$\log \text{hav} \angle F = \log \text{cosec}\, t + \log \text{cosec}\, p + \tfrac{1}{2}\log \text{hav}\,[f + (t \sim p)] + \tfrac{1}{2}\log \text{hav}\,[f - (t \sim p)]$

Working for distance by haversine formula. The following example, of a theoretical great circle passage from Yokohama to Estrecho de Magallanes (not feasible navigationally) serves to illustrate the method of working.

Yokohama	(Position F)	34° 49′ N,	140° 00′ E.	co-Lat. (*t*) 55° 11′
Estrecho de Magallanes	(Position T)	52° 25′ S,	75° 12′ W.	co-Lat. (*f*) 142° 25′
		d. Long. (∠P)	144° 48′	d. co-Lat. (*f* ~ *t*) 87° 14′

log hav. d. Long. (∠P)	9·958 36
log sin co-Lat. (*f*)	9·785 27
log sin co-Lat. (*t*)	9·914 33
sum	9·657 96
anti-log of sum	·454 96
hav. d. co-Lat. (*f* ~ *t*)	·475 87
hav distance (*p*)	·930 83
distance (*p*)	149° 30′ = 8970 miles

Note: the same distance, worked on the international spheroid, is 8973 miles.

Working for distance by electronic calculator, a more convenient formula is: $\cos (p) = \cos (f) \cos (t) + \cos \angle P \sin (f) \sin (t)$, care being taken over the signs of functions of angles or angular distance, namely when the angle is less than 90° sine and cosine are both +, and for angles of more than 90° sine is + and cosine is −.

Working for azimuth by sine formula. In the same example:

		from Yokohama		from Est. de Magallanes	
log sin d. Long. (∠P)	144° 48′	9·760 75			9·760 75
log sin co-Lat. (*f*)	142° 25′	9·785 27	(*t*) 55° 11′		9·914 33
Sum			9·546 02		9·675 08
log sin distance (*p*)	149° 30′	9·705 47			9·705 47
subtract for log sin azimuth			9·840 55		9·969 61
Azimuth angle	at F	43° 51′	at T		68° 49′
Course	043° 51′ or 136° 09′		068° 49° or 111° 11′		

By inspection, the initial course could be 043° 51′ or 136° 09′. A final course of 068° 49′ can be ruled out. In many cases of this sort, the quadrant of the azimuth can be resolved by plotting on chart 5029 (*Great Circle Diagram*) or on a gnomonic chart, but the working by ½-log haversine formula is shown below.

With reference to Diagram 2, ∠F is the initial course, and the working is therefore:

t = 55° 11′	log cosec	0·085 67	
p = 149° 30′	log cosec	0·294 53	
t ~ *p* = 94° 19′			
f = 142° 25′			
f + (*t* ~ *p*) = 236° 44′	½-log hav	4·944 45	
f − (*t* ~ *p*) = 48° 06′	½-log hav	4·610 16	
	log hav ∠F	9·934 81	∠F = 136° 09′

An alternative method, when ½-log haversine tables are not available, is by the formula

$$\text{Hav} \angle F = (\text{hav}\,f - \text{hav}\,(t \sim p))\, \text{cosec}\, t\, \text{cosec}\, p.$$

$f = 142° 25'$ Nat. hav 0·896 23
$(t \sim p) = 94° 19'$ Nat. hav 0·537 63

_____

                             Nat. hav 0·358 60   log hav   9·554 60
$t = 55° 11'$ log cosec   0·085 67   5
$p = 149° 30'$ log cosec   0·294 53

                                                                         _____

                                                                         log hav∠F 9·934 80
                                                                         ∠F = 136° 09'
                                                                                                                10

The same course, worked on the International Spheroid, is 136° 13″.

The initial course is therefore 136° 09′ and the N vertex of the great circle track lies on the extension of the great circle W of Yokohama.

Working for intermediate positions on the great circle track. It was stated in article 1.15 that calculation of   15
intermediate positions on the track depends upon their longitude E or W of the vertex. At the vertex, the track
lies at right angles to the meridian, so the problem calls for the solution of the required number of right-angled
spherical triangles.

                                                                                                                20

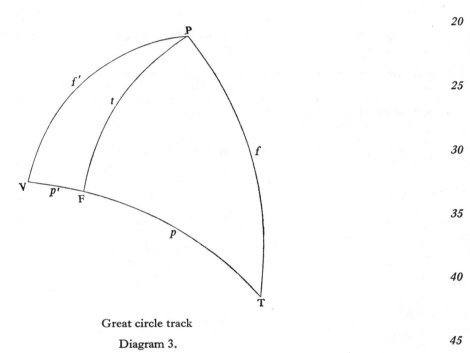

                                                                                                                25

                                                                                                                30

                                                                                                                35

                                                                                                                40

Great circle track

Diagram 3.   45

In Diagram 3, the triangle is right-angled at V. The formulae used for finding the position of the vertex of
the track are derived from Napier's Rule, and are as follows.
For the latitude: cos (Lat. of vertex) = cos (Lat. F) sin (initial course).   50
For the longitude: tan (d. Long. vertex from F) = cosec (Lat. F) cot (initial course).

        Working for latitude:
            log cos Lat. F (34° 49′)   9·914 33   55
            log sin initial course (136° 09′)   9·840 59

            log cos (Lat. of vertex)   9·754 92

            Latitude of vertex 55° 20′ N
                                                                                                                60

        Working for longitude:
            log cosec Lat. F (34° 49′)   0·243 40
            log cot initial course (136° 09′)   0·017 44
                                                                                                                65
            log tan d. Long. vertex from F   0·260 84

    d. Longitude of vertex from F 61° 15′ W (by inspection of initial course)
    Longitude of F 148° 00′ E
    Longitude of vertex 78° 45′ E   70

Plotting the track. To plot the intermediate positions on the great circle track, it is necessary to find the latitude in which the track crosses a series of meridians at given intervals of longitude (say 10°) from the vertex. The formula used is

$$\text{cot (required Lat.)} = \text{cot (Lat. of vertex) sec (d. Long. from vertex)}$$

	Position F			
1. d. Long. from vertex	61° 15′	71° 15′	81° 15′	91° 15′
2. Longitude	140° 00′ E	150° 00′ E	160° 00′ E	170° 00′ E
3. log cot (Lat. of vertex)	—	9·839 54	9·839 54	9·839 54
4. log sec (d. Long. from vertex)	—	0·492 90	0·817 80	1·661 20
5. log cot (required Lat.)	—	0·332 44	0·657 34	1·500 74
6. Latitude	34° 49′ N	24° 57′ N	12° 24′ N	1° 48′ S

The track can then be plotted through the positions given by lines 6 and 2.

The same formulae can be used to determine the longitudes in which the track cuts a series of given latitudes.

The backgrounds of the formulae used for these and other problems connected with great circle sailing are given in *Admiralty Manual of Navigation*.

1.17. Rhumb Line sailing. A rhumb line, or loxodrome, is a line on the earth's surface which cuts all meridians at a constant angle. It therefore plots on a Mercator chart as a straight line.

Rhumb line distances taken from a Mercator chart are only acceptable if measured on the latitude, or distance, scale of the chart within the band of latitude covering the distance in question, and when the difference of latitude is not great. With small-scale charts and a large difference of latitude, considerable errors may occur unless great care is taken in using the latitude scale, particularly in high latitudes.

Distances of up to 600 miles may be calculated without appreciable error by the use of plane sailing formulae, in which

$$\tan\text{ course} = \frac{\text{departure}}{\text{difference of latitude}}$$

$$\text{departure} = \text{difference of longitude} \times \text{cosine mean latitude}$$

$$\text{distance} = \frac{\text{difference of latitude}}{\text{cosine course}}$$

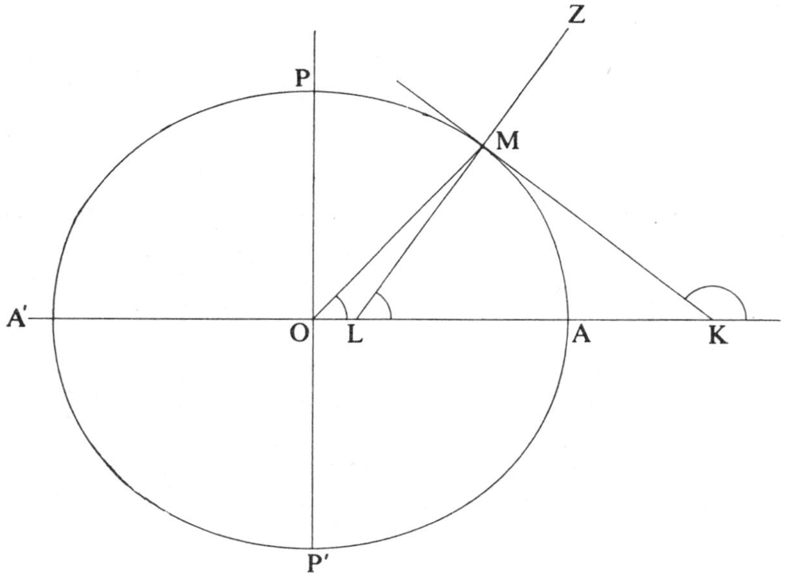

Shape of the Earth

Diagram 4.   PAP′A′ is the elliptical section of the Earth.
KM is the tangent to the meridian at M.
LMZ is the vertical at M.
∠MOA is the geocentric latitude of M.
∠MLA is the geographical latitude of M.
∠OML is the reduction from geographical to geocentric latitude.

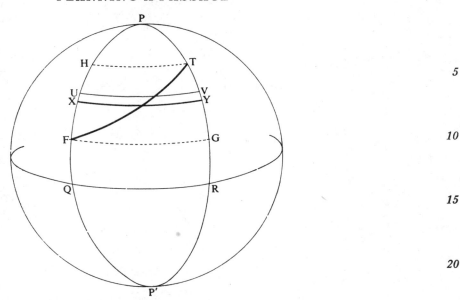

Rhumb Line track

Diagram 5.   FT is the rhumb line course.
XY is the mean latitude of FT.
UV is the middle latitude of FT.

The Traverse table may be used for obtaining departure, difference of latitude, and course for distances up to 600 miles, based on the plane right-angled triangle, if the arithmetical mean of the terminal latitudes is used when obtaining the departure. This method is not strictly accurate, but more so than the probable accuracy of navigation.

For problems demanding accuracy, it is important that allowance should be made for the shape of the earth. This entails firstly an adjustment to the terminal latitudes to reduce them from charted or "geographical" values to "geocentric", see Diagram 4, and then an adjustment to the resulting "mean" latitude to convert it to "middle" latitude. The first correction allows for the compression of the axis; it is tabulated in various books of Nautical tables and has a greatest value of −11′ 44″, at latitude 45°, for a compression of $\frac{1}{293\cdot463}$. The second correction converts the mean latitude applicable to a plane surface to that applicable to the sphere, and is needed because the convergency of the meridians varies approximately as the sine of the latitude; it is also tabulated and the corrected result is properly called "middle" latitude, see Diagram 5.

Example. To find the middle latitude for terminal latitudes of 38° 17′ 00″ and 57° 29′ 00″:

Terminal latitude	38° 17′ 00″		57° 29′ 00″
Reduction	— 11 24		— 10 39
Reduced latitude	38 05 16		57 18 21
	57 18 21		38 05 16
Sum	95 23 37	difference	19 13 05
Mean reduced latitude	47 41 48		
Correction to mean latitude	+ 51 00		
Middle latitude	48° 32′ 48″		

For distances in excess of 600 miles rhumb line problems should be worked using mercator sailing formulae and meridional parts.

The **meridional parts** of any latitude are the number of longitude units of 1′ each in the length of the meridian between the parallel of that latitude and the equator. They are tabulated in books of nautical tables. Some tables are for the sphere with a correction table for the spheroid; others tabulate the meridional parts for the spheroid, usually for a compression of $\frac{1}{293\cdot463}$ (Clarke's figure of the earth, 1880). The latitude on the sphere for a given number of meridional parts will be slightly less than the latitude for the same number of meridional parts on the spheroid, by the amount given above.

It should be noted that the International Spheroid, on which the distances given in *Ocean Passages for the World* and *Admiralty Distance Tables* are worked, has a compression of $\frac{1}{297\cdot0}$ but, for passage purposes, the differences resulting from the use of other commonly used compression figures are insignificant.

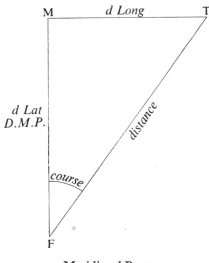

Meridional Parts

Diagram 6.

In Diagram 6, FT is a rhumb line. FM represents the difference of latitude and the difference of meridional parts between F and T, and MT represents the difference of longitude. Since the units of longitude and meridional parts are the same, the course may be found from the formula

$$\tan (\text{course}) = \frac{d. \text{ Long.}}{\text{D.M.P.}}$$

and the distance, since the units of latitude and distance are the same, may be found from the formula

$$\text{distance} = d. \text{ Lat. sec (course)}.$$

Example. To find the rhumb line course and distance between (F) 8° 10′ N, 109° 30′ E and (T) 34° 22′ N, 138° 52′ E.

Geographical Lat. F	8° 10.′0 N	Lat. T	34° 22.′0 N
Reduction for spheroid*	— 3.3		— 10.9
Geocentric Lat. F	8 06.7 N	T 34 11.1 N	
	34 11.1 N		
difference (d. lat.)	26° 04.′4 = 1564·4 miles		

* If Meridional Part tables are for the Sphere.

Geocentric Lat. F	8° 06.′7 N	mer. parts	488·34	Long. F	109° 30′ E
Geocentric Lat. T	34° 11.′1 N	mer. parts	2184·88	Long. T	138° 52′ E
d. Lat.	26° 04.′4	D.M.P.	1696·54	d. Long.	29° 22′ E
	(1564·4 miles)				(1762′)

Note: The meridional parts are taken from *Inman's Nautical Tables* which tabulates for the true sphere.

$\tan (\text{course}) = \dfrac{d. \text{ Long.}}{\text{D.M.P.}} = \dfrac{1762}{1696·54}$	log 1762	3·246 01
	log 1696·54	3·229 55
course 046° 05′	log tan (course)	0·016 46
	log 1564·4	3·194 35
distance = d. Lat. sec (course)	log sec 46° 05′	0·158 88
= 1564·4 sec 46° 05′		
= 2255·4 miles	log distance	3·353 23

By calculation on the International Spheroid, course is 046° 05′, and distance is 2258·5 miles.

The backgrounds of the formulae used in problems connected with rhumb line sailing are given in *Admiralty Manual of Navigation.*

GENERAL MARITIME METEOROLOGY

1.21. Atmospheric Pressure. The atmosphere, by reason of its weight, exerts a pressure on the surface of the earth. This pressure is normally measured in millibars, the mean value at sea level being around 1013 mb.

This pressure is in certain places semi-permanently above the mean, while in other places it is semi-permanently below the mean. These places are referred to as regions of high and low pressure respectively. There are also temporary areas of high or low pressure.

1.22. Wind. Because of the rotation of the earth, air which is drawn towards a centre of low pressure is deflected to the right in the N hemisphere and to the left in the S hemisphere. The result is an anti-clockwise circulation of wind around an area of low pressure in the N hemisphere and a clockwise circulation in the S hemisphere. Circulations around areas of low pressure are termed cyclonic. Conversely, the wind circulates in a clockwise direction around an area of high pressure in the N hemisphere and in an anti-clockwise direction in the S hemisphere, such circulations being termed anticyclonic.

The strength of the wind at any given time depends upon the pressure gradient, i.e. on the spacing of the isobars. Isobars are lines which join together places which at the same time have equal barometric pressure (reduced to sea level) and are analogous to the contour lines of a map; the closer they are together the greater the pressure gradient and the stronger the resulting wind.

Surface friction has two effects on the wind. Firstly it causes a reduction in the strength of the wind at the surface and secondly it causes the wind to be deflected some 10° to 20° across the isobars, inwards towards the centre of low pressure or outwards away from the centre of high pressure. Buys Ballot's Law sums this up as follows: If you face the wind the centre of low pressure will be from 90° to 135° on your right hand in the N hemisphere, and on your left hand in the S hemisphere. Diagram 7 shows the distribution of pressure and the winds which would result over a featureless earth.

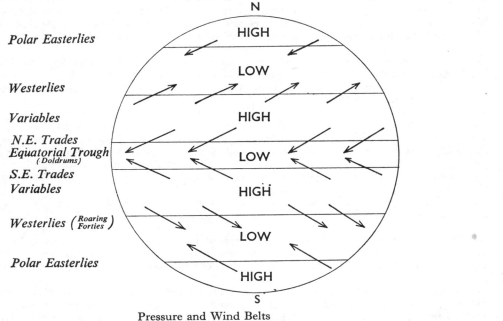

Pressure and Wind Belts

Diagram 7.

1.23. Effect of distribution of land and sea. The effect of large land masses is to modify considerably the areas of pressure and the wind, as shown in the diagram. The belts of high pressure around 30° N and 30° S are split into separate cells of high pressure (anticyclones) situated over the E part of each of the oceans. The belt of low pressure around 60° N is similarly modified into separate areas of low pressure situated near Iceland and the Aleutian Islands. In the S hemisphere there is little or no land in the area covered by this low pressure belt and consequently it extends almost without interruption around the earth. See World Climatic Charts 5301, 5302.

Superimposed upon these modifications there is a tendency for pressure to become relatively high over land masses in winter and relatively low in summer. Such seasonal changes in pressure distribution can produce large scale modifications to winds over neighbouring oceanic regions, a notable example being the Monsoon circulation over the Indian Ocean.

1.24. Effects of variations in sun's declination. The annual movement of the sun in declination causes the belts of pressure and their associated winds to move towards each pole during its summer.

This oscillation amounts to some 4° of latitude and it lags some 6 to 8 weeks behind the sun.

GENERAL CLIMATE

The distribution of wind is given in World Climatic Charts 5301, 5302. In addition these show the distribution of pressure, sea surface temperature, gales, fog, currents and ice. The notes which follow should be read carefully when studying these charts.

1.31. The Equatorial Trough (Doldrums) is an area of low pressure situated between the Trade Winds of the two hemispheres. Characteristic features of this area are light and variable winds alternating with squalls, heavy rain and thunderstorms. The Trough varies greatly in width both daily and seasonally. The type of weather experienced also varies considerably. At times a ship may cross the Trough and experience fine weather, while on another crossing squalls and thunderstorms may be encountered. Weather in the Trough is generally worst when the Trades are strongest. This is a highly simplified account of an area where the weather is complicated and not completely understood. For a more detailed description of the Equatorial Trough reference must be made to meteorological textbooks.

1.32. The Trade Winds blow on either side of the Equatorial Trough, NE'ly in the N hemisphere and SE'ly in the S hemisphere. The Trades blow with great persistence and each embraces a zone of some 1200 miles of latitude. Trade Winds, however, do not blow in all the oceans. The South-west Monsoon winds (see below) blow instead in the East Atlantic, North Indian Ocean and the W part of the North Pacific Ocean. See Climatic Chart for July. The average strength of the Trades is about Force 4, though variations occur between different oceans and at different seasons. The weather in Trade Wind zones is generally fair with small detached cumulus clouds. On the E sides of the oceans cloud amounts and rainfall are small, while on the W sides cloud amounts are larger and rainfall is frequent, being at their maximum in summer. Cloud amounts and the frequency and intensity of rain all increase towards the Equatorial Trough. Poor visibility often occurs at the E end of the Trade Wind zones, due partly to mist or fog forming over the cold currents and partly to sand and dust being carried out to sea by prevailing offshore winds. At the W end of the zones visibility is good, except when reduced in rain. Fog is rare. In certain seasons and in certain localities the generally fair weather of the Trades is liable to be interrupted by tropical storms. These are described in detail in article 1.38.

1.33. Variables. Over the areas covered by the oceanic anticyclones, between the Trade Winds and the Westerlies farther toward the poles, there exist zones of light and variable winds which are known as The Variables, and the N area is sometimes known as the Horse Latitudes (30° N–40° N). The weather in these zones is generally fair with small amounts of cloud and rain.

1.34. Westerlies. On the polar sides of the oceanic anticyclones lie zones where the wind direction becomes predominantly W'ly. Unlike the Trades, these winds, known as The Westerlies, are far from permanent. The continual passage of depressions from W to E across these zones causes the wind to vary greatly in both direction and strength. Gales are frequent, especially in winter. The weather changes rapidly and fine weather is seldom prolonged. Gales are so frequent in the S hemisphere that the zone, S of 40° S, has been named the Roaring Forties.

In the N hemisphere fog is common in the W parts of the oceans in this zone in summer. Areas where fog is likely and those where ice may be encountered are shown on the Climatic Charts.

1.35. The Polar Regions which lie on the polar side of the Westerlies are mainly unnavigable on account of ice. The prevailing wind is generally from an E'ly direction and gales are common in winter, though less so than in the zones of the Westerlies. The weather is usually cloudy and fog is frequent in summer.

1.36. Seasonal winds and monsoons. Over certain parts of the oceans the general distribution of pressure and wind in the zones described above is greatly modified by the seasonal heating and cooling of adjacent large land masses. The annual range of sea temperature in the open ocean is comparatively small, whereas large land masses become hot in summer and cold in winter. This alternate heating and cooling of the land results in the formation of areas of low and high pressure respectively. This redistribution of pressure results in a seasonal reversal of the prevailing wind over the adjacent oceans. The most important oceanic areas subject to these seasonal winds are the Indian Ocean, West Pacific Ocean and those adjacent to the coast of West Africa.

The seasons of the principal monsoons and their average strengths are shown in Table A on page 12.

1.37. Depressions. A depression, also known for synoptic purposes as a *low*, appears on a synoptic chart as a series of isobars roughly circular or oval in shape, surrounding an area of low pressure. Depressions are frequent at sea in middle latitudes and are responsible for most strong winds and unsettled weather, though not all depressions are accompanied by strong winds. Depressions vary much in size and depth. One may be only 100 miles in diameter and another over 2000; one may have a central pressure of 960 millibars and another 1000 millibars.

Note. The bracketed equivalents which follow refer to the S hemisphere.

In the N (S) hemisphere the winds blow around an area of low pressure in an anti-clockwise (clockwise) direction. There is a slight inclination across the isobars towards the lower pressure. The strength of the wind is closely related to the gradient across the isobars, the closer the isobars the stronger the wind.

Depressions may move in any direction though many move in an E direction, at speeds varying from nearly stationary to 40 knots. Occasionally, during the most active stage of its existence, a low may move as fast as 60 knots. Lows normally last around 4 to 6 days and slow down when filling.

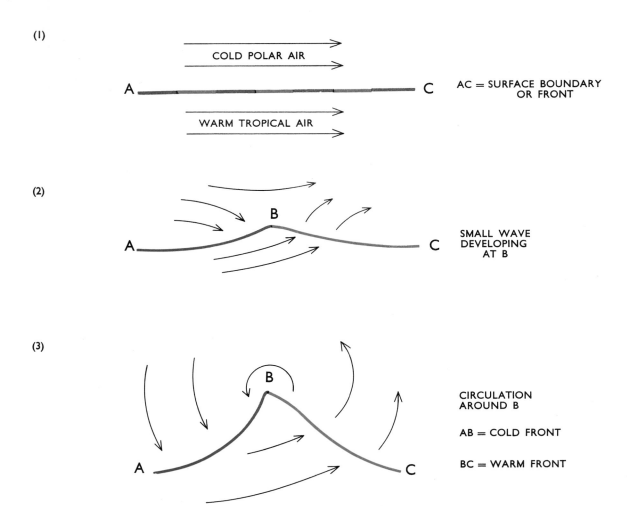

(1)

COLD POLAR AIR

A   C   AC = SURFACE BOUNDARY
OR FRONT

WARM TROPICAL AIR

(2)

B

A   C   SMALL WAVE
DEVELOPING
AT B

(3)

B

CIRCULATION
AROUND B

AB = COLD FRONT

BC = WARM FRONT

A   C

Diagram 8

Formation of Fronts in the N. Hemisphere.

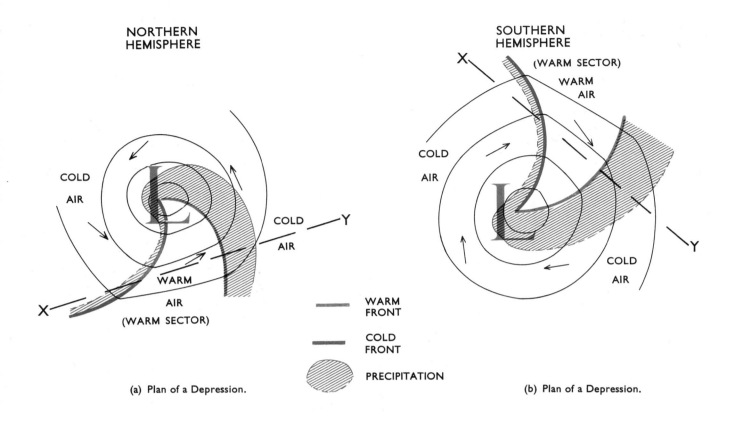

NORTHERN
HEMISPHERE

COLD
AIR

L

COLD
AIR — Y

WARM

AIR

(WARM SECTOR)

X

SOUTHERN
HEMISPHERE

X

(WARM SECTOR)

WARM
AIR

COLD

AIR

L

COLD

AIR

Y

——— WARM
FRONT

——— COLD
FRONT

PRECIPITATION

(a) Plan of a Depression.

(b) Plan of a Depression.

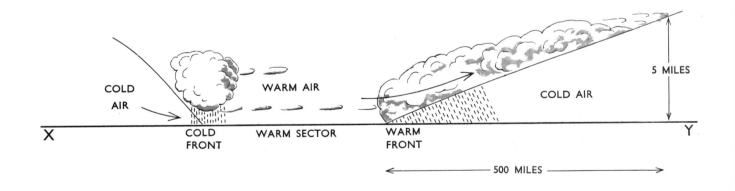

COLD
AIR

WARM AIR

WARM SECTOR

COLD AIR

5 MILES

X

COLD
FRONT

WARM
FRONT

Y

500 MILES

Diagram 9

(c) Section through Depression at XY.

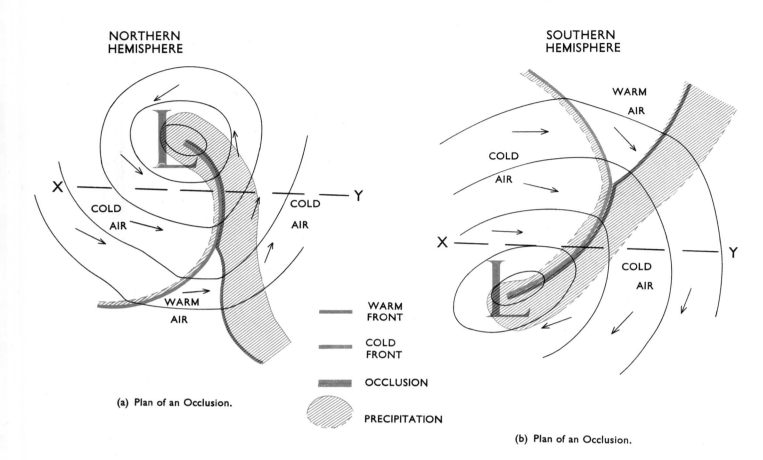

NORTHERN
HEMISPHERE

SOUTHERN
HEMISPHERE

COLD
AIR

COLD
AIR

WARM
AIR

WARM
AIR

COLD
AIR

COLD
AIR

X — — Y

X — — Y

———	WARM FRONT
———	COLD FRONT
═══	OCCLUSION
⬭	PRECIPITATION

(a) Plan of an Occlusion.

(b) Plan of an Occlusion.

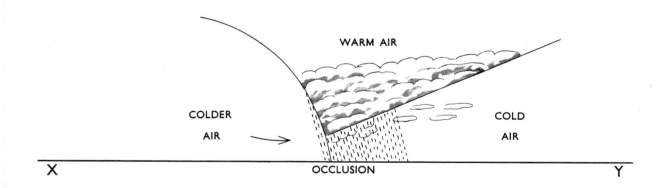

WARM AIR

COLDER
AIR

COLD
AIR

X ——————————— OCCLUSION ——————————— Y

Diagram 10

(c) Section through Occlusion at XY.

Fronts, which accompany depressions, are formed, in brief, as follows. If two air masses from different regions, such as the polar and tropical regions, are brought together, the surface boundary where they meet is known as a front. Further there is a tendency for waves to form on this front and some of these waves develop into depressions. This is shown in Diagram 8, where by stage 3 it can be seen that the depression has a circulation. The part of the front marked AB is called a cold front as along it cold air is replacing warm air. The part marked BC is the warm front since along this front warm air is replacing cold air.

Oceanic depressions usually have one or more fronts extending from their centres, each front representing a belt of bad weather, accompanied by a veer (backing) of wind, which marks the change from the weather characteristic of one air mass to that of the other. During the first two or three days of its existence a depression has a warm and a cold front, the area between the two being known as the warm sector because the air has come from a warmer locality than that which is outside the sector. This is shown in Diagram 9, (a) and (b). Warm air is lighter than cold air and it rises over the cold air ahead of the warm front as shown in Diagram 9 (c). This causes condensation of the water vapour in the warm air, forming at first cloud and later drizzle or continuous steady rain. The cloud spreads out ahead of the warm front and the highest cloud, cirrus, is often about 500 miles ahead of it. At the rear boundary of the warm sector, known as the cold front, the cold air is pushing under the warm air forcing the latter to ascend rapidly. This process is sometimes violent enough to produce squalls. The rapid ascent of the warm air causes the moisture to condense in the form of cumulonimbus clouds (shower clouds), from which heavy showers may fall.

The cold front moves faster than the warm front and gradually overtakes it, causing the warm air to be lifted up from the surface. When this happens the depression is said to be occluded and the fronts have merged into a single front, known as an occlusion. Diagram 10 shows this. Once occluded, depressions usually become less active, slow down and start to fill. Depressions normally travel in a direction approximately parallel with the isobars and the direction of the wind in the warm sector.

The following is a brief general description of depressions and the associated weather in temperate or middle latitudes of the two hemispheres. It must be emphasised, however, that individual depressions in different localities differ considerably from one another according to the temperature and humidity of the air currents of which they are composed and the nature of the surface over which they are travelling.

The approach of a depression is indicated by a falling barometer. In the N (S) hemisphere, if a depression is approaching from the W and passing to the N (S) of the ship, clouds appear on the W horizon, the wind shifts to a SW (NW) or S (N) direction and freshens, the cloud layer gradually lowers and finally drizzle, rain or snow begins. If the depression is not occluded, after a period of continuous rain or snow there is a veer (backing) of the wind at the warm front. In the warm sector, the temperature rises, the rain or snow eases or stops, visibility is usually moderate and the sky overcast with low cloud. The passage of the cold front is marked by the approach from the W of a thick bank of cloud (which however cannot usually be seen because of the customary low overcast sky in the warm sector), a further veer (backing) of wind to W or NW (SW) sometimes with a sudden squall, rising pressure, fall of temperature, squally showers of rain, hail or snow, and improved visibility except during showers. The squally, showery weather with a further veer (backing) of wind and a drop in temperature may recur while the depression recedes owing to the passage of another cold front or occlusion. If the depression is occluded, the occlusion is preceded by the cloud of the warm front; there may be a period of continuous rain mainly in front of and at the line of the occlusion, or a shorter period of heavy rain mainly behind the occlusion, according as the air in front of the occlusion is colder or warmer than the air behind it. There may be a sudden veer (backing) of wind at the occlusion.

Often another depression follows 12 to 24 hours later, in which event the barometer begins to fall again and the wind backs towards SW (NW), or even S (N).

If a depression travelling E or NE (SE) is passing S (N) of the ship, the winds in front of it are E and they back (veer) through NE (SE) to N (S) or NW (SW); changes of direction are not likely to be so sudden as on the S (N) side of the depression. In the rain area there is often a long period of continuous rain and unpleasant weather with low cloud. In winter in the colder regions the weather is cold and raw and precipitation is often in the form of snow.

Winds may be temporarily light and variable near the centre of a depression but rapid changes to strong or gale force winds are likely as pressure begins to rise and the low moves away.

Sometimes in the circulation of a large depression, usually on the equatorial side and often on the cold front, a secondary depression develops, travelling in the same direction as the primary but usually more rapidly. The secondary often deepens while the original depression fills. Between the primary and the secondary depressions, the winds are not as a rule strong but on the farther side of the secondary, usually the S (N) side, winds are likely to be strong and they may reach gale force. Thus the development of a secondary may cause gales farther from the primary than was thought likely, while there may be only light winds where gales were expected.

1.38. Tropical storms are storms which blow round an area of low pressure in a direction which is anti-clockwise in the N hemisphere and clockwise in the S hemisphere. The wind does not revolve around the centre of the low pressure in concentric circles but has a spiral movement inwards, towards the centre.

A tropical storm is not so extensive as the depressions of higher latitudes but, within 75 miles or so of the centre, the wind is often far more violent, and the high and confused seas near the centre may cause considerable damage even to large and well found ships. The danger is still greater when ships are caught in restricted waters without adequate room to manoeuvre. Due to torrential rain and sheets of almost continuous spray visibility near the storm centre (but outside the eye) is almost nil. Within 5 to 10 miles of the centre the wind is light or moderate and variable, the sky is clear or partially so, and there is a heavy, sometimes mountainous, confused swell; this area is known as the eye of the storm.

The localities, seasons, average frequencies and local names of these storms are shown in Table A. They are most frequent during the late summer and early autumn and are comparatively rare in the S hemisphere from

TABLE A: Figures in brackets after Tropical Storms show average number per year.   Figures against Monsoons show typical wind force.

Area	Jan.	Feb.	March	April	May	June	July	Aug.	Sept.	Oct.	Nov.	Dec.
WEST INDIES						↑		HURRICANES (8) ——— Worst months ↑		↑	↑	
E NORTH PACIFIC						↑		HURRICANES (7–8) ——— Worst months →	→	↑		
W NORTH PACIFIC					↑	↑ (dashed)		TYPHOONS (22) ——— Worst months →			↑ (dashed)	→
South China Sea	5–6	— NE MONSOON — 4–5	4	3 →	3 ← SW MONSOON	4	4	4–5	3–4	5	5–6	5–6
Japanese Waters	5	5	5	4–5	4–5	4	4	3–4	4	4–5	5	4–5
N INDIAN OCEAN												
Bay of Bengal	4	— NE MONSOON — 4	4 →	← CYCLONES (1–2) →	4 ← SW MONSOON	5–6	6–7	6 CYCLONES (5–6)	5 →	← CYCLONES (1–2) → 4 — NE MONSOON —	4	4
Arabian Sea												
S INDIAN OCEAN W of 80° E	——— CYCLONES (6) (5°–25° S) ——————————————→											← CYCLONES
AUSTRALIA N, NW & W coasts	WILLY-WILLIES (1) →		→									← WILLY-WILLIES —
Queensland coast	HURRICANES (2–3) ←		→									
S PACIFIC Fiji, Samoa and New Zealand, N Island area	— HURRICANES (2) ——————→											← HURRICANES

mid-May to November and in the N hemisphere from mid-November to mid-June. It should be remembered however that no month is entirely safe and that storms can occur at any time.

The locating of tropical storms has greatly improved in recent years with the aid of weather satellites, a typical satellite picture being shown in Diagram 11. Once identified by satellite, tropical circulations are carefully tracked and in some areas, e.g. the seas around the West Indies and the Philippines, weather reconnaissance *5* aircraft fly into these circulations to measure characteristics such as wind speed and pressure. Warnings of the position, intensity and expected movement of each circulation are then broadcast at regular intervals (see *Admiralty List of Radio Signals*), the following terms being then generally used to describe tropical circulations.

Tropical Depression: Winds of Force 7 and less.   *10*
Tropical Storm: Winds of Force 8 and 9.
Severe Tropical Storm: Winds of Force 10 and 11.
Cyclone, Typhoon, Hurricane, etc.: Winds of Force 12 and over.

Tropical storms generally originate between the latitudes of 7° and 15°, though some form nearer the equator.   *15* Those which affect the W part of the Pacific, South Indian and North Atlantic Oceans are usually first reported in the W parts of these oceans, though there are exceptions, such as in the North Atlantic during August and September when an occasional storm begins near Cape Verde Islands. In the N hemisphere they move off in a direction between 275° and 350°, though most often within 30° of due W. When near the latitude of 25° they usually recurve away from the equator and, by the time they have reached a latitude of 30°, the track (or path as it is more usually called) is NE. In the S hemisphere they move off in a WSW to SSW direction (usually the   *20* former), recurve between latitudes of about 15° to 20°, and thereafter follow a SE path. Many storms, however, do not recurve but continue in a WNW (WSW) direction until they reach a large land mass where they fill quickly.

The speed of the storms is usually about 10 knots in their early stages, increasing a little with latitude but seldom achieving 15 knots before recurving. A speed of 20 to 25 knots is usual after recurving though speeds   *25* of over 40 knots have been known. Storms occasionally move erratically, at times making a complete loop, but when this happens their speed is usually less than 10 knots.

Winds of force 7 are likely up to 200 miles from the centre of the storm and winds of gale force 8 up to 100 miles from the centre, at latitudes of less than 20°; but by a latitude of 35° these distances may be doubled though wind force near the centre may be diminished. Hurricane force winds are likely within 75 miles of the   *30* storm centre in the tropics and gusts exceeding 175 knots have been reported.

As already stated, warning of the position, intensity and expected movement of a storm is given by radio at frequent intervals. Sometimes, however, there is insufficient evidence for an accurate warning, or even a general warning to be given and then ships must be guided by their own observations. The first of the following observations is by far the most reliable indication of the proximity of a storm, within 20° or so of the equator. It should   *35* be borne in mind, however, that very little warning of the approach of an intense storm of small diameter may be expected.

Precursory signs of tropical storms.

If a corrected barometer reading is 3 millibars or more below the mean for the time of the year, as shown   *40* in the climatic atlas or appropriate volume of Admiralty Sailing Directions, suspicion should be aroused and action taken to meet any development. The barometer reading must be corrected not only for height, latitude, temperature and index error (if mercurial) but also for diurnal variation, as given in the climatic atlas or appropriate volume of Admiralty Sailing Directions. If the corrected reading is 5 millibars or more below normal it is time to consider avoiding action for there can be little doubt that a tropical storm   *45* is in the vicinity. Because of the importance of pressure readings it is wise to read the barometer hourly in areas affected by tropical storms.

An appreciable change in the direction or strength of the wind.

A long, low swell is sometimes evident, proceeding from the approximate bearing of the centre of the storm. This indication may be apparent before the barometer begins to fall.   *50*

Extensive cirrus cloud followed, as the storm approaches, by altostratus and then broken cumulus or scud.

Radar may give warning of a storm within about 100 miles. Diagram 12 gives an idea of how the areas of precipitation around a tropical storm may appear on radar in the N hemisphere. At times the eye of the storm can be clearly seen. It is surrounded by a large area of moderate or heavy rain and outside this area   *55* the belts of rain are arranged in bands as shown. Diagram 13 shows hurricane *Camille* in August 1969 approaching New Orleans from S. Winds of 120 to 130 knots were estimated in the circulation of this hurricane.

By the time the exact position of the storm is given by radar, the ship is likely to be already experiencing high seas, and strong to gale force winds. It should be in time, however, to enable the ship to avoid the eye   *60* and its vicinity, where the worst conditions exist.

Note: Under regulations drawn up by the International Convention for the Safety of Life at Sea, it is the duty of every ship suspecting the presence or formation of a tropical storm immediately to inform other vessels and shore authorities by all means at her disposal. Weather reports should be made by radio at frequent intervals   *65* giving as much informatioon as possible, especially corrected barometer readings (but not corrected for diurnal variation). If the barometer readings are uncorrected this fact should also be stated in the signal.

To decide the best course of action if a storm is suspected in the vicinity, the following knowledge is necessary:
(*a*) The bearing of the centre of the storm.
(*b*) The path of the storm.   *70*

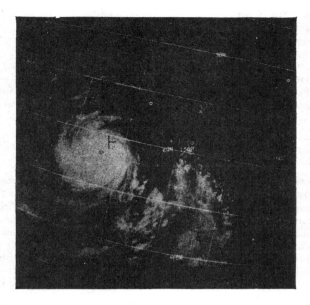

Satellite picture of Typhoon 'Elsie' off T'ai-wan, September 1969

Diagram 11.

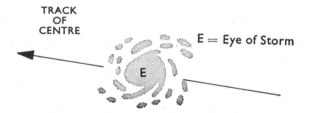

TRACK
OF
CENTRE

E = Eye of Storm

Precipitation areas shown by radar

Diagram 12.

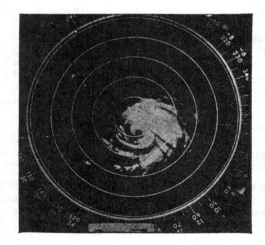

Radar Presentation of Hurricane 'Camille'

Diagram 13.

If an observer faces the wind, the centre of the storm will be from 100° to 125° on his right hand side in the N hemisphere when the storm is about 200 miles away, i.e. when the barometer has fallen about 5 millibars and the wind has increased to about force 6. As a rule, the nearer he is to the centre the more nearly does the angle approach 90°. The path of the storm may be approximately determined by taking two such bearings separated by an interval of 2 to 3 hours, allowance being made for the movement of the ship during the interval. It can generally be assumed that the storm is not travelling towards the equator and, if in a lower latitude than 20°, its path is most unlikely to have an E component. On the rare occasions when the storm is following an unusual path it is likely to be moving slowly.

Diagram 14 shows typical paths of tropical storms and illustrates the terms "dangerous" and "navigable" semicircle. The former lies on the side of the path towards the usual direction of recurvature, i.e. the right hand semicircle in the N and the left hand semicircle in the S hemisphere. The advance quadrant of the dangerous semicircle (shown shaded) is known as the dangerous quadrant as this quadrant lies ahead of the centre. The navigable semicircle is that which lies on the other side of the path. A ship situated within this semicircle will tend to be blown away from the storm centre and recurvature of the storm will increase her distance from the centre.

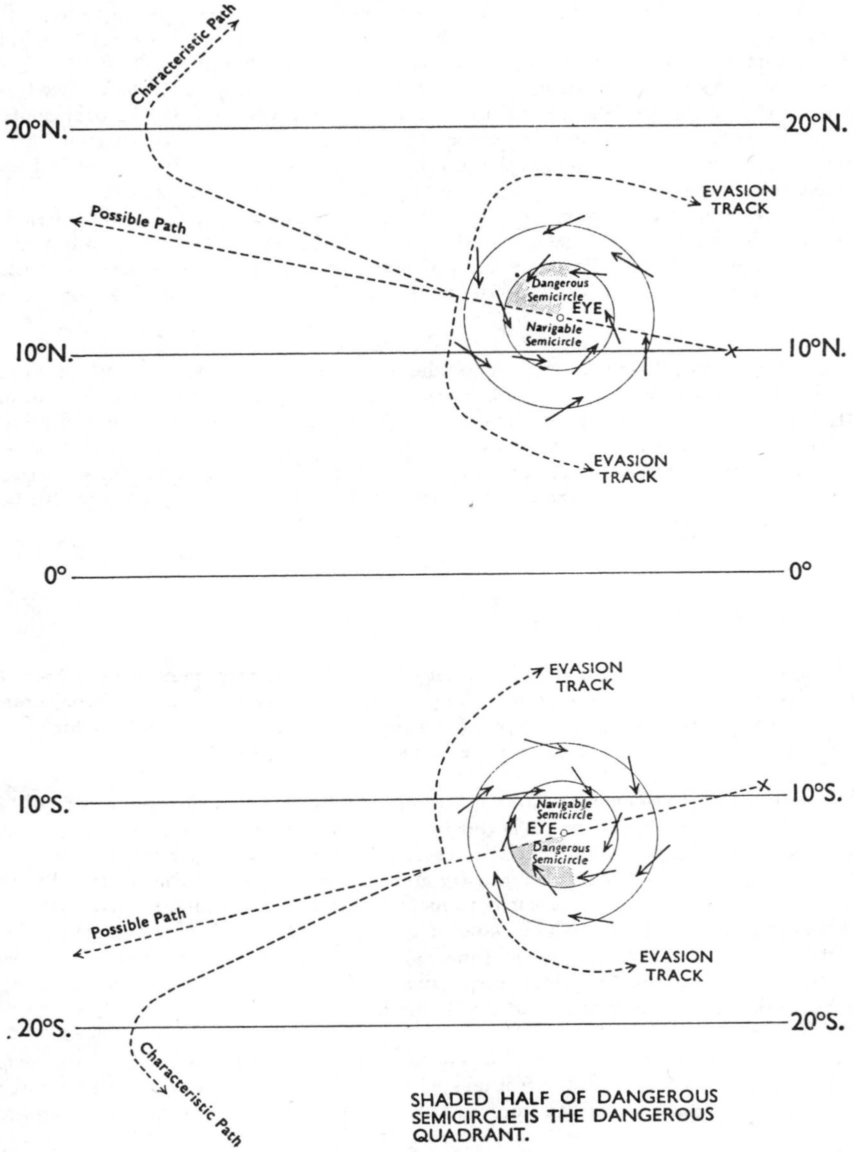

Typical paths of Tropical Storms

Diagram 14.

1.39. Avoiding tropical storms. In whatever situation a ship may find herself the matter of vital importance is to avoid passing within 50 miles or so of the centre of the storm. It is preferable but not always possible to keep outside a distance of 200 miles. If a ship has at least 20 knots at her disposal and shapes a course that will take her most rapidly away from the storm before the wind has increased above the point at which her movement becomes restricted, it is seldom that she will come to any harm. Sometimes a tropical storm moves so slowly that a vessel, if ahead of it, can easily outpace it or, if astern of it, can overtake it.

If a storm is suspected in the vicinity, the vessel, whilst observing her barometer, should continue on her course until the barometer has fallen 5 millibars (corrected for diurnal variation) below normal, or the wind has increased to force 6 when the barometer has fallen at least 3 millibars. Then she should act as recommended in the following paragraphs, until the barometer has risen above the limit just given and the wind has decreased below force 6. Should it be certain, however, that the vessel is behind the storm, or in the navigable semicircle, it will evidently be sufficient to alter course away from the centre.

In the N hemisphere (ship initially moving slowly).

If the wind is veering the ship must be in the dangerous semicircle. The ship should proceed with all available speed with the wind 10° to 45°, depending on speed, on the starboard bow. As the wind veers the ship should turn to starboard, thereby tracing a course relative to the storm as shown in Diagram 14.

If the wind remains steady in direction, or if it backs, so that the ship seems to be nearly in the path or in the navigable semicircle respectively, the ship should bring the wind well on the starboard quarter and proceed with all available speed. As the wind backs the ship should turn to port as shown.

In the S hemisphere (ship initially moving slowly).

If the wind is backing the ship must be in the dangerous semicircle. The ship should proceed with all available speed with the wind 10° to 45°, depending on speed, on the port bow. As the wind backs the ship should turn to port thereby tracing a course relative to the storm as shown.

If the wind remains steady in direction, or if it veers, so that the ship seems to be nearly in the path or in the navigable semicircle respectively, the ship should bring the wind well on the port quarter and proceed with all available speed. As the wind veers the ship should turn to starboard as shown.

If there is insufficient room to run, when in the navigable semicircle, and it is not practicable to seek shelter, the ship should heave to with the wind on her starboard bow in the N and on her port bow in the S hemisphere.

If in harbour when a tropical storm approaches, it is preferable to put to sea if this can be done in time to avoid the worst of the storm. Riding out a tropical storm, the centre of which passes within 50 miles or so, in a harbour or anchorage, even if some shelter is offered, is an unpleasant and hazardous experience, especially if there are other ships in company. Even if berthed alongside, or if special moorings are used, a ship cannot feel entirely secure.

1.40. Anticyclones. Over the E sides of the oceans the movement of anticyclones, which are also known for synoptic purposes as *highs*, is generally slow and erratic and the anticyclone may remain stationary for several days giving settled weather. The pressure gradient is usually slight, the winds are light and the weather is often fine or partly cloudy, but in winter overcast skies are common, producing gloomy conditions. Precipitation is, however, rare except on the outskirts of an anticyclone. Over the W parts of the oceans anticyclones are more likely to move quickly and consequently the weather is more changeable. Movement is generally towards the E.

FOG

1.51. Fog is caused by the cooling of air in contact with the surface to a temperature at which it can no longer maintain, in an invisible state, the water vapour which is present in it. Condensation of this vapour into minute, though visible, droplets produces fog. The type of fog depends upon the means by which the air is cooled. For details of specific areas, Admiralty Sailing Directions should be consulted.

1.52. Sea or Advection fog is associated with moist and relatively warm air flowing over a cold sea surface and is the main type of fog experienced at sea. It is most common in the late spring and early summer, when sea temperature is at its lowest compared with air temperature. To produce fog by this means the rate of cooling of the air must be high. This only occurs frequently and on a large scale, either near cold currents and at a season when the prevailing wind transports warm, moist air over them, or elsewhere where the sea temperature is appreciably lower than that of the air which blows over it. Examples of the former are the fogs which occur off Newfoundland, off California and between Japan and the Aleutian Islands; the cold currents involved being the Labrador, California and Oya Shio, respectively. The latter type is represented by the spring and summer fogs in the SW approaches to the English Channel.

1.53. Frontal fog may occur near an occlusion or ahead of a warm front and is due to the evaporation of the warm raindrops into the cold air beneath the frontal surface, raising the relative humidity to saturation point. It occurs in temperate and high latitudes and is confined to a relatively narrow belt not usually more than 50 miles in width.

1.54. Arctic Sea Smoke, or Frost Smoke, is normally confined to high latitudes and occurs when very cold air flows over a much warmer sea surface, when intense evaporation takes place from the relatively warm sea. The moisture thus evaporated is immediately chilled by contact with the cold air and condensed to form fog, giving the sea the appearance of steaming. This type of fog is often encountered where a cold wind is blowing off ice or snow on to a relatively warm sea.

1.55. Radiation fog forms over low-lying land on clear nights (conditions for maximum radiation) especially during winter months. Radiation fog is thickest during the latter part of the night and early part of the day.

Occasionally it drifts out to sea but is found no farther than 10 to 15 miles offshore as the sea surface temperature is relatively high which causes the water droplets to evaporate.

1.56. Forecasting sea fog. Warnings of the likely formation of sea fog may be obtained by frequent observations of air and sea surface temperature; if the sea surface temperature falls below the dewpoint, see Table B, fog is almost certain to form. The following procedure is recommended whenever the temperature of the air is higher than, or almost equal to that of the sea, especially at night when approaching fog cannot be seen until shortly before entering it. Sea and air (both dry and wet bulb) temperatures should be observed at least every 10 minutes and the sea surface temperature and dewpoint temperature plotted against time. See Diagram 15.

If the curves converge fog may be expected when they coincide. The example shows that by 2200 there is a probability of running into fog about 2300, assuming that the sea surface temperature continues to fall at the same rate.

In areas where a rapid fall of sea surface temperature may be encountered, which can be seen from the appropriate chartlet in Admiralty Sailing Directions, a reliable warning of fog will be given when the dewpoint is within 5°C of the sea surface temperature. To avoid fog a course should be set for warmer waters.

TABLE B: Dew-point (°C)

Dry Bulb °C	Depression of Wet Bulb																			Dry Bulb °C
	0°	0.5°	1.0°	1.5°	2.0°	2.5°	3.0°	3.5°	4.0°	4.5°	5.0°	5.5°	6.0°	6.5°	7.0°	7.5°	8.0°	8.5°	9.0°	
40	40	39	39	38	38	37	36	36	35	35	34	33	33	32	31	31	30	29	29	40
39	39	38	38	37	37	36	35	35	34	33	33	32	32	31	30	29	29	28	27	39
38	38	37	37	36	36	35	34	34	33	32	32	31	30	30	29	28	28	27	26	38
37	37	36	36	35	35	34	33	33	32	31	31	30	29	29	28	27	27	26	25	37
36	36	35	35	34	34	33	32	32	31	30	30	29	28	28	27	26	25	25	24	36
35	35	34	34	33	33	32	31	31	30	29	29	28	27	26	26	25	24	24	23	35
34	34	33	33	32	32	31	31	30	30	29	28	28	27	26	25	25	24	23	22	34
33	33	32	32	31	31	30	30	29	28	28	27	26	26	25	24	23	23	22	20	33
32	32	31	31	30	29	29	28	27	27	26	25	25	24	23	22	22	21	20	19	32
31	31	30	30	29	28	28	27	27	26	26	25	24	23	22	22	21	20	19	18	31
30	30	29	29	28	27	27	26	25	25	24	23	22	22	21	20	19	18	17	17	30
29	29	28	28	27	26	26	25	24	24	23	22	21	20	20	19	18	17	16	15	29
28	28	27	27	26	25	25	24	23	22	22	21	20	19	19	18	17	16	15	14	28
27	27	26	26	25	24	24	23	22	21	21	20	19	18	17	16	16	15	14	13	27
26	26	25	25	24	23	23	22	21	20	19	19	18	17	16	15	14	13	12	11	26
25	25	24	24	23	22	21	21	20	19	18	18	17	16	15	14	13	12	11	10	25
24	24	23	23	22	21	20	20	19	18	17	16	16	15	14	13	12	11	10	8	24
23	23	22	22	21	20	19	19	18	17	16	15	14	13	13	12	11	9	8	7	23
22	22	21	21	20	19	18	17	17	16	15	14	13	12	11	10	9	8	7	5	22
21	21	20	20	19	18	17	16	16	15	14	13	12	11	10	9	8	6	5	4	21
20	20	19	19	18	17	16	15	14	14	13	12	11	10	9	7	6	5	4	2	20
19	19	18	17	17	16	15	14	13	12	11	10	9	8	7	6	5	3	2	0	19
18	18	17	16	16	15	14	13	12	11	10	9	8	7	6	5	3	2	0	−1	18
17	17	16	15	15	14	13	12	11	10	9	8	7	6	4	3	2	0	−2	−3	17
16	16	15	14	14	13	12	11	10	9	8	7	5	4	3	2	0	−2	−4	−6	16
15	15	14	13	12	12	11	10	9	8	7	5	4	3	1	0	−2	−4	−6	−8	15
14	14	13	12	11	10	10	9	7	6	5	4	3	1	0	−2	−4	−6	−8	−11	14
13	13	12	11	10	9	8	7	6	5	4	3	1	0	−2	−4	−6	−8	−11	−14	13
12	12	11	10	9	8	7	6	5	4	3	1	0	−2	−4	−6	−8	−10	−13	−17	12
11	11	10	9	8	7	6	5	4	3	1	0	−2	−3	−5	−8	−10	−13	−17	−22	11
10	10	9	8	7	6	5	4	3	1	0	−2	−3	−5	−7	−10	−13	−16	−21	−29	10
9	9	8	7	6	5	4	3	1	0	−2	−3	−5	−7	−9	−12	−16	−20	−27	−45	9
8	8	7	6	5	4	3	1	0	−2	−3	−5	−7	−9	−12	−15	−19	−25	−25	−36	8
7	7	6	5	4	3	1	0	−1	−3	−5	−7	−9	−11	−14	−14	−18	−19	−24	−34	7
6	6	5	4	3	1	0	−1	−3	−4	−6	−8	−11	−14	−14	−18	−23	−32			6
5	5	4	3	2	0	−1	−3	−4	−6	−8	−10	−11	−15	−18	−22	−30				5
4	4	3	2	0	−1	−2	−4	−6	−8	−9	−11	−14	−17	−22	−28	−45				4
3	3	2	1	−1	−2	−4	−5	−6	−8	−11	−13	−16	−21	−27	−39					3
2	2	1	0	−2	−3	−4	−6	−8	−10	−13	−16	−20	−25	−34						2
1	1	0	−2	−3	−4	−6	−8	−10	−12	−15	−19	−24	−31							1
0	0	−1	−3	−4	−6	−8	−9	−12	−14	−18	−22	−29	−44							0
−1	−1	−2	−4	−5	−7	−9	−11	−14	−17	−21	−26	−37								−1
−2	−2	−4	−5	−7	−9	−11	−13	−16	−19	−24	−32									−2
−3	−3	−5	−6	−8	−10	−12	−15	−18	−23	−29	−44									−3
−4	−4	−6	−8	−10	−12	−14	−17	−21	−26	−36										−4
−5	−5	−7	−9	−11	−13	−16	−19	−24	−31											−5
−6	−6	−8	−10	−13	−15	−18	−22	−28	−39											−6
−7	−7	−10	−12	−14	−17	−20	−25	−32												−7
−8	−8	−11	−13	−16	−19	−23	−28	−40												−8
−9	−9	−12	−14	−17	−21	−25	−33													−9
−10	−10	−13	−16	−19	−23	−28	−39													−10
−11	−11	−15	−17	−21	−25	−32														−11
−12	−12	−16	−19	−23	−28	−38														−12
−13	−13	−17	−20	−25	−31	−47														−13
−14	−14	−18	−22	−27	−35															−14
−15	−15	−20	−24	−29	−40															−15
−16	−16	−21	−25	−32																−16
−17	−17	−22	−27	−35																−17

Interpolation must not be made between figures above and below the heavy line originating at 0°, because at temperatures above the line, evaporation takes place from a water surface, and at temperatures below the line it takes place from an ice surface.

For dry bulb temperatures below 0°C it will be noticed that, when the depression of the wet bulb is zero, i.e., when the temperature of the wet bulb is equal to that of the dry bulb, the dew-point is still below the dry bulb, and the relative humidity is less than 100 per cent. These apparent anomalies are a consequence of the method of computing dew-points and relative humidities now adopted by the Meteorological Office, in which the standard saturation pressure for temperatures below 0°C is taken as that over water, and not as that over ice.

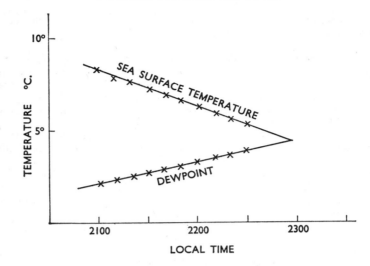

Sea Temperatures and Dew Point readings plotted against Time

Diagram 15.

EFFECTS OF WIND, SEA, AND SWELL

1.61. Weather routeing. The routes given in this book, and any which are derived from the routeing charts or other statistic-based media, are "climatic" and take account of the more usual conditions of weather, sea, and swell. A marked improvement of the route by "weather routeing" may be possible if temporary adverse conditions can either be forecast before sailing or avoided at short notice, the effect of these being most marked, except for tropical storms, on E–W voyages outside the tropics. Research conducted by the United States Naval Oceanographic Office on a "Victory" type ship of length 134 m, beam 19 m, and draft 8·4 m, with a top rated speed of 17·5 knots, has yielded enough information to show that, for average merchant ships, a reduction in speed of from 20 to 60 per cent is probable whenever head or beam seas reach state 6 or following seas reach state 7. Vessels on many conventional routes may have to reduce speed to an extent which depends on their seakeeping qualities, the route, the season, and the course. Diagrams 16 and 17 of the North Atlantic and North Pacific Oceans show isolines of probable speed reduction due to such seas on various headings in the different seasons; this information can be used either when planning a passage or during a voyage.

Apart from adjustment for sea and swell conditions as above, there are two methods of weather routeing by which the climatic route may be adjusted before and during the voyage to offset delay and damage due to short-term weather variations or such variables as the movement of ice. Both depend for their efficiency on the accuracy of forecasts, knowledge of ship characteristics, and the speed with which the necessary adjustments can be made.

The first method employs the services of a central routeing organisation ashore, staffed by meteorologists and experienced seamen, which sails the ship on the best route computed from the expected weather, ship statistics and voyage requirements, subsequently notifying the ship, as new weather trends appear or are anticipated, of advisable diversions. Such services are offered by:– Ocean Routes London, San Francisco, and Tokyo (all oceans); Meteorological Office, Bracknell, U.K. (Atlantic and Pacific); Bendix Inc., New York (Atlantic and Pacific); Alwex Inc., Washington, D.C. (Atlantic and Pacific); Weather Routeing Inc., New York (Atlantic and Pacific); K.N.M.I., de Bilt, Netherlands (Atlantic); Deusches Swetteramt, Hamburg Atlantic, W-bound only).

In the second method, the ship is self-routed, diversions being made on passage according to the judgment of the master and in the light of weather forecasts and facsimile weather and ice maps, if the ship is fitted to receive them.

1.62. The action of the wind in blowing for a time across an expanse of ocean is to produce an area of sea affected by waves of nearly constant height and period. Such waves progress in groups at half the speed at which individual waves appear to move across the surface, the latter starting at the rear of and moving forwards through the group. The fact that height and period are only nearly constant means that at times there is mutual interference between wave systems, and areas of comparatively smooth or rougher water result. Such systems of waves continue to progress across the ocean, with some attenuation, thus affecting different areas with waves that were produced by wind action elsewhere. In general, waves of this sort do not move at the same speed as the weather systems producing their generating winds and there is no relation between the wind at a point outside the generating area and these waves, which are known as **swell**. Those waves, which are being produced by the wind blowing at the time and place of observation are described as **sea**, and may usually be distinguished from swell by the fact that their crests are short and lie at right angles to the wind direction, whereas those of swell may lie in any direction relative to the wind. The similarity between sea and swell has often led to confusion in reporting, particularly when both happen to be similarly directed, only being distinguishable by differing periods.

FEBRUARY

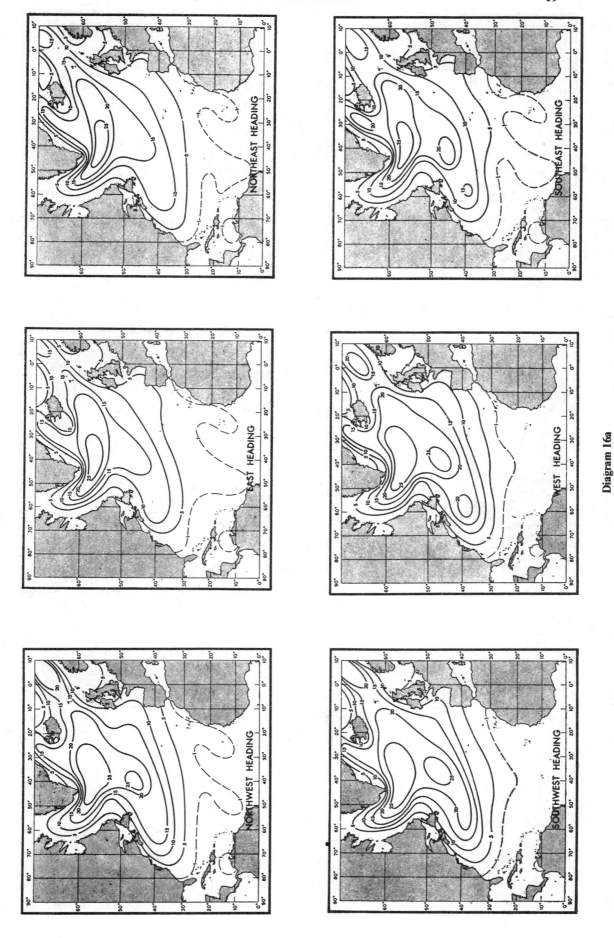

Diagram 16a

Charts show percentage of time during which a reduction of speed, due to high seas, may be expected for specified headings

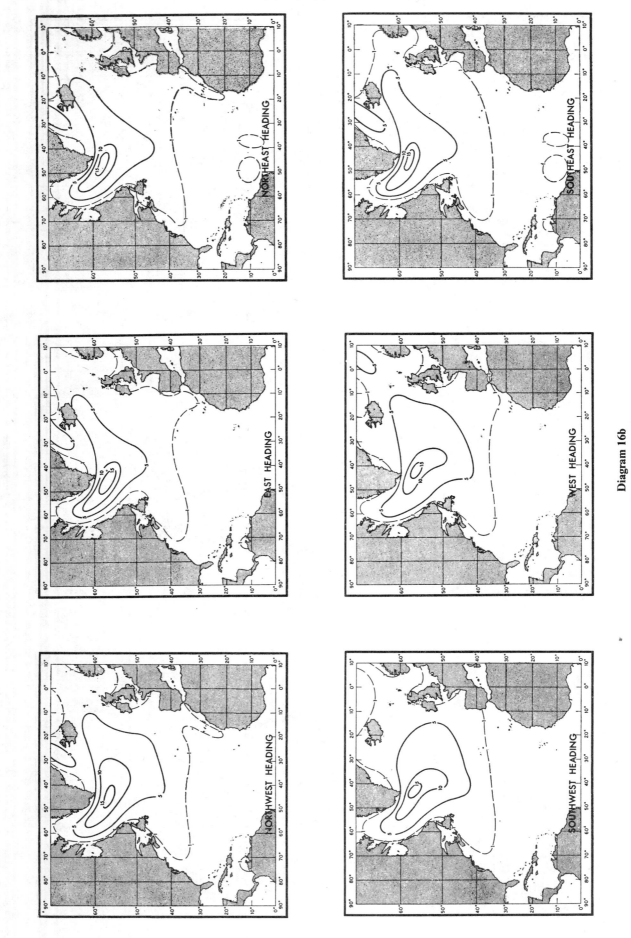

Diagram 16b

Charts show percentage of time during which a reduction of speed, due to high seas, may be expected for specified headings

AUGUST

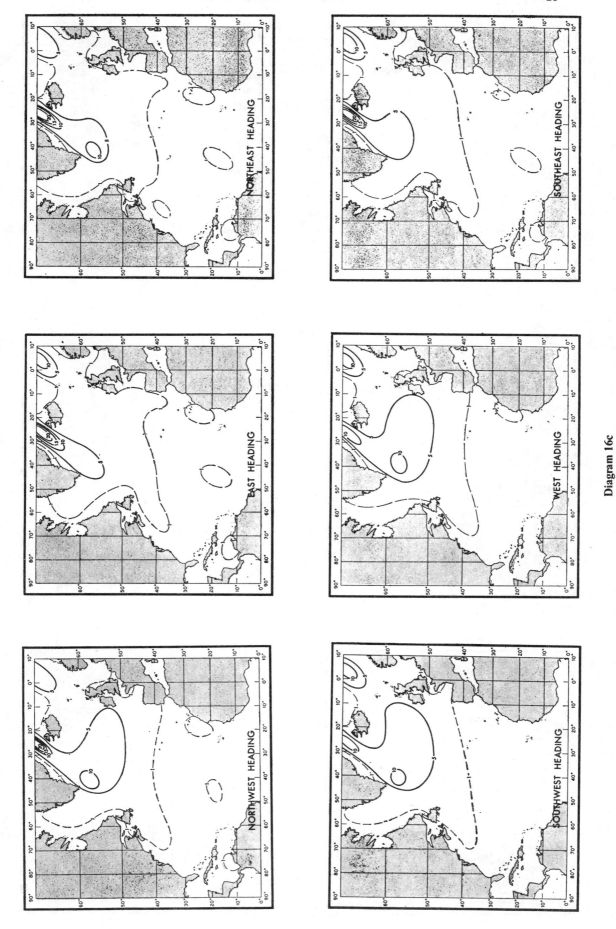

NORTHEAST HEADING

SOUTHEAST HEADING

EAST HEADING

WEST HEADING

NORTHWEST HEADING

SOUTHWEST HEADING

Diagram 16c

Charts show percentage of time during which a reduction of speed, due to high seas, may be expected for specified headings

NOVEMBER

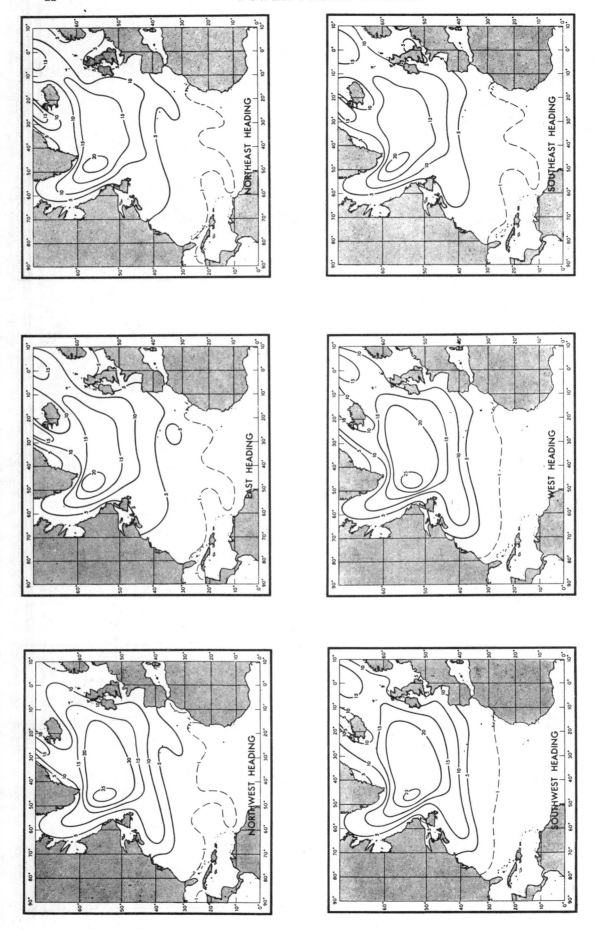

Diagram 16d

Charts show percentage of time during which a reduction of speed, due to high seas, may be expected for specified headings

FEBRUARY

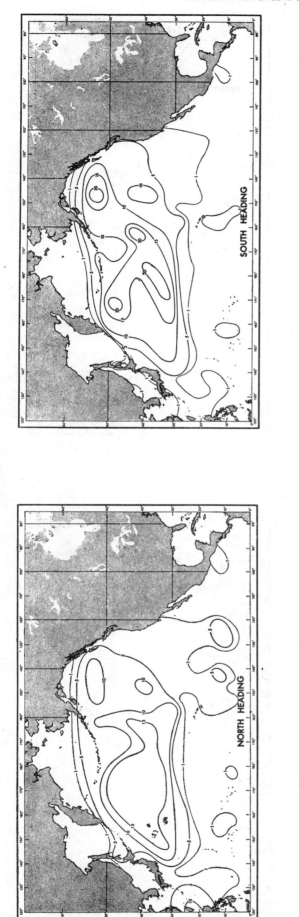

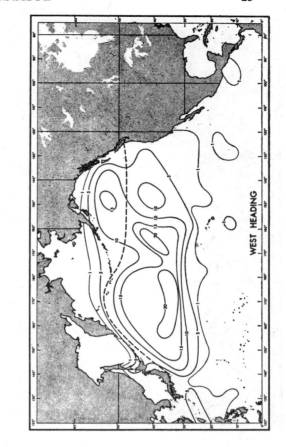

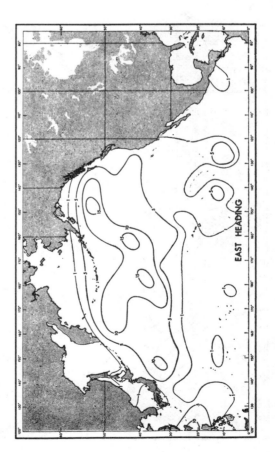

Diagram 17a

Charts show percentage of time during which a reduction of speed, due to high seas, may be expected for specified headings

MAY

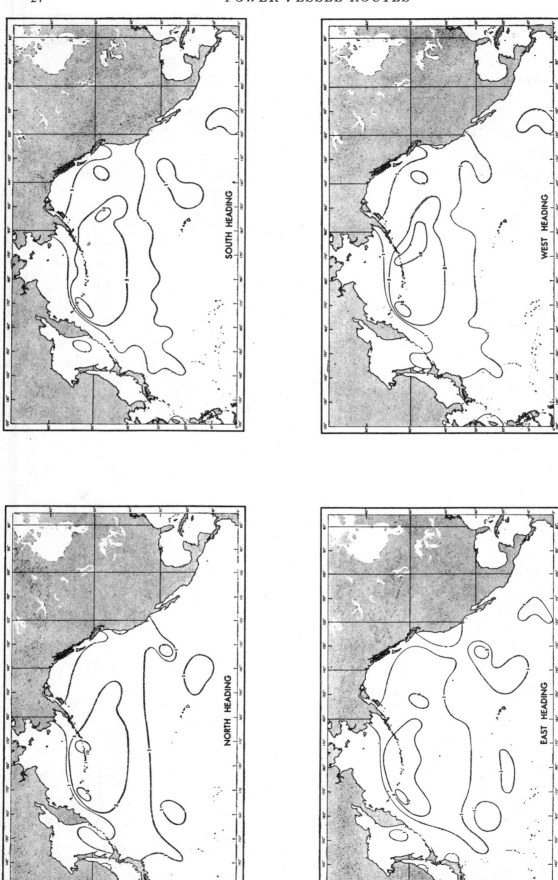

Diagram 17b

Charts show percentage of time during which a reduction of speed, due to high seas, may be expected for specified headings

AUGUST

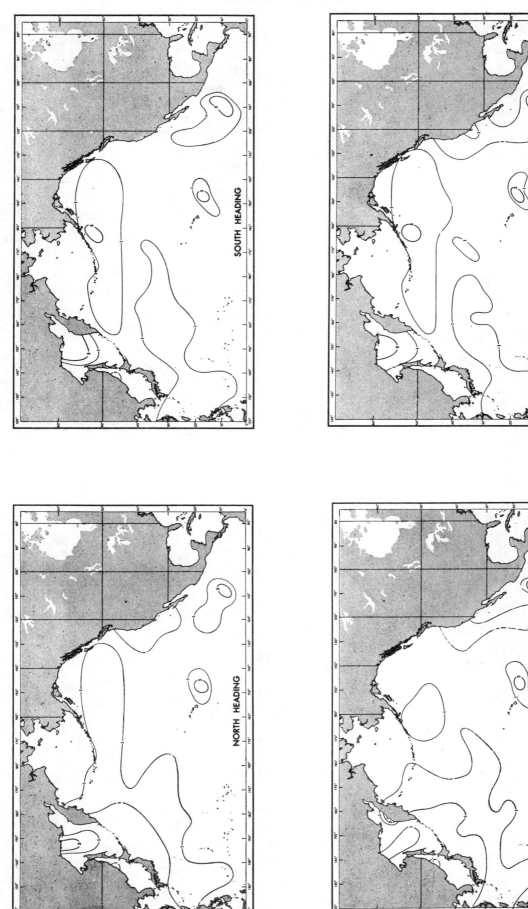

B

Diagram 17c

Charts show percentage of time during which a reduction of speed, due to high seas, may be expected for specified headings

NOVEMBER

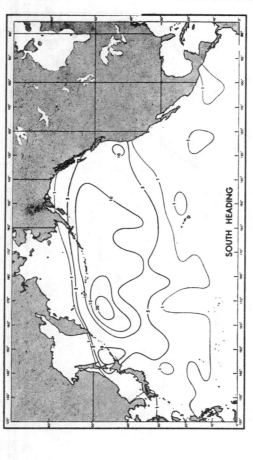

SOUTH HEADING

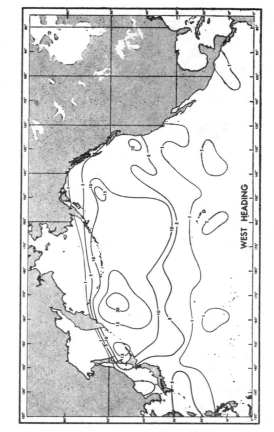

WEST HEADING

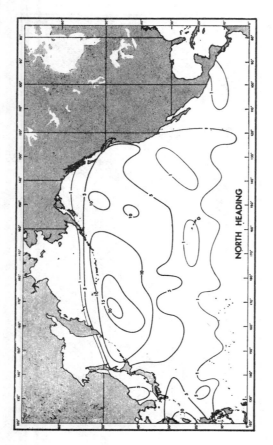

NORTH HEADING

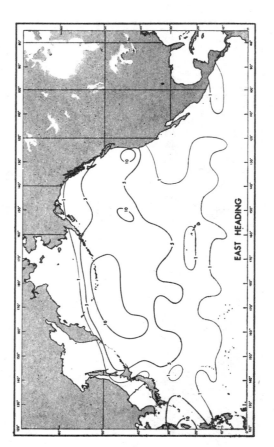

EAST HEADING

Diagram 17d

Charts show percentage of time during which a reduction of speed, due to high seas, may be expected for specified headings

1.83. BEAUFORT WIND SCALE

(For an effective height of 10 metres above sea level)

(WMO Code 100)

Beaufort Number	Descriptive Term	Mean wind speed equivalent in knots	Deep Sea Criterion	Probable mean wave height* in metres
0	Calm	<1	Sea like a mirror	—
1	Light air	1–3	Ripples with the appearance of scales are formed, but without foam crests	0·1 (0·1)
2	Light breeze	4–6	Small wavelets, still short but more pronounced; crests have a glassy appearance and do not break	0·2 (0·3)
3	Gentle breeze	7–10	Large wavelets; crests begin to break; foam of glassy appearance; perhaps scattered white horses	0·6 (1)
4	Moderate breeze	11–16	Small waves, becoming longer; fairly frequent white horses	1 (1·5)
5	Fresh breeze	17–21	Moderate waves, taking a more pronounced long form; many white horses are formed (chance of some spray)	2 (2·5)
6	Strong breeze	22–27	Large waves begin to form; the white foam crests are more extensive everywhere (probably some spray)	3 (4)
7	Near gale	28–33	Sea heaps up and white foam from breaking waves begins to be blown in streaks along the direction of the wind	4 (5·5)
8	Gale	34–40	Moderately high waves of greater length; edges of crests begin to break into spindrift; foam is blown in well-marked streaks along the direction of the wind	5·5 (7·5)
9	Strong gale	41–47	High waves; dense streaks of foam along the direction of the wind; crests of waves begin to topple, tumble and roll over; spray may affect visibility	7 (10)
10	Storm	48–55	Very high waves with long overhanging crests; the resulting foam, in great patches, is blown in dense white streaks along the direction of the wind; on the whole, the surface of the sea takes a white appearance; the tumbling of the sea becomes heavy and shock-like; visibility affected	9 (12·5)
11	Violent storm	56–63	Exceptionally high waves (small and medium-sized ships might be for a time lost to view behind the waves); the sea is completely covered with long white patches of foam lying along the direction of the wind; everywhere the edges of the wave crests are blown into froth; visibility affected	11·5 (16)
12	Hurricane	64 and over	The air is filled with foam and spray; sea completely white with driving spray; visibility very seriously affected	14 (—)

* This table is only intended as a guide to show roughly what may be expected in the open sea, remote from land. It should never be used in the reverse way, i.e., for logging or reporting the state of the sea. In enclosed waters, or when near land, with an off-shore wind, wave heights will be smaller and the waves steeper. Figures in brackets indicate the probable maximum height of waves.

5

10

15

20

25

30

35

40

45

50

55

60

65

70

1.64. Sea and swell. The following table shows the wave height and the descriptive terms used for sea states.

State	Average wave height (metres)	Descriptive term
0	0	Calm (glassy)
1	0–0·1	Calm (rippled)
2	0·1–0·5	Smooth (wavelets)
3	0·5–1·25	Slight
4	1·25–2·5	Moderate
5	2·5–4·0	Rough
6	4·0–6·0	Very rough
7	6·0–9·0	High
8	9·0–14·0	Very high
9	>14·0	Phenomenal

Swell states. The terms in general use for the height of swell are:—low (2m), moderate (2–4 m), and heavy (4 m and above). Length of swell is defined as short (less than 100 m), average (100–200 m), and long (200 m and above).

OCEAN CURRENTS

1.71. General remarks. Currents flow at all depths in the oceans, but in general the stronger currents occur in an upper layer which is shallow in comparison with the general depth of the oceans. Ocean current circulation therefore takes place in three dimensions. The navigator is only interested in the surface current circulation, which may be defined as the circulation at a depth of about half the ship's draught. This may differ slightly, especially in the case of a big ship, from that at the very surface, such as would affect a ship's boat and all drifting objects of negligible draught. A current at any depth in the ocean may have a vertical component, as well as horizontal ones; a surface current can only have horizontal components.

The main cause of surface currents in the open ocean is the direct action of the wind on the sea surface, and a close correlation accordingly exists between their directions and those of the prevailing winds. Winds of high constancy blowing over extensive areas of ocean will naturally have a greater effect in producing a current than will variable or localised winds. Thus the North-east and South-east Trade Winds of the two hemispheres are the main spring of the surface current circulation. In the Atlantic and Pacific Oceans the two trade winds drive an immense body of water W over a width of some 50° of latitude, broken only by the narrow belt of E-going Equatorial Counter-current, which is found a few degrees north of the equator in both these oceans. A similar W'ly surge of water occurs in the South Indian Ocean by the action of the South-east Trade Wind.

The trade winds in both hemispheres are balanced in the higher latitudes by wide belts of variable W'ly winds. These produce corresponding belts of predominantly E'ly sets in the temperate latitudes of each hemisphere. With these E'ly and W'ly sets constituting the N and S limbs, there thus arise great continuous circulations of water in each of the major oceans. These cells are centred in about 30° N and S, and extend from about the 10th to at least the 50th parallel in both hemispheres. The direction of the current circulation is clockwise in the N hemisphere and counter-clockwise in the S hemisphere. There are also regions of current circulation outside the main eddies, due to various causes, but associated with them or dependent upon them. As an example, part of the North Atlantic Current branches from the main system and flows N of Scotland and N along the coast of Norway. Branching again, part flows past Spitsbergen into the Arctic Ocean and part enters the Barents Sea.

In the main monsoon regions, the N part of the Indian Ocean and the extreme W of the North Pacific Ocean (China Seas and Eastern Archipelago), the current reverses seasonally, flowing in accordance with the monsoon blowing at the time.

The South Atlantic, South Indian and South Pacific Oceans are all open to the Southern Ocean, and the Southern Ocean Current, encircling the globe in an easterly direction, completes the S part of the main circulation of each of these three oceans.

The general surface current circulation of the world is shown in Chart 5310 (in the pocket at the end of the book), on which the different circulations during the two monsoon seasons are indicated. Apart from these major changes of direction, there are some minor seasonal changes of position of currents, which cannot be shown on a single general chart. One of the chief of these is the Equatorial Counter-current of the North Atlantic Ocean, which originates much farther E from January through April, in about 20° W. For details of the circulation, reference should be made to current atlases.

Over by far the greater part of all oceans, the individual currents experienced in a given region are variable, in many cases so variable that on different occasions currents may be observed to set in most, or all, directions. Even in the regions of more variable current there is often, however, a greater frequency of current setting towards one part of the compass, so that in the long run there is a flow of water out of the area in a direction which forms part of the general circulation. Some degree of variability, including occasional currents in the opposite direction to the usual flow, is to be found within the limits of the more constant currents, such as the great Equatorial Currents, or the Gulf Stream. The constancy of the more constant currents varies to some extent in different seasons and in different parts of the current. It is usually about 75 per cent or more; it rarely exceeds 85 per cent and then only in limited areas. Current variability is mainly due to the variation of wind in strength and direction. For the degree of variation to which currents are liable, reference should be made to the charts of current roses given in standard current atlases.

1.72. Warm and cold currents. The common conception of currents as either warm or cold is not very satisfactory, and needs to be amplified. Currents may be classified as follows:— 5
   (i) Currents, the temperature of which corresponds to the latitude in which they flow and in which the sea surface isotherms therefore run approximately E–W; this temperature may be warm, cold or intermediate.
   (ii) Currents, the temperature of which does not correspond to the latitude in which they flow, and in which the sea surface isotherms trend more or less markedly N or S. They are therefore either warmer or colder than currents of class (i) flowing in the same latitudes. 10

Examples of class (i) are the warm W- going Equatorial Currents of all oceans and the cold E-going Southern Ocean Current encircling the globe. Examples of class (ii) are the warm Gulf Stream and the warm Kuro Shio, which transport the warm water of the Equatorial Currents to higher latitudes, and the cold East Greenland Current, transporting cold water from the Arctic basin to lower latitudes.

Currents of class (ii), cold relatively to their latitude, may be subdivided into two kinds, depending on the 15 origin of the cold water.
   (*a*) Currents bringing the cold water of polar regions to lower latitudes, such as the East Greenland Current, the Labrador Current, the Falkland Current and Oya Shio. These currents do not form part of the main closed circulation round the high-pressure area of the appropriate ocean.
   (*b*) Currents of lower latitudes, such as the Perú Current, forming the E part of the main circulation. In these 20 cases the relative coldness is caused by colder water rising to the surface from moderate subsurface depths, near an extended coastline. This process is known as upwelling, the reason for which is given later. The upwelling water is not as cold, relatively speaking, as are the currents described under (*a*) above.

The warm currents, transporting warm water to higher latitudes, are found on the W sides of the main closed circulations in both hemispheres. These currents, and the colder ones on the E sides, can be tabulated as 25 follows:—

	Warm current on W Side of ocean	Cold current and area of upwelling on E Side of ocean
N. Atlantic Ocean	Gulf Stream	Canary Current
S. Atlantic Ocean	Brazil Current	Benguela Current
N. Pacific Ocean	Kuro Shio	California Current
S. Pacific Ocean	East Australian Coast Current	Perú Current
S. Indian Ocean	Moçambique and Agulhas Currents	

There is no upwelling on the E side of the South Indian Ocean, where no extended coastline occurs. It should be noted that the relative warmth of the warm currents on the W sides of the ocean compared with other water in the same latitude, is greatest in winter and least in summer. 45

Cold currents from high latitudes have a special significance for navigators by transporting ice to low latitudes. Cold currents also contribute to the occurrence of a high frequency of fog and poor visibility in certain regions.

1.73. Strength of currents. The information given below is generalised from the current atlases, and refers to the currents of the open ocean, mainly between 50° N and 50° S. It does not refer to tidal streams, nor to the 50 resultants of currents and tidal streams in coastal waters. Information as to current strength in higher latitudes is scanty.

The proportion of nil and very weak currents, less than $\frac{1}{4}$ knot, varies considerably in different parts of the oceans. In the central areas of the main closed oceanic circulations, where current is apt to be most variable, the weakness of the resultant, or vector, mean flow is, in general, not caused by an unduly high proportion of very 55 weak currents, but by the variability of direction of the stronger currents. There is probably no region in any part of the open oceans where the currents experienced do not at times attain the rate of at least 1 knot.

Currents of between 2 and 3 knots are found mainly in the W part of the Equatorial Currents, and in the warm currents of the W sides of the circulation in both hemispheres, with the exception of the Brazil Current. They also occur in parts of the Equatorial Counter-currents and in the monsoon areas of the North Indian Ocean and 60 China Seas. These regions are as follows.

In the Atlantic Ocean, the Guiana Current; the Florida Current and Gulf Stream W of 40° W; the Guinea Current (but not the Equatorial Counter-current as a whole); at certain seasons in the extreme W of the Mediterranean Sea; in the Falkland Current and its extension, the Brazil Counter-current; and in the region of the Cape of Good Hope. Very few observations of current exceeding 2 knots have been recorded elsewhere. 65

In the Indian Ocean, the Equatorial Current in the region of Madagascar; the Equatorial Counter-current; the Moçambique Current and its extension, the Agulhas Current; the Somali Current in both monsoons, whether flowing N or S along the coast; the South-west Monsoon Current in the Arabian Sea and Bay of Bengal; the region immediately E or S of Ceylon throughout the year. Very few observations of current exceeding 2 knots have been recorded elsewhere except S of Socotra in the South-west Monsoon. 70

In the North Pacific Ocean, occasionally in the North Equatorial Current, W of 152° E; in the Equatorial Counter-current, W of 140° E, and E of Mindanao and in the Sulawesi Sea, where the North Equatorial Current is recurving S into the Counter-current; in Kuro Shio, from Luzon to about 150° E (160° E from March to May); in the China Seas, in both monsoon periods; in the region of the Gulf of Panama, to 84° W, from November to July; in the North Equatorial Current E of 160° W at all seasons.

In the South Pacific Ocean, in the South Equatorial Current, mainly on the E side of the ocean; in the East Australian Coast Current.

Currents of more than 3 knots are confined to very restricted regions. They have been recorded in the equatorial regions of the oceans, and in the warm currents flowing to higher latitudes on the W sides of the oceans, with the exception of the Brazil Current. The regions are as follows.

In the Atlantic Ocean, in the Guiana Current except from February to April; in the Florida Current and Gulf Stream W of 58° W; in the Guinea Current, May to July only.

In the Indian Ocean, in the Somali Current and East African Coast Current especially in summer; in the Moçambique and Agulhas currents throughout the year but more frequently in the Algulhas Current; in the region immediately E and S of Ceylon, from June to December. An occasional observation is reported in the Equatorial Counter-current and in the S parts of the Arabian Sea and the Bay of Bengal.

In the North Pacific Ocean, in Kuro Shio throughout the year; in the South Equatorial Current, 0° to 4° N, between about 90° W and 160° W; E of Mindanao from June to August.

In the China Sea, off the coast of Vietnam from August to December and in February; very occasionally else-where.

In the South Pacific Ocean, in the East Australian Coast Current N of 34° S from October to April.

Some extreme values of currents have been observed in the Gulf Stream in February, at 5¼ knots; in Kuro Shio in November, at 5¾ knots; in the East Australian Coast Current in April, at 4 knots; in the Agulhas Current in September, at 5 knots; in the East African Coast Current, near the coast in September, at 5 knots; in the Somali Current, in the area S of Socotra, in August at 6 knots and in September at 7 knots. The region S of Socotra between 8° N and 11° N, during the height of the South-west Monsoon, is the area of strongest-known current in the world.

1.74. General surface circulation. The idea of oceanic circulation needs some explanation. If a small definite area of the ocean be chosen and all currents observed within that area be plotted, it will be found that they are variable, in greater or lesser degree. Surface water thus flows into and out of the area in various directions. Providing that each individual current is not exactly balanced by one of the same strength in the opposite direction, which is never the case, there will be in the long run a resultant flow of water out of the area. This flow is found by taking the vector mean of all the currents, *i.e.* a mean which takes account of the direction of each current as well as its rate. The resultant flows out of this and every similar area into which the ocean may be divided, form the general circulation.

The general circulation never exists as a whole at any given time. In many regions the actual currents at one time would be in accordance with the circulation, particularly in the regions of more constant current, but the circulation would frequently be interrupted, even in these. In the regions of more variable current, the deviations from the direction of the general circulation would be numerous, and possibly whole stretches of the circulation would be found missing if we could obtain an instantaneous view of the water movements of a whole ocean. The reality of the general circulation, in the long run, has been proved by numerous cases of the drifts of ships, bottles etc., over great distances.

1.75. Direct effect of wind in producing currents. When wind blows over the sea surface the frictional drag of the wind tends to cause the surface water to move with the wind. As soon as any motion is imparted, the effect of the earth's rotation (the Coriolis force) is to deflect the movement towards the right in the N hemisphere and towards the left in the S hemisphere. Although theory suggests that this effect should produce a surface flow, or "wind drift current" in a direction inclined at 45° to the right or left of the wind direction in the N or S hemisphere, observations show this angle to be less in practice. Various values between 20° and 45° have been reported. An effect of the movement of the surface water layer is to impart a lesser movement to the layer immediately below, in a direction to the right (left in the S hemisphere) of that of the surface layer. Thus, with increasing depth, the speed of the wind-induced current becomes progressively less but the angle between the directions of wind and current progressively increases.

Many investigators have endeavoured to determine the ratio between the speed of the surface current and the speed of the wind responsible. This is a complex problem and many different answers have been put forward. An average empirical value for this ratio is about 1:40 (or 0·025). Some investigators claim a variation of the factor with latitude but the degree of any such variation is in dispute. In the main the variation with latitude is comparatively small and, in view of the other uncertainties in determining the ratio, can probably be disregarded in most cases.

The implication that a 40-knot wind should produce a current of about 1 knot needs qualification. The strength of the current depends on the period and the fetch over which the wind has been blowing. With the onset of wind there is initially little response in terms of water movement, which gradually builds up with time. With light winds the slight current that results takes only about 6 hours to become fully developed, but with strong winds about 48 hours is needed for the current to reach its full speed. A limited fetch, however, restricts the full development of the current.

It seems reasonable to expect that hurricane force winds might give rise to currents in excess of 2 knots, provided that the fetch and duration of the wind sufficed. Reliable observations, however, are rare in these circumstances.

In the case of **tropical storms**, the effect of the very high wind speed is usually reduced by the limited fetch due to the curvature of the wind path, and by the limited period within which the wind blows from a particular direction. Thus, with these storms, it is the slow moving ones which are liable to cause the strongest currents.

In the vicinity of a tropical storm the set of the current may be markedly different from that normally to be expected. Comparatively little is known about such currents, particularly near the centre of the storm, since navigators avoid the centre whenever possible and conditions within the storm field generally are unfavourable to the accurate observation of the current.

The primary cause of the currents is the strong wind associated with the storm. The strength of the current produced by a given force of wind varies with the latitude and is greatest in low latitudes. For the latitudes of tropical storms, say 15° to 25°, a wind of force 10 would produce a current of about 1 knot. It is believed that the strength of the currents of tropical storms is, on the average, the same as that which a wind of similar force, unconnected with a tropical storm, would produce. These currents, at the surface, set at an angle of 45° to the right of the wind direction (in the N hemisphere) and therefore flow obliquely outward from the storm field, though not radially from the centre.

Unless due allowance is made for these sets, very serious errors in reckoning may therefore arise. It is reported that, in one case, a vessel experienced a SE'ly set of more than 50 miles, under conditions when the set normally to be expected was SW'ly. In another case an unexpected SSW'ly set of 60 miles was experienced in 18 hours. These are examples of currents of abnormal strength, which are ocasionally met in the vicinity of tropical storms, and which cannot be accounted for by the wind strength. The possibility of such an experience should be borne in mind, particularly near, say within 100 miles of the centre of the storm.

Other currents, not caused directly by the wind, may flow in connection with these storms, but are probably weak and therefore negligible in comparison with the wind current.

The above remarks apply to the open ocean. When a tropical storm approaches or crosses an extended coastline, such as that of Florida, a strong gradient current parallel with the coast will be produced by the piling up of water against the coast. The sea level may rise by as much as from 2 to 4 metres on such an occasion.

Whether the storm is in the open ocean or not there is a rise of sea level inwards to its centre which compensates for the reduction of atmospheric pressure. The extent of this rise is never great, being about $\frac{1}{2}$ metre, according to the intensity of the storm. It produces no current so long as the storm is not changing in intensity. If the storm meets the coast, however, the accumulation of water at its centre will enhance the rise of sea level at the coast mentioned above and so produce a stronger gradient current along the coast.

1.76. Gradient currents are caused by pressure gradients in the water. They occur whenever the water surface develops a slope, whether under the action of wind, or through the juxtaposition of waters of differing temperature and/or salinity. The initial water movement is down the slope but the effect of the earth's rotation is to deflect the movement through 90° to the right (in the N hemisphere) and to the left (in the S hemisphere) of the initial direction.

A gradient current may be flowing in the surface layers at the same time as a drift current is being produced by the wind. In this case the actual current observed is the resultant of the two.

An interesting example of a gradient current occurs in the Bay of Bengal in February. In this month the current circulation is clockwise around the shores of the bay, the flow being NE'ly along the W shore; with the North-east Monsoon still blowing, the current is setting against the wind. The explanation of this phenomenon is that the cold wind off the land cools the water at the head of the bay. A temperature gradient thus arises between cold water in the N and warm water in the S. Because of the density difference thus created a slope, downwards towards the N, develops. The resulting N'ly flow is directed towards the right, in an E'ly direction, and so sets up the general clockwise circulation.

1.77. Effect of wind blowing over a coastline. Slopes of the sea surface may be produced by wind. When a wind blows parallel with a coastline or obliquely over it, a slope of the sea surface near the coast occurs. The effect of a wind blowing obliquely over the coast to seaward is to drive water away from the coast, so that the sea level slopes down to the coast. The effect of a similar wind blowing obliquely towards the land is to bank water against the coast, so that the sea level slopes up to the coast. In either case a gradient current results. A wind more or less parallel with the coast is the most effective in creating these slopes, since the total water transport, in the layer in which wind influence occurs, being directed at 90° from the wind, is then directly on to the coast or directly away from it. Whether the water runs towards or away from the coast depends on; (i) which way the wind is blowing, along the coast; (ii) which hemisphere is being considered. For example, in the region of the Benguela Current (S hemisphere) the South-east Trade Wind blows obliquely to seaward over the coast of SW Africa, *i.e.* in a NW direction. The total transport of water is 90° to the left of this, *i.e.* in a SW direction, and therefore water is driven away from the coast.

The coastal currents on the E side of the main circulation are produced in this way, by removal of water from the coastal regions under the influence of the trade winds. As has been shown, the gradient current runs at right angles to the slope. As the slope is at right angles to the trend of the coastline, the gradient current must always be parallel with the coastline. Taking the Benguela Current as an example, the water tending to run down the slope towards the coast of SW Africa is deviated 90° to the left and therefore the gradient current is somewhat W of N, since this is the general trend of the coastline. The South-east Trade Wind is tending also to produce at the actual sea surface a drift current directed rather less than 45° to the left of NW or roughly W, and the actual current experienced by a ship will be the resultant of this and the gradient, approximately NW.

These coastal currents on the E sides of the oceans are associated with the chief regions of upwelling. In these regions colder water rises from moderate depths to replace the water drawn away from the coastal region by the wind. In consequence the sea surface temperature in these regions is lower than elsewhere in similar latitudes. The balance between the replacement of water by upwelling and its removal by the gradient current is such that the slope of the surface remains the same, so long as the wind direction and strength remain constant. The actual slope is extremely slight and quite unmeasurable by any means at our disposal. In general, it is less than one inch in a distance of 10 miles.

The Labrador Current is an example of one which is produced by the banking of water against the coast by the N to NW'ly winds prevailing during a large part of the year. Water tends to run down the slope to seaward, and being diverted 90° to the right, the current follows the coast in a S'ly direction.

1.78. Summary. The causes which produce currents are thus seen to be very complex, and in general more than one cause is at work in giving rise to any part of the surface current circulation. Observations of current are still not so numerous that their distribution in all parts of the ocean can be accurately defined. Still less is known of the subsurface circulations, since the oceans are vast and the work of research expeditions is very limited in time and place. It is known that the greatest variations of temperature and salinity occur in middle and lower latitudes, relatively near the surface, within a layer varying in depth from about 500 to 1000 metres. This layer includes the still shallower layer in which the direct influence of wind acts in impelling the water. The strongest currents are therefore confined to this layer. Below it the circulation at all depths, in the open ocean, is caused by density differences, and is relatively weak. The great coastal currents on the W sides of the ocean flow also in the deeper levels and perhaps nearly reach the bottom.

The main surface circulation of an ocean, though it forms a closed eddy, is not self-compensating. Examination of current charts makes it obvious that the same volume of water is not being transported in all parts of the eddy. There are strong and weak parts in all such circulations. Also there is some interchange between different oceans at the surface. Thus a large part of the South Equatorial Current of the Atlantic passes into the North Atlantic Ocean to join the North Equatorial Current, and so contributes to the flow of the Gulf Stream. There is no adequate compensation for this, if surface currents only be considered. There is therefore interchange between surface and subsurface water. The process of upwelling has been described; in other regions, notably in high latitudes, water sinks from the surface to the bottom. Deep currents, including those along the bottom of the oceans, also play their part in the process of compensation. Thus water sinking in certain places in high latitudes in the North Atlantic flows S along the bottom, and subsequently enters the South Atlantic.

Much, though not necessarily all, of the day to day variability of surface current is due to wind variation. Seasonal variation of current is also largely due to seasonal wind changes. It is probable that the average current will vary somewhat in successive periods of years. There is some evidence, for example, that the flow of the Gulf Stream was appreciably weaker in 1932–1939 than in 1910–1931.

ICE

1.81. Formation and distribution. For information concerning ice, its formation, characteristics, and global distribution, see *The Mariner's Handbook.*

Ice limits, and drift in particular areas, are described in the chapters dealing with the principal ocean areas.

ELECTRONIC AIDS AND POSITION FIXING SYSTEMS

1.91. Navigational aids

1.91.01. Particulars of Radio Direction Finding stations, Radiobeacons, Calibration stations, Coast radar stations providing navigational assistance, Radar beacons, and Coast radio stations giving QTG services are published in *Admiralty List of Radio Signals.*

1.92. Position fixing systems

1.92.01 The following notes outline the performance and application of the electronic position fixing systems suitable for ocean navigation. See also *Admiralty List of Radio Signals.*

The Administrations which control Position fixing systems accept no responsibility for the consequences of inaccurate positions obtained by means of such systems.

1.92.02. Consol is essentially a long range directional radiobeacon system, the position lines of which provide true bearings to the transmitting station. The major advantage of the system is the simple means by which a position line is obtained aurally using any receiver possessing long range (MF) coverage.

Typical ranges over the sea are 1000 miles by day and up to 1500 miles at night. The system is not usable within 25 miles of the transmitter.

System coverage is available in the NE part of the Atlantic Ocean and in the Barents Sea, most of the area being covered by Admiralty charts showing Consol position lines.

1.92.03. Loran (LOng RAnge Navigation), employs pairs of pulse transmitting stations which are spaced up to 600 miles apart. Two systems are currently in use, Loran A (formerly known as Standard Loran) and Loran C.

The range of Loran A over sea varies from 500 miles to 800 miles by day when groundwave signals are utilised to 1400 miles by night if use is made of skywave signals. Typical fix accuracy when using groundwaves is in the order of ±0·5 per cent of the range from the middle of the base line.

Loran A coverage is available over a major portion of the North Atlantic Ocean and of the North Pacific Ocean. Admiralty charts with a Loran A lattice are available for the North Atlantic Ocean.

Loran C, a more sophisticated system than Loran A, has a typical daytime range of up to 1000 miles, and skywave cover at night of up to 2000 miles.
As with Loran A, there is system coverage for large areas of the North Atlantic Ocean and the North Pacific Ocean, and there is coverage in the Mediterranean Sea.

1.92.04. Omega is a hyperbolic radio navigational aid which depends upon the measurement of the phase difference between signals transmitted from a pair of stations to provide lines of position. The use of very low frequencies, in the range of 10–14 kHz, enables base lines over 5000 miles in length to be used, so that only 8 land-based transmitting stations can provide continuous world-wide coverage.
Diurnal and seasonal variations in propagation cause changes in the Omega pattern which must be corrected from special tables, otherwise considerable errors in position could result. With the help of these tables, the optimum accuracy should be ±1 mile by day and ±2 miles at night.
In 1972, one station was operating on full power and three stations were on trial with a provisional service covering the North Atlantic Ocean and parts of the North Pacific Ocean in operation. Appropriately latticed plotting sheets and correction tables can be obtained from the Hydrographic Mapping Centre, Defence Mapping Agency, Washington DC 20390, U.S.A.

1.92.05. Satellite navigation. Vessels fitted with a satellite navigation receiver together with the necessary electronic computer can obtain positions by using signals transmitted from artificial satellites specially orbited for the purposes of navigation.
Depending on the number of satellites in orbit and the area, the system offers worldwide coverage with fixes obtainable at from ½ hour to 2 hour intervals.
The system uses the doppler principle of the signals emitted by the satellites as they pass within range of the vessel's radio horizon. A single channel system relying upon the doppler principle will give positions with approximately 2 mile accuracy, but with a two channel system, which takes refraction of the radio signals into account, accuracies of about ¼ mile can be obtained.

NOTES AND CAUTIONS

1.101. International Regulations concerning pollution of the sea by oil are given in *The Mariner's Handbook*. The zones to which they apply are described in Admiralty Sailing Directions and are shown on the Routeing Charts.

1.102. Fishing vessels. In 1969, it was estimated that some 9000 fishing vessels of over 100 tons gross, including about 300 factory ships and carriers, were at sea at any given time. Many operate in fleets. but their operations and traffic habits are nearly as varied as the catch they seek. It has been forecast that by the year 1980 the number of fishing vessels at sea is likely to be about 15000.
Owing to the complexity of the changes in fishing grounds and consequently in the movement of fishing vessels this volume does not attempt more than to give a general warning to mariners that they should be continually on the alert against meeting fishing vessels, on passage or at work, anywhere at sea.

1.103. Coral waters. Coral reefs are often steep-to, and depths of more than 200 m may be found within one cable of the edge of a reef. Soundings are therefore of little value as a warning of their proximity. The soundings, furthermore, shoal so rapidly that it is sometimes difficult to follow the echo sounder trace and the echo itself is often weak owing to the steep bottom profile.
Navigation among coral reefs is therefore almost entirely dependent upon the eye, and in ocean areas where these reefs abound the greatest care is required. Whenever possible, passage through the worst parts of such areas should be made in daylight, and every precaution should be taken to keep an accurate check on the ship's position.
For additional information on navigation in coral waters, see *The Mariner's Handbook*.

CHAPTER 2

NORTH ATLANTIC OCEAN

CONTENTS   *Page*

ROUTES TO AND FROM KAP FARVEL AND DAVIS STRAIT

ROUTES TO AND FROM STRAIT OF BELLE ISLE

ROUTES TO AND FROM ST JOHN'S, NEWFOUNDLAND

ROUTES BETWEEN ST LAWRENCE AND NORTHERN COAST OF UNITED STATES, AND EUROPE

ROUTES BETWEEN UNITED STATES OR WEST INDIES, AND AFRICA

ROUTES BETWEEN EUROPE AND WEST INDIES

ROUTES BETWEEN ENGLISH CHANNEL AND STRAIT OF GIBRALTAR OR INTERMEDIATE PORTS

ROUTES BETWEEN ENGLISH CHANNEL AND WEST COAST OF AFRICA

ROUTES BETWEEN NORTH AMERICA AND CABO DE SÃO ROQUE, OR INTERMEDIATE POSITIONS

ROUTES BETWEEN NORTH-EAST COAST OF SOUTH AMERICA AND EASTERN PART OF NORTH ATLANTIC OCEAN

ROUTES BETWEEN EASTERN PART OF NORTH ATLANTIC OCEAN AND RECIFE

ROUTES TO AND FROM ARQUIPÉLAGO DOS AÇÔRES

ROUTES TO AND FROM ARQUIPÉLAGO DE CABO VERDE

WINDS AND WEATHER

2.01. Equatorial Trough, or Doldrums. In the North Atlantic Ocean, the belt of calms and light variable winds which lies between the trade winds of the two hemispheres remains N of the equator throughout the year. Its mean positions for February and August respectively, when it reaches its S'ly and N'ly limits, are indicated on charts 5301 and 5302. The actual position is subject to much day-to-day variation, as is also the width of the zone, which averages about 200 to 300 miles but may at times be reduced to almost nothing by a strong burst of one or both Trade winds.

There is evidence to show that showers, squalls, and thunderstorms are more common within 200 to 300 miles from the African coast than in the W part of the area.

Visibility in the Doldrum zone is invariably good except in rain.

2.02. South-west Monsoon. In summer, the intense heating of the land mass of N Africa lowers the atmospheric pressure over that area and distorts the Equatorial Trough towards N. The South-east Trade Wind (3.02) is drawn across the equator and is caused to veer by the earth's rotation, so that it arrives off the W coast of Africa between the equator and about 15° N, E of about 20° W, as a SW wind which is known as the South-west Monsoon. This monsoon, which is accompanied by cloudy weather and considerable rainfall, lasts from about June to the middle of October; the rainfall is heavy on the coast between Gambia and Liberia. Visibility is good at this season except in rain.

During the rest of the year winds in this area are mainly N'ly between Liberia and Mauritania, but are mostly from between S and W in the Gulf of Guinea; in both cases they are generally light. Between November and February a dry, dust laden E'ly wind known as the **Harmattan** occurs at times. Weather at this season is generally fine, but visibility is often only moderate due to haze, and it may become poor while the Harmattan is blowing.

Towards the beginning and end of the rainy season, that is in April and May, October and November, violent thunderstorms accompanied by severe squalls, generally from an E'ly direction, occur at times near the coast. These are known locally as **Tornados**, but they should not be confused with the storms of that name which occur in the interior of the United States and of Australia, to which they bear no relation.

2.03. The North-east Trades form the equatorial side of the clockwise circulation round the oceanic anticyclone situated in about 30° N. They extend from the African coast as far W as the Caribbean Sea and the Gulf of Mexico, blowing from about NNE on the E side of the ocean and from a little N of E in the W part of the zone. They blow permanently with an average strength of force 4, though on rare occasions they may increase to force 7 or decrease to force 2. In the Gulf of Mexico (4.01) they are more variable both in direction and strength; between November and March they are sometimes interrupted in that area by strong or gale force N'ly winds known as **Northers.**

In the NE part of the trade wind zone the weather is generally fair or fine with small amounts of detached cumulus and little or no rain. Cloud cover and showers increase towards the Doldrums and towards the W part; in the latter area rain is comparatively frequent, particularly in summer.

Haze occurs frequently in the E part of the trade wind zone; it is caused by the dust or sand carried seaward by the prevailing offshore wind. Sea fog forms at times in the NE part of the zone over the cold water of the Canary Current (2.16). In the W part of the zone, visibility is good except in rain.

2.04. Variables (Horse Latitudes). A belt of generally light and variable winds over the oceanic area of high pressure extends across the ocean in about 30° N, oscillating from about 28° N in winter to 32° N in summer. The predominant winds in this area, E of about 20° W in winter and 30° W in summer, are from between N and NE and form an extension of the North-east Trades, particularly in summer.

Weather in the E part of the zone is fine with little cloud; in the W part there is more cloud, and rain is fairly common. Visibility in the E part is often reduced by haze and sometimes by fog for the reasons explained in article 2.03.

2.05. Hurricanes occur in the W part of the North Atlantic Ocean. They affect in particular the Caribbean Sea, the Gulf of Mexico, Florida, the Bahamas, and Bermuda, with the adjacent ocean areas. They occur from June to October and sometimes in November, with their greatest frequency in September.

More detailed information on storm frequencies will be found in Admiralty Sailing Directions. Notes on precursory signs and avoiding action are published in *The Mariner's Handbook.*

2.06. Westerlies. The N part of the Atlantic Ocean experiences predominantly unsettled weather on the polar side of the oceanic anticyclone. With the almost continuous passage of depressions across this zone in an E'ly or NE'ly direction, the wind varies greatly in both direction and strength, and there is a high frequency of strong winds. Gales are common, especially in winter. The region of highest gale frequency extends roughly from the vicinity of Newfoundland to about 58° N, 13° W; and in this region winds reach force 7 or above on 16 to 20 days a month in January and February; in July, which is the quietest month, the stormiest area remains SW of Iceland but the frequency of winds of force 7 or above is only about 7 days a month in it. Close to the coasts of Greenland, Iceland, and Norway, katabatic winds are common.

2.07. Fog and visibility. The frequencies of fog and poor visibility are indicated on the Routeing Charts and the subject is treated at length in the relevant Admiralty Sailing Directions. In the region of the Westerlies, overcast skies, with periods of rain or snow, alternate with brief fine spells. Cloud amounts are generally large. The part of the North Atlantic Ocean most affected by fog lies E and S of Newfoundland.

In the vicinity of the coasts of New England and Nova Scotia, and the Newfoundland Banks, fog is very prevalent in late spring and early summer, being due to the movement of warm, moist air from S or SW over the cold Labrador Current; over a large part of this area fog is experienced on more than 10 days a month. It is also liable to occur at times in other parts of this zone—usually in spring and early summer and in association with winds from between S and SW. Visibility is good with NW'ly winds, except in showers.

2.08. The North Polar regions. The greater part of the region lying on the polar side of the Westerlies is denied to navigation on account of ice. The prevailing wind is from some E'ly point, though, as in the case of the Westerlies, great variations in direction and strength are caused by the passage of depressions across the area. Gales are common, but less so than in the Westerlies.

Weather is generally very cloudy, and precipitation, usually in the form of snow, may occur at any time.

Fog, often of the arctic sea-smoke type, is prevalent in summer.

Further information is published in Admiralty Sailing Directions.

SWELL

2.11. Atlantic Ocean, 0°–40° N. Between the equator and 30° N, frequencies of swell greater than 4 m in height rarely exceed 2 to 4 per cent. One of the most persistent swells is from NE, between Islas Canarias and the NE coast of South America. In the extreme SE, off Freetown, S and E swells prevail.

Between 30° and 40° N, frequencies of swell greater than 4 m in height are: April, 10 per cent; May to August, 5 to 10 per cent; September to November, 10 per cent; December to March, 20 per cent. The predominant direction is from between W and NW.

2.12. Atlantic Ocean, 40° N–60° N. Frequencies of swell greater than 4 m in height are: April, 20 per cent; May to July, 10 per cent; August and September, 20 per cent; October to March, 30 per cent. In December and January, a maximum of 40 per cent is reached in an area centred on 55° N, 22° W. Throughout the year swell comes mainly from between SW and NW, with swell from W predominating.

2.13. Length of swell. Swell in the Atlantic Ocean is generally short (less than 90 m) or average (90–180 m) in length. However, long swells may be found from time to time, though they are less frequent than in the Pacific Ocean.

CURRENTS

2.15. Southern part of North Atlantic Ocean. The currents in the S part of the North Atlantic, between about 10° N and 40° N, circulate in a clockwise sense to form a roughly oval cell which occupies all the region between the African and Iberian coasts and the Atlantic coasts of the West Indies and North America. The W-setting currents on the S flank of this cell comprise the **North Equatorial Current** between about 10° N and

20° N and the **North Sub-tropical Current** between about 20° N and 30°–32° N. Of these, the former is the stronger (average ½ knot) and the more constant. Some of the North Equatorial Current continues into the Caribbean Sea (4.11); the remainder turns NW off the West Indies as the **Antilles Current** and thereafter turns progressively N so as to flow parallel with the N-going **Florida Current** and **Gulf Stream** (4.11) off Florida.

5 To the N of about 32° N, the Gulf Stream turns NE and then progressively E so that the main direction of the current N of 36° N is E'ly between 65° W and 50° W. To the E of about 50° W, the Gulf Stream fans out and weakens, to become the **North Atlantic Current** (2.16) with main directions between E and NE. In consequence of this NE'ly trend of the main flow, the currents between 36° N and 40° N change from well marked easterlies in the W part of the ocean to lighter and more variable currents E of 50° W, with SE'ly to S'ly directions

10 predominating. In the N (36°–40° N) the currents are variable with only a small preponderance of S'ly sets from about 50° W as far as the Iberian coast. Farther S, under the influence of the Trade Winds, the currents become more constant and form a wide belt of mainly SW'ly sets off the North African coast, which ultimately turns W to join the North Equatorial current.

The currents are weakest and least constant towards the central part of the circulation described in the pre-

15 ceding paragraph, near an axis which shifts somewhat with the seasons but runs roughly from near Arquipélago dos Açôres to near Bermuda. In a large area round this central region the mean rates are below ½ knot at all times. The highest average rate in the region as a whole occurs in the Florida Current (or S portion of the Gulf Stream) where it reaches about 3 knots in summer in the axis of the stream off S Florida. The rate falls off farther N to an average, in the fastest part of the Gulf Stream, of about 1 knot, N and E of Cape Hatteras.

20 S of about 10° N the currents are rather more complex, and show a decided seasonal variation. In summer, an appreciable belt of E'ly sets known as the **Equatorial Counter-current** extends from about 45° W almost to the African coast. The W part of this belt lies roughly between 5° N and 10° N, while near the African coast the belt lies between 10° N and the equator. The South Equatorial Current (3.11), which sets W, lies S of this belt; on approaching the South American continent it is diverted to form a broad NW'ly stream.

25 In winter, the Equatorial Counter-current is reduced to a small belt lying between 2° N and 6° N, E of 20° W. Farther W, the North Equatorial Current and South Equatorial Current converge, forming a broad belt of current setting W with no intervening E'ly sets. This W-setting stream is diverted along the N-facing coast of South America, as in summer. Average rates in this current reach 2 knots in the strongest parts, which extend roughly from 2° N, 47° W to 5° N, 51° W.

30 Near the African coast, at all times, the flow is predominantly SE and E, forming the **Guinea Current,** which follows the coast at an average rate which varies from about 1 knot in winter to 1¾ knots in summer. The greatest rate occurs near the coast in about 5° W. Elsewhere in this area, between the equator and 10°N, the average rates are about ¾ knot to 1 knot.

35 **2.16. Northern part of North Atlantic Ocean.** Over a large portion of the N part of the North Atlantic Ocean, the direction of the prevailing flow is NE. Immediately N of Cape Hatteras the Gulf Stream, which originates in Florida Strait as the Florida Current, begins to leave the 200 m line and gradually turns E into the ocean, S of Georges Bank and the Nova Scotian Banks. Its N edge is relatively sharply defined at all times, owing to the convergence along it of the cold water of the Labrador Current (below).

40 To the E of about 46° W, the Gulf Stream ceases to be a well defined current. It widens and weakens by fanning out along the E side of the Grand Bank. The resulting wide NE'ly flow is known as the **North Atlantic Current,** which flows across the ocean towards the British Isles and the adjacent coasts of Europe.

The S part of the North Atlantic Current turns gradually clockwise to SE'ly and then SW'ly directions over the whole ocean E of 40° to 45° W. It thus passes into the North Sub-tropical current to complete the main

45 circulation. This widely extended trend of the water, branching S from the North Atlantic Current, is called the **Azores Current,** and occupies the belt of latitude between about 42° N and 32° N. The current known as the **Portugal Current,** flowing S off the W coasts of Spain and Portugal, and as the **Canary Current** farther S, forms the coastal fringe of the general S'ly flow of the Azores current.

The N part of the North Atlantic Current does not recurve S but continues to flow in a general NE direction

50 off the W coasts of the Hebrides and Shetlands and thence to the coast of Norway. It sets N along this coast, off which it is known as the **Norwegian Atlantic Current.** In about 69° N, this current divides and the N part, known as the **West Spitsbergen Current,** sets N to the W coast of Spitsbergen and thence into the Arctic Basin. The S branch is known as the **North Cape Current** and follows the coast past Nordkapp into the Barents Sea, finally setting towards the N of Novaya Zemlya; a branch of it, known as the **Murman Coast Current,**

55 continues along the Murman coast.

The chief outflow of water from the Arctic Basin is the cold, ice-bearing current known as the **East Greenland Current,** which sets SW along the E coast of Greenland. Part of this current diverges SE from the main body N of 70° N, forming the **East Iceland Current,** which passes the NE coast of Iceland and thence N of the Faeroes, the set gradually trending E and finally NE. It joins, or runs parallel with the seaward edge of the Nor-

60 wegian Atlantic Current.

A branch of the warm North Atlantic Current turns N in the longitude of Iceland. Close SW of Iceland this current, known as the **Irminger Current,** divides. The main branch turns W and joins the East Greenland Current S of Denmark Strait. A smaller branch makes a clockwise circulation of Iceland.

The East Greenland Current rounds Kap Farvel and passes N along the W coast of Greenland, where it

65 is known as the **West Greenland Current.** This loses volume by fanning out on its seaward side, but part of it circuits the head of Baffin Bay and, reinforced by water flowing E through Jones and Lancaster Sounds, sets S along the coast of Baffin Island as the **Baffin Land Current.** N of Hudson Strait this is joined by a considerable branch from the West Greenland Current, which crosses Davis Strait. The combined current, known as the **Labrador Current,** sets past the entrance to Hudson Strait and SE along the Labrador coast to the

70 Newfoundland region.

2.17. Newfoundland Banks. After passing the Strait of Belle Isle and the E coast of Newfoundland, the Labrador Current covers the whole of Grand Bank except, during summer, the extreme S part. A large branch of the current follows the E edge of the bank; this is the part which carries ice farthest S to reach the transatlantic shipping routes. Another branch rounds Cape Race and sets SW. Although some of the water that has passed on to Grand Bank continues in a more S'ly direction, especially during August to October, the bulk of it sets *5* SW and continues, as a SW'ly set, to fill the region between Newfoundland, Nova Scotia, and the Gulf Stream.

The Labrador Current subsequently continues S along the coast of the United States as a cold current as far as about 36° N from November to January, 37° N from February to April, 38° N from May to July, and 40° N from August to October. Between the S limit of the Labrador Current and the Tail of the Bank, the warm and cold waters converge on a line which is known as the **Cold Wall**. *10*

The E end of the Cold Wall presents the greatest hydrographic contrasts to be found in the world, the water changing from the olive or bottle green of the Arctic side to the indigo blue of the Gulf Stream, with temperature changes of 11° or more over short distances.

The currents off the coasts of Labrador and Newfoundland are complex; for details, reference should be made to Admiralty Sailing Directions. *15*

2.18. North Sea. A branch of the North Atlantic Current diverges from the main flow NE of the Shetlands and flows S, fanning out E towards the S part of the Skagerrak, along the E coasts of Britain as far as the Thames estuary. It is there joined by a branch of the North Atlantic Current which passes through the English Channel and the Strait of Dover, the combined currents then flowing along the Netherlands and Jutland coasts. This *20* current then flows round the Skagerrak in a counter-clockwise direction and finally sets N along the W coast of Norway.

The outflow from the North Sea forms the **Norwegian Coastal Current** and is probably the most constant part of the circulation. In about 62° N this current rejoins the main branch of the North Atlantic Current flowing towards Nordkapp. *25*

2.19. Western approaches to English Channel. After SW or W gales, a set towards the mouth of the Channel may be expected, at a rate depending on the locality, strength, and duration of the gale. In winter, sets of up to 1½ knots are sometimes recorded, mainly in directions between ENE and SE, but the tidal streams are responsible for most of the water movement within the 200 m line. See 1.75. *30*

2.20. Bay of Biscay. Off the mouth of the Bay of Biscay the current is trending SE and S to form the beginning of the Portugal Current (2.16). A branch enters the bay and recurves W along the N coast of Spain, but over most of the bay the currents are highly variable with a tendency for directions between E and S to predominate. The speeds for the most part do not exceed 1 knot and very rarely reach 2 knots. *35*

Following W'ly or NW'ly gales E'ly sets occur off the N coast of Spain, sometimes attaining a rate of 3 knots off Bilbao and 4–5 knots at the head of the bay particularly when current and tidal stream are in the same direction.

2.21. Extreme rates. For extreme rates not mentioned in the preceding paragraphs, see 1.73.

40

ICE

2.25. General remarks. The following brief account of ice in the North Atlantic Ocean is by no means comprehensive. Before undertaking voyages through areas in which ice is likely to be met, *The Mariner's Hand-* *45* *book* and the relevant Admiralty Sailing Directions should be studied, as well as the monthly Routeing Charts, which show the ice limits. These limits are also shown approximately on Climatic Charts 5301 and 5302, but they may not always agree with the Routeing Charts which endeavour to show the extreme limits on a monthly basis as far as this is possible with the limited and variable data available.

10-day Ice charts, obtainable from the Director General, Meteorological Office (Met O 10 DWR), London *50* Road, Bracknell, Berks, should also be studied.

Facsimile broadcasts of ice charts are also available, as set out in *Admiralty List of Radio Signals*.

A factor always to be borne in mind where ice conditions are concerned is their great variability. For this reason, and on account of the sparsity of observations in many areas, the charted positions of ice limits must be regarded as approximate. The dates which follow refer to average conditions. *55*

2.26. Ice limits and drift. A glance at the Routeing Charts will reveal the influence of the ocean currents (2.16–2.17) in setting the pack over much of the Newfoundland Banks area from the latter part of January until May, while the E part of the ocean remains ice-free to high latitudes.

Almost all the icebergs which menace the North Atlantic routes originate in the glaciers of the W coast of *60* Greenland where they are calved at a rate of several thousand a year. They are carried S by the Greenland, Baffin Land, and Labrador currents, and when they finally reach the shipping routes they may be several years old. The bergs calved on the E coast of Greenland also drift S, and may be met off Kap Farvel, but they do not survive the relatively warm water of Davis Strait and are not a source of danger on the regular transatlantic routes. Icebergs may be found beyond the limits of the pack ice at all seasons, but mostly in early summer; in *65* winter many are frozen into the pack.

2.27. Ice in specific localities. *Kap Farvel.* The greatest distance at which bergs are met S of Kap Farvel usually occurs in April and May; this is generally up to about 120 miles, but in 1922 bergs extended to 150 miles S of the cape. In April, bergs may be met as far E as 66° N, 32° W. *70*

St Lawrence River below Montreal is closed by ice between early December and mid-April. Commercial navigation ceases in most parts of the Gulf of St Lawrence by mid-December; in the S part, navigation is not considered safe between early December and mid-April.

The *Strait of Belle Isle* is generally not navigable from the beginning of December until June.

Pack ice arrives from N off *Cape Race* about the end of January in an ordinary season, extending round the coasts of the Avalon peninsula in February, until April.

Between July and December inclusive, *Grand Bank of Newfoundland* is entirely free of pack-ice, which reaches the bank in January and extends farthest S in March and April, on the E edge of the bank. In very rare seasons, dangerous pack may extend to the Tail of the Bank and even S of it but, on average, the floes begin to break up on reaching 45° N.

In the region of Grand Bank, the worst season for icebergs is between March and July, with May as the month of greatest frequency. Bergs are not often found S of 40° N or E of 40° W, though occasionally they may be considerably outside these limits. They are particularly prevalent around the E flank of the bank, on which many of them ground. More detail is given in Admiralty Sailing Directions.

Denmark Strait is normally free of ice on its E side throughout the year, but on rare occasions, as in the spring of 1968, the ice spreads across from Greenland to close the strait.

The *White Sea* is normally closed to navigation from about mid-December to mid-May.

In *Kól'ski Inlet*, the N part remains open through the year but, from December to April ice forms along the shore and at times breaks away, to be carried out to sea. It may be a hindrance for three or four days at a time in exceptionally cold winters.

On the *West coast of Norway*, none of the main ports is ever closed by ice, and the closure of *Oslö* is very rare.

In the *North Sea* serious ice conditions in the entrances to German, Dutch, and Danish ports, lasting from one to four weeks, occur about two or three times in ten years at some time between mid-January and early March.

2.28. Ice reporting and advisory services in the NW Atlantic are maintained by the International Ice Patrol (U.S. Coast Guard Service) in an area SE of Newfoundland, and by the Canadian Department of Transport in respect of vessels approaching and leaving Canadian ports.

The International Ice Patrol operates from February or March, and the Canadian service opens in December. Starting and finishing dates vary according to the season.

During the ice season, vessels in the International Ice Patrol area, see *Admiralty List of Radio Signals*, are urged to assist the Patrol by reporting sighting of ice, visibility, sea temperature, and weather. Ships approaching Canadian ports are asked to report 36 hours before arrival their position, speed, destination, whether loaded or in ballast, ice classification and name of Canadian Agent, with subsequent reports of position with the object of minimising delay if assistance is needed.

For details of shore based services and ships' reporting procedures, see *Admiralty List of Radio Signals*. Details of the International Ice Patrol are also given by the Intergovernmental Maritime Consultative Organisation in their Report on the International Conference on Safety of Life at Sea, 1960; and the Canadian services are described by "Information Canada" in *Ice Navigation in Canadian Waters*.

NOTES AND CAUTIONS

2.31. Western approaches to English Channel. When navigating in these waters it is essential to assess the surface drift caused by recently prevailing wind and weather. The set of the swell should not be regarded as a precise indication of the resulting drifts. See 2.19 and Admiralty Sailing Directions.

2.32. Mariners approaching **Île d'Ouessant (Ushant)** must guard against the danger of being set E of their reckoning, and should use the greatest caution when passing it. Unless certain of the position, Île d'Ouessant should be given a wide berth and a depth exceeding 110 m should be maintained.

2.33. Bay of Biscay. There may be a strong E'ly set off the N coast of Spain after a W'ly or NW'ly gale, as described in article 2.20.

An onshore wind brings cloud that develops into fog or thick mist when it reaches the elevated land at both the N and S points of the bay.

2.34. Strait of Gibraltar. A vessel approaching the Strait in thick weather from the Atlantic should take soundings unless her position is certain. Caution is necessary, since the currents, tidal streams, and eddies between Cabo de São Vicente and Isla de Tarifa are very variable. Cape Spartel is safe to approach. In clear weather, the Strait can be approached without difficulty.

2.35. Strait of Belle Isle. A vessel approaching from E in low visibility may, if not certain of her position, be greatly assisted by sounding on the banks E of Newfoundland and Labrador.

2.36. Newfoundland coasts. As fog is exceedingly prevalent off the S coast of Newfoundland, especially in summer, vessels should guard against the set of the current and the indraught into the deep bays, particularly on their E sides.

When approaching from E in thick weather, the radio beacons on the E coast of Newfoundland and the use of soundings over Grand Bank and Ballard Bank should indicate the position with enough accuracy to enable the vessel to round Cape Race in safety. Decca coverage is available E and S of Newfoundland, see *Admiralty List of Radio Signals*.

Although the current between Grand Bank and Newfoundland ordinarily sets SW at a rate which may slightly exceed 1 knot, it is not unusual, particularly for a short period before a gale, for the current to be so disturbed as to set across its ordinary direction or even to be reversed on the surface. Close inshore, it is affected by the tidal streams.

The currents between Cape Race and St. Pierre are irregular, with a greatest rate of 1 knot, and are influenced by the wind, and, near the shore, by the tidal streams. See Admiralty Sailing Directions.

When approaching from W, Cape Pine and Cape Race should not be closed in depths of less than 55 m unless certain of the position.

2.37. When approaching **Penedos de São Pedro e São Paolo** and **Ilha de Fernando de Noronha,** caution is necessary, as the South Equatorial Current sets WNW past them at a rate of from 1 to 2 knots.

2.38. Local Magnetic Anomaly. For details of places where local magnetic anomaly has been reported, the Admiralty Sailing Directions should be consulted. On or near routes described in this chapter, anomaly has been reported in the N part of Florida Strait, in the vicinity of Bermuda, in 38° 12′ N, 60° 28′ W, and off the coasts of Canada and Iceland.

2.39. Ocean weather ships, which provide certain services to shipping, are stationed in the North Atlantic Ocean; see *Annual Summary of Admiralty Notices to Mariners* and *Admiralty List of Radio Signals.*

ROUTES BETWEEN DAVIS STRAIT AND HUDSON BAY

2.46. For directions for Davis Strait, Hudson Strait, and Hudson Bay, and for ice conditions, see Admiralty Sailing Directions, and for Ice Advisory services, see *Admiralty List of Radio Signals.*

ROUTES TO AND FROM KAP FARVEL AND DAVIS STRAIT

2.47. Kap Farvel. In view of weather and ice conditions off the coast of Greenland, see *Admiralty Sailing Directions,* the routes which follow are taken from 58° 30′ N, 43° 52′ W, about 75 miles S of Kap Farvel, or from 57° 35′ N, 43° 52′ W, about 130 miles S of Kap Farvel, as appropriate.

2.48. Nordkapp ↔ Kap Farvel. Normally, pass 20 miles S of Jan Mayen and through Denmark Strait to 58° 30′ N, 43° 52′ W; distance 1830 miles. If Denmark Strait is not navigable, passage must be made S of Iceland, distance 1950 miles.

The directive force of the earth's magnetic field is weak in the vicinity of Nordkapp, and local magnetic anomaly has been reported off the coast of Iceland.

2.49. West coast of Norway and North Sea ↔ Kap Farvel. As directly as navigation will allow. For Trondheim, pass between Iceland and the Faeröes; for Bergen, pass between the Faeröes and the Shetlands; for Lindesnes, pass between Fair Isle and the Orkneys. Distance from 58° 30′ N, 43° 52′ W: Trondheim 1500 miles; Bergen 1470 miles; Lindesnes 1580 miles.

2.50. British Isles, Biscay and northern Spanish ports ↔ Kap Farvel. Great circle in all cases. For Biscay ports, pass at least 10 miles SW of Chausée de Sein, see Admiralty Sailing Directions. Distances from 58° 30′ N, 43° 52′ W; Cape Wrath 1200 miles; Inishtrahull 1200 miles; Fastnet 1250 miles; Bishop Rock 1400 miles; Bordeaux 1710 miles; Vigo 1630 miles.

2.51. Lisbon and Strait of Gibraltar ↔ Davis strait. From 57° 35′ N, 43° 52′ W, about 130 miles S of Kap Farvel, by great circle to Lisbon, or to Cabo de São Vincente for the strait of Gibraltar. Distances: Lisbon 1760 miles; Strait of Gibraltar 2020 miles.

ROUTES TO AND FROM STRAIT OF BELLE ISLE

2.52. The Strait of Belle Isle is open to navigation from about June to November, inclusive, see Admiralty Sailing Directions. Departure position is 7 miles S of Belle Isle.

2.53. Strait of Belle Isle ↔ Nordkapp. Pass through 58° 30′ N, 43° 52′ W (75 miles S of Kap Farvel), thence through Denmark Strait and 20 miles S of Jan Mayen. Distance 2400 miles. If Denmark Strait is not navigable, passage must be made S of Iceland; distance 2520 miles.

See caution regarding local magnetic anomaly and loss of directive force in article 2.48.

2.54. Strait of Belle Isle ↔ North Sea and west coast of Norway. For Trondheim, the great circle track should be followed; distance 2060 miles. For Bergen, take the great circle but pass between the Faeröes and the

Shetlands; distance 2030 miles. For Lindesnes, take the great circle but pass between Fair Isle and the Orkneys; distance 2120 miles.

2.55. Strait of Belle Isle ↔ British Isles and Biscay ports. Proceed by great circle. Distances: Cape Wrath 1740 miles; Inishtrahull 1700 miles; Fastnet 1690 miles; Bishop Rock 1830 miles; Bordeaux 2120 miles.

ROUTES TO AND FROM ST. JOHN'S, NEWFOUNDLAND

2.56. St. John's harbour is rarely frozen over.

2.57. St. John's ↔ positions between Cape Wrath and Arquipélago de Cabo Verde. Great circle tracks should be used. Distances: Cape Wrath 1800 miles; Inishtrahull 1730 miles; Fastnet 1680 miles; Bishop Rock 1810 miles; Bordeaux 2080 miles; Vigo 1870 miles; Lisbon 1950 miles; Strait of Gibraltar 2190 miles; Horta 1200 miles; Porto Grande 2290 miles.

ROUTES BETWEEN ST. LAWRENCE AND NORTHERN COAST OF UNITED STATES, AND EUROPE

2.61. Traffic density. Owing to the density of traffic, it is recommended that E-bound and W-bound tracks should be separated in some cases. A general rule of "nothing to port of the track" should be observed unless a diversion is made; little or no distance is lost by keeping 10 miles N or S of the recommended track.

2.62. Weather routeing. On the northern transatlantic routes, mariners may gain considerable advantage by closely studying the weather with the aid of routeing advice and facsimile weather and ice maps so that, by timely adjustment of their route, they may reduce delay and damage due to wind, sea, swell, and ice. See 1.21.

2.63. Ice reporting and advisory services are described in 2.28.

2.64. Cautions. Carefully conducted tests by the International Ice Patrol have shown that radar cannot provide positive assurance for iceberg detection. An iceberg is only one-sixth as good a radar reflector as a comparatively sized ship. Seawater is a better reflector than ice. This means that unless a berg or growler is observed outside the area of sea "return" or "clutter" it will not be detected by radar. The average range of radar detection of a dangerous sized growler is 4 miles.

Radar is a valuable aid, but its use cannot replace the traditional caution exercised during a passage across Grand Banks during the ice season.

In recommending routes to and from ports SW of Cape Race, account must be taken of the seasonal movement of ice in the Grand Banks area, see 2.27. No guarantee can be given that a particular route will be clear of ice; constant study of ice reports, and the utmost vigilance at sea, are essential.

2.65. Cabot Strait is usually navigable from mid-April. The Quebec–Montreal channel is open for navigation from about April to November, inclusive.

2.66. Grand Banks. The worst season for ice is from March to July, inclusive. To reduce risk to shipping, standard "nothing to N" alter-course positions are: **CR**, from 16 May to 30 November, or when the Cape Race route is clear of ice, 46° 12′ N, 53° 05′ W, E-bound, and 46° 27′ N, 53° 05′ W, W-bound; **BN**, 11 April to 15 May and 1 December to 14 February, 45° 25′ N, 50° 00′ W, E-bound, and 45° 55′ N, 50° 00′ W, W-bound; **BS**, 15 February to 10 April, 42° 00′ N, 50° 00′ W, E-bound, and 43° 00′ N, 50° 00′ W, W-bound.

W of the standard alter-course positions, the routes between Cabot strait or Halifax and Cape Race are as direct as navigation permits. For position BN, Halifax routes are direct; for ports W of Halifax, vessels should pass not less than 60 and 40 miles S of Sable Island, E-bound and W-bound respectively. For position BS, Halifax and Boston routes pass not less than 60 and 40 miles S of Sable Island, E-bound and W-bound respectively; Nantucket, Delaware Bay and Chesapeake Bay routes are direct.

In the Grand Banks area, the International Ice Patrol advises that vessels should not venture into the pack ice N of 45° 30′ N before the middle of April.

E of the standard alter-course positions, routes are by great circle to the European landfall, except that Cape Wrath traffic should pass through 57° 50′ N, 18° 00′ W. The Nordkapp route joins the Cape Wrath routes in this position.

The track between Trondheim and Cape Race is a great circle. Between position BN and Trondheim vessels should pass 10 miles N of the Faeröes; between position BS and Trondheim the best route is 10 miles S of the Faeröes. All routes for Bergen make a landfall at Sumburgh Head.

Diagram 18 illustrates the standard alter-course positions for the main transatlantic routes.

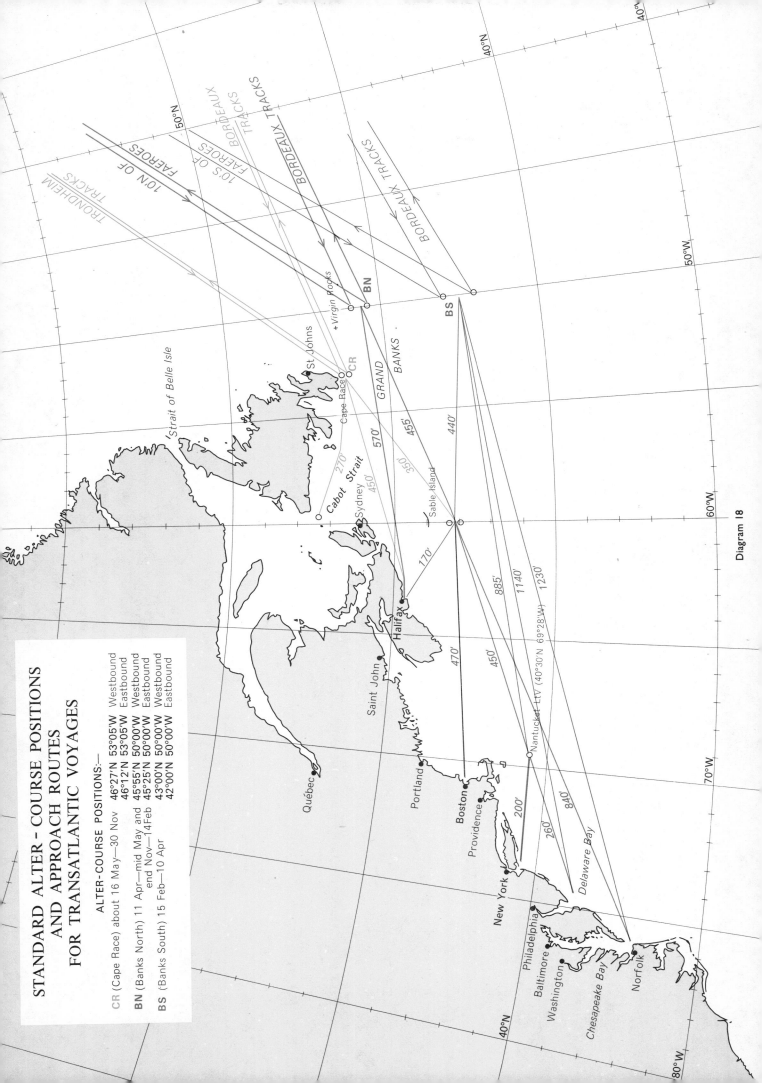

STANDARD ALTER - COURSE POSITIONS
AND APPROACH ROUTES
FOR TRANSATLANTIC VOYAGES

ALTER-COURSE POSITIONS:—

CR	(Cape Race) about 16 May—30 Nov	46°27'N	53°05'W	Westbound	
		46°12'N	53°05'W	Eastbound	
BN	(Banks North) 11 Apr—mid May and end Nov—14 Feb	45°55'N	50°00'W	Westbound	
		45°25'N	50°00'W	Eastbound	
BS	(Banks South) 15 Feb—10 Apr	43°00'N	50°00'W	Westbound	
		42°00'N	50°00'W	Eastbound	

Diagram 18

TRONDHEIM TRACKS

10°N OF FAEROES

10°S OF FAEROES

BORDEAUX TRACKS

BORDEAUX TRACKS

+ Virgin Rocks

BN

BS

St Johns

Cape Race CR

270'

GRAND BANKS

570'

455'

440'

350'

450'

'Strait of Belle Isle

Cabot Strait

Sydney

Sable Island

170'

470'

450'

885'

1140'

1230'

Québec

Saint John

Portland

Boston

Providence

Halifax

Nantucket LtV (40°30'N 69°28'W)

200'

260'

840'

New York

Delaware Bay

Philadelphia

Baltimore

Washington

Chesapeake Bay

Norfolk

50°N

40°N

40°N

50°W

60°W

70°W

80°W

2.67. Distances in miles (means of eastbound and westbound tracks). See 2.61–2.66.

	Standard alter-course positions*	Cabot Strait	Halifax	Boston	New York	Delaware Bay	Chesapeake Bay
Nordkapp	CR	3060	3240	3590	3790	3850	3980
	BN	—	3290	3650	3830	3890	4020
	BS	—	3470	3770	3950	4010	4090
Trondheim	CR	2500	2680	3050	3230	3290	3420
	BN	—	2750	3110	3290	3350	3480
	BS	—	2940	3240	3420	3470	3560
Bergen	CR	2450	2630	3000	3180	3240	3370
	BN	—	2690	3040	3220	3280	3410
	BS	—	2860	3160	3340	3390	3480
Cape Wrath	CR	2130	2310	2660	2870	2920	3050
	BN	—	2370	2720	2900	2960	3090
	BS	—	2540	2840	3020	3080	3160
Inishtrahull	CR	2060	2240	2580	2790	2850	2980
	BN	—	2280	2640	2810	2870	3000
	BS	—	2430	2730	2910	2970	3050
Fastnet	CR	1990	2180	2520	2730	2790	2910
	BN	—	2200	2560	2730	2790	2920
	BS	—	2330	2630	2800	2870	2950
Bishop Rock	CR	2130	2310	2650	2860	2920	3050
	BN	—	2330	2690	2860	2920	3050
	BS	—	2450	2750	2930	2990	3070
Bordeaux	CR	2390	2570	2910	3120	3180	3310
	BN	—	2580	2940	3120	3180	3300
	BS	—	2680	2990	3160	3220	3300

* Mean E-bound and W-bound positions. CR: 46° 20′ N, 53° 05′ W; BN: 45° 40′ N, 50° 00′ W; BS: 42° 30′ N, 50° 00′ W.

2.68. Cabot Strait ↔ Vigo, Lisbon, and Strait of Gibraltar. To avoid Virgin Rocks (46° 27′ N, 50° 47′ W) proceed to 45° 25′ N, 50° 00′ W, E-bound, and thence by great circle for the traffic lane off Cabo de São Vicente. If bound for Vigo, leave the great circle in 30° 00′ W and proceed to destination; similarly for Lisbon, leave the great circle in 15° 00′ W. W-bound, the routes are similar but pass through 45° 55′ N, 50° 00′ W and thence to Cabot Strait. Distances: Vigo 2210 miles; Lisbon 2260 miles; Strait of Gibraltar 2480 miles.

2.69. Halifax ↔ Vigo, Lisbon and Strait of Gibraltar. From 15 February to 10 April, E-bound and W-bound routes pass respectively 60 and 40 miles S of Sable Island and through 42° 00′ N and 43° 00′ N on the meridian of 50° 00′ W, and by great circle E of these positions. Distances: Vigo 2420 miles; Lisbon 2460 miles; Strait of Gibraltar 2690 miles.

From 11 April to 14 February routes are direct between Halifax and 45° 25′ N, 50° 00′ W, E-bound, and 45° 55′ N, 50° 00′ W; W-bound, E of these positions, they are as the Cabot Strait routes, namely by great circle for Cabo de São Vicente, Vigo tracks joining the great circle in 30° W and Lisbon tracks in 15° W. Distances: Vigo 2370 miles; Lisbon 2420 miles; Strait of Gibraltar 2640 miles.

Low-powered vessels, W-bound from the Strait of Gibraltar, should proceed by rhumb line S of Arquipélago dos Açôres to 36° 00′ N, 45° 00′ W; thence to Halifax.

2.70. Northern coast of United States ↔ Vigo, Lisbon, and Strait of Gibraltar. By great circle, except that from 15 February to 10 April no route may cross the meridian of 50° 00′ W to the N of 42° 00′ N, E-bound, or 43° 00′ N, W-bound. This affects Vigo routes from U.S. ports N of 31° N, Lisbon routes from ports N of Chesapeake Bay, and Strait of Gibraltar routes from Boston; tracks should be diverted accordingly. Boston routes should pass at least 60 miles and 40 miles S of Sable Island, E-bound and W-bound respectively.

Distances, in miles; by great circle routes:

	Vigo	Lisbon	Strait of Gibraltar
Boston	2700	2750	2980
New York (Ambrose Lt)	2900	2940	2990
Delaware Bay	2960	3010	3240
Chesapeake Bay	3040	3090	3310

Alternatively, some advantage in weather and currents may be obtained by vessels bound for New York from the Strait of Gibraltar, by passing 20 miles S of Ilha de São Miguel, Arquipélago dos Açôres, and thence by rhumb line to Nantucket light-vessel. Distance to Ambrose light 3210 miles.

Low-powered vessels, W-bound, should, from May to September, pass S of Arquipélago dos Açôres and steer along the parallel of 36° 00′ N as far as the meridian of 65° 00′ W, thence to destination. From October to April they should first make a position in 33° 15′ N, 20° 00′ W, thence steering on the parallel of 33° 15′ N as far as 65° 00′ W, thence to destination.

Alternatively, low-powered vessels may reduce the possibility of encountering heavy weather in the N parts of the above great circle routes by steering, on all routes, to pass through 41° 00′ N, 47° 00′ W. The farthest N position on these tracks is on the Vigo route, in 43° 15′ N, 23° 30′ W.

ROUTES BETWEEN UNITED STATES OR WEST INDIES, AND AFRICA

2.76. All routes are by great circle. See also 2.121.

Distance, in miles:

	Casablanca	Dakar	Freetown
New York (Ambrose Lt.)	3140	3330	3750
Delaware Bay	3220	3360	3770
Chesapeake Bay	3280	3370	3780
NE Providence Channel	3590	3400	3760
St. Vincent (5′ N of)	3150	2550	2830
Trinidad	3210	2550	2810

ROUTES BETWEEN EUROPE AND WEST INDIES

2.81. General notes. Routes between European departure positions and the West Indies may, if plotted on the great circle, be obstructed seasonally by ice in the region of the Newfoundland Banks. Bermuda and Arquipélago dos Açôres lie on or near some tracks. W-bound traffic on the N routes is also liable to the adverse effect of the E'ly set of the North Atlantic Current and the predominantly W'ly weather of the N part of the Atlantic Ocean, so that low-powered ships, in particular, may gain some advantage by a diversion S of the geographically shortest route. Such vessels might well consider making a mid-ocean position in 36° 00′ N, 35° 00′ W, or alternatively, passing through 36° 40′ N, 24° 45′ W and 30° 00′ N, 45° 30′ W.

2.82. Florida Strait → Bishop Rock. From 27° 00′ N, 79° 49′ W, off Jupiter Inlet, proceed through 30° 00′ N, 79° 40′ W to 35° 30′ N, 72° 40′ W; thence to join main transatlantic tracks in:
15 Feb.–10 April, 42° 00′ N, 50° 00′ W; distance 3650 miles.
11 April–14 Feb., 45° 25′ N, 50° 00′ W; distance 3620 miles.

2.83. Bishop Rock → North-East Providence Channel. By great circle. Between Bishop Rock and 43° 00′ N, 50° 00′ W, this route follows the main seasonal W-bound track from 15 Feb. to 10 April. Distance, 3500 miles, or, using route through 36° 40′ N, 24° 45′ W and 30° 00′ N, 45° 30′ W, see 2.81, 3920 miles.

2.84. Florida Strait → Bordeaux and Vigo. From 27° 00′ N, 79° 49′ W, off Jupiter Inlet, proceed through 30° 00′ N, 79° 40′ W to 35° 30′ N, 72° 40′ W; thence:—

15 Feb.–10 April, to join the main transatlantic tracks in 42° 00′ N, 50° 00′ W, thence by great circle to destination. Distances: Bordeaux, 3880 miles; Vigo 3610 miles.

11 April–14 Feb., by great circle to destination. Distances, Bordeaux 3870 miles, Vigo 3610 miles.

2.85. Florida Strait → Lisbon or Strait of Gibraltar. From 27° 00′ N, 79° 49′ W, off Jupiter Inlet, proceed through 30° 00′ N, 79° 40′ W and thence by great circle to destination. The great circle for the Strait of Gibraltar passes through Arquipélago dos Açôres. Distances: Lisbon 3630 miles; Strait of Gibraltar 3840 miles.

2.86. West Indies channels and Bermuda ↔ Europe. Subject to the avoidance of Bermuda and Arquipélago dos Açôres, great circle tracks may be used in both directions.

Distances in miles:

	Bishop Rock	Bordeaux	Vigo	Lisbon	Strait of Gibraltar
Bermuda	2760	2980	2680	2690	2890
NE Providence Channel	see 2.83	3730	3440	3450	3650
Turks Island Passage	3460	3650	3330	3310	3490
Mona Passage	3480	3650	3310	3270	3440
Sombrero Island Passage	3310	3460	3120	3060	3230
Barbados	3380	3500	3140	3050	3190

Routes in the Gulf of Mexico and the Caribbean Sea, and the approaches thereto, are continued in Chapter 4.

ROUTES BETWEEN ENGLISH CHANNEL AND STRAIT OF GIBRALTAR OR INTERMEDIATE PORTS

2.91. General Notes. With favourable weather and tidal streams Chenal du Four and Raz de Sein may be used to shorten the distance between the English Channel and ports in the Bay of Biscay. See Admiralty Sailing Directions.

When rounding Île d'Ouessant in uncertain weather great care should be taken, see 2.19, 2.31, and 2.32, and Admiralty Sailing Directions. The incidence of fog in the vicinity is high, and it is important to remember, when in fog, that it is not always possible from the land to determine the existence of fog banks in the offing and that the fog signals may not, therefore, be in operation.

Between Île d'Ouessant and Cabo Finisterre, a general E'ly set may be expected. Onshore winds bring cloud, which may develop into low visibility near the coast.

The coast between Cabo Ortegal and Cabo Finisterre is a dangerous landfall except in good weather, owing to the E'ly set of the current, the tidal streams, and the risk of poor visibility with low cloud which may obscure the lights. See Admiralty Sailing Directions.

W of Spain and Portugal, although in general a good offing is advisable, it is usual for N-bound vessels to follow the Portuguese and Spanish coasts to Cabo Finisterre more closely than the S-bound traffic. The channel between Ilha Berlenga and Cabo Carvoeiro is clear and deep and may be taken in clear weather. When uncertain of the position in the vicinity of Os Farilhões (39° 29′ N, 9° 33′ W) and Ilha Berlenga, it is vital to gain sea room since sounding gives little indication of the vicinity of these islands. For general remarks on depths off these coasts, see Admiralty Sailing Directions.

In the vicinity of Cabo de São Vicente, the currents set strongly along the coast and have a tendency towards the cape.

For the approach to the Strait of Gibraltar, see 2.34.

For fishing grounds, and for further details amplifying these notes, see Admiralty Sailing Directions.

2.92. Distances. The following table gives distances in miles between terminal positions in 48° 28′ N, 5° 24′ W (Ouessant) and 36° 56′ N, 5° 45′ W (Strait of Gibraltar). For Bishop Rock, add 55 miles to Ouessant distances.

	Ouessant		
435	Vigo		
650	230	Lisbon	
920	500	275	Strait of Gibraltar

ROUTES BETWEEN ENGLISH CHANNEL AND WEST COAST OF AFRICA

2.96. General notes. The great circle track between Bishop Rock and 20° 50′ N, 18° 10′ W, off Cap Blanc, passes 35 miles W of Cabo Finisterre and between Tenerife and Gran Canaria.

For the passages across the Bay of Biscay and off the W coasts of Spain and Portugal, see 2.91. For the W coast of Africa, see Admiralty Sailing Directions. Abnormal refraction occurs at times off the African coast. The charting of the coast between Cape Bojador and Fleuve Sénégal is reported to be inaccurate, and at night, as there are few lights, it should be given a wide berth.

If bound for ports in the Gulf of Guinea, proceed through 4° 20′ N, 9° 20′ W, off Cape Palmas. For Cape Town, leave the coastwise route in 10° 40′ N, 17° 40′ W, off Arquipélago dos Bijagós and continue by great circle, see 3.41, 3.42.

2.97. Distances. In the following table, distances are worked from positions off Ouessant, in 48° 28′ N, 5° 24′ W and off the Strait of Gibraltar, in 36° 56′ N, 5° 45′ W. For Bishop Rock, add 55 miles to Ouessant distances.

Ouessant						
920	Strait of Gibraltar					
960	170	Casablanca				
1310	680	525	Las Palmas			
2140	1500	1330	835	Dakar		
2640	2000	1850	1360	505	Freetown	
2380	1730	1580	1090	245	—	10° 40′ N, 17° 40′ W, for Cape Town
3010	2360	2210	1710	840	450	4° 20′ N, 9° 20′ W (see 3.41)

ROUTES BETWEEN NORTH AMERICA AND CABO DE SÃO ROQUE OR INTERMEDIATE POSITIONS

2.101. General notes. The main factor affecting voyages in that part of the ocean between the Gulf of St. Lawrence and the Bahamas is the NE'ly set of the Gulf Stream.

A strong current setting N will be encountered for 200 miles in the N approach to Providence NE Channel.

General directions for passages between New York and Florida Strait, and for West Indies channels, are given in Admiralty Sailing Directions.

2.102. Distances, in miles.

	NE Providence Channel	Crooked Island Passage	Turks Island Passage	Mona Passage	Sombrero Passage
Cabot strait	1570	1590	1670	1800	1750
Halifax	1300	1330	1430	1590	1560
New York (Ambrose Lt.)	890	980	1140	1360	1420
Delaware Bay	805	895	1060	1290	1350
Chesapeake Bay	685	780	960	1200	1250

2.103. Northern ports ↔ Barbados. Pass E of Barbuda and the Lesser Antilles. When making a visual landfall on Barbados at night, it is advisable to make Ragged Point light, as the low-lying N end of the island is difficult to pick up.

Distances from Barbados: Cabot Strait, 2050 miles; Halifax, 1910 miles; New York (Ambrose light), 1840 miles; Delaware Bay, 1700 miles; Chesapeake Bay, 1620 miles.

2.104. Northern ports ↔ Belém, all routes from ports N of Cape Hatteras are by great circle to 5° 00′ N, 47° 30′ W, and thence to the pilot station off Salinopolis. During the hurricane season, from July to October, ships from Delaware Bay and Chesapeake Bay should make direct for Bermuda to establish a landfall, thence passing through 26° 00′ N, 60° 00′ W; 11° 00′ N, 50° 00′ W; and 5° 00′ N, 47° 30′ W. Similarly, vessels from northern ports may with advantage also make a landfall at Bermuda.

N of Bermuda, the Gulf Stream will be felt; squally weather is frequent within its limits, and fog is prevalent along its N border.

Full allowance must be made on the S parts of these routes for the effects of the Equatorial Current and counter-current; great care must be taken not to make a landfall W of Ponta de Atalaia (*0° 35′ S, 47° 21′ W*) because, in that region, fresh to strong ESE winds and rough seas may be expected, with occasional poor visibility.

Distances from Belém: Cabot Strait, 2900 miles; Halifax, 2770 miles; New York (Ambrose light), 2840 miles; Delaware Bay, 2800 miles; Chesapeake Bay, 2700 miles.

2.105.   Northern ports ↔ Cabo de São Roque. Proceed by great circle to 4° 40′ S, 34° 35′ W, midway between Cabo de São Roque and Atol das Rocas.

Distances: Cabot Strait, 3380 miles; Halifax, 3330 miles; New York (Ambrose Light), 3460 miles; Delaware Bay, 3440 miles; Chesapeake Bay, 3400 miles.

2.106.   Caribbean Sea → Belém and Cabo de São Roque. From the Caribbean Sea, take departure in 13° 28′ N, 61° 10′ W, 5 miles N of St. Vincent, and proceed through 5° 00′ N, 45° 00′ W, or even farther N, to avoid the strength of the South Equatorial Current. From Trinidad, join this route in 11° 00′ N, 56° 20′ W.

Vessels bound for Belém should leave the route in about 6° 20′ N, 47° 30′ W. Alternatively, a curving track about 100 miles offshore will shorten the distance by about 100 miles, but the adverse current will be stronger.

From 5° 00′ N, 45° 00′ W, proceed to 4° 40′ S, 34° 35′ W, midway between Cabo de São Roque and Atol das Rocas, making allowance for the W'ly set.

From Belém, it is possible to take advantage of the tidal streams and an E-setting counter-current by keeping close inshore if conditions permit.

From Trinidad to Demerara, keep as close to the land as is safe in order to avoid the current. From Galera Point, steer to a position 30 miles N of Demerara light-beacon, which should be made on a bearing of more than 180°. As a rule the nature of the bottom when approaching Demerara River should be fine dark sand; a mud bottom indicates that the vessel is too far W. Because of the strength of the currents and the extent of the shore banks, sounding should be continuous. It is possible for a vessel set too far SW to ground before sighting land.

Distances: St. Vincent to Belém, 1330 miles; Trinidad (Galera Point) to Belém, 1250 miles; St. Vincent to 4° 40′ S, 34° 35′ W, 1940 miles; Belém to 4° 40′ S, 34° 35′ W, 825 miles.

2.107.   Cabo de São Roque → Belém and Caribbean Sea. For Belém and other intermediate ports, keep about 50 miles offshore in the strength of the current.

For the Caribbean Sea, proceed direct.

Distances from 4° 40′ S, 34° 35′ W: Belém, 835 miles; 5 miles N of Galera Point, Trinidad, 1840 miles; 10 miles N of Tobago, 1840 miles; 5 miles N of St. Vincent, 1930 miles.

ROUTES BETWEEN NORTH-EAST COAST OF SOUTH AMERICA AND EASTERN PART OF NORTH ATLANTIC OCEAN

2.111.   General notes. When approaching the coast between Trinidad and Cabo de São Roque, the effects of the Equatorial Current and Counter-current will be felt. See Admiralty Sailing Directions.

In general, great circle tracks are recommended. The following routes and distances are from Belém: Bishop Rock, 3670 miles; Bordeaux, passing 10 miles NW of Cabo Villano, 3690 miles; Vigo, 3290 miles; Lisbon, 3140 miles; Strait of Gibraltar, passing between Isla de Hierro and Isla de la Palma, Islas Canarias, 3120 miles; Casablanca, route as for Strait of Gibraltar, 2970 miles; Dakar 2000 miles; Freetown, 2110 miles; Ponta Delgada, 2580 miles; Porto Grande, 1680 miles; Las Palmas, 2530 miles.

ROUTES BETWEEN EASTERN PART OF ATLANTIC OCEAN AND RECIFE

2.116.   General notes. On voyages between the British Isles and the E coast of South America, calls may be made at intermediate ports in the E Atlantic islands with very little increase of distance.

Penedos de São Pedro e São Paolo (St. Paul rocks), Arquipélago de Fernando de Noronha, and Atol das Rocas lie on or near most of the routes, in the main W'ly set of the South Equatorial Current.

The coast S of Cabo de São Roque should be approached with caution, and the prevalence of onshore sets should be kept in mind. See Admiralty Sailing Directions.

2.117.   Routes. Landfall off Recife should normally be made in 8° 00′ S, 34° 40′ W, 10 miles E of Ponta de Olinda, but not S of this position from October to January, see 3.31 and Admiralty Sailing Directions. The great circle from Bishop Rock passes through Ilha de São Vicente; vessels using this track may pass through Canal de São Vicente or NW of Ilha de Santo Antão.

The route between the Strait of Gibraltar and Recife passes between Isla de Fuerteventura (Islas Canarias) and the African coast to 17° 30′ N, 20° 00′ W; thence direct to Recife. From Las Palmas, for Recife, pass E of Arquipélago de Cabo Verde; 45 miles W of Penedos de São Pedro e São Paolo; and about 5 miles W of Ilha de Fernando de Noronha. For destinations S of Recife, see Chapter 8.

Distances: Recife (landfall) to Bishop Rock, 3760 miles; to Lisbon, 3220 miles; to Strait of Gibraltar, 3180 miles; to Las Palmas, 2440 miles; to Porto Grande, 1590 miles.

ROUTES TO AND FROM ARQUIPÉLAGO DOS AÇÔRES

2.121. Routes. Subject to the ordinary requirements of navigation, Arquipélago dos Açôres can be approached by great circle from all directions. The islands lie in the main flow of the Azores Current, and S of the W'ly weather of the North Atlantic Ocean.

Distances, in miles:

	Horta	Ponta Delgada
Bishop Rock	1210	1140
Bordeaux	1300	1200
Vigo	940	835
Lisbon	910	770
Strait of Gibraltar	1130	970
Casablanca	1075	925
Las Palmas	920	780
Dakar	1550	1450
Porto Grande, Islas de Cabo Verde	1330	1280
Belém	2600	2670
Barbados	2220	2300
Sombrero Passage	2190	2290
Mona Passage	2370	2470
Turks Island Passage	2410	2530
North-East Providence Channel	2540	2660
Bermuda	1790	1900
Florida Strait (Jamaica Inlet)	2740	2850
Delaware Bay	2340	2500
New York	2090	2230
Halifax*	1600	1750
Cabot Strait	1460	1610
St. John's, Newfoundland	1190	1340

* From 15 February to 10 April the E-bound route passes 40 miles S of Sable Island and through 42° 00′ N, 50° 00′ W, and the W-bound route passes through 43° 00′ N, 50° 00′ W and 20 miles S of Sable Island. These diversions add about 25 miles to the great circle distances.

ROUTES TO AND FROM ARQUIPÉLAGO DE CABO VERDE

2.126. Great circle routes. Subject to the ordinary requirements of navigation, great circle sailing should be used on the following routes. Bishop Rock, 2170 miles; Belém, 1680 miles; Trinidad, 2110 miles; St. Vincent, West Indies (for Caribbean Sea), 2100 miles; North-East Providence Channel (for Gulf of Mexico), 2940 miles; Bermuda, 2330 miles; Delaware Bay, 2920 miles; New York, 2900 miles; Halifax, 2540 miles; Cabot Strait, 2540 miles; St. John's Newfoundland, 2290 miles. For Arquipélago dos Açôres, see 2.121.

2.127. Porto Grande ↔ West Africa. For Dakar and Bathurst, pass N of Ilha de Bôa Vista. For Freetown and ports S, pass S of Ilha de São Tiago. For currents, see Admiralty Sailing Directions.

Distances: Strait of Gibraltar, 1560 miles; Casablanca, 1400 miles; Las Palmas, 880 miles; Dakar, 480 miles; Bathurst, 525 miles; Freetown, 875 miles; Monrovia, 1080 miles.

For ports in the Gulf of Guinea, see 3.41, pass through 4° 20′ N, 9° 20′ W, about 90 miles W of Cape Palmas.

The E islands of Arquipélago de Cabo Verde more especially feel the force of the SW'ly set of the Canary Current and several wrecks have been caused by disregarding it. The currents between the islands of the group are frequently strong, irregular, and influenced by the wind.

Local magnetic anomaly has been reported in the vicinity of Arquipélago de Cabo Verde, especially off the W side of Ilha do Sal, off the E side of Ilha de Bôa Vista, and near Ilha do Fogo and Ilha Brava.

CHAPTER 3

SOUTH ATLANTIC OCEAN

CONTENTS

WINDS AND WEATHER

3.01. The wind system of the South Atlantic resembles that of the North Atlantic, except that the circulation round the oceanic anticyclone is anti-clockwise, and there is no wind corresponding to the South-west Monsoon of West Africa. There is no Doldrum zone, and there are no tropical storms.

3.02. The South-east Trade Winds form the equatorial side of the circulation round the oceanic anticyclone, which is centered in about 28° S to 20° S. They are the counterpart of the North-east Trades, and blow with equal persistence and constancy of direction, from about SSE on the E side of the ocean to almost E on the W part. They extend as far N as the equator in winter (July) and to within two or three degrees of it in summer (January). The average strength of the South-east Trades is similar to that of the North-east Trades except N of 10° S, E of about 10° W, where it averages only force 2–3.

Weather is similar to that of the zone of the North-east Trades, except that fog is frequent over the cold waters of the Benguela Current close to the coast of South-west Africa between about 20° and 30° S.

3.03. The Variables (Horse Latitudes), a belt of light and generally variable winds in the neighbourhood of the oceanic areas of high pressure, extend across the ocean in about 29° S, oscillating from about 26° S in winter to about 31° S in summer. Conditions are similar to those in the corresponding zone of the North Atlantic. E of the prime meridian winds are predominantly from between S and ESE, being in fact an extension of the South-east Trades. In the W part of the zone NE'ly winds are commonest, particularly in summer.

3.04. The Westerlies (Roaring Forties). S of about 35° S, W'ly winds predominate. As in the North Atlantic, the almost continuous passage of depressions from W to E causes the wind to vary greatly both in direction and strength, and winds from any direction can be experienced; the centres of the depressions generally move from the vicinity of Cabo de Hornos in the direction of South Georgia and then approximately along the 50th parallel. Gales are very prevalent; S of about 40° S, even at midsummer, winds reach force 7 on from 7 to 9 days per month, and S of about 43° S and E of about 40° W the frequency rises to about 15 days per month. In winter this latter frequency is general S of a line joining the Falkland Islands and the Cape of Good Hope, while most of the area between this line and the 30th parallel has from 5 to 10 days per month with winds of this force.

Weather is of a similarly variable nature to that experienced in the corresponding zone of the N hemisphere. Fog is not uncommon in summer, and is generally associated with winds from a N'ly direction.

SWELL

3.06. Zones. Fewer observations of ocean swell are available from the South Atlantic than from the North Atlantic. The South Atlantic, for purposes of swell, can conveniently be divided into three zones. For length of swell, see 2.13.

3.07. South Atlantic, 0°–20° S. Slight to moderate swell, rarely heavy; from SE in the E part of the zone, and from between SE and E in the W part.

3.08. South Atlantic, 20° S–40° S. The swell is mainly moderate, but sometimes heavy. In the E part of the zone, it is from S; the direction is variable in the W part, with a high proportion from between NE and N. Reports of confused swell are frequent.

3.09. South Atlantic, 40° S–60° S. The swell is mainly moderate, but in the extreme S it is often heavy. Throughout the year, the worst conditions are likely to occur between 40° S and 50° S. The depressions, which are of much the same size as those that produce the North Atlantic winter storms, move in continual succession from W to E, usually along tracks S of 50° S. The strongest winds blow from NW with a heavy overcast sky on a falling barometer; they are followed by SW winds as the barometer rises and the sky clears.

Heavy swell is present for between 30 per cent and 70 per cent of the time between 50° S and 60° S. In summer, the frequency of high seas and swell decreases towards the circumpolar trough which generally lies in about 64° S, where the mean wind speeds are less than farther N, although relatively small strong gales occur from time to time.

Most of the very high seas and swell appear to be raised by the westerlies. Freak waves, which are almost certainly due to a number of component wave trains becoming momentarily in step, are a very real possibility which appears to be increased in the vicinity of shoal water and when the wave train is moving against the current.

5

CURRENTS

10

3.11. Ocean circulation. Most of the South Atlantic Ocean is occupied by currents which form a simple anti-clockwise circulation. On the N flank the **South Equatorial Current** flows in a W'ly direction across the ocean N of about 6° S. S of this zone the general W'ly flow persists, but at a reduced rate, as far as about 20° S. This weaker and less constant current is known as the **South Sub-tropical Current.**

Most of the South Equatorial Current turns NW, towards the West Indies, as it approaches the Brazilian coast. *15* This current attains high rates especially on the equator near 45° W, where in the winter and spring of the S hemisphere average rates of 2 knots are reached. Most of the South Sub-tropical Current, on the other hand, turns SW as it approaches the coast of Brazil, giving rise to the **Brazil Current**, which is extensive and flows SW, parallel with the coast, as far as about 34° S to 37° S. A small part of the flow which impinges on the coast S of Cabo de São Roque turns N and later joins the South Equatorial Current after rounding the cape. The *20* latitude in which the N-going and S-going coastal streams diverge varies between about 7° S in December and 11° S in June.

On reaching about 25° S, the Brazil Current begins to fan out SE and E. The remaining SW'ly flow continues to about 36° S, where it turns SE and E to form the N part of the great E-flowing body of water which constitutes the S flank of the main ocean circulation. The S part of this E'ly flow is formed by the **Southern Ocean Current**, *25* which is a continuous belt of cold water flowing round the S hemisphere S of the continents. After passing Cabo de Hornos the flow turns NE to bring the Southern Ocean water as far N as about 38° S in the E part of the South Atlantic. The bulk of this water turns E and passes S of the African continent. From the Southern Ocean current a branch turns N in the neighbourhood of Cabo de Hornos to form the **Falkland Current**, which passes W of the Falkland Islands and continues N as far as the neighbourhood of the estuary of Río de La Plata in *30* November until the end of April. For the rest of the year, this current extends farther N, reaching about 25° S in June.

The main ocean circulation is completed, on the African side, by the NW-flowing **Benguela Current** which derives, in part, from the continuation, after rounding the Cape of Good Hope, of the Agulhas current (6.36). It is also fed by upwelling off the coast of South-west Africa and to a smaller extent by the NW'ly diversion of *35* some of the Southern Ocean Current. On the oceanic side of the Benguela Current there is a progressive fanning out towards W. In the higher latitudes the currents become variable towards W, but farther N the NW'ly flow turns progressively W while maintaining its average rate of about ½ knot, and feeds into the W-setting South-Sub-tropical Current. Near the African coast, the NW to N'ly flow, following the coast, extends to the equator between February and April. It is least developed between August and October, when it only extends about *40* as far as Walvis Bay, the currents farther N being variable.

45

ICE

3.16. For general remarks and references, see remarks for the North Atlantic in article 2.25, which are also applicable to the South Atlantic except for 10-day ice charts and facsimile ice broadcasts.

50

3.17. Pack-ice. The approximate mean limits of pack-ice are indicated on the Routeing and Climatic Charts. The main shipping routes of the S hemisphere are not affected by pack-ice, but in the South Atlantic its presence prevents the use of a great circle track between the Cape of Good Hope and Cabo de Hornos except during March, April, and May.

The long-term average position of the pack-ice (4/8 concentration) in September to October, at its greatest *55* extension, see chart 5302, runs from about 60° S, 60° W to a position just E of South Georgia in about 54° S, 30° W. Thence, it extends E while gradually increasing in latitude to about 55° S on the meridian of Greenwich and about 58° S in 50° E. It is stressed that this is an average position of the edge of the pack which in severe years, can be encountered appreciably farther N.

The average position of the edge of the pack in the months of least average extension (February–March) is *60* well S of the foregoing positions. In those parts where the Antarctic continent extends continuously to lower latitudes, i.e. from 10° W through 0° to 160° E, the average ice edge at this season does not extend much beyond 100 miles from the coast and in some places retreats to the coast. Off the Weddel and Ross seas the ice is more extensive, reaching its farthest N on the parallel of about 62° S between 30° W and 60° W. Again it is stressed that these are average positions.

65

3.18. Icebergs. The antarctic icebergs, unlike those of the North Atlantic, are not usually calved from glaciers, but consist of portions that have broken away from the great ice shelves which surround parts of the Antarctic continent. They are consequently flat-topped, and they may be of immense size.

The extreme limit of icebergs, irrespective of season, is illustrated on charts 5301 and 5302. In the S hemisphere, *70* icebergs are liable to be encountered in lower latitudes in the South Atlantic than in the other oceans of this hemisphere. Near the coasts of Argentina and South Brazil, icebergs may be found as far N as 31° S. Abnormally, one has even been reported in about 26° S, 26° W. In the rest of the South Atlantic, bergs are largely confined to latitudes S of 35° S.

The relatively simple nature of Antarctic geography, with an almost symmetrical flow of currents round a nearly circular continent, means that there is less cause here than in Arctic waters for a great concentration of bergs in a few comparatively narrow "lanes". Some concentration does occur due to the deflection and concentration of the E-setting circumpolar stream by the N'ly projection of Graham Land. Some of the bergs in the resulting NE flow between South America and Graham Land are carried into the Falkland current which takes them N as far as, or even beyond, the estuary of Río de La Plata. Another branch of the NE'ly flow through Drake Passage continues NE and passes E of the Falkland Islands, carrying bergs to similar latitudes in the more central parts of the South Atlantic.

Due notice should be taken of the caution in article 2.64 regarding the use of radar for detecting icebergs.

NOTES AND CAUTIONS

3.21. Coasts of South Africa. Between Saldanha Bay and Table Bay, an eddy current sets S at a distance of from 4 to 5 miles offshore during the winter months of June, July, and August; at a short distance seaward of this eddy, the current is almost constant throughout the year in a general direction between N and NW, or parallel with the coast, at a rate of from ½ knot to 1 knot, though between Table Bay and Dassen Island it sometimes runs at over 2 knots.

This current sometimes has a tendency to set a vessel towards the coast, especially during or after strong onshore winds, and it should therefore be carefully guarded against. From time to time, however, reports have been received from vessels approaching from N to the effect that when abreast the coast between Saldanha Bay and Table Bay the normal N'ly set has not been evident, but that, on the contrary, a S'ly set has been experienced, sometimes towards the land and sometimes away from it.

3.22. Caution is necessary in the vicinity of **Penedos de São Pedro e São Paolo** and **Ilha de Fernando de Noronha**, as the South Equatorial Current sets WNW past them at a rate of from 1 to 2 knots.

ROUTES OFF EAST COAST OF SOUTH AMERICA

3.31. Passages between the ports on the E coast of South America are, in fact, coastwise and will not be described in detail in this book. Generally speaking, all routes are as direct as prudent navigation permits, but off-lying shoals make wide divergence from the coast necessary in some places, notably in the vicinity of Arquipélago dos Abrolhos (*18° S*), Cabo de São Tomé (*22° S*) and Costa do Albardão (*33° 12'S, 52° 41' W*). Known dangers are fully described in Admiralty Sailing Directions, but it is emphasised that owing to the uneven character of the bottom in the vicinity of Arquipélago dos Abrolhos, as shown by soundings, it is probable that shoals other than those charted may lie within 200 miles of those islands.

In making passages along the E coast of South America the seasonal changes in the coastal currents should be noted. Detailed information is given in Admiralty Sailing Directions. Summarising this information in very general terms, it may be said that the movement of water is towards Río de La Plata; S from Recife and N from Cabo de Hornos, though the latter set is well away from the coast. Off the coast of Patagonia currents are very variable, and within 20 miles of the shore tidal influences only are felt. It is important also to remember the prevalence of onshore currents at any time of the year between Cabo de São Roque and Cabo Frio.

The important seasonal changes are, firstly, in the position, in the vicinity of Recife, in which the S-going current (3.11) starts; the latitude varies from about 7° S in December to about 11° S in June. Secondly, the **Brazil Inshore Counter-current** runs from May to July as a temporary N'ly extension of the Falkland Current. Throughout the region of the S-going Brazil Current there is always considerable variation, but during May, June, and July the proportion of N-going sets near the coast between Cabo Frio and Río de La Plata increases and, in the vicinity of Río de Janeiro, slightly predominates over the S-going sets. Advantage may be taken of this by making N-bound passages between Río de La Plata and Cabo Frio closer inshore during this period than at other times, with due regard, as always, to the possibility of a shoreward set.

3.32. Río de Janeiro ↔ Recife or Porto do Salvador. As direct as navigation permits, passing at least 20 miles E of Arquipélago dos Abrolhos unless using Canal dos Abrolhos, see Admiralty Sailing Directions. Distance, see 3.39.

3.33. Río de Janeiro ↔ Río de La Plata. As direct as navigation permits, with due precautions against onshore currents.

From May to July, while the Brazil Inshore Counter-current is setting N, S-bound vessels may with advantage keep to seaward.

Distance, see 3.39.

3.34. Río de La Plata ↔ Cabo de Hornos and intermediate ports. The N-going Falkland Current will affect voyages between Río de La Plata and the Falkland Islands or Estrecho de le Maire, or, to a lesser extent, Estrecho de Magallanes. Special attention is required in approaching Estrecho de Magallanes, as the range of the tide is great, and the tidal streams at the entrance run with great strength, causing, at times, an indraught towards Banco Sarmiento and the dangers extending from Cabo Virgenes. The tidal streams in the strait are a controlling factor in the choice of the time of arrival, see Admiralty Sailing Directions.

Courses are as direct as navigation permits, but low-powered vessels, S-bound to Estrecho de Magallanes or coastal ports, are advised to take an inshore route in order to avoid the strength of the Falkland Current which, at a distance of 50 miles offshore, has been known to set N at a rate of about 50 miles a day. S of Cabo Corrientes (38° S), only the tidal streams are felt within 20 miles of the land and, with W'ly winds, better weather is experienced close inshore than in the offing.

Low-powered vessels, N-bound between Estrecho de Magallanes and Río de La Plata, should keep between 20 and 50 miles to seaward of the rhumb line track to obtain full benefit from the Falkland Current. Over the length of this voyage, the distance is thus increased by about 40 miles.

For directions for approaching Falkland Islands, see Admiralty Sailing Directions.

Distances: see 3.39.

3.35. Routes ↔ Falkland islands. Caution. For most of the year the mean limit of icebergs lies well SE of the Falkland Islands, but during November and December it passes from about 100 miles SE of Cabo de Hornos, through the Falkland Islands, to about 43° S, 52° W, before turning E to pass about 500 miles S of the Cape of Good Hope. Icebergs N and W of this mean limit are, however, common at all times, and the risk of meeting them when on passage to or from the Falkland Islands, Estrecho de Magallanes, and Cabo de Hornos must always be borne in mind. See Admiralty Sailing Directions.

3.36. Stanley ↔ Estrecho de Magallanes. As direct as navigation will allow, passing either (1) S or (2) N of the Falkland Islands. Distances: (1) 420 miles, (2) 440 miles.

3.37. Stanley ↔ East coast of South America. As direct as navigation will allow. Distance, see 3.39.

3.38. Stanley ↔ Cabo de Hornos. As direct as navigation will allow, either through Estrecho de le Maire or E of Isla de Los Estados. Distance by either route, 435 miles.

3.39. Table of distances (in miles).

4° 40′ S 34° 35′ W								
215	Recife							
590	380	Porto do Salvador						
1290	1080	740	Río de Janeiro					
2270	2060	1730	1030	Río de La Plata				
2650	2440	2110	1410	435	Bahía Blanca			
3070	2860	2570	1860	855	525	Comodoro Rivadavia		
3350	3140	2810	2130	1170	880	465	Estrecho de Magallanes	
3480	3270	2940	2260	1350	1100	685	Cabo de Hornos	
3070	2860	2530	1860	1000	790	530	Stanley	

WEST COAST OF AFRICA

3.41. General notes. Voyages between ports on the W coast of Africa are mostly coastwise, and routes are as direct as prudent navigation allows.

The route between the English Channel and the W coast of Africa is described in 2.96 and 2.97. For Cape Town, proceed by great circle from 10° 40′ N, 17° 40′ W, off Arquipélago dos Bijagós; for ports in the Gulf of Guinea, pass through 4° 20′ N, 9° 20′ W, off Cape Palmas.

5

10

15

20

25

30

35

40

45

50

55

60

65

70

3.42 Table of distances (in miles)

10° 40′ N, 17° 40′ W									
625	**4° 20′ N 9° 20′ W**								
1080	460	**Takoradi**							
1400	780	325	**Lagos**						
1600	975	530	270	**Bonny**					
1750	1130	685	425	160	**Douala**				
1860	1240	840	680	465	445	**Gamba oil Terminal**			
2000	1380	1000	840	630	605	160	**Pointe-Noire**		
2320	1700	1380	1290	1070	1050	610	465	**Lobito**	
3370	2780	2590	2580	2400	2380	1950	1830	1430	**Cape Town**

If routeing to Indian Ocean, passing through 36° 45′ S, 19° 00′ E and S of Agulhas Current, the distance to that position from 10° 40′ N, 17° 40′ W is 3510 miles.

TRANSATLANTIC ROUTES

3.46. Northern part of South Atlantic. Great circle routes in both directions are recommended between South American ports N of Río de la Plata and ports on the African coast N of about 25° S, and between Recife or Porto do Salvador and Cape Town or Cape Agulhas.

E-bound ships wishing to avoid the Agulhas Current should pass through 36° 45′ S, 19° 00′ E from October to April.

Distances, in miles:

	Takoradi	Lagos	Bonny	Pointe Noire	Cape Town	15′ S of Cape Agulhas	36° 45′ S 19° 00′ E
Recife	2130	2450	2620	2790	3320	3410	3390
Porto do Salvador	2440	2750	2900	3020	3330	3410	3380
Río de Janeiro	2970	3270	3380	3380	—	—	—
Río de La Plata	3900	4190	4270	4170	—	—	—

3.47. Caution. Vema Seamount, over which there is a depth of 11 m, lies in 31° 40′ S, 8° 22′ E, about 500 miles WNW of Cape Town.

3.48. Southern part of South Atlantic. S of about 25° S, the main E-bound tracks are by great circle, but diversion of the corresponding W-bound tracks to rhumb lines should, in general, involve the vessel in less headwind and adverse current while entailing an extra distance of not more than about 3 per cent.

3.49. Río de Janeiro → Cape Town or Cape Agulhas. Great circle. Distances: Cape Town, 3280 miles; 15 miles S of Cape Agulhas, 3350 miles; 36° 45′ S, 19° 00′ E, to avoid the strength of the Agulhas Current, 3290 miles.

3.50. Cape Town or Cape Agulhas → Río de Janeiro. Rhumb lines. Distances: Cape Town, 3320 miles; 15 miles S of Cape Agulhas, 3390 miles.

Low-powered vessels should be routed through 29° 50′ S, 10° 00′ E; 25° 50′ S, long. 0°; 22° 50′ S, 10° 00′ W; 21° 10′ S, 20° 00′ W; 21° 10′ S, 30° 00′ W; passing S of Ilha da Trinidade and Ilhas Martin Vaz in order to take advantage of better weather and more favourable currents.

3.51. Río de La Plata → Cape Town or Cape Agulhas. Great circle. The farthest S position on the Cape Town track is 41° 00′ S, 20° 00′ W; parts of the track lie within the extreme iceberg limit. The great circle track between Río de La Plata and a position 15 miles S of Cape Agulhas reaches its farthest S in 41° 50′ S, 18° 15′ W, or if intending to pass through 36° 45′ S, 19° 00′ E to avoid the strength of the Agulhas Current, see 3.46, the farthest S position is 42° 30′ S, 17° 30′ W. Distances: Cape Town, 3610 miles; 15 miles S of Cape Agulhas, 3650 miles; 36° 45′ S, 19° 00′ E, 3570 miles.

Low-powered vessels may usually avoid ice by passing through 36° 00′ S, 40° 00′ W; thence by rhumb line to 36° 00′ S, 25° 00′ W; thence by great circle to Cape Town or Cape Agulhas, passing close S of Tristan da Cunha Group. If proceeding to the Indian Ocean via 36° 45′ S, 19° 00′ E, the farthest S position will be 38° 30′ S, 1° 00′ W.

3.52. Cape Town or Cape Agulhas → Río de La Plata. Follow a rhumb line, which lies almost along the parallel of 35° S. Distance: Cape Town 3700 miles; 15 miles S of Cape Agulhas 3750 miles.

Low-powered vessels should follow the rhumb line track for Rio de Janeiro (3.50) as far as 20° W, and thence steer by rhumb line to Río de La Plata. Although this route increases the distance by about 250 miles, lighter winds and more favourable currents are experienced.

3.53. Estrecho de Magallanes ↔ Gulf of Guinea. By rhumb line to 47° 50′ S, 60° 00′ W; thence by great circle to destination. Distances: Takoradi, 4810 miles; Lagos, 5060 miles; Bonny, 5100 miles.

3.54. Estrecho de Magallanes ↔ Pointe Noire. By rhumb line to 47° 50′ S, 60° 00′ W; thence to 43° 50′ S, 50° 00′ W; thence by great circle. Distance 4890 miles.

3.55. Estrecho de Magallanes → Cape Town or Cape Agulhas. By rhumb lines through 47° 50′ S, 60° 00′ W; 43° 50′ S, 50° 00′ W; 41° 10′ S, 40° 00′ W; 40° 20′ S, 33° 00′ W; thence by great circle, passing close S of Gough Island. Distances: Cape Town, 4150 miles; 15 miles S of Cape Agulhas, 4200 miles; 36° 45′ S, 19° 00′ E, to avoid the strength of the Agulhas Current, 4110 miles.

Low-powered vessels should proceed by rhumb lines through 36° 00′ S, 40° 00′ W; 36° 00′ S, 25° 00′ W; thence by great circle, passing close S of Tristan da Cunha Group.

3.56. Cape Town or Cape Agulhas → Estrecho de Magallanes, Stanley, or Cabo de Hornos. Follow the rhumb line track for Río de La Plata, see 3.52, as far as 35° 00′ S, 40° 00′ W; thence take rhumb line courses to destination.

Low-powered vessels should follow the rhumb line track for Río de Janeiro, see 3.50, as far as 27° 00′ S, 20° 00′ W; thence they should steer to 35° 00′ S, 40° 00′ W and to destination. Although the extra distance by this route is about 150 miles, the advantages of lighter winds and more favourable current should more than compensate for it.

Distances, in miles, for full power routes:

	Cape Town	15′ S of Cape Agulhas
Est. de Magallanes	4500	4550
Stanley	4160	4220
Cabo de Hornos	4620	4670

3.57. Stanley → Cape Town or Cape Agulhas. The great circle distance to Cape Town is 3370 miles but the track reaches 53° S, and it cannot therefore be recommended on account of ice and weather. The normal route is by rhumb lines through 43° 00′ S, 47° 00′ W; 41° 10′ S, 40° 00′ W; 40° 20′ S, 33° 00′ W; thence by great circle, passing S of Gough Island. Distances: Cape Town, 3800 miles; 15 miles S of Cape Agulhas, 3850 miles; 36° 45′ S, 19° 00′ E, to avoid the strength of the Agulhas Current, 3760 miles.

Low-powered vessels should first proceed to 36° 00′ S, 40° 00′ W; thence to 36° 00′ S, 25° 00′ W; thence by great circle, passing S of Tristan da Cunha Group.

3.58. Cabo de Hornos → Cape Town or Cape Agulhas. After passing either through Estrecho de le Maire or E of Islas de los Estados, see 3.38, pick up the Stanley → Cape Town route, see 3.57, off Stanley. Distances: Cape Town, 4240 miles; 15 miles S of Cape Agulhas, 4280 miles; 36° 45′ S, 19° 00′ E, to avoid the strength of the Agulhas current, 4200 miles.

CHAPTER 4

GULF OF MEXICO AND CARIBBEAN SEA

CONTENTS   *Page*

WINDS AND WEATHER

WINDS AND WEATHER

4.01. Over the **Caribbean Sea,** NE to E winds prevail throughout the year, while over the **Gulf of Mexico** the wind is generally lighter and more variable in direction, though frequently from between NE and SE. In coastal waters, strong N'ly winds may reach gale force at times over the Gulf. For the whole area, wind speeds are mainly light or moderate except for occasional hurricanes, see 2.05, which may affect the area from June to November. Most hurricanes track N of Cuba, and they rarely occur S of 15° N.

The weather over the area is generally partly cloudy or cloudy with scattered showers. Sunny spells are frequent and, from May to December, periods of heavy rain and thunderstorms are frequent. Squalls may occur at any time, but fog seldom occurs at sea.

Visibility is generally good throughout the year though it may at times be drastically reduced by heavy rain. For Northers, see 2.03.

SWELL

4.05. Swells are generally lower in the **Gulf of Mexico** than in the **Caribbean Sea.**

In the Caribbean Sea the prevailing direction is NE to E; in the Gulf of Mexico, from March to September it is E to SE, and from October to February it is NE.

Highest swells occur in an area round 13° N, 77° W in the Caribbean Sea, especially in June and July, when the frequency of swell greater than 4 m is 20 per cent. These swells are invariably short or average in length.

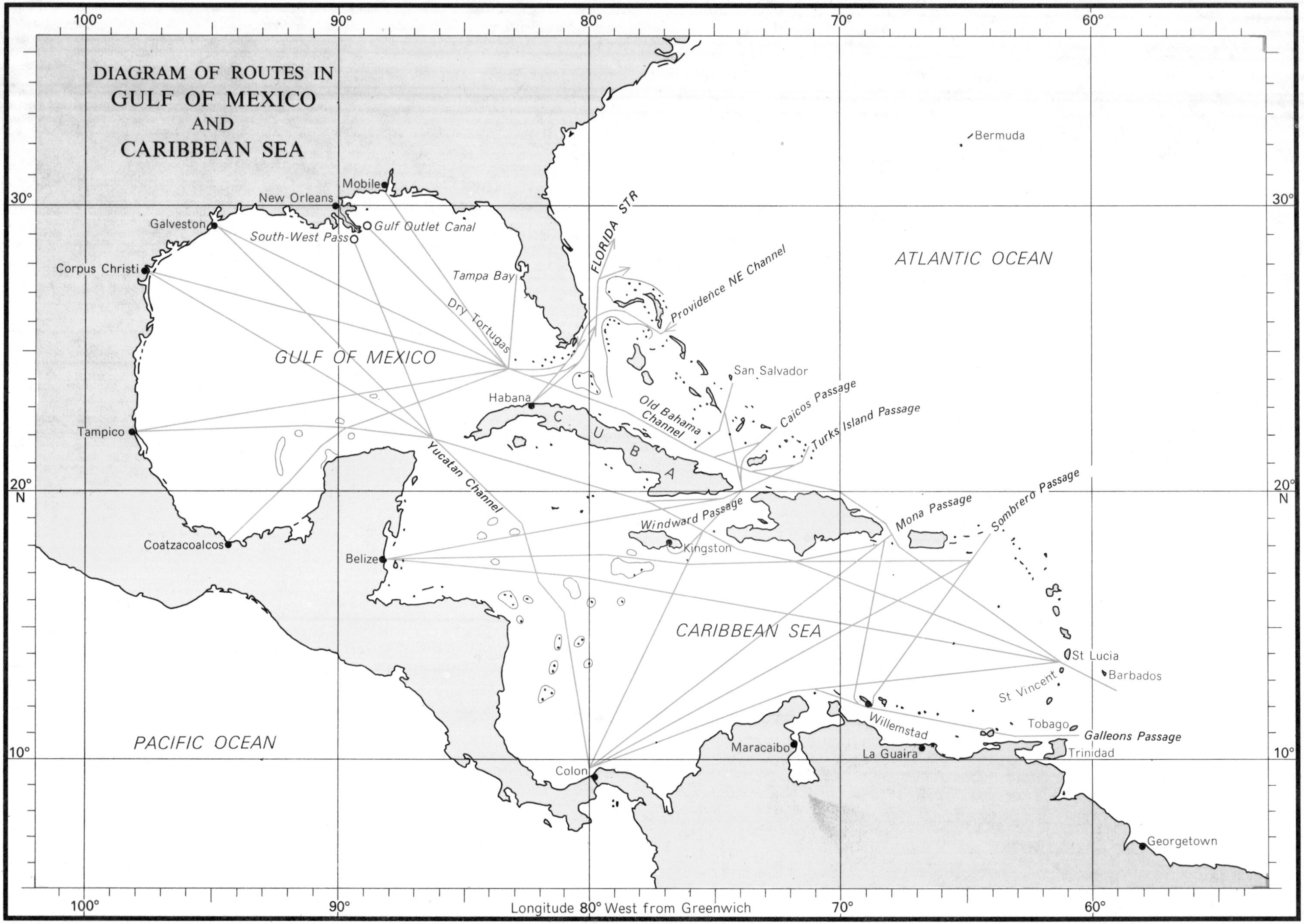
DIAGRAM OF ROUTES IN
GULF OF MEXICO
AND
CARIBBEAN SEA
100°
90°
80°
70°
60°
30°
20° N
10°
ATLANTIC OCEAN
GULF OF MEXICO
CARIBBEAN SEA
PACIFIC OCEAN
Bermuda
Mobile
New Orleans
Galveston
Gulf Outlet Canal
South-West Pass
Corpus Christi
Tampa Bay
Dry Tortugas
FLORIDA STR
Providence NE Channel
San Salvador
Habana
CUBA
Old Bahama Channel
Caicos Passage
Turks Island Passage
Tampico
Yucatan Channel
Windward Passage
Kingston
Mona Passage
Sombrero Passage
Coatzacoalcos
Belize
St Lucia
Barbados
St Vincent
Willemstad
Tobago
Galleons Passage
Trinidad
Maracaibo
La Guaira
Colon
Georgetown
Longitude 80° West from Greenwich
Diagram 19

CURRENTS

4.11. The North Equatorial Current (2.15) flows WNW through the Caribbean Sea with little change of direction until it approaches Yucatan Channel where it becomes more N'ly. It leaves an anti-clockwise eddy in the S part of the sea, S of about 12° N. There is also an E'ly counter-current close to the S coast of E and central Cuba.

In the Gulf of Mexico, part of the N-going flow from Yucatan Channel fans out in directions between SW and NW. Currents setting in these directions occupy most of the Gulf W of a line from Cabo Catoche to close W of the Mississippi delta. From the NW'ly flow along this line the water fans out NE and then shortly recurves to join the SE flow extending from the Mississippi delta to the W approaches to Florida Strait. This SE'ly stream joins the NE'ly stream which emerges from Yucatan Channel and the combined flow continues E, and through Florida Strait as the **Florida Current**. The emerging stream, meeting the NW flowing water of the North Sub-tropical Current, turns N off the E coast of Florida and forms the beginning of the **Gulf Stream**.

Along the W coast of Florida, there is a N'ly current which, with the SE'ly flow coming from the Mississippi delta, forms an anti-clockwise eddy in the E part of the Gulf of Mexico.

There is very little seasonal variation in the pattern of the currents.

The average current speeds in most of the Caribbean Sea are about 1 knot, increasing on the W side of Yucatan Channel to about 1½ knots. The strongest currents are observed in Florida Strait in about 25° 00' N, 80° 00' W and for about 300 miles N from that position. Here the average speed is nearly 3 knots in summer and 2½ knots in winter.

Over most of the Gulf of Mexico the average speeds are ½ knot to 1 knot, but stronger (N'ly) sets of 1·3 knots are reported in summer near the Mexican coast, N of Tampico.

NOTES AND CAUTIONS

4.15. Navigation. In the Gulf of Mexico, the Caribbean Sea, and in the channels leading thereto, great care is necessary in the vicinity of the cays and banks, as some of the charts are based on old and imperfect surveys.

Furthermore, the depths over the shoals may be less than those charted owing to the growth of the coral of which many of them are composed or to the imprecise nature of the least depths reported over them. Shoal water should be approached with caution at all times and given a wide berth when conditions for fixing are poor; many of the banks are steep-to.

In places, there are but few navigational aids, and the currents are variable.

ROUTES

4.21. Entrance channels. The Gulf of Mexico may be approached N of Cuba through Florida Strait; via Providence Channels and thence into Florida Strait; through Old Bahama Channel and Nicolas Channel; or S of Cuba through the Caribbean Sea and Yucatan Channel. Since the current in Florida Strait runs N with some strength, that strait is a good choice for departure, but Providence Channels or Old Bahama Channel may hold the balance for entry. The latter is approached from the Atlantic Ocean through Crooked Island Passage, Caicos Passage, or Turks Island Passage.

When navigating off the coast of Great Abaco Island, on the N side of North-East Providence Channel, caution is required on account of the current which may set onshore at a rate of more than 1½ knots.

Old Bahama Channel suffers from the disadvantage, particularly in inclement weather, that the lights are somewhat widely spaced.

Turks Island Passage is not lighted in its S approach.

In Florida Strait, most of the wrecks on Florida Reefs are of vessels S-bound at night; analysis of available data has pointed to an almost universal under-estimate of the speed of the contrary current, with a consequent over-estimate of the speed made good. When S-bound, between Fowey Rocks and Sombrero Key, it is on the side of safety to assume that the vessel is steaming against a 3- or 4-knot current and to hold a safe course from one light until the next is sighted. N-bound, it is better to under-estimate the speed of the Florida Current. Vessels are rarely stranded on Florida Reefs when N-bound, except when crossing the stream from Habana or making the reefs in reduced visibility.

Vessels proceeding through Florida Strait from the Gulf of Mexico should first make a position off Dry Tortugas in 24° 00' N, 83° 00' W.

The **Caribbean Sea** may be approached through Crooked Island Passage, Caicos Passage, or Turks Island Passage, all of which lead to Windward Passage. Crooked Island Passage is the best; it is constantly used by vessels on voyages to and from the S coast of Cuba, Jamaica, and the Panama Canal. Caicos Passage is not lighted, and Turks Island Passage is not recommended to N-bound vessels at night, since its S approach is not lighted.

Other entrances to the Caribbean Sea in common use are Mona Passage, which is much frequented and presents no difficulty; although subject to heavy squalls, it is safer than Turks Island Passage. Sombrero Passage, between the Virgin Islands and the Leeward Islands, is not lighted in its S approach. The passages between St. Lucia and St. Vincent, and on either side of Tobago, are also used.

4.22. Bermuda → Habana. Proceed by North-East Providence Channel, North-West Providence Channel, and Florida Strait. Distance 1150 miles.

C

Low-powered vessels should either stand across to Fowey Rocks from Great Isaac, thence proceeding to Sand Kay before re-crossing the Florida Current; or they may proceed S along the W edge of Great Bahama Bank preferably in daylight. For directions, see Admiralty Sailing Directions.

4.23. Habana → Bermuda. Proceed through Florida Strait, thence direct from off the NW end of Little Bahama Bank. Distance 1150 miles.

4.24. Bermuda ↔ Kingston. Proceed through Crooked Island Passage or Caicos Passage, thence W of Great Inagua Island and through Windward Passage. The greatest caution must be exercised in the vicinity of Morant Cays, where the currents vary greatly both in strength and direction. Distance by Caicos Passage 1150 miles.

4.25. Panama Canal ↔ Gulf of Mexico. From a position about 3 miles N of the breakwaters at the entrance to Limon Bay, make good a course of 352°, to pass 15 miles W of Serrana Bank South-west Cay (*14° 16′ N, 80° 24′ W*). Thence make good 354° for a position in 15° 42′ N, 80° 50′ W, whence the vessel should make good a course of 320°, passing W of Thunder Knoll and keeping in depths of more than 200 m.

From a position about 15 miles NW of Thunder Knoll, a vessel should keep in the deep water W of Grand Cayman Island, avoiding the shoals lying E of Misteriosa Bank, and then steer NW as necessary to pass through Yucatan Channel.

A vessel entering the Gulf of Mexico from the Caribbean Sea should keep in the deep water in Yucatan Channel, taking all precautions against the N'ly set of the current and constantly checking her position to identify the point of crossing the edge of Banco de Campeche. In crossing the bank a vessel should sound continuously, since it has not been subjected to a modern survey and new reports of shoal patches are often received, as indicated on the chart.

The dangers on this bank are steep-to. Discoloured water over some of these dangers is a useful guide.

The edge of the bank is generally marked by ripplings, and at only a short distance within it the water becomes discoloured.

From a position about 23 miles N of Cabo Catoche, a vessel bound for the SW part of the Gulf of Mexico should steer a W'ly course to a position about 10 miles S of Arrecife Alacrán, with due regard to the shoals N of Punta Yalkubul (*21° 32′ N, 88° 38′ W*).

For Puerto de Tampico, from the position 10 miles S of Arrecife Alacrán, the route passes N of Cayo Arenas, clear of the shoals lying E of that cay and the 18 m patch, reported in 1961, 24 miles W of it.

For Vera Cruz from the same position, the route passes midway between Triángulo Oeste (*20°59′ N, 92° 18′ W*) and Triángulo Este to a position 3 miles S of Triángulo Oeste. Care should be taken to give a wide berth to the 14·6 m shoal reported, in 1939, to lie 38 miles SSE of Cayo Arenas, and the 22 m shoal covered with Sargasso weed, reported in 1968 about 17 miles farther SSW.

A vessel bound for Coatzacoalcos from a position about 10 miles S of Arrecife Alacrán should steer to pass NW of Snake Rock to a position SE of Cayos Arcas. The least depth passed over on this track is 24 m.

If proceeding to Campeche, after passing W of Snake Rock, a SSW course may be steered so as to pass at least 22 miles W of Celestun (*20° 52′ N, 90° 24′ W*). When approaching Campeche from N, by keeping in depths of 9 m, the ridge of hills E of the city will be sighted. If the land is made in greater depths the first objects sighted will be the 98 m ridge about 3 miles SW of the city, and Castillo San Miguel.

For a vessel proceeding E the safest guide across Banco de Campeche is to keep in depths of over 36 m, avoiding Granville Shoal, bearing in mind also that after Northers there is a S-going current along the W side of Península de Yucatan, with a rate of ¾ knot at times.

In the Mississippi approach, the currents near the mouth of the river are uncertain, fog and haze are prevalent, particularly in summer and autumn, the mud banks are low, and the wind is generally from E. If approaching on soundings from S and SW, great attention should be paid to checking the latitude, for the bank is steep-to, with depths of 65 m only 3 or 4 miles from South Pass.

4.26. Yucatan Channel ↔ Eastern part of Caribbean Sea. Having given Cabo Catoche a wide berth on account of the shoals N of it, Cabo San Antonio should be made at a distance of 7 miles. Thence, course should be shaped along the S coast of Cuba, to pass about 5 miles off Cabo de la Cruz, thence E of Jamaica, passing 5 miles off Navassa Island, Pointe de Gravois, and Alta Vela. This track is mostly under the lee of the land, and it uses the E'ly counter-current mentioned in article 4.11, although off the coast of Cuba, between Cabo San Antonio and Cabo de la Cruz, special caution is required because of the occurrence of onshore sets which may sometimes run strongly.

Ships bound for Yucatan Channel from Alta Vela should pass N of Jamaica.

4.27. For South American ports and other destinations E of the Caribbean Sea, the best route from Alta Vela lies between St. Lucia and St. Vincent and S of Barbados.

4.28. Panama Canal ↔ Trinidad and Tobago. Off the N coasts of Colombia and Venezuela, coastwise voyages are best made by keeping inshore E-bound, and hauling off to take advantage of the North Equatorial Current when W-bound. The normal route passes S of Aruba and Curaçao, and between Los Frailes and Isla Margarita, and S of Cumberland Bank.

4.29. Distances between the seaward ends of the entrance channels (4.21), and between Panama Canal and various ports are expressed in miles, below.

Florida Strait, N end (*27° 00' N, 79° 49' W*) to Dry Tortugas (*24° 25' N, 83° 00' W*), 290; Coatzacoalcos, 1040; Tampico, 1110; Corpus Christi, 1070; Galveston, 980; Mississippi, Gulf Outlet canal, 725; Mobile, 725; Tampa, 485; Habana, 285.

North-East Providence Channel (*25° 50' N, 77° 00' W*) to Dry Tortugas, 370; to Coatzacoalcos, 1120; Tampico, 1190; Corpus Christi, 1150; Galveston, 1060; Mississippi, Gulf Outlet canal, 805; Mobile, 805; Tampa, 565; Habana, 370.

Crooked Island Passage from Christopher Columbus' landfall (*24° 05' N, 74° 15' W*) off San Salvador, via Old Bahama Channel to Habana, 585; via Windward Passage to Kingston, 480; Belize, 1060; Colon, 980.

Caicos Passage (*22° 10' N, 72° 20' W*) via Old Bahama Channel to Coatzacoalcos, 1400; Tampico, 1470; Corpus Christi, 1550; Galveston, 1500; Mississippi, Gulf Outlet canal, 1080; Mobile, 1340; Tampa, 840; Habana, 600. To Kingston passing W of Great Inagua Island, 400.

Turks Island Passage (*21° 35' N, 71° 10' W*) via Old Bahama Channel to Coatzacoalcos, 1480; Tampico, 1550; Corpus Christi, 1510; Galveston, 1420; Mississippi, Gulf Outlet canal, 1170; Mobile, 1170; Tampa, 925; Habana, 685; Via Windward Passage to Belize, 1020; Colon, 905; Kingston, 415.
Via Yucatan Channel to Coatzacoalcos, 1460; Tampico, 1550; to other ports N and E of Tampico Old Bahama Channel gives the shorter route.

Mona Passage (*18° 20' N, 68° 00' W*) to Kingston, 515; Curaçao, 390; Colon, 880; Belize, 1170.

Sombrero Passage (*18° 30' N, 63° 50' W*) to Kingston, 755; Curaçao, 500; Colon, 1090; Belize, 1410.

Between St. Lucia and St. Vincent (*13° 28' N, 61° 10' W*) to Bridgetown (Barbados), 90; Kingston, 940; Curaçao 470; Colon, 1150; Belize, 1580.
Via Mona Passage and Old Bahama Channel to Coatzacoalcos, 2170; Tampico, 2240; Corpus Christi, 2200; Galveston, 2100; Mississippi, Gulf Outlet canal 1850; Mobile, 1850; Tampa, 1610; Habana, 1370, Via Yucatan Channel to Coatzacoalcos, 2060; Tampico, 2160.

Galleons Passage (*10° 58' N, 60° 48' W*) to Kingston, 935; Willemstad, 505; Colon, 1190.

Colon (Panama Canal pilot) to Coatzacoalcos, 1420; Tampico, 1500; Corpus Christi, 1560; Galveston, 1510; Mississippi, Gulf Outlet canal, 1300.

CHAPTER 5

MEDITERRANEAN SEA AND BLACK SEA

CONTENTS *Page*

WINDS AND WEATHER

SWELL

CURRENTS

ICE

ROUTES

WINDS AND WEATHER

5.01. General remarks. The weather of the Mediterranean is markedly seasonal, being characterised by hot dry summers with mainly light or moderate winds, and mild rainy winters with a rather high frequency of strong winds and gales. The situation of this sea, surrounded by land, much of which is either mountainous or desert, and the indented nature of parts of the coast, leads to the occurrence of a large number of local winds, many with special names and characteristics. Information concerning these local winds will be found in Admiralty Sailing Directions.

Over the greater part of the open waters of the Mediterranean, winds from between N and W are the most frequent, though the passage of depressions across the area causes great variations in both the direction and force of the wind. From about November to March these depressions are frequent and often vigorous, while from about May to September they are less common and much less intense.

For convenience in describing the winds and weather of the Mediterranean, the area has been divided into the Western Mediterranean, W of the Sicilian Channel, and the Eastern Mediterranean, E of the Sicilian Channel.

It is emphasised that the statements which follow apply to the open sea away from the influence of the land, in the vicinity of which marked differences are likely to be found.

5.02. Western Mediterranean, November to March. In the more confined part of the area W of about 1° W, winds mostly blow parallel with the coast, westerlies being somewhat more common than easterlies from January to March, and very considerably more frequent in November and December.

Over the remainder of the area as far E as the longitude of Sardinia the most frequent wind directions are from between N and W, with a bias towards the latter direction in the S part of the area.

In the N part of the Tyrrhenian Sea there is no clearly predominant wind direction, though winds from some N'ly point are more common than those from a S'ly point. In the S part of this sea and in the Sicilian Channel the prevailing direction is NW'ly.

In January, the stormiest month in most parts of the Western Mediterranean, winds reach force 7 or above on 6–9 days per month in the NW and on 3–7 days per month elsewhere. Most of the winter gales are from between N and W, though NE'ly gales are not uncommon and gales from other directions may occasionally occur. Weather at this season is subject to rapid changes due to the passage of depressions with their associated frontal belts of cloud and rain; the rain is usually heavier but of shorter duration than in the British Isles.

Visibility over the open sea is generally good except when reduced by rain, but it may at times be only moderate with winds from a S'ly quarter.

5.03. Western Mediterranean, May to September. In that part of the area S of about 40° N and W of the longitude of Sardinia, winds are most frequently from between E and NE or from between W and SW, the former being slightly more common. Elsewhere, from June to August the most frequent wind directions are from between N and W, but in May and September there is no clearly predominant wind direction.

Winds are likely to reach force 7 or above on 1–3 days per month in the NW part of the area; elsewhere, winds of that strength are rare at this season.

Weather in July and August is generally fine with little or no rainfall, especially in the S and E. Cloud amounts are larger and rain is somewhat more common in May and September, especially in the latter month and NE of a line joining the Gulf of Lions, Sardinia, and Sicily.

Visibility is generally good, though occasional patches of sea fog may be experienced in early summer, and with winds from a S'ly quarter haze is sometimes prevalent.

5.04. Western Mediterranean, April and October. In the transitional months of April and October conditions can be taken as intermediate between winter and summer, though it must be realised that considerable variations are likely from year to year.

5.05. Eastern Mediterranean, November to March. S of about 35° N, winds are most often from between SW and N, while N of that parallel between Sicily and Greece there is no clearly prevailing wind direction.

In the greater part of the Adriatic and the N part of the Aegean, winds from between N and E are the most frequent, though these are often interrupted by winds from a S'ly quarter blowing in advance of an approaching depression.

In the S part of the Aegean, S'ly winds occur more frequently than in the N. However, winds blow mainly, as in the N, from between N and E.

The confined nature of the Adriatic gives rise to many local effects, details of which will be found in Admiralty Sailing Directions.

At the height of the season, winds are likely to reach force 7 or above on 6–9 days per month in the Aegean Sea and the E part of the Ionian Sea, and 3–6 days per month elsewhere in the area.

Weather at this season—as in the Western Mediterranean—is subject to rapid changes caused by moving depressions, and the statements made in article 5.02 for that area apply equally to the Eastern Mediterranean.

Visibility is generally good except when reduced by rain, but with winds from a S'ly quarter, which are experienced in advance of a depression, it is often only moderate.

5.06. Eastern Mediterranean, May to September. Over the whole of the Eastern Mediterranean, other than the Aegean Sea, the prevailing winds are NW'ly throughout the period, and particularly persistent in July and August and E of the 20th meridian, where winds from directions other than between N and W are uncommon.

Over the Aegean Sea, the prevailing wind is N'ly; here also, the degree of persistence is particularly high in July and August, during which months the great majority of winds are from between NE and NW.

From May to August winds are likely to reach force 7 only on rare occasions, except over the Aegean Sea in July and August, where winds of this strength may be expected on one or two days per month. In September the frequency of these winds is 1–3 days per month over most of the Eastern Mediterranean.

Over the greater part of the open waters of the area, weather at this season is fine with small amounts of cloud and little or no rain—especially in the S and E of the area in July and August. Over the N parts of the Aegean and Adriatic, some rain is likely throughout the period.

Visibility is generally good, though occasional patches of sea fog may be experienced in early summer, most often in the N part of the area; with winds from a S'ly quarter, haze is sometimes prevalent.

5.07. Eastern Mediterranean, April and October. In the transitional months of April and October conditions can be taken as intermediate between winter and summer, though it must be realised that considerable variations are likely from year to year.

5.08. Black Sea. The wind at sea is often very different from the wind near the coast. Well out to sea, NW and NE winds predominate over most of the sea; in the SE part, however, SW to W winds are common during autumn and winter, with N winds frequent during the summer. Throughout the Black Sea, sudden changes in the direction and force of the wind are common. Gales are not frequent, occurring mainly between August and March. Land and sea breezes are much in evidence during the summer.

Many depressions cross the Black Sea, especially during autumn and winter. Generally, they move in a NE'ly direction.

Visibility is generally good, apart from fog. The season for coastal fog is September to May, and in some places fog can be expected on one day in three during this period.

Detailed information on the winds and weather of the Black Sea will be found in Admiralty Sailing Directions.

SWELL

5.11. Mediterranean Sea and Black Sea. Heavy swells are more frequent in the Western Mediterranean than in the Eastern Mediterranean, but are rare in the Black Sea. The prevailing swell direction in the Black Sea is from some N'ly point while in the Mediterranean W'ly to NW'ly swells predominate.

In the Western Mediterranean, between Corsica and Islas Baleares, the percentage frequency of swell greater than 4 m is: June to September, 1 to 2 per cent; October, 2 to 5 per cent; November to March, 10 per cent; April and May, 2 to 5 per cent. These swells are invariably short or average in length.

CURRENTS

5.16. Mediterranean Sea, Adriatic Sea, and Aegean Sea. In the Mediterranean basin, the rate of evaporation is about three times as great as the inflow from the rivers which discharge into it. In consequence, there is a continuous inflow of surface water, through the Strait of Gibraltar, from the Atlantic Ocean.

Evaporation causes the Mediterranean water to increase its salinity; this denser water sinks and its excess emerges through the Strait of Gibraltar as a W-going sub-surface current, and a smaller quantity similarly reaches the Black Sea.

The main body of water entering through the Strait of Gibraltar flows E along the N coast of Africa; this is the most constant part of the main circulation, but it gradually loses strength as it penetrates E. On reaching Malta Channel part of it turns N to circulate counter-clockwise in the Western Mediterranean; the remainder continues through Malta Channel and along the African coast, turning N at the E end of the Mediterranean and then returning W along the N shores until it reaches the Ionian Sea, where it turns S to rejoin the main E'ly flow. Branches of this current enter the Aegean Sea and Adriatic Sea, giving rise to counter-clockwise circulations in those areas.

5.17. Black Sea. There is an almost continual flow of surface water from the Black Sea via the Bosporus, Marmara Denizi, and the Dardanelles. The surface circulation of the Black Sea is counter-clockwise but the currents are, in general, weak, inconstant, and affected to a great extent by variations in the outflow of the rivers and by the wind.

ICE

5.21. No ice occurs in the Mediterranean Sea. For the Black Sea, see Admiralty Sailing Directions.

ROUTES

5.26. General notes. The principal routes in the Mediterranean Sea are described in the following paragraphs. Directions for the main routes in the Adriatic Sea and the Aegean Sea are given in Admiralty Sailing Directions. In the Black Sea, routes are as direct as navigation permits. Distances are given for the routes as described in these publications or by the best navigational route.

5.27. Eastward from Strait of Gibraltar. Ships proceeding E should make use of the E-going current by keeping well away from the Spanish coast, passing 10 miles N of Isla de Alborán and about 20 miles S of Cabo de Gata. E of this longitude, vessels bound along the African coast should pass the salient points at a distance of between 10 and 20 miles and use Galite Channel, then passing about 5 miles N of Cap Serrat, Les Fratelli, Ras Enghela, Îles Cani, Cap Bon, Isola de Pantellaria, and Gozo. E of Gozo, all routes are as direct as prudent navigation allows.

In the approach to Port Said, **caution** is necessary owing to the low coast and the uncertainty of the current; vessels are advised to keep a good offing and to approach the Fairway buoy from N.

Vessels bound for ports in the region of Genova should keep at about 20 miles from the coast of Spain after rounding Cabo de Gata, and take departure for their destinations when abreast Cabo de San Antonio. For Cagliari or Napoli, take departure from Cabo de Gata and pass close S of Sardinia; for Palermo and Messina, make for the N side of Sicily, giving Keith Reef a wide berth.

5.28. Routes to the Strait of Gibraltar. Vessels bound for the Strait of Gibraltar from the Levant, or from the Aegean by the route S of Greece, should pass S of Sicily. Distances given in the table in article 5.35 are for tracks S of Sicily; for Adriatic ports and Dhiórix Korínthou (Corinth Canal), a route for Gibraltar N of Sicily and through Stretto di Messina is slightly shorter. The E-going current which flows along the N coast of Africa should be avoided by passing well N of Île de la Galite, thence making direct for Cabo de Gata and following the Spanish coast as closely as navigation permits.

From Marseille or Barcelona, make Cabo de San Antonio direct, and, after rounding Cabo de Gata, keep close to the coast.

From Italian ports, if passing N of Islas Baleares, make the Spanish coast at Cabo de Palos, or, if passing S of these islands, at Cabo de Gata.

5.29. Routes to and from Port Said. For Gibraltar, see 5.27 and 5.28; for Malta, the route is direct. For Marseille, proceed either through Stretto di Messina and Bonifacio Strait or pass S of Sicily and Sardinia; the distance for the former route is quoted in article 5.35. For the Levant, the Aegean Sea, and the Adriatic Sea, the routes are as direct as navigation permits.

5.35. Distances in miles: Mediterranean Sea, Adriatic Sea, and Aegean Sea.

Algiers

Algiers	Gibraltar	Barcelona	Marseille	Genova	Napoli	Trieste	Ákra Taíraron (C. Matapan)	Piraiévs (via Corinth Canal)	Piraiévs (via Aegean)	Mehmetçitk Burnu (C. Helles)*	Beirut	Port Said	Tarabulus	
445														Gibraltar
280	535													Barcelona
405	705	180												Marseille
525	865	350	205											Genova
580	990	555	460	345										Napoli
1290	1710	1340	1240	1150	835									Trieste
945	1360	1030	945	855	540	720								Ákra Taíraron (C. Matapan)
1020	1440	1090	995	905	595	740	—							Piraiévs (via Corinth Canal)
1080	1500	1170	1080	990	675	—	135	—						Piraiévs (via Aegean)
1240	1670	1310	1250	1160	845	950	300	—	220					Mehmetçitk Burnu (C. Helles)*
1620	2040	1700	1580	1530	1220	1380	—	—	670	695				Beirut
1500	1930	1590	1520	1430	1110	1300	—	—	600	645	220			Port Said
665	1090	760	745	720	520	935	505	625	635	805	1120	985		Tarabulus
570	1000	665	640	580	330	745	380	470	515	680	1040	935	195	Malta

* For distances onward to Black Sea ports, see 5.36.

5.36. Distances in miles: Black Sea.

Istanbul

Istanbul	Constanţa	Sulina	Odessa	Sevastopol	Zhdanov	Novorossiysk	
200							Constanţa
255	80						Sulina
350	180	105					Odessa
290	205	155	165				Sevastopol
415	475	435	450	285			Zhdanov
455	400	355	370	205	180		Novorossiysk
570	590	560	575	415	430	245	Batumi

The distance from Mehmetçitk Burnu (Cape Helles) to Istanbul is 145 miles.

CHAPTER 6

RED SEA, INDIAN OCEAN, AND PERSIAN GULF

CONTENTS   *Page*

WINDS AND WEATHER

APPROACH FROM WESTWARD TO AUSTRALIAN WATERS

COASTWISE PASSAGES OFF AUSTRALIA

ROUTES ON EASTERN SIDE OF INDIAN OCEAN

TRANS-OCEAN ROUTES

WINDS AND WEATHER

6.01. The following description of the winds and weather of the region of the Indian Ocean amplifies the general statement given in *The Mariner's Handbook*. For more precise information about oceanic winds and weather the atlas of Monthly Meteorological Charts of the Indian Ocean (MO 519), published by the Marine Branch of the Meteorological Office, should be consulted. Detailed information about specific localities should be sought in the appropriate Admiralty Sailing Directions. In reading the following description reference should be made to World Climatic Charts 5301 and 5302 and to Routeing Charts 5126 (1) to 5126 (12).

North Indian Ocean

6.02. The **winds and weather** of the whole North Indian Ocean are dominated by the alternation of the Monsoons, which are seasonal winds caused by the heating and cooling of the land mass of Asia, which gives rise to the changes of pressure which, in turn, generate the winds.

6.03. South-west Monsoon. From June to September the heating of the Asiatic land mass results in the establishment of a large area of low pressure centred approximately over the NW part of India. The South-east Trade Wind of the South Indian Ocean is drawn across the equator, is deflected to the right by the effects of the earth's rotation, and joins the cyclonic circulation round the area of low pressure mentioned above. The resulting SW wind, felt in the North Indian Ocean, the Arabian Sea, and the Bay of Bengal from June to September, is known as the South-west Monsoon. The general distribution of pressure and wind at this season is shown on chart 5302, from which it will be noted that in the E part of the Arabian Sea the prevailing wind direction is more nearly W than SW.

The strength of the wind varies considerably between different parts of the ocean. It is strongest in the W part of the Arabian Sea where, over a considerable area, the wind averages force 6 at the height of the season and reaches force 7 or above on more than 10 days per month, see chart 5302; the worst area is some 250 miles E of Socotra, where in July about half the observations report winds of force 7 or above.

In the extreme N part, and in the E parts of the Arabian Sea in July and August, the monsoon wind averages about force 4, although it often freshens to force 5 or 6, and attains force 7 on more than 3 to 6 days per month N of about 10° N.

In the Bay of Bengal the average strength of the monsoon wind is force 4 to 5; over the greater part of the Bay the wind reaches force 7 or above on 5 to 10 days per month in July and August.

Between the equator and about 5° N, and E of 60° E, winds are generally lighter and only average about force 3; they are also considerably more variable in direction, though generally from between S and W.

In Malacca Strait the wind is mostly light and is subject to considerable variation in direction and strength due to land and sea breezes and other local influences. In the N part of the strait the winds are most often SW'ly, while in the S the most frequent direction is SE. Although the Monsoon is generally light, there are often periods of stronger winds accompanied by squalls which sometimes reach gale force. The best known of these squalls are the "Sumatras", which blow from some W'ly point and occur most frequently at night; they are described in Admiralty Sailing Directions.

The weather over most of the North Indian Ocean during the South-west Monsoon season is cloudy and unsettled, with considerable rainfall, especially off the W coasts of India and Burma, where it is very heavy. In the W part of the Arabian Sea, however, cloud amount and rainfall decrease towards the N and W and both are generally small in the vicinity of the African and Arabian coasts. Rainfall is also small at this time in the immediate vicinity of the E coasts of Ceylon and India as far N as about 15° N.

Visibility is good in most parts of the area except when reduced by rain, and in the N and W parts of the Arabian Sea where it is often only moderate and sometimes poor within about 200 miles of the coast particularly during the South-west Monsoon period, when, although the sky may be clear, the surface visibility may be reduced; in this latter zone in July and August visibility is likely to be less than 5 miles on about 50 per cent of occasions because of dust haze.

6.04. North-east Monsoon. From November to March, a NE'ly wind is experienced in the North Indian Ocean, the Arabian Sea, and the Bay of Bengal. This wind is known as the North-east Monsoon. The general distribution of pressure and wind at this season is shown on Climatic Chart 5301, from which it will be observed that over the E part of Arabian Sea, and towards the equator, the prevailing wind direction is more nearly N than NE.

There are two areas in which the Monsoon is subject to considerable interruption, or in which the wind is rather variable in direction. The first is in the Arabian Sea N of about 20° N, where the variations in the direction and strength of the wind are caused by the passage of depressions across Iran or along the Makran coast, and the second is between the equator and about 5° N, and E of about 90° E, where winds, though mostly N'ly, are generally light and somewhat variable in direction.

Over the greater part of the North Indian Ocean the strength of the North-east Monsoon averages force 3 to 4 at the height of the season, though towards the equator it averages force 2 to 3, except W of about 55° E; it is also only light in the Malacca Strait. Winds are likely to reach force 7 only on rare occasions.

The weather in the Arabian Sea and Bay of Bengal is generally fine with small amounts of cloud and little or no rain. Cloudiness and rainfall increase towards the S and E, especially in December and January when considerable rain occurs in the S part of the Bay of Bengal S of a line joining the N extremities of Ceylon and Sumatra.

Visibility over the open ocean away from the effects of land is generally good or very good at this season, and fog is unknown. In the N and E parts of the Arabian Sea, however, visibility is often reduced by dust haze, especially in the latter part of the season, while in the N part of the Bay of Bengal it may be reduced by smoke haze and land mists carried seaward by the prevailing N'ly winds.

6.05. Inter-monsoon seasons. The months of April and May, and October, are characterised by the N and S shift across the area of the Equatorial Trough (6.11) and by the progressive replacement of the North-east Monsoon by the South-west Monsoon in April and May, and vice versa in October. The South-west Monsoon becomes established in the S earlier than in the N, and the reverse is true for the North-east Monsoon. The width of the Equatorial Trough, however, varies greatly from day to day and its movements are irregular; consequently the whole area can be regarded primarily as one of light winds (apart from squalls and tropical storms) with a rather high frequency of calms, and with the oncoming monsoon becoming gradually established.

Except in squalls, which are common, or in association with tropical storms, winds over the open ocean are likely to reach force 7 or above only on rare occasions, but in the W part of the Arabian Sea between 5° N and 10° N and W of 55° E, SW'ly winds of this strength may be expected on about 2 days in May. In the Malacca Strait "Sumatras" (6.03) occur occasionally.

The weather varies considerably, fair or fine conditions alternating with cloudy, squally weather with frequent heavy showers and thunderstorms; these conditions spread N during April and May, and retreat S during October. In the N part of the Arabian Sea, however, fine weather predominates during these inter-monsoon months.

Visibility over the open ocean is good except when reduced by heavy rain. Near the shores of the N and E parts of the Arabian Sea, however, it is sometimes reduced by dust haze in April and May.

Red Sea and Gulf of Aden

5   **6.06. Winds in Red Sea.** The prevailing winds in the Red Sea blow parallel with the coast. The seasonal change in pressure distribution over the adjacent land masses causes a seasonal reversal of the prevailing winds in the S part of the area.

From November to March, an extension of the Asiatic anticyclone is centred over the interior of Arabia, while another area of high pressure lies over the Sahara. The N part of the Red Sea is under the influence of
10   the Saharan anticyclone, resulting in the prevalence here of NNW winds, while S of about 18° N, from October to April, winds are influenced mainly by the Arabian anticyclone, with the result that the prevailing wind direction here is SSE. Between the NNW winds of the N part of the area and the SSE winds of the S part, lies an area of light variable winds and calms.

From June to September, with low pressure over the NW part of India, the NNW winds affect the S part of
15   the Red Sea as well. NNW winds thus prevail over the whole of the Red Sea from late May to late September. S of 18° N, May is characterised by the progressive retreat of the SSE'ly winds and by the corresponding advance of those from NNW, while the process is reversed in late September and early October.

In the Red Sea, N of 18° N, the average strength of the wind is force 4 throughout the year. Gales are most frequently, though not invariably, from NW or N; in the Gulf of Suez, gales are most common in December
20   and August, during which months winds may reach force 7 or above on about 2 days per month. Over the remainder of the area, February is the month of greatest frequency of strong winds with 1 to 2 days with winds of this strength. Gales are exceedingly rare during the South-west Monsoon season.

To the S of 18° N, the SSE'ly winds which prevail from October to April average force 4 to 5, rising to nearly force 6 near the Straits of Bāb-al-Mandab in February; the NNW'ly winds which prevail from June to September
25   average force 3 to 4. Gales are most common near the Straits of Bāb-al-Mandab in December and January, during which period winds in this area may be expected to reach force 7 or above on 3 to 4 days per month. As in the N part of the Red Sea, gales are rare during the season of the South-west Monsoon.

6.07. The winds in the Gulf of Aden form part of the monsoon circulation of Asia; the predominant winds are
30   ENE'ly from October to April, but become SE'ly in the Straits of Bāb-al-Mandab. In May, wind direction is variable, while from June to September SW'ly winds prevail.

In the Gulf of Aden, the ENE'ly winds average force 2 to 3 from December to March, and gales are rare. From June to September within the main part of the Gulf, the strength of the South-west Monsoon averages about force 4, and winds reach force 7 or above on 1 to 2 days per month. The average strength of the wind and
35   the frequency of gales, however, increase rapidly towards the E end of the Gulf, and E of Ras Asir winds are likely to reach force 7 or above on 10 to 15 days in July. Tropical cyclones are very rare in the Gulf, only 3 or 4 having been experienced in the last 50 years.

6.08. Weather and visibility. The weather over the whole of the Red Sea and the Gulf of Aden is generally
40   fine, with small amounts of cloud; when rainfall does occur it is in the form of showers and may be heavy. Total rainfall is slight.

Over the open sea, fog and mist are rare except in the extreme E part of the Gulf of Aden during the South-west Monsoon season. Sand and dust haze is however, widespread from June to August, visibility at this time of year being less than 5 miles on about 1 day in 10 in the N part of the Red Sea, 1 day in 4 or 5 in the S part
45   of the Red Sea and on the African side of the Gulf of Aden, and 1 day in 2 on the Arabian side of that Gulf. In September the frequency of haze decreases greatly, while from December to February it is not usual. Sandstorms, which N of about 22° N mostly occur from February to June, and in the S part of the Red Sea and in the Gulf of Aden from May to August or September, may occasionally reduce visibility to 50 metres or less.

50   ### Persian Gulf and Gulf of Oman

6.09. The following remarks apply to open water away from the local effect of land, in the vicinity of which land and sea breezes and other local effects are likely to cause considerable modification. Detailed information about specific localities will be found in Admiralty Sailing Directions.

In the main part of the Persian Gulf, NW'ly winds (Shamal) are the most frequent throughout the year; they
55   become more W'ly in the S part of the Gulf or even SW'ly on the W side of the Strait of Hormuz. From December to February these north-westerlies are frequently interrupted by SE'ly winds, blowing in advance of E-moving depressions; thus, during winter, an alternation between SE'ly and NW'ly winds is the characteristic feature. From March to May the SE'ly winds associated with depressions decrease rapidly in frequency, with a corresponding increase in the number of north-westerlies which, from June to September, are very persistent and
60   form part of the cyclonic wind circulation round the summer low situated over the NW part of India. In October and November the north-westerlies become less steady as a gradual return to winter conditions brings an increasing frequency of SE'ly winds.

The average strength of the wind is force 2 to 3 rising to 3 to 4 in the N part of the Gulf during the winter. The variations from the mean are, however, great, and both calms and fresh to strong winds are rather common.
65   Winds may reach force 7 or above most often from December to March, during which period winds of this strength are likely to be experienced on about 3 days per month; they also occur occasionally in summer, when they are due to a deepening of the summer low over the NW part of India, but they are rare in April, May and October. The winter gales may be from any direction, but those occurring in summer are limited to directions between N and W. Squalls, during which winds may reach gale force, are a characteristic feature of the weather
70   of the Persian Gulf and may occur at any time.

In the Gulf of Oman from December to February, winds are mainly from some N'ly point with NW as the most frequent direction. South-easterlies occur ahead of advancing depressions, but are less frequent here than in the Persian Gulf. From March to May winds are very variable, with north-westerlies decreasing and south-westerlies increasing in frequency until, by May, the latter winds predominate. From June to August the prevailing wind is SE'ly, being an offshoot of the South-west Monsoon of the Arabian Sea. From September to November the frequency of SE'ly winds decreases and that of northerlies increases, but wind direction is, in general, very variable.

The frequency of calms is higher in the Gulf of Oman than in the Persian Gulf; winds reach force 7 on about 1 to 2 days per month from December to March, but rarely attain force 8. As in the Persian Gulf, squalls are common. On rare occasions the Gulf may be affected by a tropical storm originating in the Arabian Sea.

In both the Persian Gulf and the Gulf of Oman rain and large amounts of cloud are practically confined to the period November to April, and are associated with E-moving depressions, in the intervals between which fine weather with small amounts of cloud prevails. In summer, the Persian Gulf is practically cloudless, but in the Gulf of Oman the influence of the monsoon causes an increase in cloudiness in July and August.

Visibility is for the most part good or very good from November to February; after this, dust haze causes a progressive deterioration until in June and July visibility is less than 5 miles on 10 to 12 days per month over the open sea, and still more often near the coast. Dust haze decreases considerably after July. Duststorms or sandstorms occur in all seasons, but are most frequent during June and July and least so during the winter; during their occurrence they often reduce visibility to less than 500 metres.

South Indian Ocean

6.10. The winds and weather of the South Indian Ocean are governed by the advance of the North Indian Ocean monsoon into the S hemisphere from November to February and its retreat from June to September; the result is the establishment, in this zone, of alternating seasonal winds. S of this zone the normal wind and pressure distribution, as outlined in *The Mariner's Handbook*, prevails.

6.11. Equatorial Trough (Doldrums). This region is known variously as the Equatorial Trough, the Doldrum belt, the Intertropical Convergent Zone (I.T.C.Z.), the Intertropical Front (I.T.F.), the Equatorial Front, or the Shearline. It is, in the Indian Ocean, S of the equator from about November to April, and reaches its most S'ly position in February. The winds and weather are similar to those encountered in the Equatorial Trough in other oceans, and consist of fair weather, calms, and light variable winds alternating with squalls, heavy showers, and thunderstorms. Both the width of the belt and its position vary considerably from day to day; the former averages about 200 miles but it may at times be much more, while at others it may be reduced to almost nothing by a strong burst of the South-east Trade Wind. Visibility in this zone is good except in heavy rain.

6.12. North-west Monsoon. During the period from November to March, when the Equatorial Trough is situated in the S hemisphere, the North-east Monsoon of the North Indian Ocean is drawn across the equator, deflected to the left by the effect of the earth's rotation, and is felt in the N part of the South Indian Ocean as a NW'ly wind, known as the North-west Monsoon. See Climatic Chart 5301.

Winds are in general light, and vary considerably in direction, but in the W part of the zone the prevailing direction is more nearly N than NW, and becomes NE close to the African coast and N of about 10° S. In the Moçambique Channel a N'ly wind prevails as far as 15° S to 17° S; it is here known as the **Northern Monsoon.**

In the E part of the ocean just S of Java, and in the Timor and Arafura Seas, the prevailing wind direction is between W and NW.

Except in squalls, which are common, or in association with tropical storms (6.16) winds over the greater part of the zone are likely to reach force 7 or above only on rare occasions.

The weather is generally rather cloudy and unsettled, and rain, mostly in the form of heavy showers, is frequent. Visibility is good except in rain.

6.13. The South-east Trade Wind blows on the equatorial side of the anti-clockwise circulation round the oceanic high-pressure area situated in about 30° S. In this ocean, however, the oceanic anticyclone seldom consists of a single cell; more frequently it contains a more or less regular succession of E-moving anticyclones, from the N sides of which blow the Trade Winds, which blow permanently and with little variation in direction throughout the year.

In summer, the South-east Trades extend from about 30°S to the Equatorial Trough, the general direction of the wind being from between E and SE over most of the area, but becoming S'ly off the W coast of Australia, and mainly SW'ly off its NW coast—though in the latter area the direction is much more variable than in the Trade Winds proper. In the S part of the Moçambique Channel an extension of the Trades gives prevailing S to SE winds. Climatic Chart 5301 shows the area covered by the Trades at this season.

In winter, the South-east Trades extend from about 27° S to the equator, though N of about 5° S and E of 70° E they are weak, and, though generally from some S'ly point, they vary considerably in direction. Elsewhere over the greater part of the open ocean winds are almost exclusively from between SSE and ESE, but in the E part of the area and in the Timor Sea the predominant direction is somewhat more E'ly. In the Timor and Arafura Seas the South East Trade Wind is sometimes referred to as the **South-east Monsoon** in contradistinction to the North-west Monsoon (6.12), which prevails there in summer. In the Moçambique Channel an extension of the South-east Trades gives prevailing S to SE winds over the whole length of the channel from about April to September. These winds are known as the **Southern Monsoon** in contradistinction to the Northern Monsoon (6.12), which prevails in the N part of the channel in summer. Climatic Chart 5302 shows the area covered by the South-east Trade Wind at this season.

5

10

15

20

25

30

35

40

45

50

55

60

65

70

The average strength of the South-east Trade Wind is force 3 to 4 in summer and force 4 to 5 in winter; it reaches a mean of force 5 between about 10° S and 20° S and 65° E and 100° E when at its strongest during the winter. In summer, winds are likely to reach force 7 or above on 1 to 3 days per month over the greater part of the zone, rising to 3 to 6 days per month over the central part of the area. In winter, winds of this strength are likely to be encountered on 1 to 3 days per month in the E and W parts of the zone, while over a considerable area between about 65° E and 90° E their frequency rises to 6 to 9 days per month as shown on Climatic Chart 5302. In the Timor and Arafura Seas winds are unlikely to reach force 7 on more than 1 or 2 days per month.

The weather over the open ocean is mostly fair or fine with skies about half covered, but belts of cloudy showery weather occur at intervals. To the NW and N of the Australian continent, between the NW part of Australia and Java, and in the Timor Sea and, to a lesser extent, in the Arafura Sea, cloud amounts and rainfall are small from April to September, while the South-east Trade Wind prevails in these regions. Extensive dust haze prevails here, especially in the Timor Sea and towards the end of the season. Elsewhere in the South-east Trade zone visibility is good except in rain.

6.14. Variables. To the S of the S limit of the South-east Trade Wind, there is a zone of light variable winds in the area of the oceanic high pressure region. In winter the centre of the high-pressure region is located in about 30° S, while in summer it moves to about 35° S over the greater part of the ocean, dipping somewhat farther S near the SW part of Australia.

The weather also varies considerably in this zone, alternating between fair or fine conditions near the centres of the E-moving anticyclones and cloudy showery weather in the intervening troughs of low pressure. Visibility is generally good except in rain.

6.15. Westerlies (Roaring Forties). To the S of the high pressure region mentioned in articles 6.13 and 6.14, W'ly winds predominate. As in the Westerlies of other oceans, the almost continuous passage of depressions from W to E causes the wind to vary greatly both in direction and strength; the centres of most of these depressions pass S of 50° S. Gales are very prevalent in the zone of the Westerlies especially in winter, during which season winds reach force 7 or above on 12–16 days per month S of about the 36th parallel; during summer, winds of this force are likely to be encountered on 6 to 12 days per month S of about 40° S. Climatic Charts 5301 and 5302 show the regions in which gales are most common.

As in the Westerlies of other oceans, the weather is very variable, periods of overcast skies and rain or snow associated with the fronts of E-moving depressions alternating with fairer conditions. Fine weather is, however, seldom prolonged, and cloud amounts are generally large throughout the year.

Visibility varies considerably; with winds from a S'ly point it is generally good, while N'ly winds are often associated with moderate or poor visibility. S of the 40th parallel visibility of less than 2 miles may be expected on perhaps 5 days per month, while fog is not uncommon during the summer; it is usually associated with winds from a N'ly point.

Tropical storms

6.16. Tropical storms occur in the Arabian Sea, the Bay of Bengal, and in parts of the South Indian Ocean. They are described, and advice on avoiding them is given in *The Mariner's Handbook*. Information regarding storm frequencies and tracks will be found in the appropriate Admiralty Sailing Directions, on the Routeing Charts 5126 (1) to 5126 (12), and in the atlas of Monthly Meteorological Charts of the Indian Ocean (MO 519).

Tropical storms are known as "Cyclones" in the area covered by this chapter. Alternatively, in Western Australia they are known as "Willy-Willies".

In the Arabian Sea, cyclones occur in May, June, October, and November, the periods of greatest frequency being from early May to mid-June, and from mid-October to mid-November. Although they have been recorded they are extremely rare in July, September, and December. They are unknown from January to March and in August.

In the Bay of Bengal most cyclones occur from May to November, with November as the month of greatest frequency. They occur very occasionally in March, April, and December, and are unknown almost in January and entirely so in February.

In the South Indian Ocean, cyclones occur from December to April, the month of greatest frequency being January; they also occur occasionally in November and May.

In the Timor Sea and the Arafura Sea, and off the W coast of Australia the Willy-Willy season and the month of greatest frequency are the same as for the cyclones of the South Indian Ocean, except that Willy-Willies are not known in May.

For the effect of tropical storms upon the currents, see 1.75.

SWELL

6.21. In the Arabian Sea and the Bay of Bengal, the swell is governed by the direction and strength of the monsoon winds. In the Arabian Sea a SW'ly swell becomes established during May and persists until September. A NE'ly swell becomes established during November and persists until March. There is no predominant direction in April or October and the swell is normally low or moderate in the changeover months and mainly moderate once the monsoon is established, though from June to September a heavy swell may be encountered. In the Bay of Bengal a SW'ly swell becomes established during March and persists until October. A NE'ly swell becomes established during November and persists until February. Swell is normally low or moderate except for the period from May to August when it is moderate or heavy. In **Malacca Strait** there is no predominant direction of swell. Throughout the year swell is normally low and only on rare occasions does it become moderate.

Swell in the Arabian Sea and the Bay of Bengal is normally short or average in length. However, on about 10 per cent of occasions swells of over 200 metres may be encountered; such swells are almost invariably low in height.

6.22. In the **Red Sea,** the predominant swell directions are N to NW and S to SE. From May to September the swell is everywhere N to NW but in October a S to SE'ly swell becomes established S of 18° N. This swell persists until March but is replaced in April by the N to NW swell of the N part of the Red Sea as it extends S. Swell in the Red Sea is low or moderate, but rarely heavy. The length of swell is generally short, though a small number of average swells do occur.

6.23. In the **Gulf of Aden,** a SW'ly swell occurs from June to September and an E to NE'ly swell from November to March. These swells are low or moderate. There is no predominant direction in April, May, or October, when the swell is mainly low. Swell lengths are similar to those experienced in the Red Sea.

6.24. In the **Persian Gulf,** swell is predominantly NW'ly, though from December to February, a SE'ly swell may occur. The swell is normally low or moderate, but is occasionally heavy in the S part of the Gulf in August and September.

In the Gulf of Oman, swell is NW'ly from December to February and SE'ly from June to August. At other times there is no predominant direction. The swell is normally low or moderate and only rarely heavy. Most swells in the Persian Gulf and the Gulf of Oman are short, and have periods between 3 and 6 seconds.

6.25. In the **South Indian Ocean,** swell is a regular feature. The swell generated by the depressions S of 50° S often travels to all parts of the N and S Indian Ocean; more than one swell is frequently present, and confused swell is often reported. As shown by the following table, it is normally moderate to heavy. In length, it covers the complete range from short to long; many swells are of average length but lengths of over 300 metres are not uncommon.

Freak waves may occur, see 3.09.

Zone	25° E–70° E		70° E–110° E	
	Direction	Height	Direction	Height
0°–20° S	Predominantly SE	Low or moderate, at times heavy between 10° S and 20° S.	S to SE	Mainly moderate
20° S–35° S	SE through S to SW	Moderate or heavy	Mainly SW to S	Moderate or heavy
35° S–50° S	Some NW but mainly W to SW	Moderate or heavy	Some NW but mainly W to SW	Moderate or heavy, with waves greater than 6 m quite common

6.26. Speed reduction in relation to sea conditions. During the **North-east Monsoon and Southern summer period,** from about November to March, sea conditions in the Indian Ocean do not call for particular comment except that, S of 40° S, they are such as to cause ships on W'ly headings to find it necessary to reduce speed for more than 10 per cent of their voyage time. The southern summer is, however, the season of greatest frequency of tropical storms in the South Indian Ocean, see 6.16.

At the peak of the **South-west Monsoon period,** in July, speeds of ships in the Arabian Sea may have to be reduced for more than 60 per cent of the time when steaming into, or abeam of, wind and sea, and about 20 per cent of the time in following seas. In the S hemisphere, seas in winter are higher than in summer and the South-east Trades and the Westerlies are at their strongest. It is apparent that winter storms in the South Indian Ocean have their greatest frequency in about 80° E and lesser concentrations about 60° E and 110° E.

During the **transitional periods,** in April and October, sea conditions, though less severe than in July, may affect speed on the E–W tracks across the Southern Ocean. S of 35° S, speed reduction may be necessary on these tracks for more than 10 per cent of voyage time.

CURRENTS

North Indian Ocean

6.31. The currents in the North Indian Ocean are reversed in direction seasonally under the influence of the monsoons. These comprise the currents of the Arabian Sea and Bay of Bengal, and the Somali Current, between

2° S and Ras Asir. The only current which is not so reversed is the Equatorial Counter-current, which lies mainly S of the equator but sometimes extends a few degrees N of it.

The South-west Monsoon circulation is established from May to September. October is a month of transition. In November, which is also to some extent transitional, the circulation more resembles that of the two subsequent months. The typical North-east Monsoon circulation occurs during December and January. The later North-east Monsoon period, February to April, constitutes an extended transition period, in which an intermediate type of circulation is developed. The currents are, therefore, described below for the three periods, November to January; February to April; and May to September.

6.32. North-east Monsoon period, November to January. In the open waters of the Arabian Sea and Bay of Bengal, the current sets in a general W'ly direction. Owing to the coastal conformation, the current flows round the coasts in a counter-clockwise direction. Off Somalia, the current which sets NE in November reverses during December to become SW in January. This current, known as the **Somali Current**, meets the N-going **East Africa Coast Current** and turns towards E to form the beginning of the **Equatorial Counter-current.**

6.33. Later North-East Monsoon period, February to April. During this period the resultant flow in the open waters of the Arabian Sea and Bay of Bengal remains W'ly, though the actual currents experienced are somewhat more variable than during November to January. The coastal circulation, both of the Arabian Sea and Bay of Bengal, is, however, reversed to a clockwise direction (see above). This reversal is completed in the Bay of Bengal by about the beginning of February. In the Arabian Sea it is more gradual and is not complete on all parts of the coast until the end of March. In February, the current flows SW off the African coast S of about 8° N, but farther N it sets NE. In the subsequent months the S limit of the NE flow extends progressively S and by April the flow is NE from the equator to Ras Asir.

6.34. South-West Monsoon period, May to September. The clockwise circulation of the coastal region of the Arabian Sea and Bay of Bengal persists and is strengthened. The East African Coast Current and the Somali Current continue to flow N along the coast from the equator to Ras Asir, and the latter is greatly strengthened. From the Somali Current, the flow fans off to the E. In the open waters of the Arabian Sea and Bay of Bengal there is a general E'ly drift. Very strong currents occur in this season, especially off the equatorial coasts of Somalia, and S of Socotra where they are probably stronger than anywhere else in the world. Here, mean values of 3 knots have been observed, with extreme rates up to 7 knots on occasions.

6.35. The Equatorial Counter-current. This is an E-setting current which is easily identified during the winter of the N hemisphere between the W-setting monsoon current to the N and the Equatorial Current, also setting W, to the S. In November, the N limit of the counter-current is in about 3° N. It shifts S in the following months and reaches its most S'ly positions in February, when it lies between 2° S and 3° S. It returns N thereafter and by April is in about 2° N in the W, and in about 4° N, E of 80° E.

In the South-west Monsoon season the Equatorial Counter-current cannot be distinguished in direction from the general E'ly current of the Arabian Sea and Bay of Bengal, but in the region of the counter-current, S of about 2° N, the rate of flow is stronger than in the general monsoon drift.

The course of the counter-current on the E side of the ocean is not fully known. In November to January the bulk of it appears to follow the W coast of Sumatra and the S coast of Java in SE'ly and E'ly directions. In the South-west Monsoon period there is some evidence that part of it recurves toward S in the region W of Sumatra, passing into the Equatorial current.

The S limit of the counter-current is well S of the Equator in all seasons.

South Indian Ocean

6.36. The main surface circulation of the South Indian Ocean is counter-clockwise.

There is only one true Equatorial Current in the Indian Ocean, corresponding to the South Equatorial Currents of the Atlantic and Pacific Oceans. The W-going flow of the **Equatorial Current** of the Indian Ocean lies well S of the equator, thus differing from the South Equatorial Currents of the Atlantic and Pacific, which extend in latitude to a few degrees N of the equator. Its N boundary is usually between 6° S and 10° S, varying according to longitude and season.

The N part of the W-going Equatorial Current, after passing the N extremity of Madagascar, meets the African coast in the region of Cabo Delgado. Here it divides, some of the water flowing N along the coast, while the remainder flows S into Moçambique Channel forming a strong coastal current. From Cabo Delgado to Baía de Lourenço Marques this current is known as the **Moçambique Current**. Its continuation S is known as the **Agulhas Current**; this is reinforced by water from the Equatorial Current setting past the S extremity of Madagascar.

The direction of flow of the S part of the Equatorial Current becomes more S'ly as it approaches Madagascar and, near the coast, becomes SSW. It follows the coast, becoming WSW off Cap Sainte Marie. Away from the coast, there is less variation in the direction, which is more consistently SW'ly. At distances of more than 60 miles from the coast the average speeds are mainly ½ to ¾ knot but much larger values occur within a few miles of the coast where the average speed is 1–2 knots and 3 knots or more is sometimes reported. This strong inshore current is known as the **Madagascar Current.**

Some of the water of the Agulhas Current recurves SE between about 20° E and 32° E and passes into the N part of the Southern Ocean Current. The remainder of the Agulhas Current continues along the coastline and, passing over Agulhas Bank, enters the South Atlantic Ocean, where it contributes to the flow of the Benguela Current of that ocean, see 3.11.

The S side of the main circulation is formed by the cold water of the **Southern Ocean Current**, setting across the ocean in E'ly to NE'ly directions as far as about 80° E, and in E'ly to SE'ly directions on the E side of the ocean. As above stated, some of the warm Agulhas Current water also contributes to the S side of the circulation in the W part of the ocean.

The **Southern Ocean Current** has no defined N boundary, the predominance of E'ly sets decreasing with decreasing latitude in the central longitudes of the ocean until they merge into the extensive region of variable current in the middle of the ocean S of the Equatorial Current. Some predominance of E'ly set is found as far N as 28° S or 30° S in the central longitudes.

The E side of the circulation is not well marked. It is formed by the **West Australian Current**, a weak NW'ly flow off the W coast of Australia. This passes into the Equatorial Current in about 16° S to 20° S, 95° E to 105° E. The Southern Ocean Current on approaching Australia sends off a branch which passes into the West Australian Current. The bulk of the Southern Ocean Current continues its E'ly course, S of Australia and Tasmania into the S Pacific Ocean.

Off the coast of Western Australia, S of Cape Naturaliste, the average flow is SE'ly in all seasons. N of this cape the currents near the coast, though mainly weak and inconstant, show a seasonal variation. From April till September the flow is SE along all the coast S of the latitude varying between 28° S and 32° S. Farther N, the coastal flow is N'ly. From October till April, the flow is N'ly or variable off the whole coast N of Cape Naturaliste.

The **Equatorial Counter-current** flows E across the ocean throughout the year, immediately N of the Equatorial current. It is more directly connected with the currents of the North Indian Ocean than with those of the South Indian Ocean and is more fully described in connection with the former, in article 6.35.

6.37. Extreme eastern part of Indian Ocean. The currents of this part of the ocean, including the Arafura Sea, are not well known. E of Christmas Island, between the parallels of about 10° S and 14° S, there is a predominance of W'ly sets during the greater part of the year, forming the most E'ly part of the Equatorial Current.

ICE

6.41. General remarks. The following brief account of ice in the South Indian Ocean should not be taken as complete or in any way all-embracing. More detailed information than can be given here will be found in the following publications, which should be consulted before undertaking passages S of the latitude of Cape Agulhas.

> Admiralty Sailing Directions covering the appropriate areas.
> The Mariner's Handbook.
> Charts 5126 (1) to 5126 (12)—Monthly Routeing Charts for the Indian Ocean.
> Charts 5301, 5302—World climatic charts.
> Washington, U.S. Navy, Oceanographic Atlas of the Polar Seas, H.O.705.

A general statement regarding ice, including warning signs of its proximity, is given in Chapter 1 of this book.

A factor always to be borne in mind where ice conditions are concerned is their great variability from year to year. For this reason, and on account of the sparsity of observations in many areas, the charted positions of ice limits should be regarded as approximate.

6.42. Pack-ice. The long-term average position of the pack-ice (4/8 concentration) in September to October, at its greatest extension, see chart 5302, runs from about 55° S on the meridian of Greenwich to 58° S, 50° E, and 60° S, 110° E. Continuing E, the edge lies near 61° S as far as 160° E. For least average extension, see 3.17. None of the normally inhabited places in the South Indian Ocean is affected, but great circle sailing between the more S'ly ports in South Africa and Australia is interfered with.

6.43. Icebergs. The icebergs that occur in the South Indian Ocean are not, in most cases, calved from glaciers, but consist of portions that have broken away from the great ice shelves which fringe parts of the Antarctic continent. They are consequently flat-topped, and they may be of immense size.

The mean limit of bergs reaches its farthest N between 20° E and 70° E in November and December, when it runs from about 44° S in the longitude of Cape Agulhas to about 48° S, 70° E. It is farthest N in February and March E of the 70th meridian, when it runs between the 48th and 50th parallels as far as 120° E, and thence to about 55° S in the longitude of Tasmania. In May and June the mean limit of bergs is everywhere S of the 50th parallel, and between the 120th meridian and the longitude of Tasmania it is S of 55° S.

With regard to extreme limits, the season varies considerably from one longitude to another, and, moreover, factors other than climatic may be responsible for abnormalities, so that it is probably best to regard this limit as unrelated to the time of year. Earthquakes, for example, may give rise to an excessive formation of tabular bergs. The extreme limit of icebergs, indicated on charts 5301, 5302, and on charts 5126 (1) to (12), runs from near 35° S off the coast of Africa, gradually receding S and lying in about 38° S between 70° E and 120° E. Continuing E, it recedes farther S to about 40° S, 130° E and 48° S, 120° E.

RED SEA ROUTES

6.51. General. Routes in the Red Sea to ports on its coasts are as direct as navigation permits, and are not described in this volume. A general description of the through route between the Gulf of Suez and the Gulf of Aden is, however, included. For all routes, Admiralty Sailing Directions should be consulted.

6.52. Suez ↔ Aden. Recommended routes incorporating traffic separation have been established in the Gulf of Suez, in the S part of the Red Sea, and in the Straits of Bāb-al-Mandab.

The central passage through the Red Sea, between the Gulf of Suez and Jabal at Tāir, is free from dangers, but the direct course passes much nearer the E side than the W side of the sea; it is therefore advisable, having passed E of the Brothers and on either side of Daedalus Reef, to steer for 17° 00′ N, 40° 40′ E, midway between the coastal banks, and thence to the N end of the recommended route in 16° 00′ N, 41° 46′ E. This route leads S-bound traffic through Abu Ail Channel, and N-bound traffic E of Abu Ail islands.

The recommended routes in the Straits of Bāb-al-Mandab, are in Large Strait. Small Strait is intended for coastal traffic .

Between Large Strait and Aden, the routes is as prudent navigation permits.

Distance: Suez to Aden 1310 miles.

6.53. Notes and cautions. Local cross currents, with rates that may approach 2 knots, are not infrequent in all parts of the Red Sea. Constant vigilance is called for, and a good berth should be given to the positions of outlying banks and shoals.

Currents exceeding a rate of 2 knots may occur, at times, in the Straits of Bāb-al-Mandab during the Northeast Monsoon period.

When N-bound in short visibility a vessel which has suffered a W'ly set may mistake Gifâtìn Islands for Shaker (Shadwân) Island on first sighting. Since Gifâtìn Islands are steep-to on their E side, and Shaker Island can be identified by its light-tower, visual confirmation of the landfall should be possible in these conditions.

Low-powered vessels, when N-bound, may find it to their advantage by day to use the channels W of Shaker Island which are less exposed than the Strait of Gûbal to the prevailing NW wind.

PERSIAN GULF ROUTES

6.54. Routes. For routes in the Persian Gulf, see Admiralty Sailing Directions.

From the E (Gulf of Oman) end of the Strait of Hormuz (*26° 21′ N, 56° 38′ E*), distances to various destinations are:

Jabal aẓ Ẓannah (pilots)	270 miles
Jazīrat Dās (pilots)	225 miles
Jazīrat Hālūl (anchorage)	240 miles
Bahrain (Sitrah anchorage)	340 miles
Ra's Tannūrah (anchorage)	380 miles
Mīnā al Aḥmadī (Al Fuḥayḥil loading berths)	495 miles
Khaw Al Amayah (pilots)	495 miles
Bandar Shāhpūr (pilots)	490 miles
Jazireh-ye Khārk (pilots)	415 miles

EAST COAST OF AFRICA, ARABIAN SEA, AND BAY OF BENGAL

6.55. Moçambique Channel. When planning routes which offer the alternatives of passage through Moçambique Channel or E of Madagascar, the navigational hazards presented by the islands and shoals in the N approach to Moçambique Channel should be considered, as well as the restriction they impose on freedom of manoeuvre on the approach of a tropical storm, of which little warning may be expected in these waters.

6.56. Cape Town → Durban and Moçambique Channel. The dominating factors are the Agulhas Current, which flows S and W with considerable strength, and the sea and swell generated by S'ly gales.

A counter-current will sometimes be found between 1 and 6 miles offshore between Cape Agulhas and Great Fish Point, and sometimes, during W'ly winds, between Port Shepstone and Cape Natal. When nearing Cape Natal, a strong set-off from the land may be expected.

Ships seeking to pass inshore of the Agulhas Current, with the possible benefit of a counter-current, while avoiding the heavy and dangerous seas, see Admiralty Sailing Directions, which sometimes run in the vicinity of the 200 m (110 fms) line during S'ly and SW'ly gales, and particularly off East London, must proceed with caution and, when uncertain of their position, keep in depths of more than 75 m (40 fms). They should in any case take great care to avoid the salient points, and be vigilant against indraught into bays. Tankers carrying cargo oil in excess of one-half per cent of their deadweight tonnage should keep at least 12 miles off a line joining the salient points of the South African coast.

A ship making the passage from Cape Town to Moçambique Channel can avoid the main part of the Agulhas Current by keeping to seaward of it, through 36° 45′ S, 19° 00′ E; by great circle to 34° 30′ S, 32° 30′E; thence by rhumb line, and nothing to W, to 30° 00′ S, 38° 20′E; thence steering for the E part of Moçambique Channel and passing E of Île Europa.

6.57. Moçambique Channel → Durban and Cape Town. The S-bound route through Moçambique Channel is on the W side of the channel, in the Moçambique Current. Thence, ships should hold the Agulhas Current by keeping from 20 to 30 miles from the coast as far as Mossel Bay. During SW gales off the latter part of this coast, a very dangerous sea will be experienced at or to seaward of the edge of the coastal bank, see Admiralty Sailing Directions, there is considerably less sea near the coast, and if a vessel keeps about 3 miles or less offshore the reduction in the sea will more than compensate for the loss of favourable current. As directed

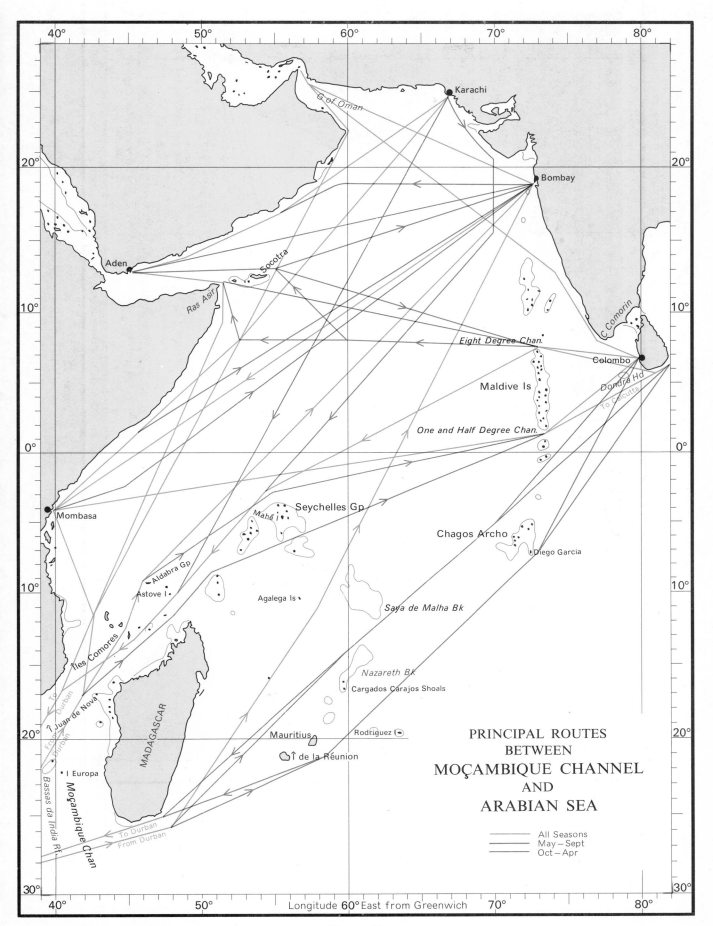

PRINCIPAL ROUTES
BETWEEN
MOÇAMBIQUE CHANNEL
AND
ARABIAN SEA

	All Seasons
	May—Sept
	Oct—Apr

Diagram 21

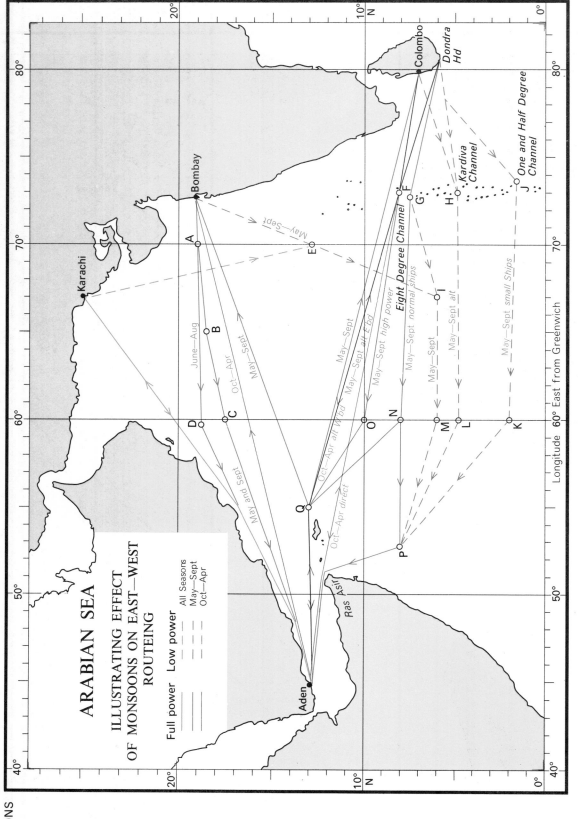

KEY TO LETTERED POSITIONS

	LATITUDE	LONGITUDE
	° ′	° ′
A	19 00 N	70 00 E
B	18 30 N	65 00 E
C	17 30 N	60 00 E
D	18 45 N	59 40 E
E	12 50 N	70 00 E
F	8 06 N	73 00 E
G	7 30 N	72 45 E
H	4 56 N	73 00 E
I	6 00 N	67 00 E
J	1 35 N	73 40 E
K	2 00 N	60 00 E
L	4 44 N	60 00 E
M	6 00 N	60 00 E
N	8 00 N	60 00 E
O	10 00 N	60 00 E
P	8 00 N	52 40 E
Q	13 00 N	55 00 E

ARABIAN SEA

ILLUSTRATING EFFECT
OF MONSOONS ON EAST—WEST
ROUTEING

	Full power	Low power
All Seasons		
May—Sept		
Oct—Apr		

Diagram 22

in 6.56, a depth of more than 75 m (40 fm) should be maintained if uncertain of the position, and, in any case, tankers carrying cargo oil in excess of one-half per cent of their deadweight tonnage should keep at least 12 miles off a line joining the salient points of the South African coast. After passing Mossel Bay, course should be shaped to round Cape Agulhas and the Cape of Good Hope at a safe distance.

6.58. Routes through Moçambique channel. The currents near the W coast of Madagascar are little known. In mid-channel and extending at least half-way towards Madagascar, the predominant flow is mostly NE, but both direction and rate are highly variable.

On the African side of the channel, the Moçambique Current sets strongly in a generally SSW direction, following the coast; in the region of Moçambique this current is thought to extend about 50 miles off the coast during most of the year, increasing to nearly 100 miles in June, July, and August.

The situation in Moçambique Channel, where strong SSW'ly currents suddenly give place to moderate or possibly strong currents in the opposite direction, has obvious dangers. The boundaries of the currents vary with season and weather, and their rates may differ by as much as 4 knots from those anticipated.

From Durban or its vicinity N-bound, haul off to about 100 miles from the coast and pass through 27° 15′ S, 36° 00′ E and 17° 00′ S, 42° 15′ E, passing 30 miles W of Bassas da India. Having passed W of Juan de Nova, steer for 11° 35′ S, 42° 50′E and thence as required. Alternatively, a route E of Île Europa will give less adverse current at the expense of about 30 miles more distance.

The S-bound route from the W coasts of the Arabian Sea passes W of Îles Comores, through 11° 35′ S, 42° 50′ E and thence, in the full strength of the Moçambique Current, about 30 miles offshore abreast Porto de Moçambique and to 25° 00′ S, 35° 30′ E.

6.59. Routes between Moçambique Channel and Aden. Coastwise, the East African Coast Current flows continually N from Cape Delgado past Mombasa, giving way to the Somali Current, which reverses its direction seasonally, in the region of the Equator. The N-going current on the coastal and offshore routes is at its strongest S of Socotra, where, at the height of the South-west Monsoon, the landfall should be made well to the S.

A definite width cannot be assigned to the coastal currents between Cape Delgado and Ras Asir; the NE-going current which prevails during the South-west Monsoon is stronger nearer the coast and decreases rapidly at a distance of over 50 miles offshore. S-bound shipping will therefore generally benefit by keeping a good offing.

The choice of route in the vicinity of Socotra presents certain problems, because it is possible to pass on either side of the island, provided that the N side is given a berth of at least 40 miles. During the South-west Monsoon the heaviest weather of the Arabian Sea is E of Socotra and, from that point of view, passage between Ras Asir and Socotra is to be preferred.

It is dangerous to try to make Ras Radressa, the E point of Sacotra, during either monsoon. In the period of the North-east Monsoon, the land may be obscured about sunset by heavy rain squalls. During the South-west Monsoon, the lower land of the mountain range is often obscured by haze. The depths off Ras Radressa are considerable, and sounding gives no warning of the dangers which extend some distance from the shore. The currents in the vicinity are strong and irregular.

As regards the passage between Socotra and Ras Asir, great care is necessary when steering NW and N towards and past Ras Asir in the South-west Monsoon, when the weather and sea are at their worst, the N-going current is at its strongest, and the land is generally covered by thick haze. In hazy weather at night, the steep fall of Ras Scenaghef may perhaps be dimly seen when it bears less than about 270°; if Ras Asir is not sighted, as often happens if the haze is thicker at sea level and obscures the light-coloured hill, Ras Scenaghef may be mistaken for Ras Asir with disastrous results. In the South-west Monsoon, Ras Hafun should be made before Ras Asir.

By day, a gradual change in the colour of the water from blue to dark green will probably be observed as the land is approached. The sea becomes smoother and the swell alters its direction to E of S, when N and W of Ras Hafun.

Full directions for the passage between Ras Asir and Socotra are given in Admiralty Sailing Directions, but, although this passage is 40 miles wide, if there is doubt about the vessel's position, she should take the route N of Socotra where there is at least sea room, if stormy.

When making Ras Alula and Ras Asir from the Gulf of Aden, allowance must be made for the possibility of a SW or onshore set, particularly during the North east Monsoon.

To summarise for passages between Moçambique Channel and the Gulf of Aden, the normal route in both directions passes between Ras Asir and Socotra, and for intermediate coastal destinations, vessels should keep coastwise in both directions. S-bound ships may, however, avoid the strongest effects of the South-west Monsoon and of the NE'ly current between Îles Comores and Ras Asir by passing through 8° 00′ N, 52° 40′ E and 1° 10′ N, 55° 00′ E, at a cost of about 220 miles of extra distance on the run from Ras Asir to Îles Comores.

Distances, in miles: N = Northbound, S = Southbound.

Cape Town

790 N, 790 S	Durban		
2620 N, 2580 S	1830 N, 1770 S	Mombasa	
4020 N, 3970 S	3230 N, 3180 S	1610 N, 1610 S	Aden

5

10

15

20

25

30

35

40

45

50

55

60

65

70

6.60. African coast ↔ Persian Gulf. S of Îles Comores, this route is described in articles 6.55–6.58. To and from Mombasa, the track follows the trend of the African coast and joins the main route in 8° 00′ N, 52° 40′ E.

N of Îles Comores, the main route passes through 8° 00′ N, 52° 40′ E, thence to the Strait of Hormuz, passing at least 50 miles clear of the E end of Socotra.

Distances from Strait of Hormuz: Cape Town 4690 miles N-bound, 4640 miles S-bound; Durban 3900 miles N-bound, 3840 miles S-bound; Mombasa 2320 miles both ways. For destinations in the Persian Gulf, add the distances given in article 6.54.

6.61. African coast → Karachi. As article 6.60, through 8° 00′ N, 52° 40′ E, thence direct. Distances: from Cape Town 4730 miles; from Durban 3940 miles; From Mombasa 2360 miles.

6.62. Karachi → Mombasa. From May to September, steer parallel with the Indian coast to 70° E, thence due S to 17° 06′ N, 70° 00′ E, and thence direct to Mombasa. Distance 2720 miles.

When the full South-west Monsoon is blowing, low-powered vessels should divert S, through 12° 50′ N, 70° 00′ E and 6° 00′ N, 67° 00′ E.

From October to April, proceed direct. Distance 2350 miles.

6.63. Karachi → Moçambique Channel. From May to September, steer parallel with the Indian coast to 70° E, thence due S to 15° 40′ N, and thence to Moçambique Channel, passing 20 miles E of Astove Atoll, bearing in mind the strong W'ly set of the Equatorial Current in that region, and about 20 miles SE of Île Mayotte. Proceed thence to pick up the S-bound track in Moçambique Channel (6.58) in 17° 00′ S, 40° 20′ E. Distances: to Durban 4180 miles; to Cape Town 4970 miles.

When the full South-west Monsoon is blowing, low-powered vessels should divert S through 12° 50′ S, 70° 00′ E, and 6° 00′ S, 67° 00′ E, rejoining the route as given above in 3° 00′ S, 54° 00′ E, NW of Seychelles Group.

From October to April, steer direct to pass 20 miles E of Astove Atoll and about 20 miles SE of Île Mayotte, thence as for the remainder of the year. Distances: to Durban 3920 miles; to Cape Town 4710 miles.

6.64. Aden ↔ Persian Gulf or Karachi. While in the Arabian Sea, follow a track as close as practicable to the Arabian coast, having regard to the variability of the current, and avoiding a close approach to the Gulf of Masīrah, see Admiralty Sailing Directions. Distances: to Strait of Hormuz 1410 miles; thence, for Persian Gulf, as 6.54; to Karachi 1460 miles.

W-bound, after passing Muscat, keep as close to the Arabian coast as navigation permits. This is especially advisable during the South-west Monsoon, when the full force of the wind, and of the NE set, will be felt only in the vicinity of Kuria Muria Islands, and off Ras al Kalb.

Ships W-bound from Karachi during the South-west Monsoon may do better by steering coastwise to the meridian of 70° E, then due S to 12° 50′ N, 70° 00′ E and thence to Aden. This route will add about 800 miles to the distance, but the head wind and heavy sea will be largely avoided. During this monsoon the weather is generally very hazy along the Arabian coast so that, though the sky may be clear, the land may not be visible until close inshore. In the Persian Gulf, during a shamal in summer or while the NE wind, known as the Nashi, is blowing in the S part of the Gulf in winter, the haze may obscure the land so completely that the surf on the beach may be the first intimation of its proximity.

6.65. Cape Town or Durban → Bombay. The N-bound routes from Cape Town and Durban through Moçambique Channel are discussed in detail in articles 6.55–6.58. To continue thence from 17° 00′ S, 42° 15′ E, W of Juan de Nova, pass between Île Anjouan and Île Mayotte to a position 30 miles W of Aldabra Islands and thence take the rhumb line to Bombay, crossing 60° 00′ E in 5° 50′ N.

Distances: Cape Town 4650 miles; Durban 3860 miles.

By night or when uncertain of the position, the foregoing route through the islands at the N end of Moçambique Channel should always be taken, owing to the strength and variability of the W-going current in the locality. By day, after passing Île Anjouan, a vessel may pass between Assumption Island and Cosmoledo Atoll.

The alternative route from South African ports to Bombay passes S of Madagascar. Traffic from Cape Town should follow the coast, see 6.55, as far as Great Fish Point, and all ships should round the S end of Madagascar at a distance of 60 miles or more offshore, to seaward of the strongest part of the Madagascar Current, see Admiralty Sailing Directions. After leaving the vicinity of Madagascar, the route passes W of Île de la Réunion, Mauritius, and Saya de Malha Bank. Agalega Islands should be given a wide berth.

Distances by alternative route: Cape Town 4700 miles; Durban 3950 miles.

Caution: During the North-east Monsoon, there is considerable haze over Bombay in the mornings and evenings, and often throughout the day, obscuring everything from view. It is particularly noticeable during the interval between the land and sea breezes.

During the South-west Monsoon a northerly set may be expected in making the land off Khānderi island.

6.66. Bombay → Durban or Cape Town. Steer by rhumb line to 10° 07′ S, 48° 05′ E, 20 miles E of Astove Atoll, and then steer to pass W of Îles Glorieuses and Geyser Reef to a position 20 miles SE of Île Mayotte. This part of the voyage should be undertaken by day, if possible, see Admiralty Sailing Directions.

When the full South-west Monsoon is blowing, low-powered vessels should divert S from Bombay through 6° 00′ N, 67° 00′ E, picking up the direct rhumb line NW of Seychelles Group in 3° 00′ S, 54° 00′ E.

From the position SE of Île Mayotte, steer to pick up the S-bound route through Moçambique Channel in 17° 00′ S, 40° 20′ E, see 6.58.

Distances: to Durban 3830 miles; to Cape Town 4620 miles. Add 80 miles for low-power route.

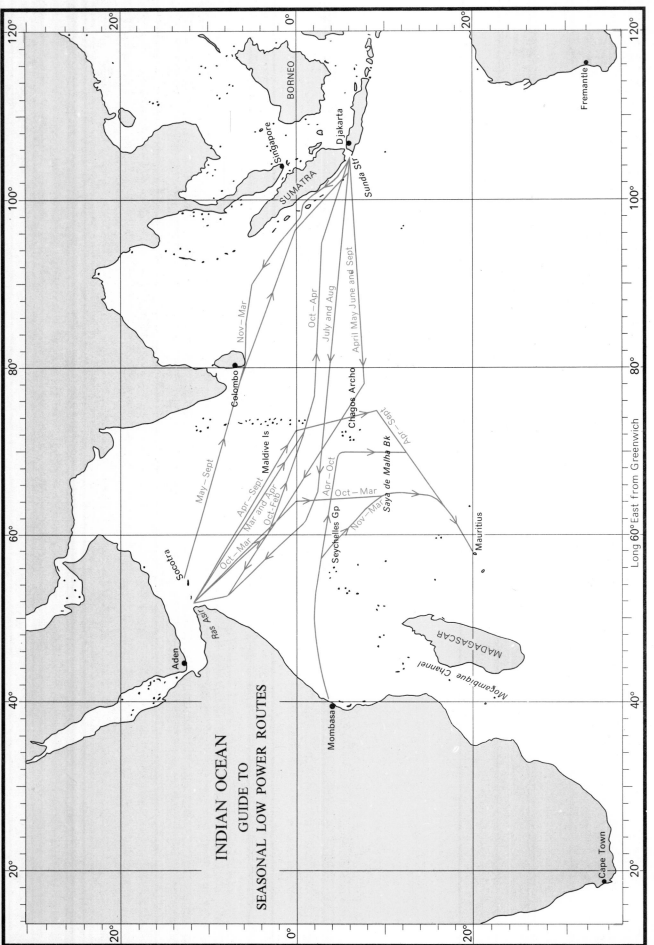

INDIAN OCEAN
GUIDE TO
SEASONAL LOW POWER ROUTES

Nov–Mar

Oct–Apr

July and Aug

April May June and Sept

Sunda Str

Djakarta

BORNEO

Singapore

SUMATRA

Chagos Archo

Apr–Sept

Saya de Malha Bk

Apr–Oct

Oct–Mar

Nov–Mar

Seychelles Gp

Mauritius

May–Sept

Apr–Sept. Maldive Is

Mar and Apr

Oct–Feb

Oct–Mar

Colombo

Socotra

Ras Asir

Aden

Mombasa

MADAGASCAR

Moçambique Channel

Fremantle

Cape Town

Long 60° East from Greenwich

Diagram 23

6.67. South coast of Africa → Colombo, Bay of Bengal, and Selat Benggala. This passage can be made either E or W of Madagascar.

If using Moçambique Channel, proceed as in articles 6.55–6.58 to 17° 00′ S, 42° 15′ E, off Île Juan de Nova. Thence, from April to October pass 30 miles E of Geyser Reef and Îles Glorieuses, to 8° 30′ S, 50° 40′ E, 30 miles NW of Wizard Reef, and so to One and half Degree Channel. From November to March pass between Île Anjouan and Île Mayotte to 9° 30′ S, 45° 30′E, 30 miles W of Aldabra Island; thence passing 50 miles N of Seychelles Group to One and half Degree Channel. Attention must be paid to the W-going current which flows strongly past the N point of Madagascar. Throughout the year, proceed thence as navigation permits, the shortest route to Rangoon being through Preparis South Channel.

To make the passage E of Madagascar, after rounding the S end of that island at about 60 miles (6.65), from May to September pass 60 miles SE of Mauritius and E of Diego Garcia; thence as navigation permits, using Ten Degree Channel if bound for Rangoon. From October to March, pass through 14° 00′ S, 60° 00′ E; 5° 00′ S, 70° 00′E; and thence as navigation permits, using Preparis South Channel if bound for Rangoon.

Distances, in miles:

	May to September		October to March	
	Cape Town	Durban	Cape Town	Durban
W of Madagascar				
Colombo	4510	3710	4640	3850
Madras	5030	4240	5160	4370
Paradip	5480	4690	5620	4830
Sandheads	5560	4770	5690	4900
Rangoon	5660	4870	5790	5000
Selat Benggala	5320	4530	5460	4670
E of Madagascar				
Colombo	4450	3690	4380	3620
Madras	4930	4170	4880	4130
Paradip	5360	4600	5310	4560
Sandheads	5430	4670	5390	4630
Rangoon	5520	4770	5470	4740
Selat Benggala	5010	4250	5090	4330

6.68. Colombo → South coast of Africa. This passage may be made either through Moçambique Channel or E of Madagascar.

For Moçambique Channel, pass through Eight Degree Channel to a position in 3° 00′ S, 54° 00′ E, NW of Seychelles Group; thence steer to pass 20 miles E of Astove Atoll and through Moçambique Channel as directed in article 6.66. This route is good for all seasons but, during the South-west Monsoon, vessels of low power should consider a S'ly diversion, steering from the Ceylon coast across the equator into the South-east Trade and passing S of Chagos Archipelago before setting course for the N end of Moçambique Channel. Distances by the full-power route are: Durban 3820 miles, Cape Town 4610 miles.

Alternatively, in April and October, One and half Degree Channel may be used, after which course should be shaped to pass 30 miles NW of Wizard Reef (*8° 50′ S, 51° 03′ E*) and thence, passing about 40 miles E of Îles Glorieuses and Geyser Reef to join the S-bound route in 17° 00′ S, 40° 20′ E as directed in article 6.66. Attention is called to the currents S of 5° S, especially near Providence Island, where they will probably be setting NW'ly, and near Îles Glorieuses and Geyser Reef, where the set is usually strong W'ly. See Admiralty Sailing Directions. Distances: Durban 3730 miles; Cape Town 4520 miles.

If taking the route E of Madagascar, from November to March steer S of Maldive Islands to 5° 00′ S, 70° 00′ E; thence to 14° 00′ S, 60° 00′ E; and thence to pass 20 miles SE of Madagascar. Distances: Durban 3620 miles; Cape Town 4360 miles. From April to October, pass E of Diego Garcia, at the SE extremity of Chagos Archipelago, and thence 20 miles SE of Madagascar. During this period ships bound for ports S of Durban are advised to make a landfall near Durban and thence proceed coastwise, to avoid the heavy weather prevalent to seaward. Distances: Durban 3670 miles; Cape Town 4460 miles.

6.69. Bay of Bengal ← South coast of Africa. Routes are in most respects similar to those from Colombo given in article 6.68, and the cautions given therein are relevant. Eight Degree Channel is not used, and the route from One and half Degree Channel to enter Moçambique Channel through a position 30 miles NW of Wizard Reef is advised as an alternative to passage E of Madagascar during April and October.

The route E of Madagascar, from November to March, passes through 5° 00′ S, 70° 00′ E; 14° 00′ S, 60° 00′ E, and 20 miles off the SE point of Madagascar. From May to September, course should be shaped to pass E of Diego Garcia, at the S extremity of Chagos Archipelago and thence 20 miles SE of Madagascar. During this period, ships bound for ports S of Durban are advised to continue to a position off Durban and thence to proceed coastwise, to avoid the heavy weather prevalent to seaward.

From June to August, ships from Rangoon may find it advantageous to pass S of Great Nicobar Island and then join the route for South Africa from Selat Benggala, see 6.70.

Distances, in miles:

	One and half Degree Channel		W of Chagos Archipelago		E of Chagos Archipelago	
	Cape Town	Durban	Cape Town	Durban	Cape Town	Durban
Madras	5050	4260	4870	4130	4950	4160
Paradip	5480	4690	5300	4560	5370	4580
Sandheads	5550	4760	5380	4630	5450	4660
Rangoon	5650	4860	5470	4730	5530	4740

6.70. Selat Benggala → ports on South coast of Africa. Steer by rhumb line, N of Mauritius, to pass 20 miles off the S end of Madagascar, making the coast off Durban or Cape Recife according to season, see 6.69. Distances: Durban 4260 miles; Cape Town 5050 miles via Durban landfall; 5000 miles via Cape Recife.

6.71. Routes in Bay of Bengal. In the Bay of Bengal there is little possibility of diversion, even at the cost of distance, to reduce the adverse effects, or to take advantage of wind and current. S-bound ships should keep well clear of the E and S coasts of Ceylon, off which the currents are irregular and sometimes strong; N–S routes off this coast should pass through 7° 25′ N, 82° 45′ E. The only passage on which a diversion can be suggested for the purpose of avoiding the South-west Monsoon is from Rangoon to Dondra Head; ships unable to thrust against the full Monsoon should steer E of Andaman Islands and Nicobar Islands and through 5° 50′ N, 94° 30′ E in June, July, and August.

Tropical depressions and cyclones are experienced in the Bay of Bengal, see 6.16.

Distances, in miles:

Dondra Hd.

545	Madras				
975	570	Paradip			
1050	650	110	Sandheads		
1150	985	680	640	Rangoon	
865	975	—	—	630	Selat Benggala

For Colombo, add 95 miles to Dondra Head distances.

6.72. Mombasa → Bombay. During the South-west Monsoon, advantage may be taken of the Africa Coast Current and the Somali Current by following the trend of the coast during the first part of the voyage.

From May to September, keep about 50 miles offshore as far as 1° 30′ N, 45° 50′ E, and then take the rhumb line to Bombay. Distance 2400 miles.

From October to April, proceed to 2° 30′ S, 44° 50′ E and thence to Bombay by rhumb line. Distance 2415 miles.

See caution about landfall given in article 6.65.

6.73. Bombay → Mombasa. The normal route is direct at all seasons. Distance 2390 miles.

During the full South-west Monsoon, low-powered vessels should steer for 6° 00′ N, 67° 00′ E and thence proceed direct.

6.74. Mombasa → Dondra Head or Colombo. At all seasons direct, via One and half Degree Channel or Kardiva Channel, the former being preferred if there is any doubt of the ship's position, as the W entrance to Kardiva Channel is not easily identified. Distance by One and half Degree Channel: Colombo 2540 miles; Dondra Head 2530 miles.

6.75. Dondra Head or Colombo → Mombasa. At all seasons direct, via One and half Degree Channel except that, from October to April, traffic from Colombo may favour Eight Degree Channel, and, from May to September, low-powered vessels should consider steering across the Equator into the South-east Trade and then passing S of Chagos Archipelago. Distances by One and half Degree Channel: from Colombo 2540 miles; from Dondra Head 2530 miles.

6.76. Aden → Bombay. From October to April, proceed direct by rhumb line, distance 1650 miles. During the North-east Monsoon, haze may considerably reduce visibility at Bombay, particularly between land and sea breezes in the morning and evening.

From May to September make a position in 13° 00′ N, 55° 00′ E, NE of Socotra, and proceed thence by rhumb line. Distance 1680 miles.

See caution about landfall given in article 6.65.

6.77. Bombay → Aden. From October to April, proceed direct by rhumb line. Distance 1650 miles.

During the South west Monsoon the best route is determined by the strength of the monsoon. In May and September, a N'ly track, through 19° 00′ N, 70° 00′ E; 18° 30′ N, 65° 00′ E; and 17° 30′ N, 60° 00′ E, with a distance of 1660 miles, is recommended. In June, July, and August, when the monsoon is at its strongest, vessels should keep on the parallel of Bombay until about 100 miles from the Arabian coast, thence proceeding coastwise; distance 1680 miles. On this passage, during the South-west Monsoon, the wind and sea are at their height between the meridians of 66° E and 60° E. The adverse current may attain a speed of 2 knots in the middle of the Arabian Sea and occasionally 3 knots in the W part of that sea and off the Arabian coast.

The route advised for low-power vessels during the South-west Monsoon is through 6° 00′ N, 67° 00′ E; 6° 00′ N, 60° 00′ E; 8° 00′ N, 52° 40′ E; and thence between Ras Asir and Socotra.

6.78. Aden → Dondra Head or Colombo. In the Gulf of Aden and N of Socotra, allowance must be made for the possibility of a set towards the S shore, see 6.59.

Vessels using Eight Degree Channel should keep nearer to Minicoy Island than to the Maldives, see *West Coast of India Pilot*.

From October to April pass between Ras Asir and the islands E of it, and thence through Eight Degree Channel. Distances: Colombo 2100 miles; Dondra Head 2160 miles.

From May to September, to avoid the heavy cross sea S of Socotra caused by the South-west Monsoon, pass N of Socotra to 13° 00′ N, 55° 00′ E; thence direct or through Eight Degree Channel. Distances: Colombo 2100 miles; Dondra Head 2160 miles.

6.79. Dondra Head or Colombo → Aden. From October to April, pass through Eight Degree Channel and S of Socotra, bearing in mind the difficulty of identifying the landfall, see 6.59. Distances: from Dondra Head 2160 miles; from Colombo 2100 miles.

Alternatively from October to April pass through Eight Degree Channel and to 13° 00′ N, 55° 00′ E; and thence N of Socotra to Aden, observing the directions given in article 6.59. Distances: from Dondra Head 2160 miles; from Colombo 2100 miles.

During the South-west Monsoon, fully-powered vessels are routed S of the more direct North-east Monsoon tracks. From May to September, large vessels of high power may pass through Eight Degree Channel to 10° 00′ N, 60° 00′ E; thence to 13° 00′ N, 55° 00′ E and N of Socotra. Distances: from Dondra Head 2180 miles; from Colombo 2130 miles. Other fully powered vessels should, having passed through Eight Degree Channel on the parallel of 7° 30′ N, continue to 8° 00′ N, 60° 00′ E and thence to Aden either through 8° 00′ N, 52° 40′ E and round Ras Asir, or through 13° 00′ N, 55° 00′ E and N of Socotra. Distances via Ras Asir and N of Socotra respectively: from Dondra Head 2290 and 2240 miles; from Colombo 2240 and 2190 miles.

From May to September, low-powered vessels should adopt one of the following routes.

Through Eight Degree Channel on the parallel of 7° 30′ N, and through 6° 00′ N, 67° 00′ E; 6° 00′ N, 60° 00′ E; 8° 00′ N, 52° 40′ E to Ras Asir.

Alternatively provided that Olivelifuri Islet can be made between sunrise and noon, pass through Kardiva Channel and through 4° 44′ N, 60° 00′ E to 8° 00′ N, 52° 40′ E and Ras Asir.

All small vessels should pass through One and half Degree Channel and then steer to cross 60° E in about 2° 00′ N, thence proceeding through 8° 00′ N, 52° 40′ E to Ras Asir.

The choice of a route depends largely on the power and sea-keeping qualities of a vessel. A factor which may influence departure from Ceylon is that the South-west Monsoon often blows fresh between the coast and 75° E.

6.80. Strait of Hormuz ↔ Colombo or Dondra Head. To avoid Bassas de Pedro and the shoals E of the Laccadive Islands, pass through 13° 00′ N, 74° 10′ E, off the Malabar coast. Distance: Colombo 1800 miles; Dondra Head 1870 miles.

6.81. Bombay or Karachi ↔ Colombo or Dondra Head. Direct; for the possibility of onshore sets, see Admiralty Sailing Directions.

Distances, in miles:

	Bombay	Colombo	Dondra Head
Karachi	500	1340	1420
Bombay	—	880	955

6.82. Selat Benggala (*5° 50′ N, 95° 00′ E*), between Pulau Breuëh and Pulau Wé, is deep, and is the best channel for E-bound or W-bound approach and departure for vessels passing through Malacca Strait. It is deep throughout; SW'ly or NW'ly winds prevail according to season. There is usually a NW-going current of 1 or 2 knots in the fairway, but near the SW shore the streams are tidal, and low-powered vessels needing anchorage while the stream is adverse may take advantage of this. See Admiralty Sailing Directions.

6.83. Malacca Strait, about 250 miles long in its narrower part, forms part of the shortest route between the Arabian Sea and Singapore. The least depth in the fairway is about 25 m but the bottom is of sandwave formation, and depths and the configuration of the channel are liable to change. Navigational aids are difficult to maintain and may be unreliable. Deep draught vessels should therefore take particular note of the latest reports of depths in or near the fairway, and all ships must appreciate that long periods of considerable vigilance are necessary. There is a considerable amount of traffic in the strait, and manoeuvring room may also be restricted by fishing vessels and their nets. The distance from Selat Benggala, at the NW end of Malacca Strait, to Singapore is 620 miles.

ROUTES TO AND FROM MAURITIUS

6.90. Port Louis ↔ Cape Town. For Cape Town, round the S end of Madagascar at about 20 miles offshore to take advantage of the Madagascar Current (6.36), and steer to make a landfall in the vicinity of Algoa Bay, thence keeping in the Agulhas Current to destination. Distance 2290 miles. From April to October, to avoid the heavy weather prevalent to seaward, a landfall at Durban and the coastwise route thereafter are preferable to the direct route; the extra distance is 45 miles.

From Cape Town, either follow the coast as far as Great Fish Point and pass at least 60 miles SE of Madagascar, or keep to seaward of the main part of the Agulhas Current by proceeding to 36° 45′ S, 19° 00′ E; thence by great circle to 34° 30′ S, 32° 30′ E and thence by great circle to destination. Distances: Coastwise 2300 miles; outside Agulhas Current 2440 miles.

6.91. Port Louis ↔ Durban. The same conditions as for article 6.90 apply to the vicinity of the S end of Madagascar. Distance 1550 miles.

6.92. Port Louis ↔ ports in Moçambique Channel. Vessels bound for the NW coast of Madagascar should always go round the N end of that island; and those bound for the W coast, or to any ports on the African coast S of 18° S, should pass round the S end.

6.93. Port Louis ↔ Mombasa. The usual route is direct in both directions. Distance 1430 miles.

Seasonal diversions are advised for vessels of low power S-bound, namely, from November to March they should pass N of Seychelles Group, keeping N of the direct route; thence steering E of Saya de Malha Bank and into the South-east Trades before setting the final course. From April to October they should take a similar route, but stand E to about 70° E before making S, well into the South-east Trades.

6.94. Port Louis ↔ Aden. The full power route is direct in both directions, passing E or W of Seychelles Group according to the circumstances. Distance 2340 miles (W of Seychelles).

As for Mombasa, seasonal diversions are advised for S-bound low power traffic. From October to March, these vessels should run from Ras Asir through the North-east and North-west Monsoons to cross the equator in about 64° E, steering thence E of Saya de Malha Bank and into the South-east Trade. From April to September they should run SE through the South-west Monsoon to cross the equator in about 72° E or even to pass through One and half Degree Channel before turning S into the South-east Trade, then passing E of Chagos Archipelago and through 10° 00′ S, 70° 00′ E.

6.95. Port Louis ↔ Karachi. The normal route is direct, passing W of Saya de Malha Bank. Distance 2740 miles.

When the South-west Monsoon is blowing strongly it is advisable, on leaving Karachi, to steer SE coastwise to 70° E and to proceed along that meridian to cross the equator continuing thence E of Cargados Carajos Shoals and to Port Louis. At this season, low-powered vessels, S-bound, should make their passage E of Laccadive Islands, Maldive Islands, and Chagos Archipelago.

6.96. Port Louis ↔ Seychelles. The normal route for fully powered vessels is direct, as navigation permits, with a distance of 950 miles.

From November to March, N-bound vessels of low power should keep rather W of the direct route until in the North-west Monsoon, while S-bound vessels should stand E, round Saya de Malha Bank and into the South-east Trade, before making for Mauritius.

From April to October, S-bound vessels of low power should stand E to about 70° E; then proceeding S until well into the South-east Trade before shaping course for Mauritius.

6.97. Port Louis ↔ Bombay. For Bombay, the route from Mauritius passes W of Cargados Carajos Shoals and Nazareth Bank and on either side, as preferred, of Saya de Malha Bank. Distance, passing W of Saya de Malha Bank, 2530 miles.

From Bombay, the equator should be crossed in about 66° 45′ E and the voyage should be continued E of Nazareth Bank and Cargados Carajos Shoals, distance 2520 miles, but at the height of the South-west Monsoon a vessel may do better by steering due S on the meridian of 70° E as far as the equator, then rejoining the foregoing route E of Nazareth Bank. At this season, low powered vessels should steer E of Laccadive Islands and Maldive Islands and Chagos Archipelago.

6.98. Port Louis ↔ Colombo. For Colombo, steer to pass through 7° 30′ S, 73° 00′ E, about 30 miles E of Diego Garcia. S-bound, pass through 7° 30′ S, 72° 35′ E, close E of that island. Distance 2140 miles.

6.99. Port Louis ↔ Selat Benggala. Proceed direct. Distance 2710 miles.

5

6.100. Port Louis ↔ Sunda Strait. (6° 25′ S, 102° 30′ E). Proceed direct. Distance 2900 miles.

6.101. Port Louis ↔ Torres Strait and Port Darwin. From October to April the route passes through 11° 30′ S, 118° 00′ E, to pass N of the usual tracks of the Willy-Willies. E of this position, the deep water route S of Timor may be used, and North Sahul Passage for Port Darwin. Alternatively, the coastwise route, see 6.125, may be *10* joined S of Cartier Islet in 12° 40′ S, 123° 45′ E. Distances, using the coastwise route, are 4920 and 4330 miles for Torres Strait and Port Darwin respectively; for the deepwater passage S of Timor add 15 miles to these distances.

From May to September the route passes through 15° 30′ S, 120° 00′ E and joins the coastwise route S of Browse Island. Distances: Torres Strait 4890 miles; Port Darwin 4300 miles. *15*

6.102. Port Louis ↔ Fremantle and Cape Leeuwin. The routes are direct. Distances: Fremantle 3220 miles; 20 miles WSW of Cape Leeuwin 3160 miles.

20

ROUTES TO AND FROM SEYCHELLES GROUP

6.106. Seychelles ↔ South Africa. For destinations on the coasts of **South Africa**, pass 20 miles E of Île *25* Mayotte and join the S-bound route through Moçambique Channel in 17° 00′ S, 40° 20′ E. Distances: Durban 2130 miles; Cape Town 2920 miles. N-bound, take the N-bound route through Moçambique Channel as far as 17° 00′ S, 42° 15′ E and continue the voyage as directly as navigation permits. Distances: Durban 2110 miles; Cape Town 2900 miles. See 6.58.

30

6.107. Seychelles ↔ Mombasa. The usual route is direct in both directions. Distance 950 miles.

From October to April, E-bound ships of low power should keep N of the direct route until the North-west Monsoon (6.12) is picked up in about 45° E. From April to October, E-bound ships of low power, if unable to make their destination on the direct route, should continue until able to make it from a N'ly direction. W-bound, such vessels should allow for the probability of the wind heading them and for the strong N'ly current off the *35* African coast.

6.108. Seychelles ↔ Aden. The normal route is direct to and from Ras Asir, except that during the South-west Monsoon Ras Hafun should be made by N-bound traffic before Ras Asir. Distance 1410 miles.

From October to March, low-powered vessels outward bound from Aden should keep along the Arabian *40* coast until able to weather Ras Asir, whence they should proceed direct. N-bound, from November to March, low-powered vessels should cross the equator in about 61° E and make into the North-east Monsoon until able to weather Socotra.

From April to September, S-bound ships of low power should steer from Ras Asir to 3° 00′ N, 60° 00′ E, thence proceeding due S across the equator into the South-east Trade. If the South-west Monsoon is still *45* blowing strongly in 3° N, 60° E, a vessel should hold her SE'ly course until its strength is lost, then turning S across the equator and to her destination.

6.109. Seychelles ↔ Bombay. The normal route in both directions is direct. Distance 1750 miles. During the full South-west Monsoon, low-powered ships on leaving Bombay should steer for 6° 00′ N, 67° 00′ E; *50* thence to cross the equator in about 59° E and so to destination.

6.110. Seychelles ↔ Colombo. The NE-bound route passes through One and half Degree Channel throughout the year. SW-bound, Eight Degree Channel should be taken from October to April and One and half Degree Channel from May to September: Distances are: by One and half Degree Channel 1680 miles; by Eight Degree *55* Channel 1740 miles.

Low-powered vessels, NE-bound, should, from November to March, proceed through 4° 00′ S, 70° 00′ E; then crossing the equator in 80° E and proceeding N to make the Ceylon coast on that meridian. From April to October, they should proceed through Eight Degree Channel or Kardiva Channel, the latter being the more direct but advisable by daylight only. *60*

Low-powered vessels, SW-bound, should, from October to April, pass through Eight Degree Channel and stand SW to cross the equator in about 54° E before making for their destination. From May to September, they should establish a good offing from the Ceylon coast and then stand S across the equator into the South-east Trades, passing S of Chagos Archipelago before making for their destination.

65

6.111. Seychelles ↔ Fremantle and south coast of Australia. E-bound, proceed to 11° 30′ S, 60° 00′ E, and thence by great circle. Distances: Fremantle 3840 miles; 20 miles WSW of Cape Leeuwin 3810 miles.

W-bound, proceed as direct as navigation permits. Distances: from Fremantle 3850 miles; from 20 miles WSW of Cape Leeuwin 3840 miles.

For continuation of route E of Cape Leeuwin, see 6.130 to 6.137. *70*

APPROACH FROM WESTWARD TO AUSTRALIAN WATERS

6.120. From Sunda Strait. Between the W entrance to Sunda Strait and Torres Strait there are three main routes, namely through the Java and Flores Seas and Wètar Strait, see Chapter 7; S of Java and through Sumba, Ombai, and Wètar Straits; and S of all the islands E of Sunda Strait, passing through 11° 30′ S, 118° 00′ E. Distances between 6° 25′ S, 102° 30′ E, which is the routeing position W of Sunda Strait, and 10° 49′ S, 140° 59′ E, the position of Carpentaria light-vessel, are similar, being respectively 2360, 2330, and 2360 miles. In the Java and Flores Seas, the current is to the advantage of E-bound shipping during the North-west Monsoon, between about November and April; otherwise, currents are predominantly W'ly on all three routes. The Java Sea route, between the shoals E of Sunda Strait and through Sapudi Strait and Wètar Passage, demands close attention to navigation. Sumba, Ombai, and Wètar Straits are wide and deep and present no difficulty, particularly to ships fitted with radar. Ships using the route S of the islands should, when S of Timor and Tanimbar Islands, keep in the deep-water gut close S of those islands.

Port Darwin can be approached from W either through Sumba and Roti Straits or from seaward through 11° 30′ S, 118° 00′ E. In the former case, the route continues through North Sahul Passage; in the latter case, the coastal shoal area is entered through 12° 40′ S, 123° 45′ E, 13 miles S of Cartier Islet. The recommended approach tracks are shown on the charts. Distances by the seaward route to Port Darwin from 6° 25′ S, 102° 30′ E are 1780 miles by North Sahul Passage, and 1770 miles by the route S of Cartier Islet.

6.121. From the South Indian Ocean, there are two initial positions for approach to the Arafura Sea. The more N'ly, 11° 30′ S, 118° 00′ E, is used on the most S'ly route between Sunda Strait and Torres Strait and therefore caters for traffic passing between Timor and the shoal area. The more S'ly position, 15° 30′ S, 120° 00′ E, is in general use for the South African traffic except during the summer Willy Willy-season, when the route is better taken through 11° 30′ S, 118° 00′ E.

COASTWISE PASSAGES OFF AUSTRALIA

6.125. The following notes on coastwise passages, of which details will be found in Admiralty Sailing Directions, have some bearing on those ocean passages in the Indian Ocean which have terminal positions in Australian waters or the Pacific.

6.126. Torres Strait, (7.53), which connects the Arafura Sea and the Coral Sea, is described in Admiralty Sailing Directions. Transit distance between Carpentaria Light-vessel and Twin Island (*10° 28′ S, 142° 28′ E*) is 90 miles, and between Carpentaria Light-vessel and Bligh Entrance 219 miles.

From the W end of Torres Strait, the shortest distance to all ports E of Adelaide is eastabout.

6.127. Many banks in the **Timor Sea** and the **Arafura Sea** are unsurveyed and caution is necessary in their vicinity. The recommended tracks have been surveyed to a width of 10 miles on either side, but less depths than charted may be found outside these limits.

On the route between Wètar Strait and Timor Strait, keep S of Duddell Shoal and Volsella Shoal.

6.128. Sahul Banks and their vicinity have only been partially surveyed, and caution is necessary in this area.

6.129. Vessels without local knowledge should keep to seaward of **Holothuria Banks, Rowley Shoals,** and **Monte Bello Islands.**

6.130. Approaching the coast between **Cape Naturaliste** and **Rottnest Island,** unless certain of her position, a vessel should not stand into depths of less than 55 m (30 fm) until N of Naturaliste Reefs (*33° 13′ S, 115° 02′ E*). Thence proceeding N, she may stand into 37 m (20 fm) coarse brown sand mixed with shells, and occasionally gravel and small stones. The depth of 37 m (20 fm), however, will be found within ½ mile of the dangers of Cape Vlaming; vessels bound to the N of Rottnest Island should, therefore, not go into less than 55 m (30 fm) as the island is approached.

6.131. When rounding **Cape Leeuwin,** it should be borne in mind that the distance to which dangers extend off a long stretch of coast about the cape, and the frequent thick weather that prevails with strong on-shore winds and an inset in the same direction, make it very desirable to give the cape a wide berth in all but settled weather. From 15 to 20 miles is a good offing to take, and the use of 34° 28′ S, 114° 45′ E, 20 miles WSW of Cape Leeuwin, as a routeing position will suit most passages without appreciable loss of distance.

The greatest caution should be used if running in to make Cape Leeuwin Light which, in doubtful visibility, may not be visible as far as Géographe Reef, 8 miles NW, and as mist may hang about the land when it is clear at sea, sounding should never be neglected, and vessels should not stand in to depths of less than 128 m (70 fm).

6.132. Between the vicinity of Cape Leeuwin and **Investigator Strait** (for Adelaide) or **Cape Otway** (for Melbourne) or **South West Cape** (for Hobart), great circle courses may be steered.

6.133. A vessel approaching **Bass Strait** from W should make a landfall off Moonlight Head or Cape Otway. In the approach, due allowance must be made for winds and currents particularly during SW'ly weather, and in thick weather a depth of over 75 m (41 fm) should be maintained. Very strong tidal streams are occasionally encountered off King Island; combined with the current the E-going tidal stream may produce a SE'ly onshore set of great strength. Many fatal wrecks have occurred on King Island, from errors in reckoning and in consequence of not making the land near Cape Otway.

In Bass Strait, the channel between King Island and Tasmania is not recommended as there may be undiscovered dangers in it.

6.134. Shark and crayfish fishing fleets operate up to 90 miles from the coast between 37° 30′ S, 140° 00′ E and 37° 00′ S, 149° 55′ E.

6.135. Routes between **Adelaide** and ports E'ward are through Backstairs Passage.

With S'ly or W'ly winds, currents setting on to the land at rates of up to 2 knots are sometimes experienced between Cape Willoughby and Cape Otway.

6.136. Routes between **Melbourne** and **Hobart** may be taken either W or E of Tasmania, keeping from 10 to 20 miles W of King Island, according to weather, in the former case, and passing either through Banks Strait or E of the Furneaux Group in the latter. There is very little in the distance, the Banks Strait route being the shortest. As mentioned above, the currents off King Island may be strong.

6.137. Distances in miles:

Torres St.

770*	Port Darwin						
1560	970	Port Hedland					
2450	1870	1000	Fremantle				
2580	2000	1130	175	Cape Leeuwin			
3780	3190	2320	1370	1190	Adelaide		
4060	3470	2600	1650	1470	460	Melbourne	
4230	3640	2780	1820	1650	750	†	Hobart

* Via Cape Van Diemen. 670 miles via Clarence Strait.
† By Banks Strait 420 miles; Bass Strait and E of Furneaux Group 465 miles; westabout 455 miles.

ROUTES ON EASTERN SIDE OF INDIAN OCEAN

6.140. Bay of Bengal ↔ North coast of Australia. The choice between an open-ocean route, W of Sumatra and S of Java, and a route passing entirely or partly through the Eastern Archipelago, is governed by considerations of draught, weather, distance, and season. For Bay of Bengal and Malacca Strait see 6.71, 6.84; for the approach to Australian waters from the Indian Ocean see 6.120 and Chapter 7; for routes through the Eastern Archipelago see Chapter 7.

Distances, in miles:

	From	Torres Strait	Port Darwin
By ocean route, S of Java and Timor	Madras	4120	3540
	Sandheads	4220	3640
	Rangoon	3880	3300
S of Java; and through Sumba, Ombai and Wètar Straits for Torres Strait, or Sumba and Roti Straits for Port Darwin	Madras	4090	3530
	Sandheads	4190	3630
	Rangoon	3850	3290
By Sunda, Sapudi, and Wètar Straits	Madras	4110	3610
	Sandheads	4200	3710
	Rangoon	3860	3360
By Malacca and Sapudi Straits; thence by Wètar Strait for Torres Strait or by Lombok Strait for Port Darwin	Madras	4040	3540
	Sandheads	3980	3480
	Rangoon	3530	3020

6.141. Western side of Bay of Bengal ↔ West coast of Australia. Routes are direct, W of Nicobar Islands for Paradip and Sandheads. Distances, in miles by great circle, are:

	Madras	Paradip	Sandheads
Port Hedland	3020	3120	3120
Fremantle	3380	3550	3560
Cape Leeuwin*	3460	3650	3670

* To join coastwise route for S coast of Australia, see 6.131–6.137.

6.142. Rangoon ↔ West coast of Australia. Either the ocean route S of Nicobar Islands and W of Sumatra, or a route through Malacca Strait and Sunda Strait may be taken. For the route through the Eastern Archipelago, see 6.140. Distances from Rangoon, in miles, are:

	Port Hedland	Fremantle	Cape Leeuwin*
By ocean route	2770	3200	3300
By Malacca and Sunda Straits	2840†	3340	3450

* The South Australian coastwise route, see 6.131–6.137, may be joined off Cape Leeuwin.
† The distance via Malacca Strait and Lombok Strait is 2780 miles.

TRANS-OCEAN ROUTES

6.150. Cape Town ↔ Sunda Strait. E-bound, steer across the W-going current to 36° 45′ S, 19° 00′ E and thence to 33° 45′ S, 36° 30′ E. Take the great circle track from that position to Sunda Strait, passing through 29° 00′ S, 60° 00′ E and 15° 50′ S, 90° 00′ E, and N of Cocos Islands. Distance 5180 miles to 6° 30′ S, 105° 00′ E, in the entrance to Sunda Strait.

W-bound, from October to April, proceed from the above position by great circle to 33° 45′ S, 36° 30′ E and then make the African coast in about 34° 00′ S, 27° 00′ E, continuing to Cape Town as directed in 6.57. Distance 5070 miles. From May to September, proceed by great circle to 30° 00′ S, 56° 30′ E; thence by rhumb line to a position off Durban, to join the coastwise route to Cape Town. Distance 5190 miles.

6.151. Durban ↔ Sunda Strait. E-bound, proceed on the parallel of 30° 00′ S to 56° 30′ E and take the great circle thence through 29° 00′ S, 60° 00′ E and 15° 50′ S, 90° 00′ E, and N of Cocos Islands. Distance 4400 miles to 6° 30′ S, 105° 00′ E, in the entrance to Sunda Strait.

W-bound, from October to April, proceed from the above position by great circle. Distance 4380 miles. From May to September, proceed by great circle to 30° 00′ S, 56° 30′ E and thence by rhumb line. Distance 4400 miles.

6.152. Mombasa ↔ Sunda Strait. Direct, passing 50 miles N of Seychelles Group and N of Chagos Archipelago. Distance 3920 miles to 6° 30′ S, 105° 00′ E, in the entrance to Sunda Strait.

6.153. Aden → Sunda Strait. From October to April, round Ras Asir and take One and half Degree Channel. Distance 3800 miles to 6° 30′ S, 105° 00′ E, in the entrance to Sunda Strait.

From May to September, pass N of Socotra, through 13° 00′ N, 55° 00′ E, and thence through Eight Degree Channel. Make Point de Galle and proceed thence to Sunda Strait. Distance 3800 miles.

Low-powered vessels, from October to April, should round Ras Asir and proceed through the following positions: 3° 00′ N, 60° 00′ E (October to February); 1° 00′ S, 72° 20′ E (March and April); 2° 20′ S, 76° 30′ E; 3° 00′ S, 94° 30′ E; and thence to Sunda Strait, passing on either side of Enggano Island. From May to September, they should follow the full-power route as far as Point de Galle; thence crossing the equator in 96° 30′ E and following either the Outer or the Middle route, see Admiralty Sailing Directions, to Sunda Strait.

6.154. Sunda Strait → Aden. From October to April, make Point de Galle and pass through Eight Degree Channel; thence steer either N or S of Socotra as directed in 6.79. Distances from 6° 30′ S, 105° 00′ E, in the entrance to Sunda Strait: N of Socotra, 3800 miles; S of Socotra 3800 miles.

From May to September, proceed through One and half Degree Channel and thence through 5° 50′ N, 60° 00′ E and 8° 00′ N, 52° 40′ E, to round Ras Asir, see 6.59. Distance 3920 miles.

Low-powered vessels should, from November to March, steer NW between Kepulanan Mentuwai and Sumatra, entering the Indian Ocean by Selat Siberut. Thence they should proceed to Point de Galle on a curving course, crossing the Equator in 97° 00′ E, and through 1° 50′ N, 95° 00′ E; 5° 00′ N, 90° 00′ E; 5° 30′ N, 85° 00′ E. W of Ceylon, they should use the full-power route described above. In April, May, June, and September they should take a route close N of Chagos Archipelago, passing through 8° 00′ S, 68° 00′ E; 8° 00′ N, 52° 40′ E;

and round Ras Asir. In July and August they should pass through 2° 30′ S, 65° 00′ E; 1° 10′ S, 61   30′ E; 8° 00′ N, 52° 40′ E; and round Ras Asir. For the approach to Ras Asir, see 6.59.

6.155. Persian Gulf and eastern side of Arabian Sea ↔ North coast of Australia. Between the Gulf of Oman and the latitude of Cape Comorin the route should be taken through 13° 00′ N, 74° 10′ E. Between Karachi or Bombay and Cape Comorin it is as direct as navigation permits. See Admiralty Sailing Directions and articles 6.79 and 6.80.

E of Ceylon, the choice between an open-ocean route and a voyage through the Eastern Archipelago will be governed by considerations of draft, weather, distance, and season. Malacca Strait is discussed in article 6.83, and the approach to Australian waters is covered by articles 6.120 and 6.121. For the Eastern Archipelago see Chapter 7.

Distances, in miles:

		Torres Strait	Port Darwin
By ocean route, S of Java and Timor	Str. of Hormuz	5750	5170
	Karachi	5280	4700
	Bombay	4820	4240
	Colombo	3960	3380
S of Java; and through Sumba, Ombai, and Wètar Straits for Torres Strait, or Sumba and Roti Straits for Port Darwin	Str. of Hormuz	5720	5150
	Karachi	5250	4690
	Bombay	4790	4220
	Colombo	3930	3370
By Sunda, Sapudi, and Wètar Straits	Str. of Hormuz	5690	5230
	Karachi	5230	4770
	Bombay	4760	4310
	Colombo	3910	3450
By Malacca and Sapudi Straits; thence by Wètar Strait for Torres Strait or by Lombok Strait for Port Darwin	Str. of Hormuz	5770	5310
	Karachi	5310	4850
	Bombay	4840	4380
	Colombo	4990	3530

6.156. Persian Gulf and eastern side of Arabian Sea ↔ West coast of Australia. Between the Gulf of Oman and the latitude of Cape Comorin the route should be taken through 13° 00′ N, 74° 10′ E. Between Karachi or Bombay and Cape Comorin it is as direct as navigation permits. See Admiralty Sailing Directions and articles 6.80 and 6.81. Between Ceylon and the W coast of Australia, routes are direct.

In the relatively low latitudes traversed by these routes, which have a strong N–S component, the distance saved by great circle sailing is of minor consequence. The following distances are calculated using great circle tracks on the oceanic parts of the routes.

Distances, in miles:

Str. of Hormuz

590	Karachi			
1010	500	Bombay		
1800	1340	880	Colombo	
4610	4160	3690	2840	Port Hedland
4880	4430	3960	3110	Fremantle
4940	4490	4020	3170	20′ SSW of Cape Leeuwin

6.157. Notes on passages between South Africa and Australia. In the South Indian Ocean, the E-going Southern Ocean Current has no defined N boundary, E'ly sets predominating as far N as 30° S, or approximately the S limit of the South-east Trade Wind. Between the South-east Trades and the Roaring Forties, there is a zone of light, variable winds, the axis of which lies on about the parallel of 35° S in summer and 30° S in winter. The rhumb line between Cape Agulhas and Cape Leeuwin coincides with the parallel of 35° S; its length is 4711 miles, and the corresponding great circle, with a length of 4501 miles, has its vertex in about 45° S. It is therefore evident that any attempt to shorten a voyage by great circle sailing between the two continents is likely, except on the most N'ly tracks, to put a vessel at risk of delay not only due to pack ice, see 6.42, but also due to weather and, in the case of W-bound voyages, due to a stronger adverse current. In practice, composite sailing is usually adopted on these routes, the E-bound tracks being given a limiting latitude of 40° S in summer and 35° 30' S in winter, while the W-bound tracks make their main westing in summer on a great circle with its vertex in 35° S, and in winter by rhumb line on the parallel of 30° S.

Voyages between South Africa and the NW and N coasts of Australia are not greatly affected by the foregoing considerations, but, in view of the frequency of tropical revolving storms (Willy-Willies) off the NW coast of Australia from November to February, vessels on the Darwin and Arafura Sea routes are advised to pass close under Sumba and Timor during that season. See 6.121 and 6.158.

6.158. Cape Town → North-west and north coasts of Australia. From October to April, cross the Agulhas Current to 36° 45' S, 19° 00' E and then steer by rhumb line to 39° 00' S, 45° 00' E. Thence, for Port Darwin or Torres Strait, take the great circle to 11° 30' S, 118° 00' E, making this N'ly latitude to avoid the Willy-Willies and continue the voyage close S of Roti and Timor, breaking off for North Sahul Passage if bound for Port Darwin. Alternatively, Port Darwin may be approached by passing S of Cartier Islet, see 6.120. For Port Hedland, leave the great cirle in 19° 00' S, 115° 00' E. From May to September, in spite of the adverse effect of the Agulhas Current, do not go S of 35° 00' S, but follow that parallel to 79° 15' E and then take the great circle to 15° 30' S, 120° 00' E, thereafter joining the coastwise route S of Browse Island, or breaking off earlier according to destination. For Port Hedland, leave the great circle in 115° E.

Distances, in miles:

Cape Town to	October to April	May to September
Torres Strait	7000	6830
Port Darwin via N Sahul Passage	6420 (1)	—
Port Darwin via coastwise route	6380 (2)	6210 (3)
Port Hedland	5430	5370

(1) Via N Sahul Passage; (2) via Cartier Islet; (3) via Browse Island.

6.159. Durban → North-west and north coasts of Australia. From October to April, for Torres Strait or Port Darwin, take the great circle to 11° 30' S, 118° 00' E, and proceed thence as directed in 6.158. For other ports, leave this great circle in about 18° 00' S, 105° 00' E. From May to September, take the great circle to 15° 30' S, 120° 00' E and join the coastwise route S of Browse Island or break off earlier according to destination. For Port Hedland, leave the great circle in 110° E.

Distances, in miles:

Durban to	October to April	May to September
Torres Strait	6300	6200
Port Darwin via Sahul Passage	5720	—
Port Darwin via coastwise route	5710	5580
Port Hedland	4860	4780

6.160. North-west and north coasts of Australia → Durban and Cape Town. From October to April, ships from Torres Strait and Port Darwin should take their trans-oceanic departure by the N'ly route from 11° 30' S, 118° 00' E and ships from Port Hedland should depart from 20° 00' S, 115° 00' E, off Monte Bello Islands. From these positions, steer by great circle either for Durban or, if bound for Cape Town, to 33° 45' S, 36° 30' E; then joining the coastal route (6.56) off Algoa Bay.

From May to September, the departure positions for traffic from the N'ly ports and Port Hedland are 15° 30' S, 120° 00' E and 20° 00' S, 115° 00' E respectively, whence great circle tracks should be steered to 30° 00' S, 56° 30' E. From this position, Durban should be made by all ships by rhumb line on 30° S; an earlier departure from this latitude would expose vessels bound for Cape Town to the risk of bad weather.

Distances, in miles:

		Durban	Cape Town
Torres Strait	Oct.–Apr.	6300	6940
	May–Sept.	6210	7000
Port Darwin	Oct.–Apr.	5720	6360
	May–Sept.	5580	6380
Port Hedland	Oct.–Apr.	4740	5360
	May–Sept.	4700	5550

6.161. Cape Town and Durban → West and south coasts of Australia. From October to April, after leaving **Cape Town** cross the Agulhas Current to 36° 45′ S, 19° 00′ E and proceed thence by rhumb line to 40° 00′ S, 55° 00′ E, and then continue along the parallel of 40° 00′ S. Vessels bound for Fremantle should break off in 77° 00′ E, and those bound for Adelaide and Melbourne in 100° 00′ E, in each case completing the voyage on a great circle. Ships bound for Hobart should follow the foregoing directions to 41° 30′ S, 122° 50′ E, on the great circle track for Melbourne, from which position they should proceed by great circle to the landfall off South West Cape, Tasmania. During this season a shorter but more boisterous route for Melbourne could be taken by steering from 36° 45′ S, 19° 00′ E through 44° 00′ S, 40° 00′ E; 45° 00′ S, 65° 00′ E; 45° 00′ S, 120° 00′ E; all by rhumb line; and thence to Cape Otway by great circle; or to Hobart by continuing on the parallel of 45° 00′ S as far as 130° 00′ E and thence to destination. This route saves some 200 miles on the voyage to Melbourne.

From **Durban**, from October to April, proceed by great circle to join the foregoing route in 40° 00′ S, 77° 00′ E.

From May to September, vessels from **Cape Town** are advised, owing to the weather, not to proceed initially S of 35° 30′ S and having made that latitude in 20° 00′ E, to keep in it for the main part of the voyage. Strictly followed, it will carry a vessel close under West Cape Howe and to Investigator Strait; traffic for Fremantle should break off in 90° E and continue by great circle; ships bound for ports E of Cape Leeuwin should proceed direct to their destinations from 35° 30′ S, 115° 08′ E, which is 68 miles S of Cape Leeuwin.

From **Durban**, from May to September, take a great circle track to join the foregoing route in 35° 30′ S, 67° 30′ E.

The possibility of finding icebergs on these routes at any time of year cannot be discounted. See 6.43.

Distances, in miles:

		Fremantle	Adelaide	Melbourne	Hobart
Cape Town	Oct.–Apr.	4840	5820	6030	6140
	May–Sept.	4870	5960	6240	6410
Durban	Oct.–Apr.	4250	5240	5440	5550
	May–Sept.	4270	5360	5630	5800

6.162. West and south coasts of Australia → Durban and Cape Town. On all voyages throughout the year, keep N of 30° 00′ S, 100° 00′ E. From the S coast of Australia and Tasmania this position should be approached through 34° 37′ S, 115° 08′ E, 15 miles S of Cape Leeuwin; from Tasmania a great circle track bypassing Cape Leeuwin might appear preferable, but it would only save about 20 miles and adverse winds with head seas would be more likely.

From 30° 00′ S, 100° E, from October to April, the route to Durban is by great circle. The route for Cape Town follows the great circle to 35° 00′ S, 65° 00′ E, after which a W'ly course should be steered for a landfall on the African coast at Cape Recife. From May to September all traffic should proceed along the parallel of 30° 00′ S to a position off Durban, whence vessels bound for Cape Town should follow the coastwise route, see 6.57.

Distances, in miles:

		Fremantle	Adelaide	Melbourne	Hobart
Cape Town	Oct.–Apr.	4960	6120	6400	6580
	May–Sept.	5200	6370	6650	6830
Durban	Oct.–Apr.	4350	5520	5800	5980
	May–Sept.	4410	5580	5860	6040

6.163. Mombasa ↔ Australian ports. To and from Torres Strait and Port Darwin, the route to Sunda Strait (6.152) and onward through the Java Sea and Flores Sea (6.120) may be used. Alternatively, from 4° 00′ S, 73° 00′ E, N of Chagos Archipelago, proceed to 11° 30′ S, 118° 00′ E and continue as directed in 6.120.

For destinations between Port Hedland and Cape Leeuwin, proceed N of Seychelles Group to a position in 10° 00′ S, 80° 00′ E; thence direct. W-bound, the passage to Mombasa is as direct as navigation permits, keeping N of 30° S, 100° E, see 6.162.

Distances:

Torres Strait:	via Sunda Strait 6120 miles
	via 11° 30′ S, 118° 00′ E 6100 miles
Port Darwin:	via Sunda Strait 5620 miles
	via 11° 30′ S, 118° 00′ E 5520 miles
Port Hedland:	E-bound 4790 miles
	W-bound 4720 miles

	Fremantle:	E-bound 4840 miles
		W-bound 4560 miles
	Cape Leeuwin:	E-bound 4860 miles
		W-bound 4530 miles

6.164. Aden → North coast of Australia. Through the Arabian Sea, the route for this passage changes seasonally, see 6.80. E of Ceylon, there is a choice of routes, see 6.155.

Route		Distance in miles	
Arabian Sea	E of Ceylon	Torres Strait W entrance	Port Darwin
6·80 (Oct.–Apr.)	Ocean route	5890	5310
	S of Java and through Straits	5860	5290
	Sunda—Wètar Straits	5880	5380
	Malacca and Sapudi Straits	6080	5580
6·80 (May–Sept.)	Ocean route	5840	5250
	S of Java and through Straits	5810	5240
	Sunda—Wètar Straits	5830	5330
	Malacca and Sapudi Straits	6080	5590

6.165. North coast of Australia → Aden. For passage from the N coast of Australia to the Indian Ocean see 6.120. Passage across the Arabian Sea should be made as follows.

From October to April, pass through Eight Degree Channel and on either side of Socotra. Distances, passing N of Socotra: from Torres Strait, W entrance 6000 miles; from Port Darwin via Cartier Islet 5390 miles.

From May to September, pass through One and half Degree Channel; thence through 5° 50′N, 60° 00′ E; 8° 00′ N, 52° 40′ E; and round Ras Asir. Distances: from Torres Strait, W entrance 6060 miles; from Port Darwin 5480 miles.

Alternatively, from May to September the passage may be made from the Arafura Sea by Wètar, Ombai, and Sumba Straits to 9° 30′ S, 113° 00′ E; thence N of Chagos Archipelago passing through 6° 30′ S, 80° 00′ E and 4° 00′ S, 73° 30′ E and crossing the Arabian Sea through 3° 00′ N, 57° 00′ E; 8° 00′ N, 52° 40′ E and round Ras Asir. If the Monsoon permits this route may be shortened by about 20 miles by steering direct from the equator in 64° 05′ E to 8° 00′ N, 52° 40′ E. Distances: from Torres Strait, W entrance 6180 miles; from Port Darwin 5600 miles.

6.166. Aden → Fremantle and south coast of Australia. Pass between Ras Asir and Socotra; thence steer to 4° 00′ S, 73° 30′ E; and thence to Fremantle or to join the coastwise route (6.132–6.137) 20 miles WSW of Cape Leeuwin. Distances: Fremantle 4920 miles; 20 miles WSW of Cape Leeuwin 4950 miles.

6.167. South coast of Australia and Fremantle → Aden. From October to April the route is the reverse of the E'bound route given in article 6.166.

From May to September, first make a position in 8° 00′ S, 68° 00′ E; thence the passage may be continued either N or S of Socotra, in the former case through 8° 00′ N, 60° 00′ E and 13° 00′ N, 55° 00′ E; and in the latter case through 8° 00′ N, 52° 40′ E. Distances via N of Socotra: from 20 miles WSW of Cape Leeuwin 5120 miles; from Fremantle 5100 miles; via S of Socotra, from 20 miles WSW of Cape Leeuwin 5010 miles; from Fremantle 4980 miles. For ports E of Cape Leeuwin, see 6.132–6.137.

CHAPTER 7

PACIFIC OCEAN, CHINA AND JAPAN SEAS, AND EASTERN ARCHIPELAGO

CONTENTS

D

NAVIGATIONAL NOTES

PASSAGES BETWEEN TORRES STRAIT AND EAST COAST OF AUSTRALIA

ROUTES BETWEEN AUSTRALIA, NEW ZEALAND, AND ISLANDS IN SOUTH PACIFIC

ROUTES IN EASTERN ARCHIPELAGO, CHINA SEA, AND EASTERN SEA

ROUTES ON WESTERN SIDE OF PACIFIC OCEAN

ROUTES ON EASTERN SIDE OF PACIFIC OCEAN

ROUTES TO AND FROM HONOLULU

ROUTES TO AND FROM PAPEETE

SOUTH PACIFIC TRANS-OCEAN ROUTES

MID-PACIFIC TRANS-OCEAN ROUTES

NORTH PACIFIC TRANS-OCEAN ROUTES

WINDS AND WEATHER   45

7.01. The following description of the winds and weather of the Pacific Ocean and adjacent seas amplifies the general statement given in *The Mariner's Handbook*. For more precise information regarding oceanic winds and weather, the mariner is referred to the atlases of Monthly Meteorological Charts of the East and West Pacific Ocean (MO 518 and MO 484 respectively), published by the Marine Branch of the Meteorological   50 Office. Similar information is also contained in Charts 5127 (1) to (12) (Monthly Routeing Charts for North Pacific Ocean) and Charts 5128 (1) to (12) (Monthly Routeing Charts for South Pacific Ocean). Detailed information about specific localities should be sought in the appropriate Admiralty Sailing Directions. In reading the following description reference should also be made to World Climatic Charts 5301 and 5302.

In the E part of the Pacific Ocean, the winds and weather conform, in the main, with the text-book description   55 of oceanic winds and weather published in *The Mariner's Handbook*. In the W part of the ocean, however, the seasonal heating and cooling of the Asiatic land mass results in the establishment here of a monsoonal regime. Conditions are further complicated, in the region between Australia and the Philippines, by numerous islands, many of which are of some size and height, causing marked differences in the winds and weather experienced in different localities. These local effects are dealt with in the Sailing Directions.   60

North Pacific Ocean

7.02. The Equatorial Trough, known also as the **Doldrums,** the Doldrum Belt, the Intertropical Convergence Zone (I.T.C.Z.), the Intertropical Front (I.T.F.), the Equatorial Front, or the Shearline, remains permanently N of the equator, in longitudes E of about 160° W. To the W of that meridian, it lies in the S hemisphere from   65 about November or December until April or May; in the summer of the N hemisphere it is virtually non-existent W of about 150° E. In the W part of the North Pacific, therefore, the Equatorial Trough is really only in evidence during the change of the monsoons, from about mid-September to mid-November, and from about mid-April to mid-May. The weather of the Equatorial Trough is that typical of the Trough in other oceans, *i.e.* light, variable winds with calm alternating with squalls, heavy showers, and thunderstorms; but W of about   70

130° W, the frequency of calms and variable winds is considerably less than in the Equatorial Trough of other oceans, and most winds are from an E'ly point. The mean positions of the Trough in January and July are shown on charts 5301 and 5302. The actual position is subject to much variation, as is the width of the zone, which averages about 150 miles. The worst weather is generally experienced when the Trade Winds of the two hemispheres 5 meet at a wide angle. Visibility is normally good, except in heavy rain.

7.03. Seasonal winds of eastern North Pacific Ocean. In summer, E of about 120° W, and between the Equatorial Trough and the equator, there is an area covered by prevailing SW'ly winds, see chart 5302. These winds are of a monsoonal nature, and result from the summer heating of the North American continent, which 10 causes a reduction of pressure over that area, and a N'ly distortion of the Equatorial Trough; the South-east Trade Wind of the South Pacific Ocean is drawn across the equator, is deflected to the right by the effect of the earth's rotation, and is felt as a SW'ly wind in the area under consideration.

Over the greater part of the area these winds prevail from about June to October, and replace the North-east Trade Winds which prevail there in winter, see 7.04. The duration of the season of these south-westerlies varies 15 with latitude, being longest near the equator, near which S to SW winds are prevalent in most months E of 100° W.

Winds are mostly light or moderate, though squalls, in which the wind may at times reach gale force, are rather common. Tropical storms, see 7.10, also produce strong winds and gales at times.

The weather is generally cloudy and unsettled, and rainfall is considerable, it is, in fact, these winds which 20 bring the rainy season to much of Mexico and Central America. Visibility over the open ocean is generally good except in rain.

7.04. The North-east Trade Wind blows on the equatorial side of the large clockwise circulation around the oceanic high pressure area situated in about 30° N. This "high" lies farther N and is somewhat more intense 25 in summer than in winter, and, while in the former season it generally consists of a single cell, in the latter it more often represents the resultant of a succession of anticyclones moving E across the North Pacific from Asia, and becoming stationary over the E part of the ocean. In summer, the Trade Wind blows in the region E of about 150° E, and between the Equatorial Trough and about 32° N; the limits are not fixed, but fluctuate considerably. To the W of 150° E the Trades give way to the South-west Monsoon of the W part of the North 30 Pacific, which is described in article 7.06.

As with the Trade Winds of other oceans, these winds are remarkable over large areas for their persistence and steadiness. The general direction and steadiness of the wind in different parts of the zone can best be seen from a study of charts 5301 and 5302, which will show that the direction becomes more N'ly (or even NW'ly) near the American coast, and mainly E'ly, in summer, in the SW part of the area covered by these winds.

35 The strength of the North-east Trade averages force 3–4, but it often freshens to 5–6. Winds are likely to reach force 7 or above on 1–3 days per month in the heart of the Trades; in the vicinity of the Mexican coast, N of about 10° N, and between about 90° W and 100° W, the frequency rises to 3–6 days per month from November to February. Apart from squalls, winds of this strength are unlikely within about 600 miles of the equator.

40 The typical weather of the Trade Wind zone is fair, with scattered showers, and skies about half covered by small cumulus cloud. At times the Trade becomes unsteady, being interrupted by a day or two of unsettled showery weather with occasional squalls. In the NE part of the zone, near the American coast, cloud amounts are generally smaller than elsewhere, and rain is rare.

Visibility over the open ocean is generally good, except in rain, but there is often a light haze which restricts 45 visibility to between 8 and 15 miles; showers, cloud, and haze usually increase when the wind freshens. Dust haze is sometimes prevalent off the American coast and is associated with fresh or strong offshore winds.

7.05. North-east Monsoon. In the winter of the N hemisphere, the cooling of the Asiatic land mass results in the establishment of an intense area of high pressure over Mongolia and the E part of Siberia. The anticyclonic 50 wind circulation resulting from this pressure distribution gives rise to the establishment, at this season, of NE'ly winds over the W part of the N Pacific S of about 30° N, and in the China Sea, and Yellow Sea. The N and E limits of the area covered by the Monsoon are not very well defined. On its E side it merges with the North-east Trade wind of the central and E parts of the N Pacific, while to the N it gives way to the prevailing westerlies of higher latitudes.

55 The time of onset of the Monsoon varies with latitude. In the N it begins about September, while towards the equator it does not become established until November. In April it becomes less steady, the prevailing direction becomes more E'ly, and winds with a S'ly component are more frequent.

The general direction and steadiness of the Monsoon are indicated on chart 5301; at the height of the season, in January, winds over the open waters of the South China Sea and E of the Philippines are almost exclusively 60 from between N and E, while in the Yellow Sea the direction becomes more N'ly, and over the S part of Japan it is NW'ly. Wind direction becomes more variable as latitude increases. The strength of the wind changes with latitude; it averages force 6 in T'ai-wan Strait, force 5 in the China Sea, and force 4 S of 10° N. It becomes less steady, lighter, and more N'ly in direction towards the equator and amongst the islands of the Sulu Sea and the Sulawesi Sea.

65 The strength of the wind over the open sea averages about force 5 in the N part of the monsoon zone, rising to 6 in T'ai-wan Strait, and decreases to force 4 S of about 10° N.

The movement of depressions in an E'ly direction across the area also affects the strength of the wind. As far E as the general longitude of Japan there is often no closed wind circulation round newly formed "lows"; their passage is marked by a slackening of the monsoon ahead of them and a freshening, often to gale force, in their 70 rear.

At the height of the season in December and January, winds are likely to reach force 7 or above on 6–10 days per month over much of the area between Vietnam, Luzon, T'ai-wan and Japan, as indicated on chart 5301; the stormiest area is E of Luzon and T'ai-wan, where winds of this strength are likely on more than 11 days per month. In the Yellow Sea their frequency is about 3–6 days per month, while S of the 10th parallel it decreases to 0–3 days per month.

To the N of about 20° N, overcast skies with periods of light rain or drizzle are typical during this season, especially from January to April, though at times there are periods of more broken skies, and in October and November generally fair conditions prevail along the SE coast of China. In the Gulf of Pohai and the Gulf of Liaotung, immediately to leeward of the Asiatic land mass, a good deal of fine and settled weather with only small amounts of cloud prevails. S of about 17° N, over the open sea, skies are only about half covered and there are occasional showers; cloudiness increases again towards the equator and showers become more frequent.

The weather in the vicinity of land is greatly affected by the degree of exposure to the prevailing monsoon. Where the monsoon blows onshore, and especially when the coast is backed by high ground, cloud amounts are larger and rainfall is heavier than over the open sea, while to leeward of high ground fairer conditions prevail. Information about specific localities is published in Admiralty Sailing Directions.

Over the open ocean, visibility is good except in rain. Off the coasts of China and Vietnam, poor visibility becomes increasingly frequent after December, and mist or fog may occur on more than 10 days per month in the vicinity of North Vietnam in February and March, and on 8–9 days per month off Hong Kong in March and April. In the Gulf of Pohai and the Gulf of Liaotung, strong NW'ly winds at times bring dust haze from the interior of Mongolia.

7.06. South-west Monsoon. In the summer of the N hemisphere, intense heating of the Asiatic land mass results in the formation of an area of low pressure centred approximately over NW India with an extension over the E part of Asia, see chart 5302. The South-east Trade Wind of the Pacific and Indian Oceans is drawn across the equator and is deflected to the right by the effect of the earth's rotation. This wind, known as the South-west Monsoon, is felt in the W part of the North Pacific Ocean and the China Sea and Yellow Sea as a prevailing S to SW wind, and in the Japan Sea as a S to SE wind. The N and E limits of the Monsoon are ill defined but, W of about 140° E and S of about 40° N, winds are predominantly from between SE and SW at the height of the season, in July. The general direction and steadiness of the winds at this period are indicated on chart 5302. The Monsoon is steadiest in the South China Sea, where nearly all winds are from S and W; farther N and E they are much more variable in direction, and in the early part of the season N of about 25° N, travelling depressions may cause winds from any direction; along the China coast between 20° N and 30° N, and in the vicinity of T'ai-wan, north-easterlies are still more common than south-westerlies in May.

The average strength of the Monsoon over the open sea is about force 3–4 in the South China Sea and force 3 elsewhere, but squalls, in which the wind may reach gale force, are fairly common. Apart from these squalls or in the vicinity of tropical storms (7.10), winds do not often reach force 7 in the Monsoon season. Land and sea breezes prevail close to the coast, and calms are not uncommon.

The weather over the open sea away from the effects of land is mainly fair, with skies about half covered, and with occasional showers. Over the coasts, especially if exposed to the Monsoon and backed by high ground, cloudy weather with frequent heavy rain prevails.

Visibility over the open ocean is good except when reduced by rain, but along the China coast there is a high frequency of sea fog in certain months, due to the spread of warm moist equatorial air over water previously cooled by the NE winds of the winter Monsoon. The water recovers its normal temperature progressively from S to N, and the foggy season reaches its maximum in April off Hong Kong (8–9 days per month), in June off Ch'ang Chiang (12 days), and in July off S Shantung (12 days). In the Japan Sea, fog occurs on 3–4 days per month, and on 5–7 days per month off N Honshū. After these months the incidence drops sharply to about 2 days per month, and fog is rare in the later part of the season.

7.07. Variables. In a belt extending across the central part of the Pacific Ocean, and situated in about 25° N–30° N in winter, and 35° N–40° N in summer, there are variable and mainly light or moderate winds in the vicinity of the oceanic anticyclone. In the E part of this zone winds are mainly N'ly in all seasons, and form a N extension of the North-east Trade around the E flank of the oceanic "high". In the W part of the zone, in summer, winds become mainly S'ly, and merge with the South-west Monsoon described in article 7.06, while in winter they give way, W of about 150° E, to prevailing NW'ly winds forming part of the circulation of the North-east Monsoon.

In summer, winds are generally light, and are likely to reach force 7 only on rare occasions except in association with tropical storms, (7.10), and E of about 140° W, where they may be expected to reach this strength on 1–4 days per month, the higher figure applying towards the American coast, near which strong N to NW winds are common. At the height of the winter season in January, winds may be expected to reach force 7 or above on 1–3 days per month E of about 140° W, and on 3–6 days per month W of that meridian, increasing to 6–10 days per month in the area covered by the North-east Monsoon W of about 150° E, described in article 7.05. The weather in summer is generally fair or fine near the normal position of the oceanic "high", see chart 5302, which, at this season, usually consists of a single cell, and rain is infrequent. Cloudier conditions prevail E and W of the area of high pressure; rainfall is light on the E side, towards the American coast, but more common to the W. In winter the "high" shown on chart 5301 usually consists of a series of E moving anticyclones, near which fair or fine weather prevails, the intervening troughs of relatively low pressure being characterised by cloudy, showery weather. Visibility in winter is mostly good except in rain, and over the open ocean fog is not common. In summer fog and poor visibility become increasingly frequent towards the N limit of the zone (40° N at this season); in the W this is due to the N'ly flow of warm moist equatorial air over progressively colder water, aggravated off the E coast of N Honshū by contact with the cold Oya Shio; in the E it is due to a similar cooling by the California Current. Over much of the zone fog may occur on 3–4 days per month at this season, rising to 5–7 days per month off the coast of California.

7.08. Westerlies. On the polar side of the oceanic anticyclone, the prevailing winds are from some W'ly point, but summer and winter conditions are markedly different, and it is convenient to treat the two periods separately.

In winter, N of 40° N, the almost continuous passage of depressions from the vicinity of China and Japan in a NE'ly direction towards the Aleutian Islands and S Alaska causes winds to vary greatly in both direction and strength, and winds from any direction may be experienced. As can be seen on chart 5301, strong winds and gales are frequent. The region of highest gale frequency extends from E of Japan to the area S of the Aleutians and the Alaska peninsula; in this region winds are likely to reach force 7 or above on 12 to 18 days per month.

The main feature of the weather is its great variability, periods of overcast skies and rain or snow alternating with fairer intervals. Fine weather is seldom prolonged and cloud amounts are generally large. Although fog is not common at this season, rain and snow often reduce visibility drastically; it is also often only moderate with winds from a S'ly point, but is generally good (except in precipitation) with N'ly or NW'ly winds.

In summer, depressions are less frequent, much less intense, and their tracks are farther N than in winter. Winds therefore, although they still vary a good deal both in direction and strength, are much lighter, and gales are far less common. Over the greater part of the zone, winds may reach force 7 or above on 1–5 days per month S of about 50° N; the quietest month is July, during which winds of this strength are unlikely on more than one day on average. N of the 50th parallel observations are scarce, but the frequency of gales is probably the same as above.

Over the greater part of the zone the weather is very cloudy and foggy; W of about 160° W fog occurs on about 5–10 days per month in most parts, rising to more than 10 days per month over large areas, see chart 5302. This high incidence is due to the N'ly flow of warm moist S to SW winds over progressively colder water, in particular over the cold waters of Oya Shio and the Kamchatka Current. E of 160° W the frequency is less but it increases again to 5–10 days per month towards the W coast of America over the cold waters of the California Current. Apart from fog, visibility is generally moderate.

7.09. Polar Easterlies. Since, in winter, the tracks of most depressions are S of the Aleutian Islands, the prevailing winds in the Bering Sea at this season are often E'ly. As in the case of the westerlies, great variations in both strength and direction occur, due to the passage of some depressions close to and across the area. The N part of the zone is not navigable on account of ice; in the S part winds may reach force 7 or more on over 10 days per month.

The weather is generally very cloudy, and precipitation, usually in the form of snow, is frequent, amounts being greatest in the S. Visibility is often poor because of snow.

7.10. Tropical storms. In the W part of the North Pacific these storms are known as **typhoons**, and in the E part as **hurricanes**. They are fully described in *The Mariner's Handbook*, with their warning signs, and advice on avoiding them.

The area mainly affected by typhoons is W and N of the Caroline Islands and Marianas Islands, and includes the N part of the Philippines, the N half of the South China Sea, the vicinity of the China coast and T'ai-wan, the Eastern Sea and Japan. Although typhoons may occur in any month, more than half are experienced from July to October, and nearly 90 per cent between May and December inclusive; September is the month with the greatest frequency with an average of just over 4 storms. The number experienced in any month varies greatly in different years.

Taking the area as a whole, no month is immune from typhoons, but some parts of it are free from them in certain months, notably the China coast, T'ai-wan Strait, and the W part of the Eastern Sea, in which areas they have not been recorded from December to April.

The area mainly affected by hurricanes is the vicinity of the Pacific coast of America between about 10° N and 30° N; they have, however, been recorded as far W as 130° W to 140° W, generally in the early part of the season.

Almost all hurricanes occur in the period from June to October, the month of greatest frequency being September, with an average of 2 storms; they are occasionally recorded in May and November, and very occasionally in December; they are unknown from January to April. As with all tropical storms, the number experienced in different years varies greatly.

More detailed information regarding the frequency of typhoons and hurricanes in different localities will be found in Admiralty Sailing Directions, and in the atlases of Monthly Meteorological Charts for the West Pacific (MO 484) and the East Pacific (MO 518) referred to in article 7.01.

South Pacific Ocean

7.15. As stated in article 7.02, the **Equatorial Trough** remains N of the equator throughout the year in longitudes E of about 160° W. In more W'ly longitudes it lies in the S hemisphere from about November or December to April or May, reaching its extreme S position in February. The seasonal movement of the belt in the W part of the South Pacific is thus large, as also is the day to day variation in its position, especially in the extreme W in the vicinity of N Australia and New Guinea. The width of the zone averages about 150 miles, but it may at times be as little as 50 miles and at others over 300 miles.

The weather is that typical of the Equatorial Trough elsewhere, in which calms and light, variable winds and fine weather alternate with squalls, heavy rain (most often in the form of showers), and thunderstorms. Conditions are generally more severe in the W part of the South Pacific than elsewhere in this ocean, due to the wide angle at which the South-east Trade Wind and the North-west Monsoon, see 7.17 and 7.16, meet. Visibility over the open sea is good except in heavy rain.

7.16. North-west Monsoon. During the summer of the S hemisphere, pressure is low over the N part of the heated Australian land mass, and the Equatorial Trough is located over that area. The North-east Monsoon of the W part of the North Pacific is drawn across the equator, is deflected to the left by the earth's rotation, and is felt over the South Pacific, W of about the 180th meridian and between the equator and the Equatorial trough as a prevailing NW'ly wind known as the North-west Monsoon. The season of this monsoon varies   *5* somewhat with latitude; in the vicinity of N Australia it is generally only firmly established in January and February, while farther N in the Java Sea and the Banda Sea it normally blows from December to March.

The general wind direction is indicated on chart 5301; winds are mainly from N and NE near the equator, and back gradually to between NW and W in more S'ly latitudes. Over much of the area the constancy of the Monsoon is not great, and winds from other directions are also experienced, though at the height of the season   *10* and away from the effects of land, winds from between S and E are uncommon; in the vicinity of the numerous islands, local effects may give rise to variation in both the direction and force of the wind.

The strength of the Monsoon is generally only light or moderate, but squalls, in which the wind may reach gale force, are rather common. Apart from these, or in the vicinity of tropical storms (7.10), winds of gale force are unlikely. The weather is generally cloudy, and rain, usually in the form of heavy showers, is frequent over   *15* most of the area. In the vicinity of land, the wind often varies greatly over short distances; off coasts exposed to the monsoon—especially if backed by high ground—rainfall is often very heavy and cloud amounts are large, while off sheltered coasts fair weather and less cloudy conditions prevail. Visibility over the open sea is generally good except in heavy rain. Information relating to specific localities is published in Admiralty Sailing Directions.

20

7.17. The South-east Trade Winds blow on the equatorial side of the oceanic high pressure area situated in about 30° S. In the E part of the zone the Trade Winds are maintained by the semi-permanent anticyclone situated towards the E side of the ocean and shown on charts 5301 and 5302, while in the W they are due to migratory anticyclones moving E from the vicinity of Australia.

Over the greater part of the ocean, the N limit of the Trades is defined by the Equatorial Trough. In the winter   *25* of the S hemisphere, E of about 120° W, and W of about 140° E, the N limit is the equator, N of which the Trades recurve to form the South-westerlies of the E part of the North Pacific, and the South-west Monsoon respectively; these winds are described above among those of the North Pacific Ocean. The S limit of the Trade winds is situated in 15° S to 20° S in winter and in 20° S to 25° S in summer.

As with the Trade Winds of the other oceans, those of the South Pacific are remarkable over large areas for   *30* their persistence and steadiness. The general direction and constancy of the wind can best be seen by studying charts 5301 and 5302. In the vicinity of the W coast of South America the Trades blow from between S and SE, while farther W the direction becomes predominantly E'ly. It becomes SE'ly again in winter W of about 160° E and over the seas N of Australia, where it is sometimes known as the **South-east Monsoon.** W of about 140° W, from November to April, the Trade Wind is unsteady over large areas, and though the predominant direction   *35* remains from between NE and SE, winds from other directions are rather frequent.

The average strength of the Trade Wind is about force 4, but it often freshens to force 5 or 6 over large areas. Over the greater part of the Trade Wind zone, winds of force 7 or above are unlikely on more than 1 or 2 days per month and, apart from short-lived squalls, are rare within 10 degrees of the equator. In an area between the NE coast of Queensland, New Caledonia, and the New Hebrides, however, the frequency rises to 3–6 days per   *40* month for much of the year.

Over the open ocean the characteristic weather of the steady South-east Trade Wind is fair with occasional showers; skies are about half covered with small cumulus clouds, and there is a slight haze which reduces visibility to between about 8 and 15 miles. Showers, cloud, and haze generally increase when the wind freshens. To the E of about the 180th meridian, and between the equator and about 8° S but varying somewhat with the   *45* season, there is a belt in which rainfall and cloud amounts are generally small. This dry belt widens towards the coast of South America to include most of the area covered by the Trade Wind; weather here is cloudier and overcast skies are common.

From November to April, W of about 140° W, but excluding the dry belt mentioned above, weather is often unsettled, the Trade becomes unsteady, and is followed by a period of cloudy, showery weather before settling   *50* in again with increased strength and some squalls from between S and E.

Over the seas N of Australia, during the season when the South-east Trade Wind prevails in these regions, namely from April to September or October, cloud amounts and rainfall are small; extensive dust haze prevails, especially towards the end of the season, due to the persistent offshore winds from the increasingly dry interior of the continent. These conditions are most marked in the Timor Sea, but are also prevalent in the Java Sea   *55* and Banda Sea, and to a lesser extent in the Arafura Sea. Visibility in haze is often less than 5 miles. Fog and mist are rather common towards the coast of South America over the cold waters of the Perú Current (7.37) but rarely occur elsewhere.

7.18. Variables. Between the S limit of the South-east Trades and the N limit of the Westerlies, there is a   *60* wide belt of variable winds of mainly moderate strength. The approximate area covered by this belt extends from 25° S to 40° S in summer, and from 20° S to 30° S in winter. It does not, however, extend completely across the ocean. To the E of about 85° W, S to SE winds prevail, forming a S extension of the South-east Trades around the E flank of the oceanic "high". Except in the E part of the zone referred to above, winds vary considerably in strength as well as in direction, and, in general, strong winds become more frequent with increasing   *65* latitude. Over the greater part of the area winds are likely to reach force 7 or above on 1–3 days per month, rising to 3–6 days per month towards the S limits of the zone. This latter frequency is also reached in many months over large areas W of about 160° W.

The weather is variable, being governed largely by the E-moving anticyclones already mentioned. Near the centres of these anticyclones it is fair or fine, while the intervening troughs of low pressure are characterised   *70* by cloudy, unsettled weather, with rainfall increasing towards the S. To the E of 85° W to 90° W, rainfall becomes progressively smaller towards the N and E, and it is very infrequent in the vicinity of the American coast. In this area, cloud amounts are often large, and overcast skies are common in winter.

Visibility is generally good in the N part of the zone except when reduced by rain, but the frequency of moderate and poor visibility increases with latitude and towards the S limits of 40° S in summer and 30° S in winter; visibility of less than 5 miles is recorded in some ten to fifteen per cent of ships' observations in summer, and five per cent in winter. It is generally associated with winds from some N'ly point.

In the extreme E part of the zone, over the cold waters of the Perú Current, fog is rather prevalent, and off the W coast of South America it occurs on 3–5 days per month towards the S limit of the zone.

7.19. The Westerlies, or **Roaring Forties**, predominate S of the belt of high pressure described in articles 7.17 and 7.18. As in the zone of the Westerlies in other oceans, the almost continuous passage of depressions from W to E causes the wind to vary greatly in both direction and strength. Gales are very common, especially in winter, during which season winds are likely to reach force 7 or above on 5–10 days per month over most of the area between 30° S and 40° S, and on more than 12 days per month S of the 40th parallel. One of the stormiest areas is to the W of NW of Cabo de Hornos, in which region winds of this strength are likely on about 20 days per month from July to September. In summer, gales are somewhat less common and occur farther S. To the E of about 150° W, and between 40° S and 45° S, winds are likely to reach force 7 or above on 5–10 days per month, and S of the 45th parallel the frequency rises to more than 10 days per month. To the W of 150° W, the area of highest gale frequency is farther S, but in few parts of the zone of the Westerlies, namely S of the 40th parallel at this season, is the frequency less than 3–5 days per month. Charts 5301 and 5302 give an indication of the distribution of gales in summer and winter respectively.

As in the Westerlies of other oceans, the weather is very variable, periods of overcast skies and rain or snow associated with the fronts of E-moving depressions alternating with fair weather. Fine weather is seldom prolonged and cloud amounts are generally large at all times.

Visibility also varies greatly; with winds from a S'ly point it is generally good, while N'ly winds are often associated with moderate or poor visibility. Fog is rather common in summer and may be expected on 3–5 days per month.

7.20. Tropical Storms are known as **hurricanes** in the South Pacific. They are described, and advice on avoiding them is given, in *The Mariner's Handbook*.

The area mainly affected is W of about 155° W and S of 8°–10°S. Most storms occur from December to April, and the season of greatest frequency is from January to March; they are not unknown at other times and the actual number of storms varies from year to year.

More detailed information about the frequency of hurricanes in specific localities will be found in Admiralty Sailing Directions and in the atlas of Monthly Meteorological Charts for the Western Pacific (MO 484) referred to in article 7.01.

SWELL

7.25. The North Pacific Ocean, east of 160° W, has large areas devoid of recorded observations of swell. Information is therefore confined to certain localities.

Off the coast of America between about 20° N and 40° N a W'ly swell, mainly low or moderate and rarely heavy, persists throughout the year.

To the N of 50° N, swell is predominantly SW to W; it is mainly moderate but the frequency of heavy swells increases to 20 per cent to 30 per cent in winter.

A NE'ly swell persists throughout the year SE of Hawaii. It is normally moderate or heavy, and may extend as far E as 130° W and, in winter, as far S as the equator.

From June to November inclusive, a SW'ly swell may be experienced off Colombia; it is normally low or moderate. Farther W, between 100° W and 150° W, a SE'ly swell which is moderate and, at times, heavy occurs between the equator and 10° N.

For monthly details, see the Atlas of Monthly Meteorological Charts of the Eastern Pacific (MO 518).

7.26. In the **North Pacific Ocean, west of 160° W**, swell waves are frequently interrupted by the many islands, particularly S of 20° N and near the Aleutian Islands. The statements which follow apply to the uninterrupted areas. In the SW part of the North Pacific, the swell is governed by the monsoons.

From the equator to 20° N, a NE'ly swell predominates from November to March inclusive. It is mainly low or moderate, but it is heavy on 10 per cent of occasions.

The South China Sea is affected by a SW'ly swell, sometimes moderate but only rarely heavy, from June to August inclusive.

To the N of 20° N and W of 140° E, there is no predominant direction, though a NW'ly swell is often found. Swell in this region is normally moderate or heavy; the frequency of heavy swells is about 30 per cent in the area close E of Japan.

7.27. The South Pacific Ocean, west of 160° W, is encumbered by islands which interrupt swell waves. The following statements therefore apply only to areas where there are few islands.

From the equator to 20° S, swell is predominantly from between NE and SE, and is mainly moderate in height.

From 20° S to 30° S, swell is frequently from between SE and SW but no direction predominates. In this region swell is normally moderate or heavy.

From 30° S to 50° S, swell is predominantly SW'ly, moderate or heavy. S of 30° S, two or even three swells are often present and reports of confused swells are frequent.

To the S of 50° S, swell comes mainly from between NW and SW, moderate or heavy.

7.28. In the **South Pacific Ocean, east of 160° W**, there are vast areas for which swell data are almost non-existent, particularly between 30° S and 50° S and between 80° W and 120° W. Available data show the following.

Off the coast of South America, between 10° S and 40° S, a S to SW'ly swell persists throughout the year, normally moderate but heavy at times.

From the equator to 20° S and from 100 miles off the coast of South America to 130° W, a SE'ly swell predominates. It is mainly moderate, though occasionally heavy.

From 30° S to 50° S and between 130° W and 160° W a moderate to heavy SW'ly swell predominates. Swells over 6 m in height are a common feature S of 35° S.

To the S of 50° S, swell comes mainly from between NW and SW, and is either moderate or heavy. As in the W part of this ocean, reports of confused swell are frequent S of 30° S.

7.29. Length of swell in Pacific Ocean. In the North Pacific, swell is normally average in length though short and long swells can also be encountered. In the South Pacific, most swells are short or average is length, but waves of more than 300 m in length occur quite often and it is in this ocean that the longest swells occur.

In the South Pacific Ocean, freak waves may occur, see 3.09.

CURRENTS

North Pacific Ocean

7.32. In essentials, the **main circulation** of the North Pacific Ocean resembles that of the North Atlantic Ocean (2.15, 2.16), though there are some differences. Owing to the extent of the ocean and the limitations of shipping tracks, the available observations of current are inadequate to support accurate details of the flow over large parts of the ocean. This particularly applies to the middle longitudes, both in the equatorial region and in the region of variable current lying farther N.

The S part of the main circulation is formed by the W-going **North Equatorial Current**. Immediately S of this current, the **Equatorial Counter-current** flows E across the ocean, so that the N boundary of this forms the S limit of the North Equatorial Current. The limits of the Counter-current are not exactly known. Its S limit lies in about 2° N to 4° N in winter. In the W part of the ocean there is not much seasonal change, but in the E there is a seasonal shift, to about 6° N (in 110° W) in summer. The N limit lies between about 6° N and 10° N, being farthest N in the E in summer. The South Equatorial Current, the N limit of which reaches to about 4° N, is described in article 7.37.

The North Equatorial Current has no defined N limit. The predominance of the North-east Trade Wind (7.04) decreases with increasing latitude and the W'ly currents accordingly decrease. The predominance of W'ly current thus gradually lessens until it is lost in the region of variable current which occupies the central part of the ocean. The latitude to which some predominance of W'ly current extends appears to vary with the season. In the middle longitudes of the ocean it is about 25° N in winter and about 30° N in late summer or autumn.

The Equatorial Counter-current flows continuously throughout the year across the whole extent of the ocean, differing in this respect from the corrresponding current of the Atlantic Ocean (2.15). It also differs in the fact of its more direct origin from one of the Equatorial currents, on the W side of the ocean. During March to November the Counter-current is formed jointly by the recurvature of the North Equatorial Current to the S, and that of the South Equatorial Current to the N. In December to February, part of the water of the North Equatorial Current is diverted S down the E coasts of the islands of the Philippine Group S of Luzon. This water turns directly E and forms the beginning of the Counter-current in about 128° E. During these months the South Equatorial Current, N of the equator, begins to turn S in about 140° E to 150° E, and finally SE, so that it plays no part in the formation of the Counter-current.

In all seasons part of the North Equatorial Current water enters the Sulawesi Sea, emerging therefrom in a NE'ly direction to contribute to the Counter-current. The Counter-current is strongest in the most W'ly part of its course, from N of Halmahera (*1° N, 128° E*) to about 145 °E.

To complete the main circulation, a large part of the water of the North Equatorial Current turns N, to the E of Luzon, and passes up the E coast of T'ai-wan to form **Kuro Shio**, a warm current which corresponds to the Gulf Stream of the North Atlantic. To the S of the Japanese islands Kuro Shio flows in a NE'ly direction. The current subsequently fans out to form the **North Pacific Current**, which sets E across the ocean to the American coast. It is joined by cold water from the Bering Sea, which flows down the E coast of Kamchatka as the **Kamchatka Current**, and subsequently turns SE and then E. The whole forms a broad belt of variable current with a predominance of E'ly sets, filling the greater part of the region between 35° N and 50° N across the ocean. The colder part of the E-going water is found N of about 42° N and is known as the **Aleutian** or **Sub-arctic Current**.

E of about 160° E, water fans out SE and S from the S part of the North Pacific Current. To the W of about the 180th meridian, this water passes into the region of variable current; between 175° W and 140° W the S-going water, comprising the whole of the rest of the North Pacific Current, turns SW and passes into the North Equatorial Current. Between about 140° W and the American coast, the bulk of the Aleutian Current turns S and SW and finally passes into the North Equatorial Current. The part of this S-going current near the coast is called the California Current.

The **California Current** does not meet the coast. From November to February a countercurrent, known as the **Davidson Current**, sets N between the California Current and the coast to about 48° N. During the rest of the year, the space between the California Current and the coast is filled by a number of irregular current eddies.

In the region of the extreme E part of the Equatorial Counter-current, great seasonal variations occur off the Central American coast, and numerous eddies are formed, which appear to vary from one year to another. In most months the Counter-current will be met between 5° N and 6° N, and in the long run the water turns W and then NW along the Central American coast, finally passing on to the North Equatorial Current. In the early part of the year some of the Counter-current branches S and enters the South Pacific Ocean, see 7.37. There is an inflow into both sides of the Gulf of Panama. Some water from the Counter-current enters its W side and some water from the Perú Current enters its E side, during the greater part of the year. There is a resultant outflow in the middle of the Gulf, crossing 80° W and turning SW to pass into the South Equatorial current.

7.33. Northern part of North Pacific Ocean. Not much is known about the currents of the **Bering Sea**, but there is a general counter-clockwise circulation round the coasts, N'ly on the E side and S'ly on the W side. This cold S-going current is the Kamchatka current referred to in article 7.32; it continues along the coast of Kamchatka and passes the Kuril Islands, where it becomes known as **Oya Shio**. Oya Shio continues along the E coast of the main Japanese island of Honshū, until it meets the N edge of Kuro Shio in about 36° N. Oya Shio thus corresponds to the Labrador Current of the North Atlantic Ocean. Between 34° N and 36° N Oya Shio turns E. Water also fans out SE and E all along the course of the current S of Kamchatka. The resulting E'ly current flows parallel with and adjacent to the North Pacific Current, being known as the Aleutian Current as already stated. It has also been stated that the bulk of the Aleutian Current sets S, on the E side of the ocean, to form the California Current. The remainder inclines NE, and then sets NW past Queen Charlotte Islands and along the coast of SE Alaska. This current is known as the **Alaska Current**. It is reinforced, during November to January, by water from the Davidson Current, which then sets up the American coast in a N'ly direction as far as the region of Vancouver Island. The Alaska Current follows the coastline of the Gulf of Alaska, setting in a W'ly direction across its head and subsequently flowing W along the S coasts of the Aleutian Islands. To the W of the meridians of 155° W to 160° W, water recurves from the Alaska Current in S and SE directions to rejoin the E-going Aleutian Current. The general circulation of the Gulf of Alaska thus forms a large counter-clockwise eddy. The remainder of the W-going current S of the Aleutian Islands recurves N, perhaps between Tanaga Island and Amchitka Island and so enters the Bering Sea. Thence turning NE and E, it forms the E side of the Bering Sea circulation, referred to above.

7.34. China Sea and regions west of main Pacific circulation. In the China Sea and in the Java Sea the currents are monsoonal. During the South-west Monsoon, the general direction of the current is W in the Java Sea, NE in the China Sea and the Eastern Sea, and N in the Yellow Sea. During the North-east Monsoon, these directions are reversed to S in the Yellow Sea, SW in the Eastern Sea, and the China Sea and E in the Java Sea. In the S part of the China Sea there is an area of variable current W of Borneo and Palawan where caution is advised, see 7.113, in both monsoons, but a weak monsoonal current runs along the W coasts alternating between NE and SW during the year. The E part of the East China Sea is occupied by Kuro Shio.

In the China Sea, the NE current is found from May to August inclusive. September is the transition month, but the NE current still persists in the S part of the China Sea. In October the SW current becomes established everywhere, and this continues till the middle or end of March. April is the transition month.

In the Java Sea, the W'ly current runs from June to September and the E'ly current from November to March. April, May, and October are transition months.

In the Japan Sea, the general circulation is counter-clockwise throughout the year, the N-going current on the E side of the sea being a branch of Kuro Shio which has passed through Korea Strait. Part of the N-going current branches off through Tsugaru Kaikyō and flows into Oya Shio, and another part branches off through Sōya Kaikyō.

There is little or no current in the central part of the Sea of Okhotsk. A counter-clockwise current flows round the coastal regions.

South Pacific Ocean

7.37. The main surface circulation of the South Pacific Ocean is counter-clockwise. Less is known about the currents of the South Pacific than about those of the other oceans S of the equator, on account of its great extent and the large areas, particularly on the E side of the ocean, which are not traversed by the normal shipping tracks.

The **South Equatorial Current** of the Pacific Ocean has its N limit from 1° to 4° or 5° N of the equator in different longitudes and seasons, the limit being defined by the E-going Equatorial Counter-current of the North Pacific Ocean, which flows immediately N of it. The South Equatorial Current lies farthest N of the equator in the summer of the S hemisphere and only just N of the equator in the winter.

To the S of about 6° S, there is, generally speaking, a considerable reduction in the average strength of the South Equatorial Current, though the general W'ly direction remains. In the region between about 6° S and 20° S, this weaker and less constant W'ly current is known as the **South Sub-tropical Current**.

On the W side of the ocean, the course of the South Equatorial Current varies seasonally. In June to August the whole current follows the N coast of New Guinea in a NW'ly direction and then recurves to the N and NE, passing into the E-going Equatorial Counter-current of the North Pacific Ocean, to which the North Equatorial Current of that ocean also contributes. In September to November and in March to May some water also recurves from the N part of the South Equatorial Current into the Equatorial Counter-current. It recurves SW and S and flows past the N coast of New Guinea in a SE'ly direction. There is thus a complete reversal of current along this coast during the year.

Water flows SW from the South Sub-tropical Current past Ellice Islands, the New Hebrides, and New Caledonia, but the currents experienced in this region, so far as they are known, show considerable variation. Little is known of the currents of the Coral Sea except that in the N part the resultant set is towards Torres Strait and in the S part it is SW or S'ly, towards the **East Australian Coast Current**, which sets S along the SE coast of Australia.

The S side of the main circulation is formed by the **Southern Ocean Current**, setting in E'ly or NE'ly directions. Observations of this current are scanty over the great extent of the ocean. They appear to show that the current is in general weaker and more variable than it is in the longitudes of the South Atlantic Ocean and the Indian Ocean, and that N'ly sets are not infrequent.

Between Australia and New Zealand the current is variable with some predominance of E'ly sets. The bulk of the East Australian Coast Current mixes with the water of the Southern Ocean Current that flows in an E'ly direction S of Tasmania and through Bass Strait. Some of this combined water sets as a NE'ly current along both the W and E coasts of South Island, New Zealand.

The bulk of the Southern Ocean Current passes direct into the South Atlantic Ocean, S of Cabo de Hornos. The N part of this current, however, meets the coast of Chile between Isla Chiloé and Golfo de Peñas. There it divides, part going N to form the beginning of the Perú Current and part following the coast SE to rejoin the main body of the Southern Ocean Current S of Cabo de Hornos.

The E side of the main circulation is formed by the relatively cool **Perú Current**, sometimes known by its older name of **Humboldt Current**. It follows the coastline in a N'ly direction to the equator. Between Golfo de Guayaquil and the equator, the bulk of the Perú Current trends seaward and passes into the South Equatorial Current. The Perú Current is of considerable width, perhaps 300 miles or more. The part near the coast is sometimes called the **Perú Coastal Current**, while the part at some distance from the coast, which does not follow the minor irregularities of the coastline, is called the **Perú Oceanic Current**.

A branch of the Perú Current continues N off the coast during the greater part of the year and enters the Gulf of Panama, see 7.32.

During the winter of the N hemisphere, in the more E'ly longitudes of the North Pacific Ocean, the E-going Equatorial Counter-current (7.32) extends farther S than at other seasons. At this time, a branch of this current turns S along the coast of Ecuador into the South Pacific Ocean, but in most years its S limit is only a few degrees S of the equator. This warm S-going current is called **"El Niño"**, or the **Holy Child Current**. While sometimes it begins to flow about the time of Christmas, it is more regularly observed in February and March. In exceptional years, it extends farther S along the coast of Perú, occasionally to beyond Callao.

7.38. Central oceanic region. On account of the great width of the South Pacific Ocean there is a vast central area, between about the 20th and 45th parallels of S latitude, while forms the largest area of variable currents in the world. Over the greater part of this area, current observations are scanty, particularly on its E side. Certain regions show a slight predominance of current in various directions; in other regions the number of currents observed in all directions are almost equal. No general trend of current over any extensive area is shown during any part of the year. Between New Zealand, Norfolk Island, Fiji, and Tonga, currents in any direction may be experienced, but there is some predominance of currents between N and E, particularly in the half-year May to October.

ICE

7.41. General remarks. The following brief account of ice in the Pacific Ocean should not be taken as complete or in any way all-embracing. More detailed information than can be given here will be found in the following publications, which should be consulted, as appropriate, before undertaking passages through areas in which ice is likely to be encountered.

Admiralty Sailing Directions covering the appropriate areas.

The Mariner's Handbook.

Washington, U.S. Navy, *Climatological and Oceanographical Atlas for Mariners, Vol. II, N. Pacific Ocean,* 1961.

Washington, U.S. Navy, *Oceanographic Atlas of the Polar Seas,* H.O. 705.

Charts 5127 (1) to 5127 (12)—Monthly Routeing Charts for the North Pacific Ocean.

Charts 5128 (1) to 5128 (12)—Monthly Routeing Charts for the South Pacific Ocean.

Charts 5301, 5302—World Climatic Charts.

Monthly Ice charts for the North Pacific Ocean.

A general statement regarding ice is given in Chapter 1 of this book.

A factor always to be borne in mind where ice conditions are concerned is their great variability from year to year. For this reason, and on account of the sparsity of observations in many areas, the charted positions of the limits should be regarded as approximate.

North Pacific Ocean

7.42. Pack-ice. Charts 5301 and 5302 indicate the mean limits of 4/8 pack in March and September respectively, in which months it attains its greatest and least extent. The Routeing Charts indicate the maximum limit of pack-ice in any particular month. An examination of these limits reveals the marked influence of winds and currents; on the W side of the ocean the N'ly winds of winter and cold Kamchatka Current and Oya Shio bring the ice to relatively low latitudes, while on the E side, except in the N part of the Bering Sea, open water is maintained by the warm North Pacific Current.

During an average winter, navigation off the E coasts of Asia is impeded as far S as about 45° N. By mid-November, coastwise navigation is interrupted as far S as 60° N, and is closed N of 62° N; ice is also present in all coastal waters of the N and W parts of the Sea of Okhotsk, in the N part of the Gulf of Tartary, and E of Ostrov Sakhalin N of 50° N. In December, navigation is closed to all ports N of 60° N, and ice may be found anywhere in the Gulf of Tartary N of 47° N, as well as along the E coast of Ostrov Sakhalin and along the coasts of the Russian Maritime Province as far S as 43° N.

From January to March, the whole of the coastal waters of the Russian Maritime Province, the greater part of the Gulf of Tartary, and the coasts of N Hokkaidō and the SW Kuril Islands are encumbered with ice in varying degrees, as also is the whole of the Sakhalin area and the greater part of the Sea of Okhotsk, except the deep central portion. Ice is also present in the vicinity of the NE Kuril Islands and along much of the E coast of Kamchatka and the coast farther N.

In April the ice edge begins to retreat N, and by mid-May, after an average winter, there is little or no ice S of about 52° N. By mid-June, ice is confined to the SW part of the Sea of Okhotsk, the N part of Penzhinskiy Zaliv, Proliv Litke, Zaliv Olyutorskiy, and from Anadyrskiy Zaliv to the N. By late July, vessels can generally pass through Bering Strait.

The months during which ports are closed to navigation vary not only with the severity of the season and the prevailing winds, but also with the availability of ice breakers; detailed information should be sought in Admiralty Sailing Directions.

Ice may also be found in the shallow waters of the Gulf of Pohai and the Gulf of Liaotung between the middle of November and the end of March; the port of Ying k'ou (Newchwang) at the head of the latter gulf is closed to navigation from December to March.

Along the Alaskan coast in the average winter, ice extends as far as 56° N from December to April; in very severe winters the extreme NE Aleutian Islands may be affected. The ice edge advances S during October and November and retreats N during May and June, and ice is not normally found frrom July to September except near the Bering Strait.

During the ice season, the N half of the Bering Sea is filled with pack-ice, though it is not solidly frozen.

7.43. Icebergs are not a feature of the North Pacific Ocean, because there are no breeding grounds for them. Occasional floebergs may be expected among the pack ice, particularly in the W part of the Bering Sea.

South Pacific Ocean

7.44. Pack-ice. Charts 5301 and 5302 indicate the mean limits of 4/8 pack in February–March and September–October, in which months it attains its least and greatest extent respectively. None of the normally inhabited places in the South Pacific Ocean is affected, but great circle sailing between Australian or New Zealand ports and the more S'ly ports of South America is prevented.

7.45. Icebergs. The icebergs that occur in the Southern Ocean are not, in most cases, calved from glaciers, but consist of portions that have broken away from the great ice shelves which fringe parts of the Antarctic continent. They are consequently flat-topped, and they may be of immense size.

In November and December, when the mean limit reaches its farthest N, it runs from about 100 miles S of Cabo de Hornos along the 57th parallel to 90° W, whence it curves N to 52° S, 120° W. Between 120° W and the 180th meridian it is situated between 50° S and 52° S, whence it continues in a SW'ly direction to about 55° S in the longitude of Tasmania.

In May and June the mean limit of icebergs is everywhere S of the 55th parallel. W of 150° W it lies within a degree or two of 60° S.

With regard to the extreme limit of icebergs, information for many parts is too scanty for a confident description. The season of greatest extent varies from one longitude to another. Moreover, factors other than climatic may be responsible for abnormal numbers or abnormal movement of bergs. Earthquakes, for example, may increase the number calved. Accordingly, it is probably best to regard the extreme limit of icebergs as unrelated to the time of year.

The extreme limit is indicated on charts 5301, 5302, and on charts 5128 (1) to (12).

NAVIGATIONAL NOTES

7.48. Soundings and dangers. Very large areas of the Pacific Ocean are unsurveyed, or imperfectly so. In many areas no sounding at all has been recorded.

The presence of a single sounding on the chart can only prove the non-existence of a shoal or reef within a very limited area, and it may be said, as an approximation, that no shoal is likely within a radius of 7 miles from a sounding of 3660 m; within $3\frac{1}{2}$ miles of a sounding of 2740 m; or within 2 miles of a sounding of 1830 m. A danger may lie within $\frac{1}{4}$ mile, or less, of a depth of 900 m, so precipitous is the rise of a coral reef or a vigia from the ocean bed.

Many reefs, shoals, and patches of discoloured water were reported in the years 1943 to 1945, when many vessels were navigating off the usual routes.

The routes laid down in this book are those considered most likely to lead clear of dangers, but owing to the reasons stated above, the only safeguards are a good look out, and careful sounding. In the interests of all vessels it cannot be stressed too strongly that a sounding should be obtained (from a boat is possible), over any suspected danger.

7.49. Currents among the islands. Particular and constant attention must be paid to the current when navigating amongst the groups, for, when near the islands, it is sometimes deflected and always accelerated. Again, most of the islands are so low that it is almost impossible to see them at night, and ships may be driven on the barrier or fringing reefs with no warning from sounding, the reefs having, in general, very deep water close to.

PASSAGES BETWEEN TORRES STRAIT AND EAST COAST OF AUSTRALIA

7.51. Southern part. Coastwise passages off the S part of the coast of Queensland and the Pacific coast of New South Wales are affected by the East Australian Coast Current, which sets S at all times off most of this part of the coast. Between 32° S and 34° S the strength and constancy of the current are decreased by reason of the diversion of water in a SE'ly direction towards the open ocean. Between 34° S and Cape Howe currents may set in any direction, sometimes with an onshore component; close inshore there may be a predominantly N-going current at times.

Cape Pillar and Tasman Island may be rounded at a distance of 1 mile, but the rest of the E coast of Tasmania should not be closed within 5 miles. Because of the current, ships navigating off the mainland coast should keep well inshore, and inside of Montagu Island when N-bound; S-bound, they should maintain an offing of about 15 miles.

7.52. Northern part. Between ports S of Brisbane and Torres Strait, ships may take either the **Outer Route**, E of Great Barrier Reefs and through the Coral Sea, or make the N part of the passage inshore of the Reefs by the **Inner Route**. The Outer Route is not normally used, as numerous large reefs have to be given a wide berth, especially at night, owing, to the strong and variable sets which can often be experienced. The most satisfactory Outer Route track leads from off Sandy Cape to the passage between Saumarez Reef and Frederick Reef (*21° 00′ S, 154° 20′ E*), which are both lit, and thence E of Lihou Reef, E of Eastern Fields, N of Lagoon Reef, and to Great North East Channel by the recommended track which is shown on the charts.

On the Inner Route, adequate navigational aids are available and the saving in distance is considerable. It is described in Admiralty Sailing Directions. For the purposes of this book, it is assumed that pilots are embarked or disembarked off Cartwright Point, Brisbane, and that Capricorn Channel is used.

7.53. Torres Strait (6.126) itself has not been properly surveyed, but, of the several channels through the Strait, Prince of Wales Channel has been surveyed in considerable detail and is the best and most commonly used. This channel is approached from E either from the Inner route through Adolphus Channel, or from the Coral Sea through Bligh Entrance (*9° 12′ S, 144° 00′ E*) and Great North East Channel. The approach from W is made from the vicinity of Carpentaria Shoal, through Gannet Passage, where the controlling depth will probably be found, see Admiralty Sailing Directions, which also publish the latest information on pilotage and limitation of draught.

7.54. Distances: Bligh Entrance, 9° 12′ S, 144° 00′ E to junction with Inner route off Twin Island, 129 miles; thence to 10° 50′ S, 140° 59′ E, SW of Carpentaria Shoal, 90 miles; total for Torres Strait as quoted in this book 219 miles. Between ports on E and S coasts of Australia and the position SW of Carpentaria Shoal, using Inner Route distances are:

SW of Carpentaria Shoal

SW of Carpentaria Shoal	Brisbane	Sydney	Melbourne	Adelaide	Hobart
1370	Brisbane				
1820	470	Sydney			
2360	1000	540	Melbourne		
2780	1430	945	460	Adelaide	
2440	1080	620	see 6.138	750	Hobart

Routes passing through Torres Strait. Directions and distances for routes passing through Torres Strait will be found from the references given below. Distances E and W of Torres Strait are worked from the W entrance in 10° 50′ S, 140° 59′ E, SW of Carpentaria Shoal.

    Cape of Good Hope   6.121, 6.157, 6.158, 6.160
    Red Sea   6.164, 6.165
    Persian Gulf   6.155
    Bay of Bengal   6.140
    Singapore   7.163
    Sunda Strait   6.120
    Australian coastwise   6.125–6.137 and 7.51–7.54
    New Zealand   7.81, 7.82
    South Pacific Ocean   7.83–7.86, 7.240, 7.241

ROUTES BETWEEN AUSTRALIA, NEW ZEALAND, AND ISLANDS IN SOUTH PACIFIC

7.57. Hobart ↔ Bluff Harbour. By great circle between Cape Pillar and Solander Island. Distance 920 miles.

7.58. Hobart ↔ Wellington. By great circle between Cape Pillar and Cape Farewell, in the W approach to Cook Strait. Distance 1270 miles.
Alternative routes are SE of South Island. Distance, passing S of Stewart Island, 1410 miles; through Foveaux Strait, 1370 miles.

7.59. Hobart ↔ Auckland. By great circle between Cape Pillar and a position between Three Kings Islands and Cape Reinga, thence coastwise. Distance 1520 miles.

7.60. Melbourne ↔ Bluff Harbour. Pass through Banks Strait and thence steer by great circle to the landfall at Solander Island. Distance 1170 miles.

7.61. Melbourne ↔ Wellington. After clearing Bass Strait proceed by great circle to pass N of Cape Farewell and thence steer for Cook Strait. Distance 1450 miles.

7.62. Melbourne ↔ Auckland. By great circle between Wilson Promontory and a position midway between Three Kings Islands and Cape Maria van Diemen, thence coastwise. Distance 1620 miles.

7.63. Sydney ↔ Bluff Harbour. By great circle between Port Jackson and Solander Island. Distance 1100 miles.

7.64. Sydney ↔ Wellington. By great circle between Port Jackson and the W entrance to Cook Strait. Distance 1220 miles.

7.65. Sydney ↔ Auckland. As direct as navigation permits, passing on either side of Three Kings Islands. Distance 1250 miles.

7.66. Sydney ↔ Papeete. By great circle, passing between Raoul or Sunday Island and Macaulay Island, in the Kermadec Islands, and on either side of Mangaia ($21°\ 55'\ S$, $157°\ 55'\ W$). See Admiralty Sailing Directions. Few soundings are charted on this route E of about 175° W. Distance 3300 miles.

7.67. Sydney ↔ Nouméa. By great circle, passing about 40 miles NW of Middleton Reef. Distance 1050 miles.

7.68. Sydney ↔ Tongatapu. By great circle between Sydney and $21°\ 00'\ S$, $175°\ 24'\ W$, in the W approach to Ava Lahi. This track passes close S of Ball's Pyramid, and close N of Norfolk Island, and about 30 miles NW of Minerva Reef. See Admiralty Sailing Directions. Distance 1940 miles.

7.69. Sydney ↔ Suva. The great circle track between Sydney and Kandavu Passage, which should be followed, passes about 22 miles SE of Elizabeth Reef, 18 miles SE of Hunter Island, and 32 miles NW of Conway Reef. Caution is necessary near Elizabeth Reef owing to the variability of the currents. Distance 1730 miles.

7.70. Sydney ↔ Apia. The route is by great circle between Sydney and $19°\ 50'\ S$, $180°\ 00'\ W$; E of which position it passes 10 miles SE of Ongea Ndriki, 20 miles NW of Curaçoa Reef, and through Apolima Strait. Distance 2360 miles.

7.71. Sydney ↔ Ocean Island. As direct as possible, passing NW of Bampton Reefs. This track passes close to Selfridge Bank and the position of the 25 m (14 fm) shoal reported in 1960 about 68 miles ENE of Bird Islet, on Wreck Reef. Distance 2210 miles.

7.72. Brisbane ↔ Bluff Harbour. By great circle between the approach to Brisbane and Solander Island Distance 1420 miles.

7.73. Brisbane ↔ Wellington. By rhumb line to the W entrance to Cook Strait. The rhumb line track clears Lord Howe Island and Ball's Pyramid better than the great circle. Distance 1390 miles.

7.74. Brisbane ↔ Auckland. By rhumb line to pass 13 miles N of Three Kings Islands. This track gives better clearance of Middleton Reef than does the great circle. Distance 1290 miles.

7.75. Brisbane ↔ Papeete. Take the great circle track to $21°\ 00'\ S$, $159°\ 50'\ W$, about 10 miles N of Rarotonga, and pass 10 miles S of Mauke. This track passes clear of all known dangers but there are few soundings E of 177° W. Distance 3210 miles.

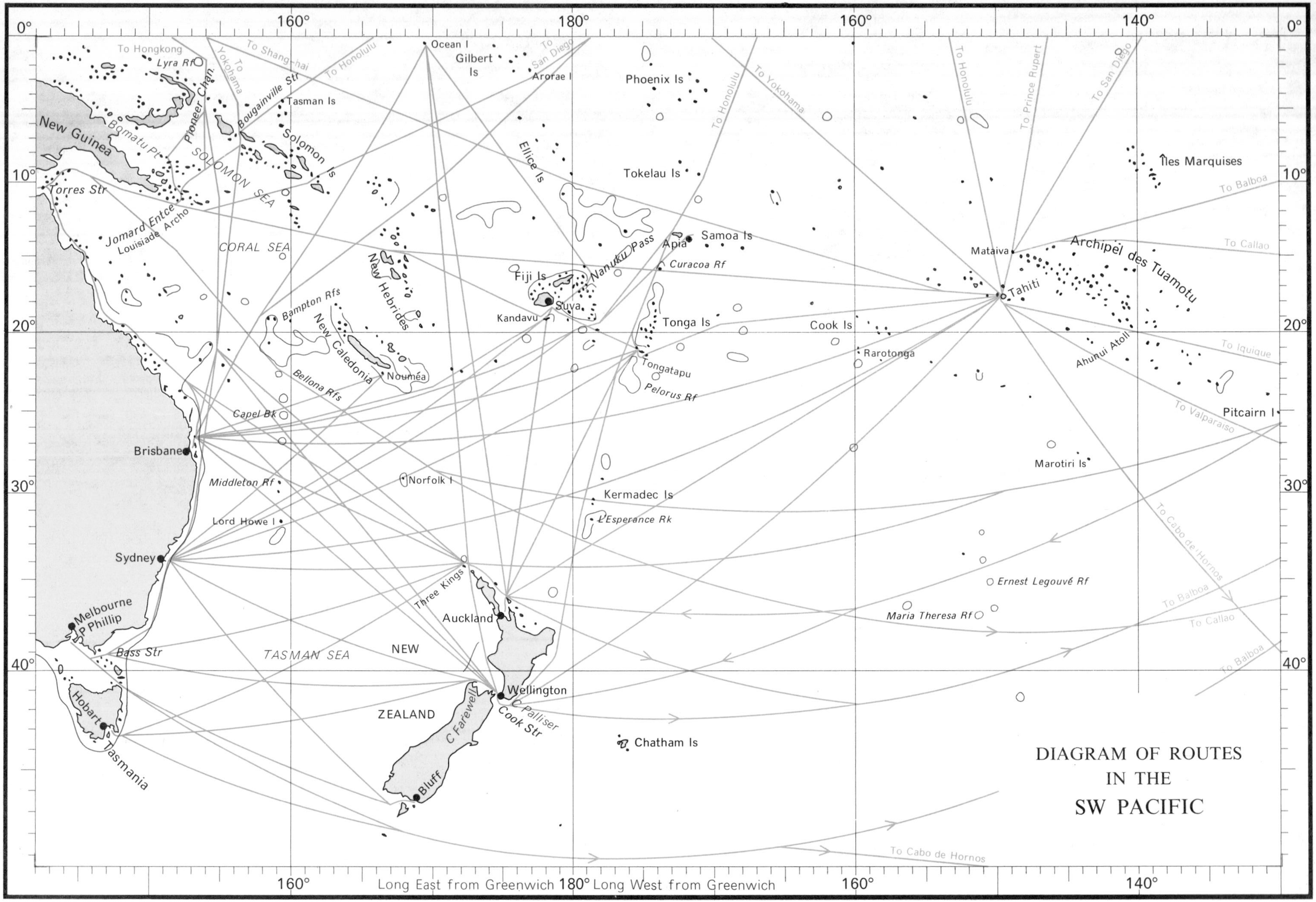

DIAGRAM OF ROUTES
IN THE
SW PACIFIC
Long East from Greenwich 180° Long West from Greenwich
New Guinea
Torres Str
Bomatu Pt
Pioneer Chan.
Lyra Rf
To Hongkong
To Yokohama
To Shang-hai
To Honolulu
Bougainville Str
Tasman Is
Solomon Is
SOLOMON SEA
Jomard Entce
Louisiade Archo
CORAL SEA
Ocean I
Gilbert Is
To San Diego
Arorae I
Ellice Is
Phoenix Is
Tokelau Is
Samoa Is
Apia
Nanuku Pass
Curacoa Rf
Fiji Is
Suva
Kandavu
New Hebrides
Bampton Rfs
New Caledonia
Nouméa
Bellona Rfs
Capel Bk
Brisbane
Middleton Rf
Norfolk I
Lord Howe I
Sydney
Melbourne
P Phillip
Bass Str
TASMAN SEA
Hobart
Tasmania
Three Kings
Auckland
NEW
ZEALAND
Wellington
C Farewell
C Palliser
Cook Str
Bluff
Chatham Is
Kermadec Is
L'Esperance Rk
Tonga Is
Tongatapu
Pelorus Rf
Cook Is
Rarotonga
Tahiti
Mataiva
Archipel des Tuamotu
Îles Marquises
Ahunui Atoll
Pitcairn I
Marotiri Is
Ernest Legouvé Rf
Maria Theresa Rf
To Prince Rupert
To Balboa
To Callao
To Iquique
To Valparaiso
To Cabo de Hornos

Diagram 24

7.76. Brisbane ↔ Nouméa. By rhumb line, passing midway between Capel Bank and Kelso Bank. Distance 765 miles.

7.77. Brisbane ↔ Tongatapu. Direct, by great circle between Brisbane and the entrance to Ava Lahi. Distance 1770 miles.

7.78. Brisbane ↔ Suva. Pass S of Capel Bank, through 25° 40′ S, 160° 00′ E and 23° 20′ S, 170° 00′ E to clear the reported banks and dangers SE of New Caledonia. Proceed thence direct to Kandavu Passage, passing midway between Matthew and Hunter Islands. Distance 1510 miles.

7.79. Brisbane ↔ Apia. Take the great circle track between Brisbane and 20° 00′ S, 178° 45′ W, about 30 miles WSW of Vatoa, keeping nothing to N of this track when in the vicinity of the reef reported, in 1943, to lie about 42 miles W of Vatoa. From this position, steer to pass 20 miles NW of Curaçoa Reef and thence through Apolima Strait. Distance 2150 miles.

7.80. Brisbane ↔ Ocean Island. Pass between Cato Island and Wreck Reef to 21° 30′ S, 156° 05′ E; thence by great circle to Ocean Island. Distance 1810 miles.

7.81. Torres Strait ↔ Wellington. Take the Inner route between Great Barrier Reef and Capricon Channel (7.52), thence proceeding by rhumb line to pass N of Middleton Reef and to Cook Strait. Distance: Torres Strait (W entrance) to Wellington 2710 miles.

7.82. Torres Strait ↔ Auckland. Take the Inner route between Great Barrier Reef and Capricorn Channel (7.52), thence to round Cape Brett and coastwise to Auckland. Distance: Torres Strait (W entrance) to Auckland 2600 miles.

7.83. Torres Strait ↔ Papeete. From Great North East Channel (7.52) steer to round the N point of Espiritu Santo Island (New Hebrides) and thence continue N of Fiji Islands to Tahiti, passing S of Niua Fo'ou and Niuatoputapu. Balmoral Reef, Zephyr Bank, and Durham Shoal lie on the S side of this track. Distance: Torres Strait (W entrance) to Papeete 4140 miles.

7.84. Torres Strait ↔ Suva. From Great North East Channel (7.52) proceed as navigation permits to pass N of Cape Cumberland and the N point of Maewo Island, New Hebrides, to Kandavu Channel. Distance: Torres Strait (W entrance) to Suva, 2340 miles.

7.85. Torres Strait ↔ Apia. From Great North East Channel (7.52) steer to pass either N or S of Banks Islands. Thence steer to pass midway between Îles de Horne and the shoal reported in 1944 to lie about 70 miles NW. From this position proceed direct to Apolima Strait. Distance: Torres Strait (W entrance) to Apia 2850 miles. passing N of Banks Island; add 10 miles for passage S of that island.

7.86. Torres Strait ↔ Ocean Island. Cross the Solomon Sea either between Jomard Entrance and Bougainville Strait or by passing S of Louisade Archipelago and between Guadalcanal and San Cristóbal Islands to a position N of Ulawa Island. In the fomer case, pass S of Ontong Java Group; in the latter, pass 25 miles E of Stewart Islands. Distance from Torres Strait (W entrance) via Bougainville Strait 2000 miles; via Ulawa 2020 miles.

7.87. Wellington ↔ Papeete. As direct as navigation permits. The great circle track passes through the charted position of Haymet Rocks, the existence of which is doubtful, in 27° 11′ S, 116° 13′ W, and about 30 miles SE of Îles Maria. Distance 2340 miles.

7.88. Wellington ↔ Auckland. Coastwise. Distance 545 miles.

7.89. New Zealand ↔ Tongatapu. The bottom between Kermadec Group and Fiji and Tonga Islands is very uneven, and the region extending about 250 miles S from the latter group must be regarded with suspicion, see Admiralty Sailing Directions. Taking this into account, a track from Wellington passing through 31° 20′ S, 179° 30′ W to 22° 30′ S, 177° 00′ W and 21° 25′ S, 176° 00′ W passes W of Kermadec Islands, Pelorus Reef, and other charted dangers. Vessels from Auckland should join this track W of Pelorus Reef in 22° 30′ S, 177° 00′ W. Distances: Wellington 1420 miles; Auckland 1100 miles.

7.90. New Zealand ↔ Ocean Island. As navigation permits, bearing in mind that much of the N part of the route is not surveyed and that several dangers have been reported near it. The positions of these reports, which are charted, should be given a wide berth. Distances: Auckland 2170 miles; Wellington, passing W of North Island 2440 miles; passing E of North Island 2580 miles.

7.91. New Zealand ↔ Apia. The route from Wellington and South Island ports passes through 31° 20′ S, 179° 30′ W, thence W of Kermadec Islands and Pelorus Reef to 22° 30′ S, 177° 00′ W. The route from Auckland is direct to this position. Thence, the New Zealand routes pass W of Tonga Islands to 15° 17′ S, 173° 55′ W, W of Curaçoa Reef, and through Apolima Channel. The region S of Tonga Islands must be navigated with caution, see article 7.89. Distances: Auckland 1580 miles; Wellington 1890 miles.

7.92. New Zealand ↔ Nouméa or Suva. The routes from Auckland are direct in both cases; from Wellington and ports in South Island, proceed W of North Island. Distances from Auckland: Nouméa 970 miles; Suva 1130 miles; from Wellington: Nouméa 1210 miles; Suva 1460 miles.

7.93. New Zealand ↔ Papeete. Proceed by great circle in either direction. Distances: Auckland 2210 miles; Wellington 2340 miles.

7.94. Suva ↔ Ocean Island. This passage may be made either W or E of Fiji Islands, but the E route through Nanuku Passage is preferred although it is the longer by about 140 miles. N of about 12° S, both routes are in unsurveyed waters; the W route passes through the area between Charlotte Bank and Penguin Bank where many shoals have been reported, and close to Balmoral Reef. Distance by E route 1350 miles.

7.95. Suva ↔ Tongatapu. Proceed as directly as navigation permits. Distance 410 miles.

7.96. Suva ↔ Papeete. The route is direct between Tahiti and either Nanuku or Lakemba Passage. Although the distance by Lakemba Passage is some 30 miles the shorter, this passage is not recommended except in fine weather with extreme visibility. Distance via Nanuku Passage 1880 miles.

7.97. Suva ↔ Apia. The route is direct. via Nanuku Passage and N of Zephyr Bank. Distance 640 miles.

7.98. Tongatapu ↔ Apia. Pass E of Tonga Islands and through Apolima Strait. Distance 570 miles. Passage E of Upolu Island entails about 15 miles extra distance.

7.99. Tongatapu ↔ Papeete. Steer to pass N of Aitutaki (*18° 52′ S, 159° 45′ W*) in the Lower Cook Islands and about 20 miles S of Niue (*19° 00′ S, 169° 55′ W*). Distance 1530 miles.

7.100. Apia ↔ Papeete. The route is as direct as navigation permits. Distance 1300 miles.

ROUTES IN EASTERN ARCHIPELAGO, CHINA SEA, AND EASTERN SEA

7.111. Singapore ↔ Sunda Strait or Djakarta. The choice lies between a route passing E of all the islands immediately S of Singapore Strait and thence through Selat Gelasa (Gaspar Strait), and one of the slightly shorter and better sheltered routes through Selat Bangka. The route through Selat Gelasa has better depths in general. Details of the various routes are given in Admiralty Sailing Directions. Distances from Singapore to Sunda Strait, NE entrance: 570 miles via Selat Gelasa; 550 miles via Selat Durian and Selat Bangka. Between Singapore and Djakarta, the distance is 565 miles by either route.

7.112. Singapore ↔ Bangkok or Saigon. The distances by the most direct routes are: Bangkok 825 miles; Saigon 600 miles.

During the **South-west Monsoon** low-powered ships bound for the Gulf of Thailand may find it advantageous, after passing Pulau Redang, to steer along the W shore of the Gulf. If bound for Saigon and certain of the position, they should pass W of Poulo Condore during this monsoon. S-bound, if proceeding from Bangkok to Singapore, they should keep along the W shore of the Gulf of Thailand as far as Pulau Redang, thence passing inside Pulau Tenggol and keeping close inshore for the rest of the voyage. From Saigon, they should keep coastwise along the coast of Cambodia, then steering across to the Malay coast and passing inshore of Pulau Tioman and Pulau Sibu.

During the strength of the **North-east Monsoon**, in December and January, it is probably better for low-powered ships N-bound to pass E of Anambas Kepulauan if bound for the Gulf of Thailand and E of Natuna Kepulauan if bound for Saigon. S-bound from Bangkok, they should steer along the E side of the gulf inshore of Koh Tang and Poulo Panjang, see Admiralty Sailing Directions; thence E of Pulau Tenggol to Singapore Strait. From Saigon, they should pass E of Poulo Condore and thence direct.

7.113. North ↔ South routes through China Sea. There is a considerable area of dangerous ground in the SE part of the China Sea, lying between the parallels of 7° 30′ N and 12° 00′ N, separated on its SE side from Palawan and the adjacent islands by the comparatively narrow Palawan Passage and, on its NW side, from the Cambodian Peninsula by a wider and less encumbered part of the sea.

Vessels are recommended, when possible, to follow the tracks indicated on the charts.

The principal axial routes, known as the Main Route and the Eastern Route, pass W of the dangerous ground, the Main Route being suitable N-bound for fully powered ships at all times and for S-bound ships in the North-east Monsoon, while the Eastern Route has some advantage N-bound during the North-east Monsoon, when it is recommended for ships of moderate power. During the strength of the South-west Monsoon smoother water may be found nearer the coast of the Cambodian Peninsula.

The **Main Route** passes W of Anambas Kepulauan; thence E of Îles Catwick and between Macclesfield Bank and the Paracel Islands.

The **Eastern Route** also passes W of Anambas Kepulauan; thence about 30 miles W of Prince of Wales Bank and North Danger and about 30 miles E of Macclesfield Bank.

Palawan Passage is deep, but there may be less depth than charted off the W coast of Palawan, and when in that vicinity a depth of at least 180 m should therefore be maintained. Furthermore, off the NW coast of Borneo and in Palawan Passage, between latitudes 2° N and 11° N, currents may set in any direction throughout the year, with rates of up to 1 knot or more; they have caused the stranding of vessels on either side of the passage.

Particular attention is drawn to the remarks on currents in Admiralty Sailing Directions.

Palawan Passage is useful for low-powered ships N-bound during the North-east Monsoon, but its use is reported to be declining.

Pratas Reef, about 160 miles SE of Hong Kong, is a serious danger to vessels in its vicinity, particularly in low visibility during the North-east Monsoon. Ships should always pass to leeward of this reef during the strength of either monsoon.

7.114. Java Sea ↔ China Sea. The customary route between the China Sea and Sunda Strait or Djakarta is through Selat Gelasa (Gaspar Strait) and E of Pengiki Besar (*0° 15′ N, 108° 03′ E*). From October to March the route E of Borneo, through Makassar Strait, is generally used by low-powered vessels N-bound.

Between the E part of the Java Sea and Singapore or the China Sea, Karimata Strait is generally used.

7.115. Singapore → Palawan Passage. From Singapore Strait, steer to pass about 5 miles N of Subi Kechil, carefully allowing for the current, then steer to make good 077° for a distance of about 230 miles, whence the course is clear up to the entrance to Palawan Passage, passing between South Luconia Shoals and Tanjong Baram, and keeping as close as circumstances may make convenient to the Borneo coast, until abreast of that point.

As an alternative, steer from Singapore Strait to pass S of Kaju Ara and thence a safe distance S of Muri (St. Petrus). Pass through Api Passage, favouring its N side, and thence to the position off Tanjong Baram. This route is very slightly the shorter.

The narrowest and most dangerous part of Palawan Passage, where it is only 29 miles wide between dangers, lies abreast Royal Captain Shoal and after passing Balabac Island. If it is necessary to make a landfall to establish the position, the island may be closed to a distance of 12 miles in clear weather, but it should not be approached within that distance on account of off-lying shoals. With a W'ly wind and thick cloudy weather the island should not be approached within 30 miles; with such winds there is usually a strong E'ly set through Balabac Strait. Off the SW end of Balabac Island it is not unusual, about September and October, for the wind, especially in squalls, to veer to WNW or sometimes NW, blowing with violence. Under these conditions it is prudent to pass Royal Captain Shoal in daylight.

If uncertain of the vessel's position, the safest part of the edge of the 180 m bank to obtain soundings lies NW of Balabac Island, N of 8° 05′ N and S of 8° 30′ N, with Balabac Peak bearing between 120° and 160°. Experience shows that even in the thickest weather the land is seldom totally obscured for any length of time, but generally presents a well defined outline between the squalls. When soundings are obtained on the edge of the bank, haul off to the NW, to give the edge a berth of about 10 miles and then steer a mid-channel course until past Bombay Shoal, whence a course parallel with the bank and from 8 to 12 miles off it may be steered.

7.116. Singapore → Hong Kong. For general remarks on the routes for this passage, see article 7.113.

The usual route in both Monsoons is the Main Route. Distance 1450 miles. During the strength of the South-west Monsoon, rather smoother water will be found by keeping closer to the coast of Vietnam, and passing W of the Paracel Islands. By this route the distance is lessened by 20 miles. Alternatively, the Eastern Route may be taken during the North-east Monsoon, when it is recommended for vessels of only moderate power; the distance by this route is 1540 miles.

The distance from Singapore to Hong Kong by Palawan Passage is 1920 miles.

7.117. Hong Kong → Singapore. During the North-east Monsoon, the Main Route (7.113), may be used, distance 1450 miles. Alternatively, a route passing 30 miles W of the Paracel Islands, from 15 to 20 miles E of Cap Varella, and E of Îles Catwick will make good use of the predominant current of this Monsoon, flowing S'ly in the W part of the China Sea.

During the South-west Monsoon, steer to pass 30 miles W of the Paracel Islands and, if the monsoon is strong, make a landfall off Cu Lao Ré and keep about 10 miles offshore as far as Mui Dinh (Cape Padaran), steering thence to make Pulau Aur and Singapore Strait. In light monsoon weather, steer direct for Cap Varella from the position W of the Paracel Islands. It is advisable to pass E of Îles Catwick unless the weather is clear or the position well established.

7.118. Hong Kong ↔ Shang-hai and northern ports. Except against a strong North-east Monsoon, the route between Hong Kong and Shang-hai is as direct as safe navigation permits, keeping from 5 to 10 miles E of the outer islands. Against a strong North-east Monsoon, keep as close to the coast as safety permits until N of Chou-shan ch'ün-tao.

When navigating along this part of the coast care is necessary at all times, as the tidal streams are very strong in places, especially in the vicinity of Nan-p'eng ch'ün-tao, (Lamock Islands), Hsia-men (Amoy), Wu-ch'iu hsü (Ockseu Islands), Yin shan (Tung-yung), T'ai-chou lieh-tao (Taichow Islands), Chou-shan ch'ün-tao (Chusan Archipelago), and the approach to Ch'ang Chiang.

From time to time vessels have stranded on outlying islands on the coast of China between Fokai Point and the entrance to Ch'ang Chiang, and, in most cases, the stranding would not have occurred if attention had been paid to the necessity of constantly sounding in thick or misty weather. Many lighthouses on the islands are of considerable elevation, and often the upper parts of the islands and the lights are obscured by fog, so, as a general rule, if a light is not seen when a vessel is within its distance of visibility, she should sound at once, even if the weather is apparently quite clear, and proceed out to a safe depth, continuing sounding until the position is ascertained.

Large fleets of fishing junks may be met with off the coast of China; they often carry no lights.

Low-powered vessels should not attempt to proceed N during the North-east Monsoon or during the typhoon season, except by the inshore passage which is described in Admiralty Sailing Directions.

Distances: Shang-hai 775 miles; Vladivostok 1650 miles.

7.119. Singapore → Shang-hai. During the South-west Monsoon proceed by the Main Route of the China Sea (7.113) to a position NW of Macclesfield Bank, steering thence between Pratas Reefs and Vereker Banks and through T'ai-wan Strait W of T'ai-wan Banks, and thence as direct as safe navigation permits, keeping from 5 to 10 miles E of the outer islands. Distance 2140 miles.

During the North-east Monsoon, take the Main Route as above and keep as close to the coast of China as safe navigation permits. See 7.118. Distance 2160 miles.

In a strong North-east Monsoon the track E of Macclesfield Bank through Pescadores Channel and N along the coast of T'ai-wan may be taken.

In addition to getting smooth water and a favourable current, a great advantage obtained by vessels using Pescadores Channel is the absence of the big fleets of fishing junks which are encountered along the China coast and which, on a dark night, are a source of great anxiety. The channel is well lighted.

7.120. Shang-hai → Singapore. Normally, proceed by T'ai-wan Strait and by the Main Route of the China Sea (7.113). From May to August, if the South-west Monsoon is very strong, an alternative is to pass W of the Paracel Islands, thence making a landfall off Cu Lao Ré and completing the voyage as in article 7.117. Distance by Main Route 2140 miles.

7.121. Singapore ↔ Nagasaki. Pass E of Macclesfield Bank to the S point of T'ai-wan, and thence coastwise in Kuro Shio, E of T'ai-wan, thence to Nagasaki as navigation permits. Distance 2420 miles.

If the Main Route of the China Sea and T'ai-wan Strait be taken, as in article 7.119, the distance is also 2420 miles.

The S-bound route is governed by the same considerations as the route from Shang-hai, see 7.120. Kuro Shio flows NE'ly along the E coast of T'ai-wan throughout the year; in the Eastern Sea and T'ai-wan Strait the currents change direction according to the monsoons.

7.122. Singapore ↔ Yokohama. Steer W of Prince Consort Bank and E of Macclesfield Bank, thence through Balintang Channel and direct to Yokohama. Distance 2890 miles.

7.123. Flotsam. In navigating the waters of the Philippines during the rainy season a sharp look-out must be kept for flotsam. Trees of immense size will be frequently met afloat. They have been found especially numerous on the south coast of Luzon; in one case, near Marinduque island, a group of them was adrift, still upright and resembling an island.

7.124. Singapore ↔ Manila. Follow the Eastern Route (7.113) as far as North Danger, after rounding which at about 30 miles distance, steer a direct course to Manila. Distance 1330 miles.

Alternatively, during the North-east Monsoon, Palawan Passage (7.115) may be used, with a distance of 1370 miles.

7.125. Singapore ↔ Sulu Sea and Basilan Strait. Proceed by Palawan Passage (7.115) Balabak Strait (Nasubata or Main Channels), and thence as navigation permits. Distances: Iloilo 1290 miles, Cebu 1380 miles; Basilan Strait 1200 miles; S point of Mindanao for Central Route (7.269) 1470 miles. For Sandakan, see 7.132.

7.126. Singapore, Sunda Strait, and Djakarta ↔ Lombok and Wètar Straits. From Singapore, pass through Karimata Strait and on either side of Pulau Bawean. From Sunda Strait or Djakarta, proceed coastwise along the N coasts of Java and Madura. Both routes then pass S of Kangean Kepulanan (by day) or through Sapudi Strait, an extra distance of 15 miles (at night), continuing to Lombok Strait or to a position on 8° 00′ S midway between Maddang Island and Sakuntji (Maria Regensburgen Banks), thence along 8° 00′ S to Wètar Strait.

Distances, in miles:

	Lombok Strait N approach	Wètar Strait N approach
Singapore	965	1500
Sunda Strait N approach	650	1190
Djakarta	610	1140

7.127. Singapore ↔ Ambon. Pass through Karimata Strait to a position S of Bawean, thence S of Gosong Taka Rewataja (De Bril Bank) and through Saleier Strait and Buton Passage. This is probably a better route to the Molukka Sea, in both monsoons, than a passage N of Borneo. Distance 1690 miles.

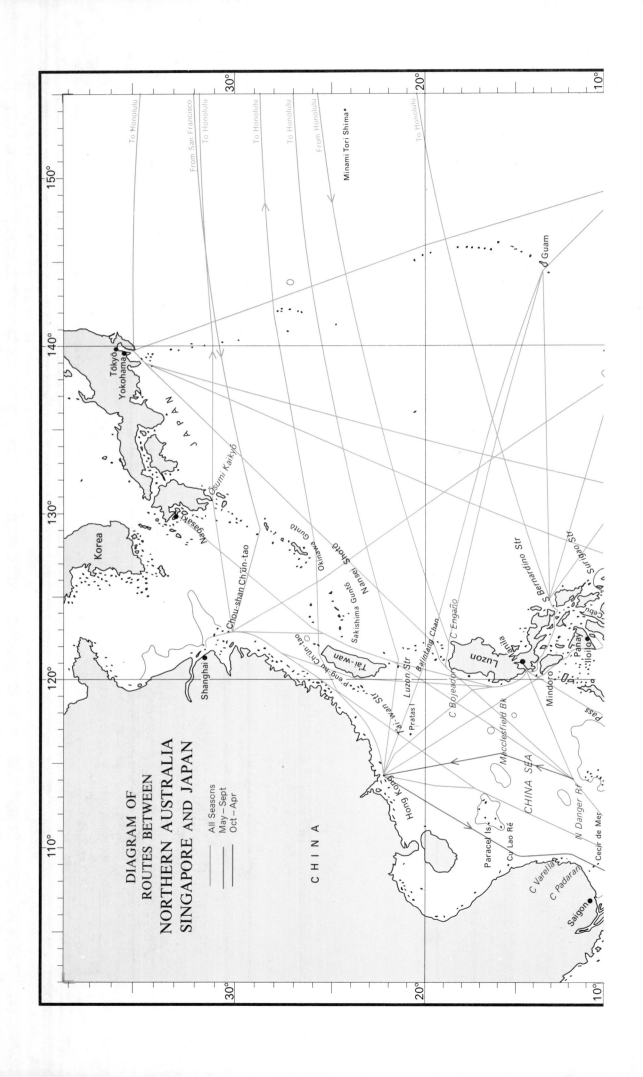

DIAGRAM OF
ROUTES BETWEEN
NORTHERN AUSTRALIA
SINGAPORE AND JAPAN

All Seasons
May – Sept
Oct – Apr

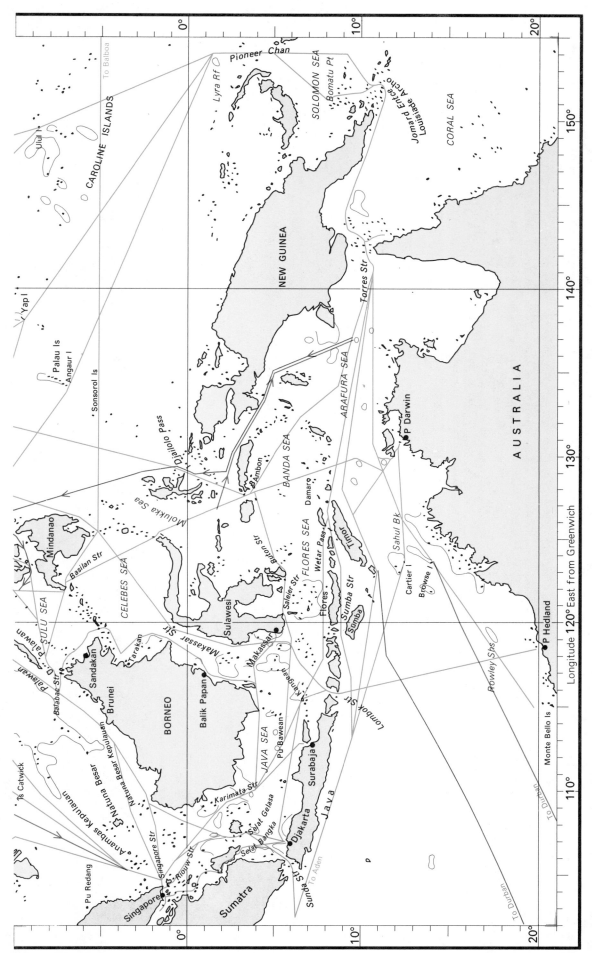

Diagram 25

CAROLINE ISLANDS

Uiui I

Yap I

Palau Is
Angaur I

Sonsorol Is

To Balboa

Pioneer Chan

Lyra Rf

SOLOMON SEA

Bomatu Pt

Jomard Entrce
Louisiape Archo

CORAL SEA

NEW GUINEA

Torres Str

ARAFURA SEA

BANDA SEA

Ambon

Djailolo Pass

Molukka Sea

Damar

FLORES SEA

Wetar Pass

Timor

Buton Str

Saleier Str

Flores

Sumba Str

Sumba

Sahul Bk

Cartier I

Browse I

P Darwin

AUSTRALIA

Mindanao

Basilan Str

SULU SEA

CELEBES SEA

Sulawesi

Makassar

Makassar Str

Tarakan

Sandakan

Balabac Str

Palawan

Palawan Str

BORNEO

Brunei

Balik Papan

JAVA SEA

Pu Bawean

Kangean

Kendiwangan

Lombok Str

Rowley Shs

P Hedland

Monte Bello Is

To Durban

Is Catwick

Pu Redang

Anambas Kepulauan

Natuna Besar Kepulauan

Natuna Besar

Singapore Str

Riouw Str

Singapore

Sumatra

Karimata Str

Selat Gelasa

Selat Bangka

Djakarta

Java

Surabaja

Sunda Str

To Aden

To Durban

Longitude 120° East from Greenwich

0°

10°

20°

0°

10°

20°

0°

10°

20°

110°

130°

140°

150°

7.128. Singapore ↔ Makassar. Pass through Karimata Strait and through the Java Sea. Enter Makassar Strait S of Pulau Laut, pass N of Laurel Reefs, and approach Makassar through the swept channel. Distance 1110 miles.

7.129. Singapore ↔ Surabaya. Pass through Karimata Strait and thence direct. Distance 760 miles.

7.130. Singapore ↔ Balik Papan. Pass through Karimata Strait, through the Java Sea and Makassar Strait as navigation permits. Distance 1070 miles.

7.131. Singapore ↔ Tarakan. Proceed either N of Borneo, through Balabac Strait and Sibutu Passage, distance 1350 miles; or S of Borneo, through Karimata Strait, Java Sea and Makassar Strait: distance 1420 miles.

7.132. Singapore ↔ Sandakan. Proceed through Api Passage and one of the channels between Borneo and Balabak. The shortest route is via Banggi South Channel, distance 1030 miles.

7.133. Bangkok and Saigon ↔ Ports in Eastern Archipelago. In all cases proceed as directly as navigation permits, bearing in mind the advice given in article 7.113 on the principal axial routes through the China Sea, and in article 7.117 on the S-bound passage from Hong Kong during the South-west Monsoon.

Distances, in miles:

	Hong Kong	Manila	Djakarta
Bangkok	1550	1450	1260
Saigon	925	870	1040

The Singapore route is described in article 7.112.

7.134. Hong Kong ↔ Sunda Strait, Djakarta, or Surabaya. S-bound, during the North-east Monsoon, the Main Route (7.113), may be used for the N part of the voyage. Alternatively, a route passing 30 miles W of the Paracel Islands, from 15 to 20 miles E of Cap Varella, and E of Îles Catwick will make good use of the predominant current of this monsoon, flowing S'ly in the W part of the China Sea.

After passing W of Vanguard Bank (7° 30′ N, 109° 30′ E), course should be shaped to pass E of Pengiki Besar (0° 15′ N, 108° 03′ E) and thence through Selat Gelasa (Gaspar Strait) for Sunda Strait or Djakarta, or Karimata Strait for Surabaya and the E part of the Java Sea.

N-bound, reverse the tracks given above for the S part of the voyage, and join the Main Route W of Vanguard Bank.

Distances: Sunda Strait 1790 miles; Djakarta 1780 miles; Surabaya 1930 miles.

7.135. Hong Kong ↔ Sandakan. Proceed through Palawan Passage (7.115), and Balabac Strait. Distance via North Balabac Strait 1200 miles.

7.136. Hong Kong ↔ Tarakan, Balik Papan, or Makassar. The Sulu Sea may be entered through Mindoro Strait, or Verde Island Passage if it is desired to avoid the weather side of Mindoro during the South-west Monsoon, or Balabac Strait. The track used for the following distances passes through Mindoro Strait by Apo East Pass and Cuyo East Pass. Distances are similar if Verde Island Passage is used and 90 miles greater if Balabac Strait is used.

After crossing the Sulu Sea, pass through Sibutu Passage into the Sulawesi Sea and Makassar Strait. When navigating Sibutu Passage, great attention should be paid to the tidal streams. Distances: Tarakan 1360 miles; Balik Papan 1640 miles; Makassar 1840 miles.

7.137. Hong Kong ↔ Ambon. Proceed through either Mindoro Strait or Verde Island Passage, thence to Basilan Strait. Round the NE end of Sulawesi either by passing between Biaro and Talisei, or through Bangka Strait, and thence through Manipa Strait to Ambon. Distance 1830 miles.

7.138. Hong Kong ↔ Manila. As directly as navigation permits. Distance 625 miles.

7.139. Hong Kong ↔ Iloilo. From Hong Kong steer for Verde Island Passage and Tablas Strait. During the North-east Monsoon, pass through Tablas Strait and thence coastwise off the W coast of Panay to Iloilo. Distance, entering Strait of Iloilo from SW, 910 miles.

During the South-west Monsoon, after passing Dumali Point on the E coast of Mindoro, steer E of Maestre de Campo Island and S of Simara Island; thence through Romblon Pass and Jintotolo Channel, passing thence along the E coast of Panay to Iloilo. Distance to pilot at NE end of Iloilo Strait 920 miles.

7.140. Hong Kong ↔ Cebu. From Hong Kong steer for Verde Island Passage and, after passing Dumali Point on the E coast of Mindoro, steer E of Maestre de Campo Island and S of Simara Island; thence through Romblon Pass and Jintotolo Channel. Then proceed to Malapascua Island, off the N end of Cebu Island and thence S to Cebu. Distance to pilot at NE entrance 960 miles.

7.141. Manila ↔ Sunda Strait or Djakarta. Proceed by Palawan Passage and Selat Gelasa, passing E of Pengiki Besar, see 7.114. Distances via Palawan Passage: Sunda Strait 1580 miles; Djakarta 1570 miles.

7.142. Manila ↔ Surabaya, Makassar, Balik Papan or Tarakan. Between Manila and the Sulu Sea Verde Island Passage should be used during the South-west Monsoon, and Mindoro Strait otherwise. Use Sibutu Passage to pass from the Sulu Sea to the W end of the Sulawesi Sea. Distances, via Mindoro Passage: Surabaya 1650 miles; Makassar 1300 miles; Balik Papan 1100 miles; Tarakan 820 miles.

7.143. Manila ↔ Sandakan, Cebu, or Iloilo. Between Manila and Sandakan, it is better to use Verde Island Passage during the South-west Monsoon, and Mindoro Strait otherwise. Distance via Mindoro Strait 650 miles.

For Cebu, proceed through Verde Island Passage and, after passing Dumali Point steer E of Maestre de Campo Island and S of Simara Island; thence through Romblon Pass and Jintotolo Channel. Then proceed to Malapascua Island and Cebu. Distance to pilot at NE entrance 395 miles.

For Iloilo, take Verde Island Passage and, during the North-east Monsoon, pass through Tablas Strait and thence coastwise off the W coast of Panay. Distance to pilot at SW entrance 355 miles. During the South-west Monsoon, after passing Dumali Point steer E of Maestre de Campo Island and as above as far as Jintotolo Channel, passing thence along the E coast of Panay to the NE entrance of Iloilo Strait, Distance 360 miles.

ROUTES ON WESTERN SIDE OF PACIFIC OCEAN

7.160. Australia and New Zealand ↔ Asiatic shores of Pacific Ocean. The complicated pattern of N–S routes on the W side of the Pacific Ocean gives a variety of choice when planning a passage. In selecting the most direct route, the circumnavigation of Australia, the comparative merits of the various routes through the Eastern Archipelago or the Solomon Sea, and the depth required to suit the vessel's draught, may be important factors. The seasonal variations of winds, currents, and weather in an area extending 45° or more N and S of the equator must also play a large part in determining a route agreeable to the characteristics of the vessel and the object of the voyage.

The basic routes are:

Between Cape Leeuwin and the Japan Sea, by Sunda Strait, Selat Gelasa, the China Sea, and the Eastern Sea, with a least charted depth of about 20 m in the NE approach to Sunda Strait. An alternative is a deep water route through Lombok Strait, Makassar Strait, and the Sulawesi Sea, and into the Pacific to make northing E of the Philippines.

Between the E coast of Australia or New Zealand and Japan, by Torres Strait and a seasonal route through the Eastern Archipelago, on which the controlling depth is in the Torres Strait, see Admiralty Sailing Directions, or by an ocean route which passes through the Solomon Sea. Where applicable, passage through the Solomon Sea is recommended using Jomard Entrance and the tracks recommended by the charts, or passing E of Adele Islet, at the E end of Louisade Archipelago, to Pioneer Channel rather than Bougainville Strait, which is probably not attractive to deep-draught ships. The passages E and W of Guadalcanal Island and Malaita Island appear to be deep and safe.

Between the SE coast of Australia and the China Sea, either a S'ly route across the Great Australian Bight to Cape Leeuwin and Sunda Strait, or an E'ly route through Torres Strait. These routes are limited in depth as stated above, but deeper access to the China Sea is possible from the Indian Ocean through Lombok Strait and thence W of Borneo through Karimata Strait, or by a deep route from Lombok Strait, E of Borneo through Makassar Strait, and thence through Sibutu Passage and either Balabak Strait or Mindoro Strait.

As regards distance, voyages via Torres Strait and via Cape Leeuwin are roughly the same each way between Singapore and Sydney and between Hong Kong and Melbourne.

7.161. North and east coasts of Australia, and New Zealand ↔ China and Eastern Seas. There are two principal routes, one through Torres Strait and the Eastern Archipelago (Torres Strait Route) and the other E of New Guinea and the Philippine Islands (Ocean Route), see article 7.162.

The Torres Strait Route, described below, is approached from Australian ports by the Inner Route (7.52), or from New Zealand ports as directed in articles 7.81 and 7.82. Thence the N-bound route as far as Manila varies according to the monsoon. The route from Port Darwin passes through Sermata Islands between Sermata and Babar, and E of Damar, to join the Torres Strait Route in Manipa Strait.

N-bound, after leaving Torres Strait, during the South-east Monsoon from May to September, pass S of Le Cher Bank and the unexamined shoals W of it, give the S end of Pulau-pulau Aru a wide berth, and enter the Banda Sea between Tanimbar Islands and Pulau-pulau Ewab (Kai Islands). Pass through Manipa Strait and between Obi Major and Sula Islands into the Molukka Sea. Thence pass round the NE end of Sulawesi, or through Bangka Strait if desired, cross the Sulawesi Sea to Basilan Strait, and proceed through Mindoro Strait to Manila or onward to Hong Kong or Shang-hai, see articles 7.138 and 7.167.

N-bound during the North-east Monsoon from December to March, after leaving Torres Strait give False Cape (8° 22′ S, 137° 35′ E) a wide berth, see Admiralty Sailing Directions, pass between the New Guinea coast and Pulau-pulau Aru and Ceram, and into the Pacific Ocean by Djailolo Passage. Thence, for Manila or Hong Kong, steer E of Mindanao, through Surigao Strait (7.176) into the Sulu Sea, and through Tablas Strait and

Verde Island Passage to Manila and into the China Sea. In this monsoon Hinatuan Passage, between the NE end of Mindanao and the off-lying islands, gives some protection against the weather but Surigao Strait is normally recommended. The route through Tablas Strait and Verde Island Passage is clear, although care must be taken near Baco Islets, SE of Verde Island; it is a favourite N-bound route during the North-east Monsoon because of the lee given by Negros and Panay, and the sheltered water E of Lubang and under the W coast of Luzon, which gives the opportunity of avoiding the strong monsoon that is generally felt on clearing Lubang Islands.

If bound for Shang-hai during the North-east Monsoon, the route through Djailolo Passage should be considered as an alternative to a continuation N from Manila, see paragraph 7.167. Having made Djailolo Passage, as described above, steer to pass E of T'ai-wan through 22° 55′ N, 122° 40′ E, and thence to destination. The reverse of this route is not recommended S-bound against Kuro Shio.

S-bound from the China Sea the route is the reverse of the above, namely through Mindoro Strait and Basilan Strait and to the passage between Obi Major and Sula Islands. Thence, the usual route passes through Manipa Strait, and between Tanimbar Islands and Pulau-pulau Ewab to Torres Strait. In July and August S-bound ships in particular may be affected by the high seas which are raised in the Arafura Sea by the South-east Monsoon, and a diversion after passing Obi Major, N of Ceram, Pulau-pulau Ewab and Pulau-pulau Aru will give the advantage of smoother water although the route is a little longer and not so well known as the Banda Sea passage. Distances for the usual S-bound route are the same as for the N-bound route in the South-east Monsoon.

Distances, in miles:

	Port Darwin	Brisbane	Sydney	Melbourne	Auckland	Wellington
SE MONSOON						
Manila	1840	3550	4000	4540	4780	4890
Hong Kong	2380	4090	4540	5080	5320	5430
Shang-hai	2920(1)(3)	4610	5070	5640	5860	5960
NE MONSOON						
Manila	1840(1)	3510	3960	4500	4740	4850
Hong Kong	2380(1)	4050	4500	5040	5280	5390
Shang-hai {	2910(1)(2)	4820(2)	5280(2)	5810(2)	6060(2)	6160(2)
		4360(3)	4820(3)	5350(3)	5600(3)	5700(3)

(1) W of Philippines; (2) W of T'ai-wan; (3) E of T'ai-wan. Djailolo Passage not included in Port Darwin routes.

7.162. Ocean route between east coast of Australia, and New Zealand ports ↔ North-west shores of Pacific Ocean.

The routes through Torres Strait and the Eastern Archipelago to the China Sea are described in article 7.161, with a continuation N in articles 7.167 and 7.168. The Ocean route, E of New Guinea and the Philippine Islands, passes through the Solomon Sea and continues NW through the Caroline Islands and Marianas Archipelago to destinations in China Japan, and on the N Asiatic coast.

To pass through the Solomon Sea from Brisbane and ports S, steer to pass 20 miles E of Frederick Reef, or to make a landfall on it, and thence midway between Adele Islet and Pocklington Reef at the E end of Louisade Archipelago for Pioneer Channel (5° S, 154° E) or 30 miles E of Pocklington Reef for Bougainville Strait. From New Zealand ports, steer to 21° 00′ S, 157° 30′ E, avoiding Kelso Bank and the shoals S and W of Bellona Reefs, and enter the Solomon Sea as above. From Torres Strait, enter the Solomon Sea by Jomard Entrance and leave it by Bougainville Strait or Pioneer Channel.

From Pioneer Channel or Bougainville Strait, all routes pass E of Lyra Reef.

From a position E of Lyra Reef, vessels bound for Yap, Manila, or Hong Kong should pass 20 miles S of Sorol Atoll. Manila should be approached through San Bernardino Strait after passing close S of Yap Island. For Hong Kong, pass through Balintang Channel.

From the position E of Lyra Reef, vessels bound for Guam and other destinations W of 150° W should pass through the Caroline Islands at 20 miles W of Ulul Island at the W extremity of Namonuito Islands (8° 45′ N, 150° 00′ E). Thence, for Hong Kong, pass through Balintang Channel; for Shang-hai, pass through Nansei Shotō between Okinawa Guntō and Sakishima Guntō at 25° 30′ N, 126° 30′ E, and approach through Hsiao-pan-men (Steep Island Pass); for Yokohama and Hakodate, proceed direct, in the former case passing at least 20 miles E of the Marianas Archipelago and Ogasawara Guntō.

For Petropavlovsk and Dutch Harbour, ships from Australia pass through the Solomon Sea as above and thence through the Caroline Islands between Oroluk Lagoon and the Senyavin Islands (7° 00′ N, 158° 00′ E). The following distances are quoted in miles, via Pioneer Channel. The alternative route, through Bougainville Strait, is slightly the longer for passages to destinations W of 150° E, and shorter for passages to ports E of that meridian.

	Torres Strait (W entrance)	Sydney	Brisbane	Auckland	Wellington
Manila	3550	4280	3830	4840	5010
Yap	2410	3140	2690	3690	3860
Hong Kong	4140	4870	4420	5430	5600
Shang-hai	3920	4650	4200	5200	5370
Guam	2320	3050	2600	3600	3770
Yokohama	3590	4320	3870	4880	5050
Hakodate	3960	4690	4240	5240	5410
Petropavlovsk	4510	5240	4790	—	—
Dutch Harbour	5270	6000	5550	—	—

7.163. Singapore and Hong Kong ↔ Eastern and southern coasts of Australia. The distances between Singapore and Sydney are much the same whether the passage is made N of Australia through Torres Strait or S of the continent, across the Great Australian Bight. Similarly, the distances between Hong Kong and Melbourne are about the same by either route. If proceeding from Sydney S-about, the beneficial effect of the S-going East Australian Coast Current must be weighed against the frequency of W'ly and NW'ly gales S of Australia.

Passages north of Australia are routed by the Inner Route, see articles 7.52 to 7.54, and Torres Strait. Routes between Torres Strait and Singapore are described below; for routes between Hong Kong and Torres Strait see 7.161.

The N-bound route from Torres Strait to Singapore, from April to October, passes S of Timor, in depths of more than 180 m to avoid the shoal area in the Arafura Sea, through Roti Strait and either Alas Strait or Lombok Strait to the Java Sea, and thence to Singapore via Karimata Strait, see 7.126. Alternatively, ships may pass N of Timor through Ombai Strait, and thence through Sumba Strait, thus avoiding most of the dangerous areas in the Arafura Sea and making use of the bold shores of the straits as aids to navigation. From November to March the route is through Wètar Strait and Wètar Passage into the Flores Sea and Java Sea; thence to Singapore as above. The passage may also be made S of all the islands and through Sunda Strait at any time of year, but the distance is greater and the only advantage is ease of navigation over much of the route.

The S-bound route from Singapore to Torres Strait, from April to October, passes through Karimata Strait, the Java and Flores Seas, and Wètar Passage and Wètar Strait as described in article 7.126. From November to March the passage should be made through Lombok Strait or Alas Strait, Roti Strait, and S of Timor.

Distances between Singapore and Sydney for passages N of Australia are as follows; for Brisbane subtract 460 miles.

For N-bound route passing S of Timor and through Roti, Sumba and Lombok Straits 4350 miles; passing N of Timor and through Ombai, Sumba and Lombok Straits 4340 miles; through Wètar Strait, Flores Sea, and Java Sea 4260 miles; S of Java and through Sunda Strait 4660 miles.

Distances between Hong Kong and ports between Torres Strait and Melbourne, for passages N and E of Australia, will be found in article 7.161.

Passages south of Australia. From Singapore, proceed to Sunda Strait as directed in article 7.111; and thence to make Cape Leeuwin, passing about 20 miles E of Christmas Island. From Hong Kong, proceed to Sunda Strait as directed in article 7.134. Between Cape Leeuwin and Adelaide in either direction, follow the parallel of 35° 30′ S; between Cape Leeuwin and Cape Otway proceed by great circle. E of Cape Otway passages to mainland ports are coastwise, except that when making S off the coast of New South Wales, a vessel should keep about 15 miles offshore, in depths of about 180 m, to obtain the full effect of the S-going East Australian Coast Current, see 7.51, while, in general, not allowing the land to dip. The land should be closed again off Cape Howe.

Distances between Singapore or Hong Kong and Australian ports, via Sunda Strait and Cape Leeuwin, in miles:

Brisbane					
470	Sydney				
1030	565	Melbourne			
1410	945	460	Adelaide		
2590	2160	1650	1370	Fremantle	
4810	4350	3860	3580	2280	Singapore
6050	5590	5100	4820	3520	Hong Hong

7.164. West coast of Australia ↔ China Sea and north-west Pacific. The route to Singapore and the China Sea through Sunda Strait is described in articles 7.111, 7.114, 7.134, and 7.163. It is continued to Shang-hai in article 7.119, to Nagasaki in article 7.121, and to Yokohama in article 7.122.

For deep draught ships, the most direct passage is by Lombok Strait, whence the voyage may be continued through Makassar Strait, Sibutu Passage, and Mindoro Strait to Manila, Hong Kong, and the China coast; or through Makassar Strait and the Sulawesi Sea to enter the Pacific S of Mindanao, for Shang-hai (alternative to the China Sea route), Japanese ports, and destinations farther N.

Distances in miles:

	Manila	Hong Kong	Shang-hai		Yokohama
			via China Sea	via Pacific	
Lombok Strait (S Entrance)	1580	2120	2650	2730	3090
Cape Leeuwin (20′ WSW of)	3130	3670	4200	4280	4650
Fremantle	3020	3560	4080	4160	4530
Port Hedland	2280	2820	3350	3430	3790

7.165. Sydney ↔ Balik Papan. Passage may be made E-about via Torres Strait or W-about via Cape Leeuwin.

For the passage via Torres Strait, proceed from Sydney via the Inner Route (7.52), and after passing through Torres Strait and the Arafura Sea enter the Flores Sea through Wètar Strait. There are two routes between Wètar Strait and Makassar Strait, either close N of Flores to 8° 00′ N, 121° 00′ W and thence E of Postiljon Kepulauan and Gosong Taka Rewataja (De Bril Bank), and thence as navigation permits, with a distance of 3520 miles; or through Saleier (Salayar) Strait, with a distance of 3490 miles.

For the passage via Cape Leeuwin, proceed from Sydney to a position 20 miles WSW of Cape Leeuwin as directed in article 7.163, and approach Makassar Strait via Lombok Strait. Distance 4090 miles.

7.166. Sydney ↔ Tarakan. The routes described in article 7.165, for Balik Papan, are good at all seasons for Tarakan, departure being made off Cape William (2° 38′ S, 118° 50′ E). Distances via Torres Strait and Saleier Strait 3750 miles; via Cape Leeuwin 4350 miles.

In the South-east Monsoon, after passing through Torres Strait, N-bound ships may steer to enter the Banda Sea between Tanimbar Islands and Pulau-pulau Aru. Thence they should steer a NW'ly course for Manipa Strait and the passage between Obi Major and Sula Islands, continuing through the Molukka Sea to round the NE end of Sulawesi either through Bangka Strait or to seaward of Bangka and Talisei. Thence they should proceed direct to Tarakan. This passage is only recommended N-bound. Distance 3560 miles. See also 7.160.

7.167. Manila ↔ Shang-hai. In the South-west Monsoon, from May to September, pass E of T'ai-wan and from 15 to 20 miles E of P'eng-chia Hsü (Agincourt Island). The influence of the N-going Kuro Shio will be felt during the greater part of this voyage. Distance 1080 miles.

In the North-east Monsoon, from December to March, pass W of T'ai-wan through P'eng-hu Chiang-tao (Pescadores Channel) or W of P'eng-hu Ch'ün-tao (Pescadores Islands) as desired. Distance via Peng-hu Chiang-tao 1090 miles.

Great caution should be observed when approaching T'ai-wan Banks, on account of uneven depths, overfalls and currents. See Admiralty Sailing Directions.

7.168. Manila ↔ Yokohama. N-bound, full advantage should be taken of the Kuro Shio by steering E of T'ai-wan to a position in 26° 00′ N, 123° 00′ E, and thence through Nansei Shotō, passing between Amami Guntō and Tokara Guntō. Distance 1830 miles.

S-bound, and alternatively N-bound though less favourable N-bound as regards current, steer by rhumb line between Balintang Channel and the approach to Yokohama. Distance 1760 miles.

7.169. Hong Kong ↔ Japan. N-bound, keep as close as prudent to the coast of China during the North-east Monsoon until abreast Tung-yin Shan (Tung Yung Island) (26° 22′ N, 120° 30′ E). Thence for Nagasaki, proceed direct; for Yokohama, steer either to pass through Osumi Kaikyō south of Kyūshū Island, and thence direct, or, if preferred, to pass between Tokara Guntō and Amami Guntō at about 29° 20′ N, and thence to destination. There is practically no difference in distance, and Kuro Shio sets strongly NE of either route.

For Hakodate, steer to pass through Korea Strait on either side of Tsushima and thence to destination.

S-bound off the S coast of Japan, keep as close to the coast as safety permits, to avoid the strength of Kuro Shio. In these circumstances it must be remembered that there is often a strong indraught into the deep bays especially between Ō Shima and Mikomoto Shima, with E'ly winds, and that during the typhoon months the currents in this locality are subject to great irregularity. Departure from Japanese waters should be taken through Osumi Kaikyō and the S-bound route should be continued through T'ai-wan Strait.

Distances from Hong Kong: Nagasaki 1070 miles; Yokohama 1590 miles; Hakodate via Korea Strait 1810 miles.

7.170. Shang-hai ↔ Yokohama. Pass round the S end of Kyūshū through Ōsumi Kaikyō. Distance 1030 miles.

Alternatively, passage may be made through Naikai (The Inland Sea of Japan), see Admiralty Sailing Directions.

7.171. Yokohama or Hakodate ↔ Petropavlovsk. As direct as navigation permits. Pack-ice may be found off the SE coast of Hokkaidō during February, March, and April. As regards current, it may be possible to reduce the effect of the SW-going Oya Shio by keeping 60 miles or more off the Kuril Islands. Distances: Yokohama 1400 miles; Hakodate 1050 miles.

7.172. Yokohama → Dutch Harbour. Proceed by great circle from the approaches to Yokohama to 44° 40′ N, 163° 40′ E. Thence proceed by rhumb line tracks through 49° 00′ N, 180° 00′ to Akutan Pass or Unimak Pass, according to weather. Distance via Unimak Pass 2770 miles.

Alternatively, to pass N of the Aleutian Islands, proceed by great circle to 51° 06′ N, 179° 30′ E; thence pass through Amchitka Pass and steer N of the islands to destination. Distance 2560 miles.

7.173. Hakodate → Dutch Harbour. Proceed as directly as navigation permits, passing N or S of the Aleutian Islands. The latter route may also be taken by proceeding by rhumb line to 49° 00′ N, 180° 00′ and thence to Akutan or Unimak Pass, according to weather, See Admiralty Sailing Directions. Distances: N of islands, 2240 miles; S of islands 2450 miles; via 49° 00′ N, 180° 00′ and Unimak Pass 2490 miles.

7.174. Dutch Harbour → Hakodate or Yokohama. The route is S of the Aleutian Islands, as navigation permits, to 50° 30′ N, 180° 00′. Thence, for Hakodate, the winter route from 1st November to 31st March passes through 50° 30′ N, 175° 00′ E; 50° 10′ N, 170° 00′ E; 49° 30′ N, 165° 00′ E; 48° 20′ N, 160° 00′ E; 46° 30′ N, 155° 00′ E; 44° 00′ N, 150° 00′ E, after which it is as direct as navigation permits. Distance via Unimak Pass 2460 miles. The summer route for Hakodate, from 1st April to 31st October, passes through 50° 00′ N, 175° 00′ E; 49° 15′ N, 170° 00′ E; 48° 20′ N, 165° 00′ E; 47° 10′ N, 160° 00′ E; 45° 20′ N, 155° 00′ E; 44° 00′ N, 152° 00′ E, after which it is as navigation permits. Distance via Unimak Pass. 2570 miles

For Yokohama, in winter, take the route given above as far as 44° 00′ N, 150° 00′ E and proceed thence by rhumb line as navigation permits. Distance 2770 miles. In summer, take the route given above to 44° 00′ N, 152° 00′ E and proceed thence as navigation permits. Distance 2760 miles.

7.175. Torres Strait ↔ Yap or Guam. The route passes through Djailolo Passage as directed for the North-east Monsoon in article 7.161. Between Torres Strait and Djailolo Passage give False Cape a wide berth, and pass between the coast of New Guinea, NE, and Pulau-pulau Aru and Ceram, SW. The ocean part of the passage is direct, as navigation permits. Distances: Yap 1860 miles; Guam 2300 miles.

7.176. Singapore ↔ Yap. There are three alternatives for this passage. The shortest route is coastwise between Singapore and Balabac Strait; thence through the Sulu Sea and Surigao Strait.

Surigao Strait is the only passage for large vessels from the Pacific to the interior waters of the Philippine Archipelago, with the exception of San Bernardino Strait; it is of advantage to vessels going to the southern Philippines or to the Sulu Sea, and is normally recommended (76.11) for ships from Australia who wish to escape the full force of the North-east Monsoon.

The main strait is safe and deep throughout its length, and the shores of the islands that border it are steep-to. The entrance to the strait from the Pacific is between Suluan Island, N, and Dinagat Island, S; the W side of the strait is formed by the SE side of Leyte, and Panaon, and the E side by the islands lying N of the NE part of Mindanao.

Alternatively, a route may be taken S of Mindanao, through the Sulawesi Sea, Makassar Strait and Java Sea, and Karimata Strait, see 7.114 and 7.128.

The third alternative is through San Bernardino Strait and Verde Island Passage to join the Eastern Route through the China Sea (7.113) NW of North Danger.

Distances: via Surigao Strait 2260 miles; via Java Sea 2520 miles; via San Bernardino Strait 2400 miles.

7.177. Apia and Suva ↔ Yap, Manila, and Hong Kong. All routes pass close S of Yap. From Apia, pass S of Ellice Islands through 10° 00′ S, 180° 00′ to cross the equator in 154° 00′ E and thence to Yap. From Suva, proceed by Kandavu Passage to pass S of Vanikoro Islands (*11° 40′ S, 166° 50′ E*) and between Santa Cruz Islands and Solomon Islands, passing N of Tasman (Nukumanu) Islands and thence to Yap. From Yap for Manila, pass through San Bernardino Strait and Verde Island Passage; for Hong Kong, pass through Balintang Channel. Distances from Apia: Yap 3320 miles; Manila 4460 miles; Hong Kong 4890 miles. From Suva: Yap 2970 miles; Manila 4120 miles; Hong Kong 4540 miles.

7.178. Yokohama ↔ Guam or Yap. By rhumb line from the approach to Yokohama. The track for Guam passes through Nanpō Shotō between Kazan Rettō and Ogasawara Guntō. In Nanpō Shotō, caution is called for owing to volcanic activity in the area, see Admiralty Sailing Directions. Distances: Guam 1340 miles; Yap 1570 miles.

7.179. Apia ↔ Yokohama. The great circle track between the two ports passes through Marshall Islands and Gilbert Islands. This part of it, though navigable, is not advised as a standard route in the existing state of hydrographic knowledge concerning these waters and owing to the uncertainty of the currents.

The great circle track should be followed between the approach to Yokohama and 18° 00′ N, 160° 00′ E. SE of this position, the recommended route passes between Eniwetok Atoll (*11° 30′ N, 162° 20′ E*) and Ujelang Atoll. 120 miles SW; W of Marshall Islands and Gilbert Islands; and between Gilbert Islands and Ellice Islands to Apia, having crossed the equator in 172° E.

Distance by recommended route 4130 miles; by great circle 4040 miles.

7.180. Suva ↔ Yokohama. Direct, by great circle to or from Kandavu Passage. The track passes between Kusaie (*5° 20′ N, 163° 00′ E*) and Pingelap Atoll, 140 miles NW. Distance 3950 miles.

7.181. Apia ↔ Guam and Shang-hai. From Apia, proceed as for Yokohama (7.179) as far as 3° 00′ S, 175° 00′ E, between Gilbert Islands and Ellice Islands, and thence to a position close S of Guam, passing N of Kusaie Island and Caroline Islands. From Guam proceed as directed in article 7.162 through Nansei Shotō at 25° 30′ N, 126° 30′ E to Hsiao-pan-men. Distances: Guam 3000 miles; Shang-hai 4730 miles.

7.182. Suva ↔ Guam and Shang-hai. From Suva, proceed by Kandavu Passage to pass S of Vanikoro Islands (*11° 40′ S, 166° 50′ E*) and between Santa Cruz Islands and the Solomon Islands to join the E Australia ↔ Guam route (7.162) at 20 miles W of Ulul. Distances: Guam 2820 miles; Shang-hai 4460 miles.

ROUTES ON EASTERN SIDE OF PACIFIC OCEAN

7.190. Dutch Harbour ↔ North and Central America. The routes between Dutch Harbour and destinations on coasts to the SE, N of San Diego, are as direct as navigation permits. For destinations farther S, the coastal route should be joined in 28° 14′ N, 115° 20′ W, W of San Benito Islands, the passage from Dutch Harbour having been made by great circle. Distances: Dixon Entrance 1270 miles; Juan de Fuca Strait 1620 miles; San Francisco 2060 miles; San Diego 2480 miles; Panama 5270 miles.

7.191. Passages between ports on Pacific coasts of North and Central America. On many passages N of Juan de Fuca Strait the choice may be made between an ocean route and a passage inshore of the islands fringing the cost. The inshore passages are fully described in Admiralty Sailing Directions. They afford smooth water and suitable anchorages at moderate distances apart, and protection against the oceanic weather. Navigation is, however, intricate in many parts and it should be constantly borne in mind that many of the minor passages may have only been partially examined.

Navigation along the Pacific coast of the United States requires to be carried out with all due caution, as the courses between salient points are, in general, long, and must be traversed during frequent periods of thick weather, with the vessel subject to the action of currents, the rate and direction of which are uncertain.

From a study of the investigations made into the causes of strandings on this coast, it was found, however, that a large percentage of the strandings were due to the lack of the ordinary precautions essential to safe navigation, *e.g.*, sounding, knowledge of the errors of the compass, etc. The recommended track S of the Strait of Juan de Fuca is discussed in detail in Admiralty Sailing Directions. In general, an inshore route as direct as possible is recommended, on account of the better use that can be made of navigational aids and soundings, and in order to avoid the heavy seas in the offing. Offshore, the California Current flows SE, but, from November to January or February, the Davidson Current flows N'ly, close inshore between the California Current and the coast, N of Point Conception or sometimes farther S.

Between San Francisco and Panama, the coast may be followed as closely as navigation permits.

For distances, see 7.196.

7.192. San Francisco or San Diego ↔ Callao or Iquique. Steer through 26° 40′ N, 115° 00′ W and thence direct to Callao by rhumb line, passing E of Archipiélago de Colón. For Iquique, proceed as navigation permits after crossing the equator. For distance, see 7.196.

7.193. San Francisco or San Diego ↔ Valparaiso. Proceed through 26° 40′ N, 115° 00′ W; 7° 00′ N, 90° 00′ W; and thence by great circle. For distance, see 7.196.

7.194. San Francisco ↔ Estero de Magallanes. Pass W of Isla de Guadalupe (*29° 11′ N, 118° 18′ W*) and then take a great circle track to cross the equator in 106° 30′ W, thereafter taking a second great circle to Cabo Pilar.

The track passes through Islas Revilla Gigedo between Roca Partida and Clarion Island; it also passes about 70 miles W of Clipperton Island, and some 45 miles W of Germaine Bank (*5° 09′ N, 107° 35′ W*). For distance, see 7.196.

7.195. Panama ↔ Pacific coast of South America. In all cases take as direct a route as navigation permits. Off this coast, the Perú Current flows predominantly N, particularly near the land. Fog is most frequent off the coast of Perú, and least so in the parts N of 6° S, and except in April and May, between 15° and 30° S. The highest and lowest frequencies of fog, over the region as a whole, occur in April and October respectively. For distance, see 7.196.

7.196. Distances, in miles:

Strait of Juan de Fuca	San Francisco	San Diego	Panama	Callao	Iquique	Valparaiso	Estrecho de Magallanes
680	San Francisco						
1110	435	San Diego					
3920	3220	2840	Panama				
4650	3960	3570	1340	Callao			
5280	4590	4210	1980	650	Iquique		
5800	5100	4720	2600	1290	780	Valparaiso	
6620	5940	5560	3710	2430	1970	1210	Estrecho de Magallanes

ROUTES TO AND FROM HONOLULU

7.200. Honolulu ↔ Sydney or Brisbane. The Sydney route passes from off Sugarloaf Point through positions 30 miles E of Cato Island and 30 miles NW of Bampton Reefs, thence midway between Torres Island and Vanikoro; through 10° 00′ S, 170° 00′ E; midway between Nanumea Atoll and Arorœ Island, to cross the equator in 178° 50′ W and thence by great circle. Distance 4490 miles.

The Brisbane route passes between Cato Island and Wreck Reef, through 21° 30′ S, 156° 05′ E and thence to a position 30 miles NW of Bampton Reefs, where it joins the Sydney route. Distance 4090 miles.

7.201. Honolulu ↔ Torres Strait. There is a choice of three routes for this passage. The shortest passes through Jomard Entrance and Bougainville Strait and between Gilbert Islands and Marshall Islands. Distance 4080 miles.

The route passing about 5 miles S of Tagula Island and thence between Guadalcanal Island and San Cristobal Island and N of Ulawa Island, thence S of Gilbert Islands to Honolulu has a length of 4160 miles.

The third route passes S of Indispensable Reef, S of Santa Cruz Islands and between Gilbert Islands and Ellice Islands. Distance 4270 miles.

7.202. Honolulu ↔ New Zealand. From Auckland, steer to pass 20 miles W of Curaçoa Reef; thence W of Savaii and between Tokelau Group and Swains Island (*11° 05′ S, 171° 03′ W*). Distance 3800 miles.

From Wellington, pass through 31° 20′ S, 179° 30′ W; and 22° 30′ S, 177° 00′ W, joining the Auckland route W of Curaçoa Reef. See 7.89, New Zealand ↔ Tongatapu. Distance 4120 miles.

7.203. Honolulu ↔ Apia. By great circle. Distance 2250 miles.

7.204. Honolulu ↔ Suva. Proceed, using Nanuku Passage, either by great circle, which entails passage through Phoenix Islands, all low and not easily sighted, and the islands and dangers NE of Fiji Islands or by a clear route passing E of these dangers. Distances: by great circle 2760 miles; via a position NW of Savaii and thence as article 7.202, 2840 miles.

7.205. Honolulu ↔ Ocean Island. As navigation permits, passing N of Abaiang Atoll (*1° 49′ N, 173° 00′ E*). Distance 2330 miles.

7.206. Honolulu ↔ Tongatapu. As navigation permits, passing 20 miles W of Curaçoa Reef. Distance 2730 miles.

7.207. Honolulu ↔ Guam or Yap. By great circle. The track for Guam passes close to Wake Islet which, although only 6 m high, is a good radar target. The immediate vicinity of Wake Islet is a prohibited area. Ulithi Atoll (*10° 00′ N, 139° 40′ E*) lies on the track about 85 miles ENE of Yap. Distances: Guam 3320 miles; Yap 3750 miles.

7.208. Honolulu ↔ Papeete. The direct track passes between Caroline Island (*10° 01′ S, 150° 14′ W*) and Vostok Island and close to the position of the breakers reported in 1926 about 30 miles SW of Filippo Reef (*5° 31′ S, 151° 40′ W*). Distance 2370 miles.

7.209. Honolulu ↔ Singapore. E-bound, take the Main Route through the China Sea to Cape Bojeador; thence pass through Babuyan Channel and proceed by great circle to Honolulu. Distance 6070 miles.

W-bound, proceed to 26° 00′ N, 180° 00′ by rhumb line, and thence by great circle to Cape Engano; thence through Babuyan Channel, to join the Main route for Singapore. Alternatively, Balintang Channel may be used. Distance via Babuyan Channel 6090 miles.

The passage may also be made in either direction via the Eastern Route through the China Sea, leaving it near North Danger Reef and passing thence through Verde Island Passage and San Bernardino Strait, proceeding thence to Honolulu by great circle. Distance 6010 miles. Via Guam, the distance is 6050 miles.

Alternatively, if it is desired to use Palawan Passage, the voyage may be routed NW of Borneo through Balabak Strait, the Sulu Sea, and Surigao Strait. Distance 5910 miles.

For routes through the China Sea, see 7.113 and 7.115.

7.210. Honolulu ↔ Manila. Through Verde Island Passage and San Bernardino Strait. Distance 4780 miles.

7.211. Honolulu ↔ Hong Kong. From Hong Kong, steer for 21° 25′ N, 121° 00′ E in Bashi Channel, and thence steer by great circle to 26° 00′ N, 180° 00′. Thence steer by rhumb line to Honolulu, keeping S of the Hawaiian Islands. This route can be used in either direction. Distance 4880 miles.

Alternatively, E-bound, the passage may be made via T'ai-wan Strait. After passing through the strait, steer round the N end of T'ai-wan and then proceed by rhumb line to 25° 50′ N, 127° 40′ E. Thence pass N of Muko-shima Rettō through 28° 00′ N, 142° 00′ E, after which steer by great circle to Honolulu, passing S of the Hawaiian Islands. Distance 4870 miles.

7.212. Honolulu ↔ Shang-hai. The route passes from Shang-hai, S of Japan by Ōsumi Kaikyō, and crosses the meridian of 140° E in 30° 10′ N between Tori Shima and Sōfu Gan. It then follows the great circle to Midway Island (*28° 13′ N, 177° 21′ W*) and passes along the N side of the Hawaiian Islands. Distance 4350 miles.

7.213. Honolulu ↔ Yokohama. The rhumb line track, on which good weather is usually experienced, passes about 20 miles S of the Hawaiian Islands. Distance 3440 miles.

The great circle track between Kauai Channel and the landfall off Nojima Saki passes 15 miles N of Midway Island. Distance 3390 miles.

7.214. Honolulu ↔ Hakodate. By great circle between Kauai Channel and the E approach to Hakodate. Distance 3310 miles.

7.215. Honolulu ↔ Dutch Harbour. By great circle between Kauai Channel and Unimak Pass. Distance 2100 miles.

7.216. Honolulu ↔ Prince Rupert. By great circle between Kaiwi Channel and Dixon Entrance. Distance 2370 miles.

7.217. Honolulu ↔ Juan de Fuca Strait, San Francisco, or San Diego. By great circles between Kaiwi Channel and destination. Distances: Juan de Fuca Strait 2280 miles; San Francisco 2080 miles; San Diego 2270 miles.

7.218. Honolulu ↔ Panama. By great circle between Kaiwi Channel and landfall off Isla Coiba, avoiding Guardian Bank (*9° 10′ N, 87° 15′ W*). Distance 4710 miles.

The E-bound voyage may also be made by the Central Route, distance 5030 miles, see 7.265.

7.219. Honolulu ↔ Pacific coast of South America. Routes are by great circle, departure being taken from the NE side of the Hawaiian Islands for destinations N of about 35° S. The great circle track for a vessel intending to round Cabo de Hornos passes about 40 miles E of Îles Marquises and Henderson Island. Distances: Callao 5720 miles; Iquique 5920 miles; Valparaiso 4760 miles; Cabo Pilar for Estrecho de Magallanes 6140 miles; 20 miles S of Islas Diego Ramirez 6430 miles; Cabo de Hornos 6470 miles.

ROUTES TO AND FROM PAPEETE

7.225. Papeete ↔ Guam. E-bound, steer N of the Caroline Islands, cross the equator in 171° 30′ E, and pass S of Tamana and Arorae in the Gilbert Islands. Pass S of Nukunonu Atoll and Fakaofo Atoll and N of Swains Island. Tahiti should be approached S of Suvorov Islands (*13° 15′ S, 163° 05′ W*) and the Society Islands. Landfall should not be attempted on Île Manuae at night or in thick weather. W-bound, reverse these directions. Distance 4360 miles.

7.226. Papeete ↔ Hong Kong or Manila. Proceed via a position close S of Yap, crossing the equator at about 154° E. For Manila, approach through San Bernardino Strait; for Hong Kong, approach through Balintang Channel. Distances: Manila 5760 miles; Hong Kong 6190 miles. To Yap, the distance from Papeete is 4620 miles; from Hong Kong 1580 miles; from Manila 1170 miles.

7.227. Papeete ↔ Shang-hai. Proceed, as in 7.225, between Guam and Papeete, and as in 7.181, through Hsiao-pan-men and 25° 30′ N, 126° 30′ E, between Shang-hai and Guam. Distance 5990 miles.

7.228. Papeete ↔ Yokohama. Take the great circle track, which passes 30 miles NE of Wake Island and between Tongareva and Rakahanga (*10° 03′ S, 161° 06′ W*) at a distance of about 80 miles from the former. Distance 5130 miles.

7.229. Papeete ↔ Prince Rupert. The route is by great circle between 14° 45′ S, 148° 55′ W, NW of Matahiva, and either Dixon Entrance or Hecate Strait. Distance via Dixon Entrance 4470 miles.

7.230. Papeete ↔ ports south of Prince Rupert. Ports on the Canadian, United States, and Mexican coasts as far S as the Gulf of California are on clear great circle tracks from a position NW of Matahiva, passing NW of Îles Marquises. Distances: Juan de Fuca Strait 4170 miles; San Francisco 3650 miles; San Diego 3550 miles.

7.231. Papeete ↔ Panama. Pass W and N of Archipel des Tuamotu, and thence by great circle to and from the Gulf of Panama. Distance 4600 miles.

7.232. Papeete ↔ Callao. There are two routes, of which the longer passes W and N of Archipel des Tuamotu and uses the great circle track between a position N of Îles du Désappointement (*14° 10′ S, 141° 20′ W*) and Callao. Distance 4370 miles. The shorter and more S'ly route passes through Archipel des Tuamotu S of Ahunui (*19° 40′ S, 140° 28′ W*), using the great circle track between that position and Callao. Distance 4210 miles.

7.233. Papeete ↔ Iquique. The route passing S of Archipel des Tuamotu and using the great circle track between Pitcairn Island and Iquique, passing close N of Isla Sala y Gomez, has a distance of 4510 miles. Alternatively, the shorter direct great circle track, passing through Archipel des Tuamotu S of Ahunui (*19° 40′ S, 140° 28′ W*) and N of Tureia and Marutea has a distance of 4480 miles.

7.234. Papeete ↔ Valparaiso. The route passes at a safe distance S of Hereheretue Atoll and Group d'îles Duc de Gloucester (*20° 41′ S, 143° 03′ W*), and thence by great circle direct to Valparaiso. The track passes close S of Islas Alejandro Selkirk (Más a Fuera) and Robinson Crusoe (Juan Fernández). Distance 4260 miles.

7.235. Papeete ↔ Estrecho de Magallanes. The great circle track is recommended, in both directions. Distance 4020 miles.

7.236. Papeete ↔ Cabo de Hornos. Steer by great circle to 55° 00′ S, 80° 00′ W, on the Southern Route (7.240), and thence by rhumb line to a position 20 miles S of Islas Diego Ramirez or to Cabo de Hornos. Distance 4240 miles to the position S of Islas Diego Ramirez; 4280 miles to Cabo de Hornos.

SOUTH PACIFIC TRANS-OCEAN ROUTES

7.240. Southern routes across Pacific Ocean. The most S'ly route usually adopted by E-bound traffic passes through 48° 30′ S, 165° 00′ W; 50° 00′ S, 140° 00′ W; 51° 30′ S, 120° 00′ W; 52° 45′ S, 100° 00′ W; 55° 00′ S, 80° 00′ W. When the great circle track between the terminal positions passes S of this route, vessels are advised to steer, by great circle if possible, to join it at the most convenient position. Similarly, they should leave the route at a position which enables them to make their destination, by great circle if possible, without passing S of the track described above, which is referred to as the **Southern Route**. For ice, see 7.44 and 7.45.

W-bound routes across the South Pacific lie far N of the Southern route, following the parallel of 30° S for various distances between the meridians of 120° W and 150° W.

The passages for which the Southern route, or part of it, are appropriate are best seen by plotting it on chart 5098, the gnomonic chart for the South Pacific and Southern Oceans. The following are the best joining and leaving positions.

From	*Join in*
Hobart or Snares Islands	48° 30′ S, 165° 00′ W
Cook Strait	49° 30′ S, 150° 00′ W
Auckland	50° 00′ S, 140° 00′ W

For	*Leave in*
Callao	48° 30′ S, 165° 00′ W
Iquique	49° 30′ S, 150° 00′ W
Valparaiso	50° 00′ S, 140° 00′ W
Estrecho de Magallanes	52° 45′ S, 100° 00′ W
20′ S of Islas Diego Ramirez	55° 00′ S, 80° 00′ W

From Cook Strait to Callao the route is direct after passing N of Chatham Islands.

From Auckland to Iquique and Callao the route is direct after clearing the New Zealand coast.

From Sydney or Brisbane for destinations S of and including Callao, proceed via Cook Strait. Alternatively, from Sydney, the route S of New Zealand is practicable for Valparaiso and ports S, and only slightly longer. Approaching Cabo de Hornos from W, pass 20 miles S of Islas Diego de Ramirez.

Distances, in miles, E-bound by the above routes:

	Callao	Iquique	Valparaiso	Estrecho de Magallanes	Islas Diego de Ramirez	Cabo de Hornos
Hobart	6780	6700	6110	5400	5620	5660
Melbourne	7030	6950	6370	5660	5870	5910
Sydney (via Cook St.)	6940	6880	6290	5580	5800	5840
Sydney (via Snares)	—	—	6320	5540	5830	5870
Brisbane	7115	7050	6460	5760	5970	6010
Wellington	5720	5660	5070	4360	4570	4610
Auckland	5840	5820	5150	4440	4650	4700

Note: Passages from Auckland to Iquique or Callao do not use the Southern Route. For Iquique, the route is by great circle direct; for Callao it is by great circle to 41° 40′ S, 160° 00′ W, as in article 7.244, and thence by great circle.

7.241. Torres Strait → South America. Pass S of Bellona Reefs to 28° 30′ S, 170° 00′ E, NE of Norfolk Island; thence by great circle to join the Southern Route (7.240) in 50° 00′ S, 140° 00′ W if bound for Cabo de Hornos or Estrecho de Magallanes, or direct for Valparaiso or Iquique. If bound for Callao, steer by great circle to 38° 00′ S, 150° 00′ W and thence to destination.

Distances from W Entrance: Cabo de Hornos 7450 miles; Islas Diego de Ramirez 7400 miles; Estrecho de Magallanes 7130 miles; Valparaiso 7850 miles; Iquique 8390 miles; Callao 8350 miles.

7.242. Hobart → Panama. Proceed by great circle to 47° 50′ S, 167° 50′ E, ENE of Snares Islands; thence by great circle to Cabo Mala. Distance 7640 miles.

7.243. Wellington → Panama. The direct great circle track between Cook Strait and the Gulf of Panama crosses the meridian of 150° W in about 38° 30′ S. The area immediately N of this position has in it several reported dangers, including Maria Theresa and Ernest Legouvé Reefs. For this reason it is considered that a better route, about 45 miles longer, is by great circle to 41° 40′ S, 160° 00′ W; thence by great circle crossing the meridian of 150° W in 40° 00′ S, to a position on the equator in 83° 00′ W. From this position, steer direct to Panama, passing E of Isla Malpelo. Distance 6540 miles.

7.244. Auckland → Panama. Proceed by great circle to 41° 40′ S, 160° 00′ W; thence by great circle to a position on the equator in 83° 00′ W; thence direct to Panama, passing E of Isla Malpelo. Distance 6630 miles. See 7.243.

7.245. Panama → New Zealand. Steer to 2° 10′ S, 90° 00′ W, about 50 miles S of Archipélago de Colón. Steer thence by great circle to 25° 40′ S, 130° 00′ W, 30 miles S of Pitcairn Island, passing about 25 miles S of Henderson Island, and then take another great circle to 36° 30′ S, 160° 00′ W, with due regard to the reports of breakers N of Ernest Legouvé Reef (*35° 14′ S, 150° 38′ W*). From the position on the 160th meridian, proceed to destination by great circle. Distances: Auckland 6530 miles; Wellington 6530 miles.

7.246. Chile and Perú → East coast of Australia, and New Zealand. The parallel of 30° S forms part of all routes, see 7.240. To reach this parallel, proceed from the departure position by great circle, ships from Estrecho de Magallanes or Cabo de Hornos to 30° 00′ S, 140° 00′ W; from Valparaiso (passing either side of Archipiélago de Juan Fernández), Iquique and Callao to 30° 00′ S, 120° 00′ W. If bound for a New Zealand port, steer from 30° 00′ S, 140° 00′ W by great circle to 36° 30′ S, 160° 00′ W, with due regard to the reports of breakers N of Ernest Legouvé Reef (*35° 14′ S, 150° 38′ W*), and thence to destination by great circle. For Australian ports, keep on 30° S as far as 150° W and then proceed to destination, passing N of New Zealand, or via Cook Strait if desired.

Distances, in miles:

	Wellington	Auckland	Sydney
Cabo de Hornos	5670	5670	6870
Estrecho de Magallanes	5390	5390	6590
Valparaiso	5800	5800	7000
Iquique	6090	6090	7290
Callao	5950	5950	7150

7.247. Apia ↔ South America. For Callao, in both directions, the route is by great circles meeting in 19° 46′ S, 140° 26′ W, SE of Ahunui Atoll, Archipel des Tuamotu.

For Iquique, the route is direct by great circle in both directions, passing close to Pitcairn Island and Isla Sala y Gomez.

For Valparaiso, the E-bound route is direct by great circle passing close to Rarotonga, the dangers SE of Îles Australes, and Île Rapa and Marotiri Islands. W-bound, from Valparaiso proceed by great circle to 30° 00′ S, 120° 00′ W as directed in article 7.246, and thence along the parallel of 30° 00′ N to 139° 00′ W and by great circle as on the E-bound route to Valparaiso.

Distances: Callao 5500 miles; Iquique 5760 miles; Valparaiso 5460 miles E-bound and 5510 miles W-bound.

7.248. Suva ↔ South America. For Callao, the route is the same in both directions. From Suva, proceed from Nanuku Passage by rhumb line to 18° 44′ S, 159° 47′ W, N of Aitutaki Island; and thence to 19° 46′ S, 140° 26′ W, SE of Ahunui Atoll, Archipel des Tuamotu; thence by great circle.

For Iquique, the route is the same in both directions, from Suva as for Callao to the position N of Aitutaki Island; thence by rhumb line to 24° 55′ S, 130° 10′ W, N of Pitcairn Island; thence by great circle.

For Valparaiso E-bound, proceed to 17° 30′ S, 173° 00′ W and thence by great circle. W-bound, proceed by great circle to 30° 00′ S, 120° 00′ W; thence along the parallel of 30° 00′ S, to 139° 00′ W; thence by great circle to 17° 30′ S, 173° 00′ W, a track which passes near Beveridge Reef and Niue Island; thence to Suva.

Distances: Callao 6060 miles; Iquique 6300 miles; Valparaiso 5920 miles E-bound and 5990 miles W-bound.

MID-PACIFIC TRANS-OCEAN ROUTES

7.260. Central Route. The constant W'ly flow of water in the equatorial part of the Pacific Ocean between, roughly, the latitudes of Hawaii in the N and Fiji and the Society Islands in the S, together with the North-east Trade and South-east Trade Winds which blow on either side of the Equatorial Trough, tend to lengthen voyage times and to increase fuel and maintenance costs on ships E-bound through these waters. All passages from ports between Hong Kong and Sydney to destinations on the coasts of Central America and equatorial South America may be affected enough to merit the diversion of part of the route into the E'ly flow of the Equatorial Counter-current (7.32) which, as described in Admiralty Sailing Directions and below, flows across the ocean from W to E in a narrow belt a few degrees N of the equator. Also the central and E part of the Ocean is favoured by the light weather of the Equatorial Trough.

Although the limits of the Equatorial Counter-current are often sharply defined at sea, they have not been precisely delineated by observation. It is known that there is some seasonal shift which tends to be N'ly or S'ly following the declination of the sun. W of 160° E, the limits are about 3° N to 9° N from May to November, and about 5° N to 7° N from December to April. To the W of 140° E average speed is about 1 knot, and over 2 knots has been recorded; farther E the average is ½ to ¾ knot. Between 160° E and 165° W the current is at its narrowest in March, April and May, when it flows between about 4° N and 8° N. It extends to about 2° N, W of 150° E, from June to December. From long. 180° to 110° W the S edge of the current lies permanently in about 4° N, while the N edge, continuing on 8° N, shifts towards 10° N as the year progresses from June towards November.

The Central Route, quoted in this book, is an average counter-current route between the Sulawesi Sea and the Gulf of Panama, with an overall length of 9250 miles between 5° 00′ N, 125° 30′ E, S of Mindanao, and 7° 00′ N, 80° 00′ W, off the Gulf of Panama. It passes between Sonsorol Islands and Pulau Anna on 5° N, continuing on that parallel to a position S of Kusaie Island in about 163° E; thence to a position S of Palmyra Island in 5° 30′ N, 162° 00′ W, and to make Cabo Mala. Positions for joining and leaving the route depend on local as well as climatic considerations; with this in view Panama-bound ships from Hong Kong might join in 168° E, between the Marshall and Caroline Islands, at a cost of 820 miles over the shortest navigable distance of 9270 miles. Ships from Sydney, joining in 150° W, would accept an extra distance of about 700 miles compared with the 7700 miles of the route via Cook Strait (7.64 and 7.243). Several joining routes are described in the following articles.

7.261. Sydney → Central Route. Steer by great circle to 19° 50′ S, 180° 00′; thence, after passing about 10 miles S of Ongea Ndriki (*19° 12′ S, 178° 24′ W*) and W of Savaii, steer to join the Central Route (7.260) in 5° 30′ N, 150° 00′ W. Distance to Panama 8390 miles.

7.262. Brisbane → Central Route. Steer by great circle to 22° 05′ S, 175° 00 E, about 30 miles SE of Conway Reef; thence to 19° 50′ S, 180° 00′; thence, after passing about 10 miles S of Ongea Ndriki (*19° 12′ S, 178° 24′ W*) and W of Savaii, steer to join the Central Route (7.260) in 5° 30′ N, 150° 00′ W. Distance to Panama 8180 miles.

7.263. Torres Strait → Central Route. Steer to pass about 5 miles off the reefs S of Tagula Island and thence, between Guadalcanal Island and San Cristobal Island and midway between Gilbert Islands and Ellice Islands to cross the equator in about 175° 00′ W. Thence, steer by rhumb line to join the Central Route (7.260) in 5° N, 160° W. Distance to Panama 8670 miles.

Alternatively, pass through Jomard Entrance and Bougainville Strait; thence S of Ontong Java and N of Abaiang Atoll (*1° 58′ N, 172° 50′ E*) to join the Central Route on the 180th meridian in about 5° 15′ N. This will increase the total distance by about 90 miles but will allow favourable weather and current to be carried for an additional 1200 miles.

7.264. Suva and Apia → Central Route. From Suva, pass through Nanuku Passage and close W of Savaii; from Apia proceed direct. In both cases, join the Central Route (7.260) in 5° 30′ N, 150° 00′ W. Distances to Panama: Suva 6660 miles; Apia 6040 miles.

Alternatively, join the Central Route in 140° W; but this will reduce the chance of a favourable Equatorial Counter-current by about 600 miles while only reducing the distance by 110 miles.

7.265. Honolulu → Central Route. As navigation permits to join the Central Route (7.260) in 5° 50′ N, 134° 00′ W. Distance to Panama 5030 miles.

7.266. Guam → Central Route. After rounding the S point of Guam steer to join the Central Route (7.260) in 5° 00′ N, 168° 00′ E, to pass between Namorik Atoll and Ebon Atoll. Distance to Panama 8300 miles.

7.267. Yap → Central Route. Direct, to join the Central Route (7.260) in 5° 00′ N, 150° 00′ E. Distance to Panama 8670 miles.

7.268. Ocean Island → Central Route. Pass N of Abaiang Atoll (1° 58′ N, 172° 50′ E) to join the Central Route (7.260) in 5° 15′ N, 180° 00′ Distance to Panama 6840 miles.

7.269. Basilan Strait → Central Route. From the E entrance to Basilan Strait steer across the Sulawesi Sea to join the Central Route (7.260) S of Mindanao, in 5° 00′ N, 125° 30′ E. Distance from Basilan Strait to Panama 10090 miles; from the position S of Mindanao to Panama 9360 miles.

7.270. San Bernardino Strait → Central Route. From the E entrance to San Bernardino Strait steer to pass S of Palau Islands and thence to join the Central Route (7.260) in 5° 00′ N, 150° 00′ E. Distance from San Bernardino Strait to Panama 9530 miles.

7.271. Balintang Channel → Central Route. From 19° 45′ N, 122° 10′ E, in Balintang Channel, pass close S of Guam and join the Central Route (7.260) in 5° 00′ N, 168° 00′ E, to pass between Namorik Atoll and Ebon Atoll. Distance to Panama 9620 miles.

7.272. Melbourne and Sydney → Panama. Cross the Tasman Sea from Bass Strait or Sydney by great circle, to pass N of New Zealand, on either side of Three Kings Islands with due regard to the tidal streams in that locality, see Admiralty Sailing Directions. To the E of New Zealand the routes follow a common track, by great circle to 30° 00′ S, 150° 00′ W, thence by rhumb line to 25° 40′S , 130° 00′ W, S of Pitcairn Island; thence by great circle to 2° 10′ S, 90° 00′ W. S of Archipiélago de Colón and to Cape Mala. Distance: Melbourne 8050 miles; Sydney 7700 miles.

Alternatively, passage from Sydney may be made via Papeete (7.66 and 7.231), or via Suva (7.69 and 7.285) and thence, leaving the Fiji Islands by Nanuku Passage or Lakemba Passage (7.96) proceeding by great circle to 6° 30′ S, 120° 00′ W, on the route between Papeete and Panama. Distance via Papeete 7900 miles; via Suva 7980 miles. For Central Route, see 7.261.

7.273. Panama → Sydney. From the Gulf of Panama, steer to 2° 10′ S, 90° 00′ W, S of Archipiélago de Colón and thence by great circle to 25° 40′ S, 130° 00′ W, S of Pitcairn Island. Then steer by rhumb line to 30° 00′ S, 150° 00′ W and then by great circle to pass N of New Zealand to a position 5 miles N of Three Kings Islands, whence a great circle track may be taken for Sydney. Distance 7700 miles.

7.274. Brisbane → Panama. This passage may be made via Papeete (7.75 and 7.231) or via Suva as in 7.78 and 7.285. Distance via Papeete 7810 miles; via Suva 7860 miles. For Central Route, see 7.262.

7.275. Panama → Brisbane. Follow the Panama → Sydney route (7.273) as far as 30° 00′ S, 150° 00′ W, thence proceeding by rhumb line to pass N of the Kermadec Islands. Distance 7740 miles.

7.276. Torres Strait ↔ Panama. The great circle track between 13° 10′ S, 160° 30′ E, S of Indispensable Reefs, and the Gulf of Panama is encumbered with dangers between Indispensable Reefs and Îles Marquises. The distance, neglecting navigational diversions, is 8570 miles. A recommended route, comparatively free as regards navigational hazards, is by the routes given in article 7.85, Torres Strait ↔ Apia and article 7.285, Apia ↔ Panama, with a distance of 8590 miles. Both the above distances are from the W entrance to Torres Strait. For Central Route, see 7.263.

7.277. Ocean Island ↔ Panama. By great circle between the Gulf of Panama and Ocean Island. Distance 6760 miles. See 7.268 for the Central Route as alternative.

7.278. Singapore → Panama. There is a choice between several routes, each with different characteristics of depths, navigational hazard, shelter, weather, currents, and bunkering facilities.

The principal routes are as follows, the distances including fuelling stops at the ports mentioned.

To Yokohama 2890 miles; thence to Panama; total 10530 miles. Articles 7.122, 7.304 refer.

To Yokohama 2890 miles; thence to Honolulu 3440 miles; thence to Panama; total 10510 miles. Articles 7.122, 7.213, 7.218 refer.

E

Through the China Sea by the Eastern Route to Balintang Channel, thence by great circle across the Pacific Ocean to join the coastal route off Manzanillo in about 19° 00′ N, 105° 00′ W. Distance 10510 miles. Articles 7.113, 7.191 refer.

Through the China Sea to Verde Island Passage, as directed in 7.124, and San Bernardino Strait to Guam 2740 miles; thence to Panama as in 7.281; total 10780 miles.

Through San Bernardino Strait as above and by great circle to join the coastal route off Manzanillo, see 7.191; total distance 10620miles.

Through Balabac Strait and Basilan Strait, to join the Central Route S of Mindanao; see 7.125, 7.269. Total distance 10830 miles.

Through the Eastern Archipelago to Torres Strait, see 7.163; thence to Panama by Central Route, see 7.263 Total distance, depending on route used through the Eastern Archipelago, about 11200 miles.

7.279. Panama → Manila or Singapore. By keeping N of the E-bound Central Route (7.260), the North Equatorial current can be carried for most of the ocean crossing and, if fuel is needed, little distance is lost by calling at Honolulu (7.218) or Guam (7.280).

For this direct route, after clearing Cabo Mala, take a great circle to 13° 30′ N, 170° 00′ E and then pass between Bikar Atoll and Taongi Atoll; thence passing close S of Guam and to San Bernardino Strait and Verde Island Passage.

Having entered the China Sea, join the Eastern Route NW of North Danger and continue to Singapore. See 7.113. Distances: Manila 9580 miles; Singapore 10810 miles.

7.280. Panama → Guam. Proceed either by the direct route given in article 7.279, or via Honolulu (7.218 and 7.207). Distance by direct route 8090 miles; via Honolulu 8040 miles.

7.281. Guam → Panama. Proceed by great circle, which passes through Hawaiian Islands between Gardner Pinnacles and Brooks Bank, and between Islas Revilla Gigedo (*19° 00′ N, 112° 00′ W*). Distance 8040 miles. Alternatively, use the Central Route (7.266); distance 8300 miles.

7.282. New Zealand, Suva, and Apia ↔ North America. Suva and Apia lie near the route NE from New Zealand (7.202), which passes close W of the Samoa Islands and on towards Honolulu. Great circle tracks for voyages between New Zealand ports and North American coast ports pass through areas S of the equator which are encumbered with dangers and which, in parts, lack charted soundings. Similarly, the great circle tracks between Suva or Apia and the North American coast are obstructed to some extent and, unless the great circle track is clear, as in the case of Apia ↔ San Francisco or San Diego, a track passing E of Tokelau Islands, through about 10° 30′ S, 171° 00′ W and keeping to the great circles, subject to navigational hazards, is recommended for each route.

Although the great circle tracks between New Zealand and the equator, and through Phoenix Islands, should be avoided, these direct distances, neglecting navigational diversions, are given below for comparison with those recommended.

Distances, in miles; D = direct, R = recommended.

		San Diego	San Francisco	Juan de Fuca Strait	Prince Rupert
Wellington	D	5830	5870	6290	6440
	R	6090	6040	6370	6490
Auckland	D	5650	5660	6040	6160
	R	5770	5720	6050	6160
Suva	D	4790	4730	5030	5110
(by Nanuku Passage)	R	4800	4750	5080	5200
Apia	D	4180	4140	4480	4600
	R	4180	4140	4890	5010

7.283. Sydney or Brisbane ↔ North America. The portion of the direct route S of the equator is common to all passages. It is described in article 7.200. From the position on the equator in 178° 50′ W the routes are by great circle to each destination. The great circle track for San Francisco should be diverted slightly to pass through Alenuihaha Channel, between Hawaii and Maui. For Juan de Fuca Strait, the track passes close SE of the reported position of Wilder Shoal (*8° 17′ N, 173° 29′ W*) and through the Hawaiian Islands E of Nihoa. For Hecate Strait, it passes E of Necker Island and for Dixon Entrance it passes E of French Frigate Shoal.

On all the direct routes, a diversion to Honolulu for fuel presents no problem. If Suva is used as a fuelling stop on the San Diego or San Francisco routes, great circle courses may be steered between those ports and a landfall at Savaii, Samoa Islands.

Distances by direct routes, in miles:

	San Diego	San Francisco	Juan de Fuca Strait	Prince Rupert (by Dixon Entrance)
Sydney	6700	6550	6740	6750
Brisbane	6300	6150	6340	6350

7.284. Torres Strait ↔ North America. The direct great circle track between Bougainville Strait and San Diego passes close to Honolulu, and those for ports farther N pass through Marshall Islands and the Hawaiian Islands. The clearest routes are therefore via Honolulu; the table below refers to the relevant paragraphs for each composite route, and gives the direct great circle distance, not allowing for the avoidance of navigational hazards, for the benefit of those considering a direct route. Distances are from Torres Strait (W entrance), in miles.

	Direct	via Honolulu	Reference	
San Diego	6570	6580	7.201	7.217
San Francisco	6350	6380	7.201	7.217
Juan de Fuca Strait	6390	6590	7.201	7.217
Prince Rupert	6260	6670	7.201	7.216

7.285. Suva and Apia ↔ Panama. The routes between Apia or Suva and 10° 45′ S, 136° 35′ W, SE of Îles Marquises, are by great circle, and again by great circle between that position and Panama. Distances: Suva 6350 miles; Apia 5740 miles. For E-bound passages by central route, see 7.264.

7.286. Guam or Yap ↔ North America. Routes are as nearly great circle tracks as navigation permits. Distances, neglecting navigational diversions, are, in miles.

	San Diego	San Francisco	Juan de Fuca Strait	Prince Rupert
Guam	5410	5080	4830	4570
Yap	5830	5500	5260	4980

7.287. Guam ↔ Manila or Singapore. The normal route from Guam is by great circle to San Bernardino Strait, Verde Island Passage, and Manila, continuing to pick up the Eastern Route in the China Sea, NW of North Danger, see 7.113 and 7.124, and so to Singapore. Distances from Guam: Manila 1510 miles, Singapore 2740 miles.

Alternatively, a direct passage may be made between Singapore and Guam, particularly E-bound in the Northeast Monsoon, by Balabac Strait and Surigao Strait. Distance 2640 miles.

7.288. Hong Kong ↔ Guam ar Yap. As navigation permits, through Balintang Channel. The vicinity of Pratas Reef and Vereker Banks should be avoided, see 7.113 and Admiralty Sailing Directions. Distances: Guam 1840 miles; Yap 1580 miles.

NORTH PACIFIC TRANS-OCEAN ROUTES

7.295. General Notes. Broadly speaking, the trend of the coastline bordering the North Pacific basin follows the arc of a great circle. In fact, a great circle drawn between a position in Luzon Strait and a position on the coast of British Columbia will pass through the Sea of Japan and the Bering Sea, while a great circle between Luzon Strait and the coast of California will pass close to Yokohama and not far S of the Aleutian Islands.

A high-latitude route for the trans-ocean voyage is therefore attractive on the score of distance, but it has disadvantages in weather and currents, to some extent seasonal, which oblige consideration of a route in lower latitudes particularly when W-bound in winter.

With regard to the weather, in summer, fog is frequent over the whole NW part of the ocean. In winter, snow often reduces visibility. The E coast of Japan is fully exposed to the strong E'ly gales prevalent in Spring.

General notes on winds, weather, currents and ice will be found in articles 7.01–7.10, 7.25, 7.26, 7.32–7.34, 7.41–7.43.

In these circumstances, the choice of an E-bound route depends mainly on the currents likely to be met and the navigational requirements. Fuelling ports are reasonably available. W-bound, it may be desirable to take a more S'ly route, based on the parallel of about 35° N or even farther S in which a compromise is effected between extra distance and the reduced influence of wind and current, and which allows for the possibility of refuelling at either Honolulu or Guam.

7.296. Singapore → North America. Yokohama, at a distance of 2890 miles from Singapore (7.122), and near the great circle joining Singapore with positions on the North American coast, is a convenient fuelling point. If calling at or passing close to Yokohama, onward routes are as follows:

For	*Route reference*	*Total distance (miles)*
Dutch Harbour	7.172	5650 (S of Aleutian Is.)
Prince Rupert	7.306	6740
Juan de Fuca Strait	7.306	7070
San Francisco	7.305	7410
San Diego	7.305	7810

7.297. Manila → Panama. The direct route passes N of Luzon, crossing the Pacific Ocean from Balintang Channel by great circle to join the American coastal route in about 19° 00′ N, 105° 00′ W, off Manzanillo. Distance 9380 miles.

To make the passage by the Central Route, proceed by Verde Island Passage and San Bernardino Strait to join the Central Route in 5° 00′ N, 150° 00′ E as instructed in article 7.270. Distance 9870 miles.

Composite routes are via Yokohama, see 7.168 and 7.304, distance 9530 miles; or via Guam and Honolulu, see 7.287, 7.207, and 7.218. Distance 9540 miles. These distances allow for fuelling stops at the ports indicated.

7.298. Manila → San Diego or San Francisco. The direct route crosses the Pacific Ocean by great circle from Balintang Channel direct to either destination. Distances: San Diego 6620 miles; San Francisco 6240 miles.

Composite routes are via Yokohama, see paragraphs 7.168, 7.305; distances to San Diego 6760 miles; to San Francisco 6360 miles; or via Guam and Honolulu, see 7.287, 7.207, and 7.217, distances to San Diego 7100 miles; to San Francisco 6910 miles. These distances allow for fuelling stops at the ports indicated.

7.299. Manila → Juan de Fuca Strait or Prince Rupert. For the direct route, take a great circle track from Balintang Channel to 41° 00′ N, 157° 00′ E; then steer by rhumb line to 49° 00′ N, 180° 00′ and by rhumb line to destination. Distances: Juan de Fuca Strait 5910 miles; Prince Rupert 5570 miles.

Composite routes are via Yokohama, see 7.168 and 7.306; distances to Juan de Fuca Strait 6040 miles; to Prince Rupert 5700 miles; or via Guam and Honolulu, see 7.287, 7.206. 7.216, 7.217: distances to Juan de Fuca Strait 7110 miles; to Prince Rupert 7200 miles. These distances allow for fuelling stops at the ports indicated.

7.300. Hong Kong → Panama. Steer as directed in article 7.169 to a position off Yokohama and then take the great circle tracks to join the North American coastal route as directed in article 7.304. Distance 9270 miles.

To make the passage by the Central route, proceed through Luzon Strait, passing between Babuyan and Balintang Islands, and then, after passing close S of Guam, join the Central route (7.271), in 5° 00′ N, 168° 00′ E. Distance 10090 miles.

7.301. Hong Kong → San Diego or San Francisco. By a small margin, the shortest route is via T'ai-wan Strait, Korea Strait and Tsugaru Kaikyo, calling at Hakodate if necessary, and thence, having cleared Erimo Misaki, by great circle to destination. The vertex of the great circle to San Francisco is in 50° 30′ N, 175° 00′ W, about 80 miles S of the Aleutian Islands, See 7.308.

Alternatively, the passage may be made via the approaches to Yokohama (7.169), and onward by great circle, see 7.305. Distances via Tsugaru Kakyo and Yokohama respectively are: San Diego 6450 and 6460 miles; San Francisco 6050 and 6060 miles.

A favourable current may be expected over most of the passage if the route is taken as above, but, on the other hand, the vessel will be exposed to the weather of the North Pacific. Better weather, but less favourable current, is likely to be experienced on the longer routes via Honolulu (7.211, 7.218), or via Guam and Honolulu (7.288, 7.207, 7.218). Distances, calling at Honolulu: San Diego 7140 miles; San Francisco 6940 miles; calling at Guam and Honolulu: San Diego 7430 miles; San Francisco 7240 miles.

7.302. Hong Kong → Juan de Fuca Strait or Prince Rupert. The most direct route is via T'ai-wan Strait, Korea Strait and Tsugaru Kaikyo, calling at Hakodate if necessary, see 7.169, 7.309. Thence, after clearing Erimo Misaki, proceed by rhumb line to 49° 00′ N, 180° 00′; and continue by rhumb line to destination. Distances: Juan de Fuca Strait 5720 miles; Prince Rupert 5390 miles. Alternatively, the passage may be made via the approaches to Yokohama, see 7.169, and onward by the routes given in article 7.306. Distances: Juan de Fuca Strait 5740 miles; Prince Rupert 5400 miles.

7.303. Shang-hai → North America. The shortest route is via the Sea of Japan and Tsugaru Kaikyō, following the directions given in articles 7.307, 7.308, and 7.309 after clearing Erimo Misaki. Distances: Panama 8540 miles; San Diego 5760 miles; San Francisco 5350 miles; Juan de Fuca Strait 5020 miles.

7.304. Yokohama ↔ Panama. Take the great circle track between the approaches to Yokohama and 22° 40′ N, 110° 00′ W, S of Cabo Falso on the North American coastal route, continuing on that route to Panama. Distance 7650 miles.

Alternatively, a route via Honolulu is recommended, particularly to ships W-bound. It avoids the generally E-going current which can be expected on the great-circle route, and it carries the probability of better weather with an opportunity of fuelling midway on the route. See 7.213 and 7.218. Distance by shortest combination of tracks 8100 miles.

7.305. Yokohama → San Diego or San Francisco. The direct routes are by great circle in both cases, with a highest latitude on the route to San Francisco of 47° 30′ N, in 170° 00′ W. Distances: San Diego 4930 miles; San Francisco 4530 miles.

Alternatively, to avoid bad weather, the reverse of the most S'ly return routes (7.313) may be taken, namely from Yokohama to 35° 00′ N, 141° 00′ E; to 35° 00′ N, 140° 00′ W; thence direct to San Diego or via 37° 00′ N, 130° 00′ W to San Francisco. Distances: San Diego 5250 miles; San Francisco 4860 miles.

7.306. Yokohama → Juan de Fuca Strait or Prince Rupert. Proceed by great circle to 44° 40′ N, 163° 40′ E; thence by rhumb line to 49° 00′ N, 180° 00′; and thence by rhumb line to either destination. This route is usually in a warm E-going current throughout. Distances: Juan de Fuca Strait 4200 miles; Prince Rupert 3870 miles.

7.307. Hakodate → Panama. Proceed by great circle to 28° 40′ N, 118° 20′ W, S of Isla de Guadalupe, and thence as navigation permits. Distance 7430 miles.

7.308. Hakodate → San Diego or San Francisco. Passage may be made either direct, on a great circle track, or by a more S'ly track whose most N'ly point is in 47° 30′ N, 167° 00′ W. By the latter route a favourable current may be expected; this is doubtful on the more direct route.

On the direct route, if bound for San Diego take the great circle track from off Erimo Misaki, bearing away S when nearing the Californian coast so as to round Point Conception, at the entrance to Santa Barbara Channel. For San Francisco, the great circle track, with its vertex some 80 miles S of the Aleutian Islands, is direct to the traffic separation route in the approach. Distances: San Diego 4650 miles; San Francisco 4240 miles.

The more S'ly route is by great circle or rhumb line from off Erimo Misaki to 46° 15′ N, 180° 00′ for San Diego and 47° 00′ N, 180° 00′ for San Francisco. Thence, for San Diego, proceed by great circle to Santa Barbara Channel; for San Francisco, proceed by great circle direct. Distances: San Diego 4670 miles; San Francisco 4260 miles.

7.309. Hakodate → Juan de Fuca Strait or Prince Rupert. Proceed by rhumb line to 49° 00′ N, 180° 00′ and thence by rhumb line to either destination. Distances: Juan de Fuca Strait 3910 miles; Prince Rupert 3580 miles.

7.310. Panama → Hong Kong or Shang-hai. The passage recommended is via Guam, proceeding thither either direct or via Honolulu, see 7.280. From Guam, proceed to Hong Kong via Balintang Channel; for Shang-hai, proceed as directed in article 7.162 through Nansei Shotō to Hsiao-pan-men. Distances (using direct passage to Guam): Hong Kong 9890 miles; Shang-hai 9720 miles.

7.311. San Diego or San Francisco → Singapore, Manila, and China Seas. The following seasonal routes, for vessels not making an intermediate port of call, are recommended.

1st June to 30th September. Proceed by great circle to Luzon Strait. A composite great circle track passing through Nanpō Shotō at 31° 00′ N, 140° 00′ E and continuing to Cape Engaño will observe the caution advised by Admiralty Sailing Directions in the volcanic area of Nanpō Shotō, while entailing less opposition from Kuro Shio than a more N'ly track. For Manila and Singapore, continue through Babuyan Channel and, for Singapore, by the Eastern Route (7.113), unless the strength of the monsoon dictates a more W'ly route in the China Sea. For destinations S of Fu-chou, sue Balintang Channel or Bashi Channel; for Fu-chou, leave the great circle as convenient to pass S of Okinawa Guntō; for Shang-hai, leave it after passing through Nanpō Shotō, or as for Fu-chou. In working the distinces given below, the departure position for Shang-hai is 31° 00′ N, 140° 00′ E.

For the rest of the year, a route based on a rhumb line crossing of the Pacific is recommended. In the transitional months of April, May, October, and November, owing to the possibility of heavy weather in the N part of the ocean, a direct rhumb line should be taken to Luzon Strait. From 1st December to 31st March an even more S'ly rhumb line, from 30° 00′ N, 140° 00′ W to Luzon Strait, is advised. For Manila or Singapore, continue by Babuyan Channel and as navigation permits, using the Eastern Route (7.113), for Singapore. For destinations S of Fu-chou, use either Balintang Channel or Bashi Channel, and for Fu-chou and destinations farther N, leave the trans-ocean rhumb line in 150° E and continue S of Kazan Retto and Okinawa Gunto.

Distances in miles (1) June-Sept. (2) April, May, Oct, Nov. (3) Dec.-Mar.:

		San Diego	San Francisco
Singapore	(1)	7770	7380
	(2)	8110	7710
	(3)	8120	7920
Manila	(1)	6650	6250
	(2)	6980	6580
	(3)	6990	6800
Hong Kong	(1)	6660	6270
	(2)	7010	6600
	(3)	7020	6820
Shang-hai	(1)	5980	5590
	(2)	6660	6250
	(3)	6630	6440

7.312. Juan de Fuca Strait or Prince Rupert → Singapore, Manila, and China Seas. As suggested in article 7.295, the shortest route in all cases is via Tsugaru Kaikyō and Korea Strait. Directions as far as Hakodate are given in articles 7.317 and 7.318; the route continues through the Sea of Japan and the China Sea as directed in articles 7.169 and 7.113.

To avoid the worst of the adverse current and the winter weather of a route in N latitudes vessels bound for China ports may proceed first by great circle to 30° 00′ N, 180° 00′ and then approach the Asiatic coast on about that parallel, passing through Nanpō Shotō between Tori Shima and Sōfu Gan, and for Shang-hai as in 7.212. For ports in S China, pass through Nansei Shotō between Tokara Guntō and Amami Gunto, but Kuro Shio runs NE on the W part of this route.

A second alternative, effective for Hong Kong and destinations farther S, is to proceed to Guam by great circle (7.286) and thence to destination by the appropriate route given for Singapore and Manila in article 7.287 and for Hong Kong in article 7.288.

This route, which also avoids the worst of the adverse current and winter weather, allows for re-fuelling at Guam. From Guam a favourable current will be carried, except during June, July, and August, when it will be adverse in the China Sea.

Distances in miles for all seasons: (1) via Sea of Japan; (2) via 30° N, 180°, (3) calling at Guam.

		Juan de Fuca Strait	Prince Rupert
Singapore	(1)	7010	6670
	(2)	7500	7330
	(3)	7570	7300
Manila	(1)	5970	5630
	(2)	6360	6190
	(3)	6340	6070
Hong Kong	(1)	5660	5320
	(2)	6320	6150
	(3)	6670	6410
Shang-hai	(1)	4960	4620
	(2)	5780	5610
	(3)	—	—

7.313. San Diego or San Francisco → Yokohama. The summer route, for June, July, and August, is by great circle. A contrary current is likely throughout the voyage. Distances: from San Diego 4930 miles; from San Francisco 4530 miles.

From September to May, a more S'ly route is recommended, see 7.295. From San Diego, proceed by rhumb line to 35° 00′ N, 140° 00′ W; from San Francisco, proceed by rhumb lines through 37° 00′ N, 130° 00′ W to that position. Thence proceed by rhumb line to Yokohama. On this route, bad weather is unusual, and the strength of the contrary current should not be felt until approaching Japan. Distances: from San Diego 5160 miles; from San Francisco 4850 miles.

7.314. Juan de Fuca Strait → Yokohama. Proceed as for Hakodate, see 7.317, as far as 50° 30′ N, 180° 00. The route thence is seasonal as far as 44° N. Over this section the winter route, from 1st November to 31st March, passes through 50° 30′ N, 175° 00′ E; 50° 10′ N, 170° 00′ E; 49° 30′ N, 165° 00′ E; 48° 20′ N, 160° 00′ E; 46° 30′ N, 155° 00′ E; to 44° 00′ N, 150° 00′ E. The summer route, from 1st April to 31st October, passes through 50° 00′ N, 175° 00′ E; 49° 15′ N, 170° 00′ E; 48° 20′ N, 165° 00′ E; 47° 10′ N, 160° 00′ E; 45° 20′ N, 155° 00′ E; to 44° 00′ N, 152° 00′ E. From either of these seasonal positions, the route is by rhumb lines tō 34° 00′ N, 140° 00′ E, making a landfall at Inubō Saki (*35° 42′ N, 140° 52′ E*) or, if preferred, at Kinkasan tō (*38° 17′ N, 141° 35′ E*).

These routes, which lead close S of the Aleutian Islands, are usually N of the W'ly winds and are in the track of the W-going current throughout.

Distances: winter 4180 miles; summer 4160 miles.

7.315. Prince Rupert → Yokohama. Proceed as for Hakodate, see 7.317, as far as 50° 30′ N, 180° 00′; and thence by the appropriate seasonal route, see 7.314, to Yokohama. Distances: winter 3820 miles; summer 4000 miles.

7.316. San Diego or San Francisco → Hakodate. There is a seasonal route through the N part of the Pacific Ocean and an alternative route farther S. On these routes, a contrary current may be expected throughout the voyage. If refuelling is desired, a call at Dutch Harbour entails a slightly longer passage, less favourable as regards weather but with a favourable current in parts.

The routes from the seaward end of Santa Barbara Channel (for San Diego), and from the approaches to San Francisco are by great circle to 50° 30′ N, 180° 00′ throughout the year, and thence the winter route, from 1st November to 31st March, passes through 50° 30′ N, 175° 00′ E; 50° 10′ N, 170° 00′ E; 49° 30′ N, 165° 00′ E; 48° 20′ N, 160° 00′ E; 46° 30′ N, 155° 00′ E; 44° 00′ N, 150° 00′ E and thence as navigation permits. The summer route, from 1st April to 31st October, passes through 50° 00′ N, 175° 00′ E; 49° 15′ N, 170° 00′ E; 48° 20′ N, 165° 00′ E; 47° 10′ N, 160° 00′ E; 45° 20′ N, 155° 00′ E; 44° 00′ N, 152° 00′ E, and thence as navigation permits. Distances are the same by winter and summer routes, namely 4660 miles from San Diego and 4250 miles from San Francisco.

The alternative route is by great circle to 44° 40′ N, 163° 40′ E, with a highest latitude on the route from San Francisco of 47° 30′ N, 170° 00′ W, and thence to Hakodate by rhumb line. Distances from San Diego 4680 miles; from San Francisco 4270 miles.

7.317. Juan de Fuca Strait → Hakodate. The route throughout the year, as far as 50° 30′ N, 180° 00′ passes through 49° 30′ N, 130° 00′ W; 50° 10′ N, 135° 00′ W; 50° 35′ N, 140° 00′ W, 50° 45′ N, 145° 00′ W; 50° 50′ N, 150° 00′ W; 50° 50′ N, 160° 00′ W; 50° 40′ N, 165° 00′ W; 50° 30′ N, 170° 00′ W; 50° 30′ N, 175° 00′ W; thence it is seasonal as on the routes given from San Diego or San Franciso in 7.316. Distance: 3860 miles (all seasons).

7.318. Prince Rupert → Hakodate. The route throughout the year, as far as 50° 30′ N, 180° 00′ W, passes through 54° 40′ N, 135° 00′ W; 54° 50′ N, 140° 00′ W; 54 °50′ N, 145° 00′ W; 54° 30′ N, 150° 00′ W; 54° 10′ N, 155° 00′ W; 53° 40′ N, 160° 00′ W; 53° 00′ N, 165° 00′ W; 52°15′ N , 170° 00′ W; 51° 30′ N, 175° 00′ W. This part of the route passes about 30 miles S of the Aleutian Islands, and is favourably affected by the W-going Alaska current. W of the 180th meridian, the route is seasonal, as given for San Diego or San Francisco in article 7.316. Distance: 3520 miles (all seasons).

5

10

15

20

CHAPTER 8

MISCELLANEOUS INFORMATION FOR POWER VESSELS

CONTENTS

Page

THROUGH ROUTES

THROUGH ROUTES

8.01. General remarks. Passages made through the sea areas covered by more than one chapter of this book
are described in detail in the chapters concerned. The following articles contain information and advice which
may be helpful in transferring from one chapter to another.

8.02. English Channel ↔ Gulf of Mexico. Proceed W-bound to North-East Providence Channel (2.83),
or E-bound through Florida Strait (2.82). Alternatively, the passage may be made in either direction via Turks
Island Passage (2.86, 4.30), and Old Bahama Channel or Windward Passage.

8.03. English Channel ↔ Caribbean Sea. For Belize, Providence Channels (2.83) or Turks Island Passage
and Windward Passage (2.86, 4.30) are suitable.
    For Kingston or Colon, Turks Island Passage and Windward Passage (2.86, 4.30) are suitable in either
direction.
    For Colon or Curaçao, Mona Passage or Sombrero Passage (2.86, 4.30) are suitable in either direction.

8.04. English Channel ↔ east coast of South America. Between the English Channel and a landfall off
Cabo de São Roque, proceed by great circle, with caution in the region of the W-going South Equatorial Current
(2.39, 2.111, 2.116, 2.117). For passages off the E coast of South America, see 3.31.

8.05. English Channel and European ports ↔ West coast of Africa. For passages between the English Channel and Cape Palmas, see 2.96, 2.97. For continuation off the west coast of Africa, see 3.41, 3.42. If calling at Arquipélago de Cabo Verde, see 2.126, 2.127.

An outward bound route that has been used by some shipping lines is to pass Île d'Ouessant at a distance of 30 miles and Cabo Finisterre at 50 miles; thence between Isla de Tenerife and Isla Gran Canaria, and at least 60 miles off Cape Blanc, Cap Vert, and Bijagós Breaker (*11° 32′ N, 16° 54′ W*), crossing the equator in 10° W, and then steering a direct course for a landfall off Cape Town. If not calling at Cape Town, pass 50 miles W of the Cape of Good Hope and join the E-bound route given in Chapter 6.

8.06. Rounding the Cape of Good Hope.

8.06.01. From the South Atlantic Ocean, to pass S of the Agulhas Current, pass through 36° 45′ S, 19° 00′ E and thence by great circle to 34° 30′ S, 32° 30′ E.

Alternatively, by keeping close inshore (6.56), it may be possible to take advantage of local counter-currents.

8.06.02. From the Indian Ocean, the Agulhas Current should be sought, but there can be a dangerous sea off the edge of the coastal bank (6.57, 6.150).

8.07. Cape Town ↔ Cabot Strait, Halifax, or New York. Steer by great circles, for Cabot Strait and Halifax passing through 14° 40′ N, 24° 55′ W, SW of Arquipélago de Cabo Verde; and for New York, direct. Distances from Cape Town: Cabot Strait 6430 miles; Halifax 6470 miles; New York 6810 miles.

8.08. Cape Town → Galleons Passage and Colon. Follow the great circle track to 4° 40′ S, 34° 35′ W, between Cabo de São Roque and Atol das Rocas, and proceed thence to 10° 58′ N, 60° 48′ W, in Galleons Passage. For continuation to Colon, see 4.29, 4.30. Distances: Galleons Passage 5260 miles; Colon 6450 miles.

8.09. Cape Town → ports in Gulf of Mexico and Caribbean Sea. Follow the great circle track as 8.08 to Cabo de São Roque and then proceed to enter the Caribbean Sea through 13° 28′ N, 61° 10′ W, about 5 miles N of St. Vincent. For continuation, see 4.26, 4,27, 4.30. Distance from Cape Town to St. Vincent 5350 miles.

8.10. Colon and ports in Caribbean Sea and Gulf of Mexico → Cape Town. The E-bound route in the Atlantic Ocean is somewhat N of the W-bound routes described in 8.08 and 8.09. It passes (see 2.106 and 4.28) through 13° 28′ N, 61° 10′ W, about 5 miles N of St. Vincent, and continues first to 5° 00′ N, 45° 00′ W; and thence to 4° 40′ S, 34° 35′ W, between Cabo de São Roque and Atol das Rocas; thence to Cape Town by great circle. Distance from Colon 6520 miles; from St. Vincent 5370 miles.

8.11. Europe and north-west coast of Africa ↔ Gulf of Mexico and Caribbean Sea. Routes and distances across the Atlantic Ocean are discussed in 2.81–2.86; the channels between the islands of the West Indies, and navigation in that area, are dealt with in Chapter 4. Owing to the complex variety of voyages and ships' requirements, the choice of a route must depend, in the main, on these factors, and on comparison between the distances involved.

8.12. Europe and north-west coast of Africa ↔ East coast of South America. Routes in the North Atlantic Ocean are discussed in 2.39, 2.111, 2.116, 2.117; for passages off the coast of South America see 3.31–3.39.

8.13. Gulf of Guinea ↔ Canada and northern United States ports. Pass SW of Arquipélago de Cabo Verde, using great circle tracks where possible. See 2.126, 2.127.

Distances, in miles:

	Takoradi	Lagos	Bonny	Douala	Gamba Oil Terminal	Pointe-Noire	Lobito
Halifax	4220	4540	4740	4890	5000	5140	5460
New York	4560	4880	5070	5230	5340	5480	5800

8.14. Gulf of Guinea ↔ Colon

8.14.01. From ports between Takoradi and Douala, proceed to 4° 20′ N, 9° 20′ W, off Cape Palmas and continue by great circle to 11° 35′ N, 60° 35′ W, about 10 miles N of Tobago. Steer thence as navigation permits to Colon.

From Pointe Noire and Lobito, proceed by great circle to Galleons Passage (*10° 58′ N, 60° 48′ W*) and thence direct to Colon.

Distances by the above W-bound routes are from Takoradi 4730 miles; Lagos 5050 miles; Bonny 5240 miles; Douala 5400 miles; Gamba Oil Terminal 5490 miles; Pointe Noire 5630 miles; Lobito 5840 miles.

8.14.02. Vessels W-bound between ports in the Gulf of Guinea and Colon may obtain considerable help by making use of the W-going South Equatorial Current (3.11) and the North Equatorial Current (2.15, 4.11). W-bound from ports farther S, the South Sub-tropical Current (3.11) should be beneficial during the ocean crossing.

E-bound routes from Colon to the Gulf of Guinea are, in general, subject to unfavourable currents but it may be possible to find the E-going Equatorial Counter-current; and the Guinea Current sets permanently to the E; see 2.15.

8.15. East coasts of Canada and U.S.A. ↔ Gulf of Mexico and Caribbean Sea. See 2.101, 2.102, 2.103 for routes in the Atlantic Ocean, and Chapter 4 for the Gulf of Mexico and the Caribbean Sea. Owing to the variety of voyages and ships' requirements, the choice of a particular route must rest on scrutiny of the charts and publications covering the area and comparison between the distances involved.

8.16. East coasts of Canada and U.S.A. ↔ East coast of South America. See 2.39, 2.105 for North Atlantic Ocean and 3.31–3.39 for the coast of South America.

8.17. Gulf of Mexico and Caribbean Sea ↔ East coast of South America. For passages in the Gulf of Mexico and the Caribbean Sea, see Chapter 4. For passages off the NE coast of South America, see 2.106, 2.107; for the E coast of South America, see 3.31–3.39.

8.18. Cape of Good Hope or Durban ↔ Singapore. Passage may be made either through Malacca Strait or Sunda Strait, in either direction, except W-bound for Durban, when Malacca Strait is advised. See 6.70, 6.82, 6.150, 6.151, 7.111.

8.19. Mauritius ↔ Singapore. Via Malacca Strait, see 6.81, 6.99.

8.20. Aden ↔ Singapore. Via Malacca Strait (6.70, 6.77, 6.78, 6.81) in either direction, or, E-bound only, via Sunda Strait (6.153, 7.111).

8.21. Colombo ↔ Singapore. Via Malacca Strait, see 6.70, 6.81.

8.22. Madras ↔ Singapore and Eastern Archipelago. If distance is the main consideration, the following table of voyage distances by Malacca Strait and Sunda Strait will assist the choice of route. See 6.70, 6.81, 7.125–7.132.

To	Via Malacca Strait (miles)	Via Sunda Strait (miles)
Singapore	1590	—
Ambon	3260	3360
Balik Papan	2660	2790
Djakarta	2160	2045
Makassar	2700	2810
Sandakan	2620	3330
Surabaya	2350	2190
Tarakan	3010	3130

8.23. Cape of Good Hope → New Zealand and Pacific Ocean. East-bound, from October to April, proceed as directed in 6.161 as far as 41° 30′ S, 122° 50′ E and thence by great circle to 47° 50′ S, 167° 50′ E, ENE of Snares Islands, or alternatively by great circle passing close S of Tasmania, to Cook Strait.

If the shorter route for Melbourne (6.161) is taken, departure for Snares Islands or Cook Strait should be made from 45° 00′ S, 130° 00′ E.

From May to September, follow the directions given in 6.161 as far as 35° 30′ S, 115° 08′ E, 68 miles S of Cape Leeuwin and continue thence by great circles to a landfall off South West Cape, Tasmania and thence to Snares Islands or Cook Strait.

8.24. Aden → New Zealand and Pacific Ocean. East-bound, from October to April, pass between Ras Asir and Socotra and to 4° 00′ S, 70° 30′ E. Proceed thence by great circle to 41° 30′ S, 122° 50′ E and thence as directed in 8.23.

From May to September proceed as above to 4° 00′ S, 70° 30′ E, and thence by great circle to 35° 30′ S, 115° 08′ E, 68 miles S of Cape Leeuwin. Continue thence by great circles to a landfall off South West Cape, Tasmania, and onward to Snares Islands or Cook Strait.

8.25. Routes between ports in Indian Ocean and on east coast of Australia. Two criteria, both of which vary, govern the basic choice between routes N and S of Australia. The distance on any particular route may vary owing to seasonal changes in the route, and, in cases where the distances N-about and S-about are similar, the balance between climatic conditions may vary seasonally.

In the following table of distances, Brisbane is taken as the central Australian port, and distances are quoted from it in miles. A comparison for Sydney may be obtained by adding 460 miles to the N-about distances given below and subtracting that amount from the S-about routes.

Seasonal routes are quoted O–A = October to April or M–S = May to September.
 *via Malacca Strait.

Between Brisbane and	E-bound		W-bound		References and Remarks common reference 7.51–7.54
	S-about	N-about	S-about	N-about	
36° 45′ S, 19° 00′ E	O–A 6820	O–A 8180	—	—	For E-bound traffic from S Atlantic (O–A only)
Cape Town	O–A 7000	O–A 8370	O–A 7370	O–A 8300	6.157, 6.158, 6.160, 6.161,
	M–S 7210	M–S 8190	M–S 7620	M–S 8360	6.162
Durban	O–A 6410	O–A 7670	O–A 6770	O–A 7670	6.157, 6.159, 6.160, 6.161,
	M–S 6600	M–S 7560	M–S 6830	M–S 7580	6.162
Mombasa	7300	7470	6970	7470	6.163
Aden	7390	O–A 7230	O–A 7380	O–A 7370	6.164, 6.165, 6.166, 1.167
		M–S 7180	M–S 7410	M–S 7430	
Strait of Hormuz	7380	6910	7380	6910	6.155, 6.156
Karachi	6930	6440	6930	6440	6.155, 6.156
Bombay	6460	5980	6460	5980	6.155, 6.156
Colombo	5610	5130	5610	5130	6.155, 6.156
Madras	5900	5410*	5900	5410*	6.140, 6.141
Sandheads	6110	5340*	6110	5340*	6.140, 6.141
Rangoon	5740	4890*	5740	4890*	6.140, 6.142

8.26. Straits and passages in Eastern Archipelago. The following brief notes are for use when planning passages between the Indian Ocean and the North Pacific Ocean. Admiralty Sailing Directions should also be consulted.

Strait or passage	Geographical position	Remarks
Alas Strait	8° 40′ S, 116° 40′E	Indian Ocean to Makassar and Sapudi Straits. No dangers. An alternative to Lombok Strait if anchorage is desired.
Alor Strait	8° 15′ S, 123° 55′ E	Sawu Sea to Flores Sea. Deep. Usually only used for local navigation. Strong tidal streams.
Bali Strait	8° 10′ S, 114° 25′ E	Seldom used except by local traffic.
Bangka Strait	1° 45′ N, 125° 05′ E	Molukka Sea to Sulawesi Sea. Shortest route round NE end of Sulawesi but not lighted.
Selat Bangka	2° 30′ S, 105° 45′ E	Between coast of Sumatra and Bangka, the shortest route between Sunda Strait and Singapore.
Basilan Strait	6° 54′ N, 122° 04′ E	Between Sulu Sea and Sulawesi Sea, the shortest route SW of Mindanao. Deep.
Berhala Strait	1° 00′ S, 104° 20′ E	Between coast of Sumatra and Singkep on the inner route between Singapore and Sunda Strait. Lighted. Controlling depth 10 m at NW end.
Boling and Lamakera Straits	8° 25′ S, 123° 20′ E	Sawu Sea to Flores Sea. Deep. Somewhat exposed. Strong tidal streams.
Buton Passage	5° 20′ S, 123° 15′ E	Deep, wide, and clear. Lighted.
Buton Strait	4° 56′ S, 122° 47′ E	Coastal route, easy to navigate by day. 18 m in South Narros. No routeing advantage over Buton Passage.
Dampier Strait	0° 40′ S, 130° 40′ E	Connects Pacific Ocean with Ceram Sea NW of New Guinea.
Djailolo Passage	0° 00′, 129° 00′ E	Between Ceram Sea and Pacific Ocean. Deep.
Durian Strait	1° 00′ N, 103° 35′ E	Entrance to Singapore Strait from inner route from Sunda Strait. Swept to 14 m (1934).
Flores Strait	8° 25′ S, 122° 55′ E	Sawu Sea to Flores Sea. Deep and clear except for Narrows at N end. Strong tidal streams in parts, calling for a good reserve of power.
Selat Gelasa	3° 00′ S, 107° 15′ E	Frequently in use between Java Sea and China Sea as alternative to Selat Bangka.
Hinatuan Passage	9° 40′ N, 125° 45′ E	Connects Pacific Ocean with S end of Surigao Strait.
Karimata Strait	3° 00′ S, 109° 00′ E	Wide passage connecting China Sea with E part of Java Sea.
Lombok Strait	8° 30′ S, 115° 30′ E	Wide. Easy to navigate. The most important passage between Makassar Strait and Indian Ocean.
Makassar Strait	2° 00′ S, 118° 00′ E	About 400 miles in length, connecting Sulawesi Sea with Java Sea and Flores Sea.

Strait or passage	Geographical position	Remarks
Malacca Strait		About 250 miles long in its narrower part connecting Bay of Bengal with Singapore Strait and Durian Strait. Depths irregular, from about 25 m. See. 6.83.
Manipa Strait	3° 15′ S, 127° 20′ E	Wide and deep passage connecting Ceram Sea with Banda Sea.
Mindoro Strait	11° 30′ N, 121° 20′ E	Wide and deep strait in frequent use between Manila and islands to the S.
Obi Strait	1° 15′ S, 128° 00′ E	Wide and deep. Connects Molukka Sea with Halmahera Sea and Djailolo Passage.
Ombai Strait	8° 30′ S, 125° 00′ E.	Wide and deep, between Alor Islands and Timor.
Pantar Strait	8° 20′ S, 124° 20′ E	Connects between Flores Sea and Ombai Strait. Used by local traffic.
Riouw Strait	0° 55′ N, 104° 20′ E	Approach from S to Singapore Strait. Well lighted and buoyed. Main channel carries 18 m.
Roti Strait	10° 25′ S, 123° 30′ E	Connects between Sawu Sea and Arafura Sea, SW of Timor. Deep.
Sagewin Strait	0° 55′ S, 130° 40′ E	Connects Pacific Ocean with Ceram Sea NW of New Guinea.
Saleier Strait	5° 40′ S, 120° 30′ E	Deep. Usual route between Java Sea and Molukkas.
San Bernardino Strait	13° 00′ N, 124° 30′ E	Wide and deep. Important passage on Pacific routes.
Sape Strait	8° 30′ S, 119° 20′ E	Connects between Sumba Strait and Flores Sea.
Sapudi Strait	7° 00′ S, 114° 15′ E	Regularly used between Java Sea and Lombok Strait or Flores Sea. Lighted.
Sele Strait	1° 10′ S, 131° 05′ E	Connects between Pacific Ocean and Ceram Sea, NW of New Guinea.
Sumba Strait	9° 00′ S, 120° 00′ E	Wide and deep passage between Sumba Island and Flores Island.
Sunda Strait	6° 15′ S, 105° 00′ E	Principal connection between Indian Ocean and Java Sea but limited for deep draught vessels by lack of water NE.
Surigao Strait	10° 30′ N, 125° 20′ E	Connects between Pacific Ocean and Mindanao Sea to Sulu Sea. Safe and deep.
Wètar Strait	8° 15′ S, 126° 25′ E	Connects between Arafura Sea and Flores Sea through Wètar Passage; used for main routes between Singapore and Australia.

OPINIONS AND COMMENTS

8.40. The notes which follow are derived from information which has been received from time to time by the Hydrographer of the Navy, or issued in response to specific requests. Reports and suggestions from sea are invaluable, and masters and ship operators are freely invited to suggest new routes or to comment on their experience of established routes, giving full supporting reasons. Such information may, after evaluation, be embodied in this book or in Admiralty Sailing Directions.

8.41. Persian Gulf → African coast. In June 1931, SS *British Dominion*, bound from the Persian Gulf to the Cape of Good Hope, after rounding Ras al Hadd, steered S on the 60th meridian with the object of crossing the South-west Monsoon area as soon as possible and, consequently, meeting less adverse current. On reaching 6° 30′ N, course was altered direct for Îles Comores. This route, though longer than that recommended in 6.60, was found to be advantageous.

On the other hand, Captain P. J. Davies has reported that in about 1959 he followed the track of *British Dominion* and "got the hammering of his life". He was of the opinion that the track recommended in 6.60 was preferable.

8.42. Torres Strait → Manila via Obi Strait. In 1969, the Eastern Australian Steamship Company Limited proposed a route for the South-east Monsoon (May to September) passing S of False Cape (*8°22′ S, 137° 35′ E*); E of Pulau-pulau Aru and Ceram; thence NE of Obi Islands (*1° 30′ S, 127° 45′ E*), to join the route given in 7.161 in the Molukka Sea.

8.43. Japanese ports to ports in T'ai-wan. In 1969, Captain R. N. Firth of SS *Pando Gulf* commented on the passage from Yokohama to Kao-hsiung Chiang, on the SW coast of T'ai-wan, in the South-west Monsoon period (May to September), to the effect that he preferred the slightly longer route E of Okinawa to that through T'ai-wan Strait, on account of Kuro Shio. On the other hand, from Kobe, T'ai-wan Strait was preferred.

8.44. Dampier Archipelago → Yokohama or Osaka. In 1964, the Hydrographer of the Navy suggested the following route for a ship drawing 48 feet (15 m 8). From Dampier Archipelago (*20° 10′ S, 116° 40′ E*) proceed to 9° 35′ S, 123° 05′ E, thence through Ombai Strait and between Alor Island and Kambing Island to Manipa Strait

(*3° 15′ S, 127° 20′ E*). Pass through Manipa Strait and between Obi Islands and Sula Islands to 0° 05′ N, 126° 28′ E and enter the Pacific Ocean in 4° 00′ N, 127° 50′ E. Proceed thence by great circle. Distances: Yokohama 3700 miles; Osaka 3580 miles.

8.45. Routeing deep-draught ships round Cabo de Hornos or through Estrecho de Magallanes. In 1970 the Hydrographer of the Navy, in response to a request, gave the opinion that no difficulty could be foreseen in passing between Cabo de Hornos and Islas Diego de Ramirez. There are no radio aids to navigation, but Cabo de Hornos is lighted. The SW coast of Chile is inhospitable and there are no lights; vessels should keep well to seaward of it. Tankers in ballast W-bound SW of Chile may pound in. W'ly weather.

Passage through Estrecho de Magallanes, with a saving of about 350 miles, is possible. There are several lights, but tidal streams are strong and there is a weather hazard. Strangers should first make the passage in ballast and in good conditions.

In 1972, the master, MV *Adelaide Star*, reported, after completing a W-bound passage of Estrecho de Magallanes without a pilot, that the collective opinion of masters of his acquaintance, experienced in the Strait and in the passage round Cabo de Hornos, favoured the passage of the Strait both W-bound and E-bound, and particularly for vessels W-bound and in ballast.

See Admiralty Sailing Directions.

8.46. North-south passages through Caroline Islands. In 1972, Captain A. J. Murdoch, of SS *Cathay*, reported that he considered the passage between West Fayu Island (*8° 04′ N, 146° 43′ E*) and Pikelot Island, 53 miles farther E, to be unsafe for a large vessel owing to existing and reported shoal depths. He preferred to pass 10 miles W of Fayu Island.

Notes

PART II

SAILING VESSEL ROUTES

CONTENTS

INTRODUCTORY REMARKS

Although it may be argued that a standard work on Ocean Passages ought to be confined to the needs of contemporary seamen and that therefore directions for sailing ships are out of place, a shortened version of the information and advice given on the subject in previous editions of this book is given here, for the benefit of towing masters and of craft specially susceptible to the main wind and current circulation of the oceans, and, of course, for ocean-going sailing vessels. It must be stressed, however, that the routeing advice in this section was originally intended for large sailing vessels able to stand up to, and take advantage of, the heavy weather to be expected on many of the passages.

In addition to the routes described in this volume, chart 5309—*Tracks followed by sailing and low-powered steam vessels*—shows many routes.

As regards distances traversed, it has been considered more useful to express them as the average number of days taken in ordinary weather by a well-found sailing vessel of about 2000 tons, which in good conditions could log speeds of 10–12 knots but generally averaged 100–150 miles a day. The following list, supplied by Messrs. Hardie and Company, of Glasgow, gives the duration of a number of voyages.

	Number of days
English Channel to New York, winter	35–40
English Channel to New York, summer	40–50
English Channel to New Orleans	45–55
English Channel to Río de Janeiro or Pôrto de Santos	45–60
English Channel to Río de La Plata	55–65
English Channel to Valparaiso (around Cabo de Hornos)	90–100
English Channel to Callao (around Cabo de Hornos)	95–120
English Channel to San Francisco (around Cabo de Hornos)	125–150
English Channel to Cape Town	50–60
English Channel to Durban	60–65
English Channel to Bombay	100–110
English Channel to Calcutta	100–120
English Channel to Rangoon	100–120
English Channel to Sunda Strait	90–100
English Channel to Hong Kong (South-west Monsoon)	100–120
English Channel to Adelaide	80–90
English Channel to Melbourne	80–90
English Channel to Sydney (or Newcastle)	85–100
New York to English Channel	25–30
New York to Cape Town	65–70
New York to Río de La Plata	60–65
New York to Melbourne	100–120
New York to Sunda Strait	100–110
Cape Town to Melbourne	35–40
Cape Town to Wellington	40–45
Cape Town to Río de La Plata (across the Atlantic)	45
Cape Town to Río de La Plata (around Cabo de Hornos)	110
Cape Town to Calcutta	40–50
Cape Town to Shang-hai (via Sunda Strait, South-west Monsoon)	60
Calcutta to Sydney	60
Calcutta to Cape Town	45
Calcutta to English Channel	90–100
Hong Kong to English Channel (North-east monsoon)	110–120
Hong Kong to San Francisco	40
Hong Kong to Sydney	50–60
Melbourne to Valparaiso	40–50
Melbourne to San Francisco	60–70
Melbourne to Río de La Plata (around Cabo de Hornos)	70–80
Melbourne to English Channel (around Cabo de Hornos)	80–100
Melbourne to Hampton Roads	80–95
Wellington to San Francisco	60–70
Wellington to Valparaiso	30–35
Wellington to Río de La Plata	55–60
Wellington to English Channel	80–100
Valparaiso to English Channel (around Cabo de Hornos)	80–90
Valparaiso to New York (around Cabo de Hornos)	75–85

CHAPTER 9

ATLANTIC OCEAN AND MEDITERRANEAN SEA SAILING ROUTES

CONTENTS

ROUTES FROM PORTS ON EASTERN SIDE OF ATLANTIC OCEAN AND FROM MEDITERRANEAN SEA

9.01. From Norwegian and Baltic ports

9.01.01. For Canadian and eastern United States ports, there are two main routes, Northern and Southern, and a direct route.

On the **Northern Route,** which should only be taken in autumn, when it is clear of ice, vessels should pass N of Orkney Islands or of Shetland Islands if the weather so dictates. Thence, they should stand W to cross 30° W in about 55° N, and continue the Northern Route as in 9.04.02.

On the **Southern Route,** vessels should pass N of Orkney Islands or Shetland Islands if necessary, and stand W far enough to ensure weathering the British Isles. When clear, they should stand S to join the Southern Route from the English Channel (9.04.03).

The **Direct Route** is seldom taken, since it is almost directly against the prevailing winds and the North Atlantic Drift. To follow it, round Orkney Islands or Shetland Islands as above, make W to at least 10° W, and thence SW to join the Northern Route in about 47° N, 40° W.

9.01.02. For other Atlantic ports, Cabo de Hornos, or the Cape of Good Hope, use the Southern Route (9.01.01) and join the appropriate route from the English Channel (9.10) in about 40° N.

9.02. From North Sea ports

9.02.01. For east coasts of Canada and United States, there are three main routes as in 9.01. On the Northern Route with W'ly winds in summer a vessel will probably do better by going N-about round the British Isles than by beating down the English Channel. On the Southern and Direct Routes the latter is preferable.

9.02.02. For other Atlantic ports, Cabo de Hornos, or the Cape of Good Hope, proceed via the English Channel and the appropriate route from 9.05, 9.06, or 9.07.

9.03. From Irish Sea and River Clyde

9.03.01. For Atlantic Ocean ports. If taking the Northern or Direct Routes (9.01) to Newfoundland, Canada or the United States when bound from Liverpool or the Clyde, it is generally better to pass N of Ireland with W'ly winds in summer. On the Southern Route, and on the routes to other ports the weather at the time of sailing will determine the most advantageous course to join the routes from the English Channel described below.

9.04. English Channel to Canada and United States

9.04.01. There are two principal routes, a Northern, and a Southern, and also a direct route. The Northern Route should, as a rule, only be taken in autumn, when it is free from ice.

9.04.02. On the Northern Route, although heavy weather is frequently experienced, the winds are generally more favourable, and the currents from the Arctic assist in the latter part of the voyage.

When clear of the British Isles stand W and cross the meridian of 30° W in about 55° N; then steer, according to destination, for the Strait of Belle Isle, for St. John's, or for Canadian or United States ports.

For Gulf of St. Lawrence or Halifax, either try to make Cape Race by passing N of Virgin Rocks, or, in order to avoid the ice, cross the banks on the parallel of 44° N, and haul up on the proper course on reaching 55° W, heavy ice being seldom met with W of that meridian. Make Cape Race if the weather is clear, and thence steer for a position S of St. Pierre Island. While on Grand Bank during fog, or when there is uncertainty regarding the position, soundings should be obtained frequently, and an indraught towards the S coast of Newfoundland must be guarded against.

Notes: The S coast of Newfoundland, E of Cape Ray, is broken, rocky and dangerous, and the tidal streams are influenced by the winds. S'ly, E'ly, and often also SW'ly winds, bring a thick fog, which is most dense near the lee shore. This coast therefore should not be approached, except with a decidedly N'ly wind and clear weather.

Sable Island should be given a wide berth, as it is a very dangerous locality owing to the prevalent fogs and variable currents near it. Sounding should never be neglected in crossing the banks, and should be continuous whether bound for a Nova Scotia or a United States port. In thick weather, the thermometer is also a useful guide in approaching the banks off Newfoundland, as the temperature of the water falls on nearing them.

With SW'ly winds, while foggy E of the meridian of Flint Island, Cape Breton Island, it is frequently clear for some miles off the land W of it.

Between St. Pierre and Cape Breton Island, when feeling the way by sounding, in foggy weather, the edges of the deep water channel running through the banks into Cabot Strait are especially good guides. Cape Pine should not be approached within depths of 70 m nor Cape St. Mary within depths of 90 m in fog. There is deep water, of 180 m to 260 m in the approach to Placentia Bay.

9.04.03. The Southern Route is the best route to be followed during the whole of the year except autumn, on account of the better weather likely to be experienced, the certainty of the wind, and the avoidance of both fog and ice off the Newfoundland banks, during the spring and early part of the summer.

By this route, leaving the English Channel with a fair wind, steer a direct course as long as it lasts, and at least ensure sufficient westing to avoid the danger of being set into the Bay of Biscay. When the fair wind fails, take the Madeira route (9.07.01), and if the wind permits pass midway between that island and Arquipélago dos Açôres into the North-east Trade Wind, but if the wind does not favour, the Trade Wind will usually be gained sooner by passing nearer to Madeira. In that neighbourhood, it is usually found in the summer season between 32° and 31° N; in winter, a degree or so farther S.

For Halifax, or Canadian ports, when well within the Trade Wind limits, run W until in about 48° W, and thence edge off to the NW passing about 200 miles E of Bermuda, and direct for Halifax, allowing for the Gulf Stream setting ENE across the track.

For New York, or other United States ports, when well into the Trade Wind limits, run W, keeping S of 25° N until in about 65° W; then steer NW for any United States port, hauling out rather earlier for ports on the N part of this coast. The Gulf Stream will have to be crossed in the latter part of this route.

9.04.04. The Direct Route across the Atlantic, from the English Channel or New York, which is about 1000 miles shorter than the Southern Route, can seldom be taken on account of the prevailing W'ly winds, and of the North Atlantic Current and Gulf Stream combined, running contrary to the desired track. It is, however, recommended by some navigators, making as directly as possible from the Channel, to cross 50° W at 45° N, and thence to the desired port.

9.05. English Channel to Bermuda

9.05.01. There are two routes, the Direct and the Southern. By the **Direct Route,** proceed generally as directed in 9.04.04. By the **Southern Route,** proceed as directed in 9.07.01 as far as Madeira, and thence steer SW until within the N limit of the North-east Trade Wind (which will be entered when the sun is in the northern tropic between the parallels of 31° and 32° N, and when it is near the southern tropic between those of 30° and 31° N), when the course should be altered gradually towards W keeping within the limit of the Trade Wind. Cross 40° W in 25° N, which parallel should be preserved until the meridian of 60° W is reached, when a course for Bermuda may be steered.

Caution: When approaching the islands every opportunity should be taken to verify the vessel's position, and should it be at all doubtful and the weather unfavourable for seeing the lights, the parallel of the islands should not be crossed during the night, for the 180 m contour line is too close to the reef for soundings to give warning.

9.06. English Channel to West Indies, Gulf of Mexico and north coast of South America.

9.06.01. First proceed as directed in 9.07.01 as far as Madeira. After passing Madeira try to cross the parallel of 25° N between 25° and 30° W, the object being to reach the North-East Trade Wind as soon as possible. The season must be taken into consideration, as to how far S it will be necessary to go to insure holding the Trade Wind. Continue as follows:—

9.06.02. For Cuba, if bound to Habana or Puerto Matanzas pass through North West Providence Channel close along the W edge of Great Bahama Bank, round the elbow of Double-headed Shot cays, Cay Sal bank, and across towards Punta Guanos, on the western side of Matanzas, out of the stream. Old Bahama Channel may also be used or, if approaching from W, Cabo San Antonio may be rounded.

Bound to any port on the S side of Cuba, it is better to pass N of Puerto Rico and Santo Domingo-Haiti during the period of S'ly winds, which is the rainy season, and S of these islands when N winds are prevalent.

9.06.03. For the Leeward Islands, Jamaica, Belize, or the Gulf of Mexico, cross 40° W in about 18° N, and thence steer direct to pass between Antigua and Guadaloupe; thence pass close S of Haiti and Jamaica, and thence continue nearly direct.

Notes: The channel between Antigua and Guadeloupe is 30 miles wide, and there is generally much less current here than farther N or S. It will be better, however, in using this channel, to keep the Antigua shore on board, and to sight the island on the parallel of 17° N. Vessels sometimes pass between Antigua and Barbuda; this may be done without much risk by day, but by no means at night, for the soundings are so irregular that in running down it would be difficult to tell whether to haul N or S.

To ports in the Gulf of Mexico, North West Providence Channel is used by a great number of vessels, keeping on the edges of the banks, to avoid the strength of the current. Old Bahama Channel is also used, but less commonly.

9.06.04. For the north coast of South America, Trinidad, and the Guianas, proceed as follows:

For the Venezuelan, Colombian, and Caribbean ports, as far W as San Juan del Norte (Greytown) (*10° 53' N, 83° 43' W*), cross the meridian of 40° W in about 13° N; thence steer direct to the NE extreme of Trinidad and thence W to the desired port, keeping in the strength of the prevailing W'ly current.

For the islands northward of Trinidad, the season must be considered as to how far S it will be necessary to go to ensure holding the Trade Wind. In making for any of the Windward Islands get in the parallel of the island about 100 miles E of it.

For Cayenne, cross the meridian of 40° W in 9° N; thence steering to make the parallel of the port from 100 to 200 miles to windward, to allow for the strong W'ly current which prevails at all seasons, thence gradually closing the shore in depths of from 13m to 18 m.

For Surinam and Demerara, cross the meridian of 40° W between the parallels of 11° N and 12° N, and thence steer to make the land to windward as for Cayenne.

9.07. English Channel to South America

9.07.01. English Channel to Arquipélago de Cabo Verde. On leaving the English Channel at once make westing, as the prevailing winds are from that direction. With a fair wind from the Lizard, steer a WSW'ly course to gain an offing in 10° or 12° W.

If the wind should be from W keep on the tack which enables most westing to be made to get a good offing, and keep clear of the Bay of Biscay, even standing NW until well able to weather Cabo Finisterre on the starboard tack. By making a long board to the W nothing is lost, as the wind will generally be found to veer, so that a change of wind will be favourable, and even permit a vessel to pursue a course with a free wind; whilst if embayed in the Bay of Biscay, any change of wind to the W would necessitate beating to windward against the current.

It must be borne in mind that the prevailing winds and currents have a tendency to set towards Île d'Ouessant, and into the Bay of Biscay when S of it. To get well to the W is therefore of the greatest importance. Île d'Ouessant should, in no case, be sighted.

From 10° or 12° W, shape course to pass Madeira at any convenient distance, giving a wide berth to Cabo Finisterre, in passing it, as the current from the Atlantic usually sets right on-shore there. In winter it is preferable to pass W of Madeira, for the strong W'ly gales which occur in November, December and January produce eddy winds and heavy squalls E of the island.

From Madeira the best track is to pass W of, but just in sight of Arquipélago de Cabo Verde as the winds are stronger and steadier W of than E of them.

9.07.02. Arquipélago de Cabo Verde to north coast of Brazil. No particular crossings of the equator are necessary (see 9.07.03), as the E coast of South America has not to be weathered. From abreast Arquipélago de Cabo Verde steer a direct course, taking care to make the coast E of the destination, and thence steering along the coast in depths of from 18 m to 27 m.

9.07.03. Arquipélago de Cabo Verde to the equator. In considering where to cross the equator it is necessary to bear in mind that if a vessel crosses far to the W there will be a less interval of doldrum to cross, but it may be requisite to tack to weather the coast of South America, and these crossings vary during the year, as the direction of the South-east Trade Wind is more S'ly when the sun is N of the equator than when S of it.

After passing Arquipélago de Cabo Verde, stand S between the meridians of 26° and 29° W, being nearer 26° W from May to October, and nearer 29° W from November to April. The equator should be crossed at points varying according to the season, as follows:—

Between January and April, when the North-east Trade Winds are well to the S, continue on a S'ly course, and cross the parallel of 5° N between 25° and 28° W, and the equator between 28° and 31° W.

In May and June the S'ly winds will be met with between 5° and 10° N. On meeting them, stand on the starboard tack so as to cross the parallel of 5° N between 18° and 20° W. Between 5° and 4° N, go round on to the port tack, and cross the equator between 25° and 23° W.

In July, August and September, the S'ly winds will be met between 10° and 12° N. On meeting them steer on the starboard tack so as to cross 5° N between 17° and 19° W. Go round then on the port tack, and cross the equator, as in May and June, between 25° and 23° W.

In October, November and December, the S'ly winds will be met between the parallels of 8° and 6° N. On meeting them, steer so as to cross 5° N between 20° and 23° W, then take the tack which gives most southing, and cross the equator between 29° and 24° W.

Caution: The South Equatorial Current is not so strong in the winter of the N hemisphere as in summer and autumn; but the mariner must remember that the strength of the current increases as it advances towards the American coast.

9.07.04. From the equator southward. Having crossed the equator as recommended, stand across the South-east Trade Wind on the port tack, even should the vessel fall off to about 260°, for the wind will draw more to the E as the vessel advances, and finally to due E at the S limit of the Trade. When in the vicinity of Penedos de São Pedro e São Paolo, frequent astronomical observations should be made, the current should be watched and allowed for, and a good lookout should be kept, as these rocks are steep-to, and can only be seen on a clear day from a distance of about 8 miles. The same precautions are necessary, if passing westward of Ilha de Fernando de Noronha, when approaching the dangerous Atol das Rocas.

On approaching the Brazilian coast between March and September, when the wind is from SE and the current near the coast sets N, it will be better to keep from 120 to 150 miles off the land until well S, and steer so as to be to windward of the port of destination; but from October to January, when the NE'ly winds prevail and the current sets SW, the coast may be approached with prudence, and a vessel may steer according to circumstances for her intended port.

9.07.05. For Río de Janeiro, from October to March make Cabo Frio and give the coast a prudent berth, as a constant and sometimes heavy swell sets in. The islands at the entrance to the harbour should not be approached until the sea breeze is well set in, as a vessel may run into a calm and be exposed to the swell and current.

9.07.06. For Montevideo or Río de La Plata, stand direct through the South-east Trades, passing about 200 miles E of Río de Janeiro.

9.07.07. For Bahía Blanca and ports southward. Bound to Bahía Blanca, or if, having called at Montevideo, and S-bound after leaving, or passing Río de La Plata, keep well in with the coast. This can be done with safety, as the winds are almost always from W, and an E'ly gale never comes on without ample warning. Pass Cabo Corrientes at a distance of 40 to 50 miles, and make the land S of Cabo Blanco and afterwards keep it topping on the horizon until the entrance to Estrecho de Magallanes has been passed.

This western route cannot be too much insisted on, and a vessel would do well to make a tack in-shore, even though with apparent loss of ground, to maintain it. As long as the wind does not back to the E of S the water will be smooth, and more sail can be carried than if farther out; and should the wind come from SE (unless when just off Cabo Blanco), the land recedes so much as to afford plenty of sea room.

9.08. Atlantic Ocean to Pacific Ocean

9.08.01. Estrecho de Magallanes is not advised as a sailing route. The passages of the old navigators, some of whom were more than 80 days between Puerto del Hambre and Cabo Pilar, the violence of the squalls, and the lack of sea room, sufficiently attest this.

9.08.02. Rounding Cabo de Hornos westbound, the usual track is take as direct a course as possible from a position 200 miles E of Río de Janeiro to about 45° S, 60° W, and from thence so as to pass 30 or 40 miles E of Isla de los Estados. This track lies between 120 and 200 miles E of the Patagonian coast, and is the most direct route for a large and well-found ship. The older navigators, however, recommend that sailing ships should keep within 100 miles of this coast, in order to avoid the heavy sea that is raised by the W'ly gales and to profit by the variableness of the inshore winds when from a W'ly direction.

Near the coast from April to September, when the sun has N declination, the winds prevail more from WNW to NNW than from any other quarter. E'ly gales are of very rare occurrence, and even when they do blow, the direction being obliquely upon the coast, it is not hazardous to keep the land aboard.

From October to March, when the sun has S declination, though the winds shift to the S of W, and frequently blow hard, yet as it is a weather shore, the sea goes down immediately after a gale. The winds at this time are certainly against making quick progress, yet as they seldom remain fixed in one point, and frequently back or veer 6 or 8 points in as many hours, advantage may be taken of the changes so as to keep close in with the coast.

When passing Isla de los Estados the usual course is E of the island, but there is, off its E extremity, a heavy tide-rip which extends for a distance of 5 or 6 miles, or even more, to seaward. When the wind is strong and opposed to the tidal stream, the overfalls are overwhelming, and very dangerous, even to a large and well-found vessel. Seamen must use every precaution to avoid this perilous area.

Estrecho de le Maire provides the shortest route round Cabo de Hornos with a valuable saving, when the difficulty of making westing is considered, of some 60 miles. Furthermore, a vessel is to some extent protected from W'ly gales and heavy seas when between Estrecho de le Maire and Cabo de Hornos, and she will avoid the NE'ly current which is encountered between the E extremity of Isla de los Estados and Cabo de Hornos.

On the other hand, the conditions must be suitable. Passage of Estrecho de le Maire is best attempted during daylight, with a fair wind and tide; the best time for beginning the passage through being at one hour after high water. A vessel should, if necessary, heave-to off the entrance to the strait until that moment. Under these conditions, even should the wind fail, or come adverse, a vessel would probably drive through rapidly, for the tidal streams are strong. With a S'ly wind, it would not be advisable to attempt the strait, for, with a weather-going tide, the sea is very turbulent, and might severely endanger the safety of a small vessel, and do much damage to a large one. In calm weather it would be still more imprudent, unless the W side of the strait can be reached, where a vessel might anchor, on account of the tidal streams which set towards Isla de los Estados where, if it became necessary to anchor, it would be in very deep water, and close to the land.

Should the wind fail, and the tidal stream not be sufficiently strong to carry a vessel through, there is a convenient anchorage in Bahía Buen Suceso.

N'ly and NE'ly winds are often accompanied by thick, misty weather; vessels approaching the strait are thus often compelled to lie-to for a time.

June and July are the best months for making a W-bound passage around Cabo de Hornos, as the wind is then often in the E quarter. The days are short, however, and the weather is cold. August and September are bad months, heavy gales with snow and ice occurring at about the time of the Equinox. From October to March, in summer, the winds are almost invariably W'ly. In April and May, the winds are slightly more favourable.

The passage from E to W around Cabo de Hornos should usually be made in about 57° S, or at about 100 miles S of the cape, but if, after passing Isla de los Estados, the wind be W'ly, the vessels should be kept upon the starboard tack, unless it veers to the S of SSW, until in 60° S, and then on the tack upon which most westing may be made. On this parallel the wind is thought by some persons to prevail more from the E than any other quarter.

It would usually be necessary to stand S in this manner from August to March; but from April fair passages have been made by keeping nearer the land and sighting Islas Diego Ramirez. There is no advantage to be gained by attempting, even with a fair wind, to go close to Cabo de Hornos; for the E-going Southern Ocean Current sets close past the cape, and appears to flow with greater velocity under the land than farther seaward on the route from Cabo San Juan.

9.09. Southbound from English Channel

9.09.01. General directions. For all destinations, at once make westing, as the prevailing winds are from that direction. With a fair wind, from the Lizard, steer to the WSW to gain an offing in long. 10° 12° W.

9.09.02. For western French ports, the above WSW'ly course should be modified, according to weather, in order to reach the destination more directly; but it must be borne in mind that the prevailing winds and currents have a tendency to set a vessel toward Île d'Ouessant and the many surrounding dangers. If circumstances require it, shelter may be obtained in one of the French anchorages until the weather improves, but Pointe de Penmárc'h should never be made.

9.09.03. For Lisbon, having gained an offing in 10° or 12° W, and with the wind from the W, haul to the wind on the tack which will best enable the approach to the proper course to be made without being drawn into the Bay of Biscay, which is especially to be avoided. During and after SW'ly gales the indraft of the Bay is strongest, and is most to be guarded against.

Should S'ly and SE'ly gales have been experienced the vessel will have been driven W, and in this case the aim should be to make progress S. On the other hand, if W'ly gales have prevailed, and the vessel has become embayed, it may be found difficult to weather Cabo Finisterre or even Cabo Ortegal; in these circumstances refuge may be found in El Ferrol, La Coruña, Ría del Barquero, or Ría de Vivero; and, in extreme cases, in the ports and roadsteads of France from the Gironde to Brest.

Rather than run any risk of becoming embayed in this manner, it will be better to make a long board to the W (as described above), and since W'ly winds generally veer, if a good offing has been made, the course can afterwards be pursued a point or two free, making allowance for a SE'ly set.

Proceeding S from off Cabo Finisterre, shape course to clear Os Farilhões and Ilha Berlenga, which should be given a wide berth in thick weather; with SW'ly winds it is better to keep off the land, to avoid the N'ly current that sets along the coast with those winds, as well as to be in a position to profit by any change of wind to the W and NW. In short, it is better to run to the S at some distance from the coast of Portugal, as W'ly winds make it a lee shore, and in winter these gales are frequent, blowing with great strength, and continuing for several days together.

Bound to Lisbon, when abreast Ilha Berlenga, steer for a position off Cabo da Roca.

9.09.04. For the Strait of Gibraltar, take the Libson route as directed in 9.09.03 to clear Os Farilhões and Ilha Berlenga, and then continue down the coast as far as Cabo de São Vicente; thence shape a course for the Strait of Gibraltar, as follows—

Cabo de São Vicente should be sighted, and then, after rounding it, as the vessel proceeds SE, the state of the wind and weather, and the indraft and current of the Strait of Gibraltar, must be considered and allowed for.

With the wind from NW, through N, to NE, make Cabo Trafalgar; with it from W, through S, to E, make Cabo Espartel.

In thick weather the safety of the vessel may be assured by making the bank which extends about 20 miles from the coast abreast Cabo Trafalgar, but care must be taken, on nearing Isla de Tarifa, to avoid Los Cabezos.

Cabo Espartel is safe to approach and can be seen from a long distance. To the S of Cabo Espartel, the land falls, and has been mistaken for the mouth of the strait; so that at night, when the light is not seen, caution is necessary. If an E'ly wind be met, and it is too strong to beat against, shelter will be found under Cabo Espartel, the vessel either keeping under weigh, or anchoring off Playa de Jeremias, about 3 miles S of the cape.

When working through the Strait of Gibraltar against an E'ly wind, keep in mid-channel to have the advantage of the current whilst the W-going tidal stream is running, but with the E-going stream either shore may be approached, with a chance of meeting favourable slants of wind. When Tarifa is passed, the force of the wind lessens.

When the E'ly wind inclines to the N, it is advisable to keep on the Spanish coast, avoiding La Perla, but when it inclines to the S, the African coast is preferable.

9.10. English Channel to Cape of Good Hope

9.10.01. General directions. Follow the directions given in 9.07.01 between 23° W and 31° W according to season (see 9.07.03), passing W of Arquipélago de Cabo Verde, and, having crossed the equator, stand across the South-east Trade on the port tack, even if the vessel cannot make a better course than WSW, for the wind will draw more to the E as the vessel advances, and finally to E at the S limit of the Trade. When in the vicinity of Penedos de São Pedro e São Paolo and Ilha de Fernando de Noronha precautions should be taken as in 9.07.04. During the greater part of the year the South-east Trade fails on a line drawn from the Cape of Good Hope to Ilha da Trindade (*20° 30′ S, 29° 19′ W*) and Ilhas Martin Vaz. This limit varies according to season.

When S of the South-east Trade, fresh winds variable in direction will be met. Those from NE through N to NW, if accompanied by cloudy weather, often shift suddenly to SW or S, but sometimes the wind steadies between W and WSW. From Ilha da Trindade shape course to the SE to cross the parallel of 30° S in about 22° W, and the meridian of Greenwich in about 35° to 37° S; whence to the Cape of Good Hope winds from W and S usually prevail. If E-bound round the Cape of Good Hope, cross the meridian of Greenwich in about 40° S.

After passing the meridian of Greenwich, a strong N'ly current will be frequently experienced; and on nearing the land, when bound to Table Bay, great attention is required, as there it will be found almost constantly running strongly to the N and, if it is disregarded, a vessel may have difficulty and lose time in reaching the bay. If bound to Simons Bay during the southern summer, it will be better to make the land about Cape Hangklip, as a strong current sets at that period across the entrance to False Bay towards Cape Point.

If near the coast at night, and the land is not visible, keep to the SW until the position is ascertained. In any circumstances, at night, there is great difficulty in judging the distance of lights situated under high land. Therefore, the prudent course for a stranger to pursue when making Table Bay is to keep off and on until daylight, far enough W of Green Point to prevent being becalmed near the land and set in upon the coast by the heave of the sea.

For continuation to the Indian Ocean, see 9.70.

Note: As the wind seldom, if ever, blows from E or NE (*i.e.*, directly off the peninsula), sailing vessels bound either for Table Bay or round the Cape of Good Hope should ensure a weatherly position to the N or S, according to the season. Those for Simons Bay have been detained many days by south-easters off Lion's Head and Hout Bay, in consequence of their making the land too far to the N during the summer season. The same winds would have been fair for them had they been 30 miles farther S. On the other hand, a vessel bound for Table Bay in the winter season will find it difficult to make her port from a position off Cape Point, during the continuance of N and NW winds, notwithstanding the general prevalence of NNW'ly current.

9.11. English Channel to West African ports

9.11.01. For Bathurst or Freetown, follow the directions given in 9.07.01, as far as Madeira. Thence steer so as to pass 60 to 100 miles W of Islas Canarias and from abreast these islands take one of the following routes, according to season.

From November to April, steer due S to about 20° N, and then edge over to the African coast, and steer as directly as possible to destination.

From May to October, keep more to the W, so as to sight Arquipélago de Cabo Verde; and, after picking up the South-east Trade in about 10° N, stand on the starboard tack direct to destination.

Note: Some navigators recommend standing to the W of Arquipélago de Cabo Verde, from abreast Islas Canarias; the North-east Trade being sometimes held longer by doing so, and turning E after passing them.

9.11.02. For Lagos or Calabar River, follow 9.11.01, as far as Islas Canarias, and then take the following seasonal routes.

From November to April, after edging over towards the coast as in 9.11.01, keep it at about 60 miles distance until abreast the port of destination.

From May to October, keep about 200 miles off the African coast during the South-west Monsoon. Turn to the E in about 6° or 7° N, 15° W and, closing the land to keep in the Guinea Current, steer to destination.

9.12. English Channel to St. Helena

9.12.01. The usual route is as for the Cape of Good Hope (9.10.01) to beyond the South-east Trade, then making enough easting to be able to enter the Trade again and weather St. Helena, which should be approached from SE. As a rule, avoid going on the starboard tack, or decreasing latitude, until St. Helena bears about 035°.

9.12.02. Northern Route. From January to April another route, known as the Northern Route, is, by some authorities, deemed preferable; that is, pass E of Arquipélago de Cabo Verde and along the African coast until past Cape Palmas, and thence, keeping in the Guinea Current, pass close to Ilha de São Thomé. In March, try to reach about lat. 7° S or 8° S, and long. 4° E, or 5° E, from whence St. Helena will generally be fetched on the port tack; but in June and early July it will probably be sufficient to get as far as 4° S or 5° S in the same longitude, as the wind is then generally more E'ly.

9.13. Bay of Biscay and west coasts of Spain and Portugal to Atlantic Ocean and English Channel

9.13.01. The usual route. Whether N-bound or S-bound, the importance of making to the W as quickly as possible, to join the routes to or from the Channel, cannot be too strongly stressed. From the Bay of Biscay, it may even be advisable to postpone sailing until a favourable wind enables a vessel to avoid all risk of being embayed. The indraft of the Bay is strongest after SW'ly gales.

See articles 9.04–9.12 from English Channel and article 9.14 from Gibraltar.

9.14. Gibraltar to English Channel

9.14.01. General directions. The W-bound passage through the Strait of Gibraltar against the general E-going current is, even with a fair wind (especially during neap tides), somewhat difficult for sailing vessels, but with W'ly winds, which increase the strength of the current, it is, for a large ship, almost impossible.

From Europa Point work along the coast of Spain during the W-going tidal stream until reaching Isla de Tarifa, and, if necessary, anchor there to await the next favourable stream. If from Algeciras, get under way at half ebb and so reach Punta del Acebuche by the commencement of the W-going stream.

If successful in doubling Isla de Tarifa by keeping to the Spanish coast, continue working up Playa de los Lances while the tidal stream remains favourable. After gaining Punta de la Pena tower (if it be preferred not to work inshore of Los Cabezos) cross to the African coast and work up under that as directed below. If the wind be from SW with moderate weather keep to the Spanish coast, as by crossing to the African coast, where the wind will probably be less, a vessel will be set to leeward. Should the wind shift to WNW or NW, the Spanish coast should still be kept.

If unable to fetch Tangier by following these directions cross to the African coast and work up that coast with the favouring stream, anchoring when necessary, until Tangier Bay is reached. But Isla de Tarifa should be fetched before standing across, otherwise there will be no certainty of weathering Punta Cires, and, should a vessel fall to leeward of it, it will be difficult even to regain Gibraltar Bay. Having weathered Punta Cires, work within the counter-current and near the shore to take advantage of any slant of wind that may occur, and then doubling Malabata Point, gain Tangier Bay, whence it will be easy to regain the Spanish coast. When the meridian of Tangier is passed, there is less current and a more manageable wind than in the narrows.

Note: With W'ly winds, if a small vessel makes Peninsula de la Almina, Ceuta, instead of Europa Point, she may work up on the African coast within the limits of the tidal streams, anchoring during the E-going stream.

From S of Ceuta to Gibraltar work up as far as Punta Cires, then taking advantage of the W-going stream, cross the strait, sailing a point free. If the wind is SW this is more easily done, with the favourable slants of wind met with on the African coast.

In light winds, preserve a good offing when in the vicinity of Cabo de São Vicente, as the currents generally set strongly along the land, and have a tendency towards the cape. Ripples are occasionally seen about 3 miles SW of and off the cape. After passing Cabo de São Vicente stand out to the NW on the prevailing N'ly winds until a favourable wind is met. Get an offing of at least 100 or 150 miles to avoid the S and SE'ly current near the coast of Portugal.

If a S'ly wind should be met with, stand to the N keeping sufficiently to the W to be able easily to weather Île d'Ouessant and do not steer an E'ly course until N of the parallel of that island.

9.15. Gibraltar to Halifax or New York

9.15.01. General Directions. Having cleared the Strait of Gibraltar as described in article 9.14, stand to the SW into the North-east Trade Wind. Thence continue as directed in article 9.04.03.

9.16. Gibraltar to West Indies, South America, Cabo de Hornos or Cape of Good Hope

9.16.01. General directions. Having cleared the strait as described in article 9.14, stand SW and join the appropriate route (9.05–9.10).

ROUTES IN MEDITERRANEAN SEA

9.19. Gibraltar to Gulf of Lions and Genova

9.19.01. After leaving Gibraltar, keep in mid-channel whether the wind be from E or W; thence follow the *5* summer or the winter route described below.

9.19.02. Summer route. Pass between Islas Baleares and Spain. A vessel bound to Marseille should sight Cabo de San Sebastian or Cabo Creus before crossing the Gulf of Lions; but if bound to Golfo di Genova she should make the land about Îles d'Hyères. In most cases, when bound to Genova or Livorno, the sooner *10* the coast of Provence is made, the more secure the voyage, unless the wind should be settled from SE to SW.

9.19.03. Winter route. Keep along the coast of Spain up to Cabo Creus, where shelter may be obtained in Bahia de Rosas in case of a N'ly gale or bad weather, and thence, if bound to Marseille, stand across the Gulf of Lions and pass well W of Île de Planier, but in case of a SE wind try to make easting as quickly as possible as *15* far as 5° E. If bound to Golfo di Genova make Îles d'Hyères.

9.19.04. Cautions. Sailing vessels rounding Cap Corse, the N end of Corsica, in the winter, should give it a berth of 6 or 8 miles, as within that distance dangerous whirlwinds and squalls come off from the cape.
When approaching the N shore of the Gulf of Lions, with S'ly winds, the greatest caution is necessary, as *20* the currents with these winds set strongly N and NW, and many vessels have been wrecked.

9.20. Gibraltar to Sardinia, Sicily, or Napoli

25

9.20.01. Summer route. With a fair wind, pass between Isla de Alborán and the coast of Spain and midway between Islas Baleares and the coast of Africa, along the S coast of Sardinia, and N or S of Sicily according to the port to which bound.
With an E'ly wind, work to windward in mid-channel, and then between Islas Baleares and the coast of Africa, keeping nearer the coast of Africa with the wind to the S of E, but nearer the islands with the wind to the *30* N of E.

9.20.02. Winter route. Keep along the coast of Spain as far as Cabo de Palos, and thence make for the S end of Sardinia, and pass N or S of Sicily.

35

9.21. Gibraltar to Malta

9.21.01. Summer route. From May to September, steer midway between Spain and Africa until abreast Cabo de Gata, and thence keep to the African coast as far as Cap Bon to profit by the E'ly current, passing N of Île *40* de la Galite. Thence proceed direct for Malta, passing N or S of Isola di Pantelleria and the Maltese islands according to circumstances.

9.21.02. Winter route. From October to April, W'ly winds (SW to NW) principally prevail, making it desirable to keep along the coast of Spain as far as Cabo de Palos, and then to steer for the S coast of Sardinia. In all cir- *45* cumstances the African coast should be avoided in the winter, as the N'ly gales make it a dangerous lee shore. From S of Sardinia make for Cap Bon, and pass N of Isola di Pantelleria and Gozo. With a strong SW'ly wind, however, the African coast may be kept as far as Cap Bon.
Note: If leaving Gibraltar with an E'ly wind, work to windward in mid-channel as far as Cabo de Palos, and thence to the S end of Sardinia. Thence make for Cap Bon, and pass N or S of Isola di Pantelleria and the *50* Maltese islands according to circumstances.

9.22. Malta to Gibraltar

55

9.22.01. Usual route. With a fair wind, after passing Cani Rocks, keep well off the African coast to avoid the E'ly current, and make the Spanish coast about Cabo de Palos, afterwards keeping along it to Gibraltar.
Great care is needed in making the Strait of Gibraltar in the thick weather which usually accompanies E'ly winds, as vessels mistaking the Rock of Gibraltar for Sierra Bullones and supposing they were passing through the strait and vice versa, have been wrecked in Bayía Mala and Ensenada de Tetuan, where the land is low. *60*
With NW'ly winds work along the coast of Sicily to Isola Marettimo and then work across to the S coast of Sardinia and the S coast of Spain. The difficulty of getting to windward with a W'ly wind increases as the Strait of Gibraltar is approached, vessels being frequently obliged to remain some days at anchor off the coast. Short tacks should be made along the Spanish coast to avoid the E'ly current in mid-channel.
If a NW'ly gale be encountered between Malta and Isola di Pantelleria, it is better to put back to Malta rather *65* than risk straining the ship in the heavy sea then met in that channel.

9.22.02. An alternative route, recommended as a better one, is, on leaving Malta, to stand on the starboard tack towards the coast of Africa, and work along it up to Cap Bon, subsequently keeping well off the coast of Africa. *70*

9.23. Napoli, Sicily, or Sardinia to Gibraltar

9.23.01. General directions. At all times of the year pass along the S coasts of Sardinia and Islas Baleares, and keep along the coast of Spain from Cabo de Palos, noting the remarks in article 9.22.01.

9.24. Genova and Gulf of Lions to Gibraltar

9.24.01. General directions. At all times of the year make for Cabo de San Antonio, and then keep along the coast of Spain, noting the remarks in 9.22.01.

ROUTES FROM PORTS ON WEST COAST OF AFRICA AND FROM ATLANTIC ISLANDS

9.25. Freetown or Arquipélago de Cabo Verde to English Channel

9.25.01. General directions. Stand to the NW into the North-east Trade Wind. Run through the Trade, passing W of Arquipélago de Cabo Verde, and then follow the route recommended for sailing vessels from Cape Town to England in article 9.40.01.

9.26. Freetown to Ascension Island

9.26.01. General directions. When clear of St. Ann Shoals run along the coast, within 50 miles of the land, until past Cape Palmas, when an endeavour should be made to cross the equator between the meridians of 3° 00′ W and 8° 00′ W, and then, without making a tack, Ascension Island will be fetched. During November long-continued calms and a strong NW'ly current are experienced in the vicinity of St. Ann Shoals.

9.27. Gold Coast, Nigeria or Bight of Biafra to Freetown or intermediate ports

9.27.01. For Freetown, stand S from the N part of the Bight of Biafra and, if possible, pass W of Fernando Póo and cross the equator as soon as possible, unless the vessel can point as high as WNW. When S of the equator stand W in the South Equatorial Current, and as westing is made the wind will be found to shift gradually round to the SE. When in about 10° W recross the equator and shape course for Freetown.

From any place in the Gulf of Guinea E of Cape Palmas, stand S into the South Equatorial Current, and then proceed as above.

9.27.02. For intermediate ports, in working to windward in the Bight of Benin, it is advisable to stand off on the starboard tack during the day, and inshore on the port tack by night, tacking if the wind should veer. If going some distance along the Guinea coast it is advisable to stand across the equator and make westing in the South Equatorial Current.

In the Harmattan season (November to February) the Guinea Current near the land in this bight is checked, and inshore a W'ly set is felt.

9.28. Gold Coast, Nigeria or Bight of Biafra to English Channel

9.28.01. General directions. Stand S of the equator into the South Equatorial Current, and then make westing, as from the Bight of Biafra to Freetown (9.27.01). Re-cross the equator in about 20° W, and then, as from the Cape of Good Hope (9.40.01) run through the North-east Trade, and shape a course for the English Channel.

9.29. Gold Coast, Nigeria or Bight of Biafra to South America

9.29.01. Via St Helena. Keep in the Guinea current until in the Bight of Bíafra, and then work along the coast as far as 6° S, whence there will generally be little difficulty in reaching St. Helena by keeping on the port tack. From Cape Palmas (4° 22′ N, 7° 44′ E) a vessel on the starboard tack will generally reach Cap Lopez (0° 38′ S, 8° 42′ E) and often S of Annobon (1° 28′ S, 5° 38′ E).

From St. Helena, keep in the South-east Trade, at about 20° S, until leaving Ilha da Trindade, when edge off for Río de Janeiro, or directly thence to the required destination.

9.29.02. Via Ascension, stand S on the starboard tack, generally weathering Ilha de São Thomé, as far as the equator; then stand W, taking care to keep in the South Equatorial Current. Progress will be slow at first, but as westing is made, the South-east Trade Wind will be felt.

From Cape Coast castle (5° 06′ N, 1° 14′ W) stand across the equator on the starboard tack, and then as above.

For vessels from the coast S of the equator the winds are always favourable, gradually backing from SW to SE as the island is approached.

From Ascension, stand through the South-east Trade Wind, to pick up the route from the English Channel to South America (9.07) and by it proceed direct to the required destination.

9.30. Gold Coast, and Bight of Biafra, to Cape Town and Cape of Good Hope

9.30.01. For Cape Town. Along the whole shore of the Bight of Biafra work to windward with the land and sea breezes, anchoring when necessary to prevent being set N by the current, especially during April and May, the season of calms and tornadoes.

From Cap Lopez to the Congo maintain a good offing, only approaching the shore to take advantage of the land breezes, which begin to blow at, or a few hours before, sunrise. In February, and sometimes in October, the sea breeze extends so well to the W as to enable vessels to head along the coast on either tack, but during May the wind blows steadily along the coast from S and S by E, night and day, with a N'ly current of 1 knot.

To cross the Congo Stream (see Admiralty Sailing Directions) either keep 200 miles off the coast or keep in anchoring ground; the latter is preferable. The usual course is to beat alongshore as far as Ponta Vermelha (*5° 39′ S, 12° 09′ E*), keeping on the bank of soundings in order to anchor if the wind falls light, crossing the Stream when the sea breeze has well set in.

From the Congo to Luanda, anchor every night when the sea breeze falls light; weigh with the first of the land breeze and continue on the port tack until about 1300; then tack, and by the time the sea breeze fails good progress will have been made to the S.

From Luanda to Baía de Mossamedes. In the neighbourhood of Ponta das Palmeirinhas, the current sets N with considerable force, and a good tack off the land for 50 or 60 miles will enable the vessel to weather the point; it seldom answers to work alongshore. Do not get away from the land more than 50 or 60 miles, as beyond these limits the sea breeze declines in force and draws more to the S, which would necessarily cause a loss of ground of the inshore tack, besides which the advantage of the alternate land and sea breezes, which are almost invariably experienced closer inshore, would be lost.

To the southward of Cabo Negro there is no difficulty in working S if advantage is taken of the variations of the wind, and the tacks are arranged accordingly. As rollers are frequent, the shore must be given a good berth. To the S of Cape Frio, N'ly winds may be expected from May to August.

9.30.02. For the Cape of Good Hope, stand off and run through the Trade Wind, and approach the Cape as when bound from England. See 9.10.01.

9.31. Ascension to English Channel

9.31.01. General directions. Ascension Island lies on the direct route from Cape Town to the English Channel. Follow the relevant part of the directions in paragraph 9.40.01.

9.32. Ascension to South America.

9.32.01. General directions are given in articles 9.29.02 and 9.07.

9.33. Ascension to St. Helena

9.33.01. General directions. Proceed S on the port tack, and when beyond the limit of the Trade Wind make easting and re-enter the Trade Wind far enough to windward to ensure weathering St. Helena Island. Avoid going on the starboard tack, or decreasing the latitude, until St. Helena Island bears about 010°.

9.34. Ascension to Cape Town or Cape of Good Hope

9.34.01. General directions. Run to the S on the port tack through, and then out of, the South-east Trade. Then stand SE with the object of crossing the Greenwich meridian between 35° S and 37° S. The parallel of 30° S will be crossed probably not W of about 14° W.

Continue between the parallels of 35° S and 37° S, and make destination from SW.

If bound to the Indian Ocean without calling at an intermediate port, proceed as directed in article 9.70.01.

9.35. Ascension to equatorial and south-western coasts of Africa

9.35.01. Notes and precautions. Leaving Ascension Island on the starboard tack, a vessel will fetch the coast of Africa, according to the season at some point between Cap Lopez and Luanda or even farther S. In May, however, the wind tends to be more E'ly and a vessel may not weather Annobon; on the other hand, a good vessel, sailing well, may make a landfall S of Congo River. Two precautions are, however, necessary, the first is not to get N of the parallel of 3° 00′ N or 4° 00′ N, and the second, not to bring the port of destination to bear more than 160°; an occasional short tack, as the wind shifts a little, may therefore be necessary, but the whole passage may sometimes be made with a free wind.

9.36. St. Helena to South America

9.36.01. General directions. Proceed as directed in 9.25.01, and if bound to Montevideo pass about 100 miles S of Ilha da Trindade; steer thence as directly as possible to destination.

9.37. St. Helena to Ascension and English Channel

9.37.01. General directions. Since both St. Helena and Ascension lie on, or very close to the route from Cape Town to the Channel, follow the relevant directions in 9.40.01.

9.38. St. Helena to west coast of Africa

9.38.01. Notes. Vessels will generally fetch as far S as Benguela, except in May, when the South-east Trade has more easting in it and the lee current is strong. To all places N of Benguela, therefore, the winds are favourable. They veer from SE to S and SW as the coast is approached.

9.39. St. Helena to Cape Town or Cape of Good Hope

9.39.01. General directions. Run S on the port tack through and out of the Trade, and then stand SE, crossing the meridian of Greenwich between 35° S and 37° S (probably not getting W of 10° to 14° W). Then keep between these parallels, as in the passage from England to Cape Town (9.10.01) and make Cape Town or the Cape of Good Hope from SW.

If bound to the Indian ocean without calling at an intermediate port, follow the directions in 9.70.01.

9.40. Cape Town or Cape of Good Hope to St. Helena, Ascension, English Channel, or Bordeaux

9.40.01. For the English Channel, first obtain a good offing to the NW as squalls from NW and WNW are not infrequent near the coast, and have been experienced in both seasons. Then shape course for St. Helena.

From St. Helena steer a direct course for Ascension, passing it on either side, and crossing the equator between 25° W and 30° W (in July between 20° W and 25° W, to ensure better winds). Then make a N'ly course to reach the North-east Trade as soon as possible (in July and August crossing the parallel of 10° N to the W of 30° W), and run through it. The North-east Trade Wind will probably be lost in about 26° N to 28° N, and 38° to 40° W, when W'ly winds may be expected, and on reaching these shape course for the English Channel.

It is seldom advisable to pass E of Arquipélago dos Açôres but should the wind draw to the NW when near them the most convenient channel through them may be taken. If E'ly winds are experienced after passing Arquipélago dos Açôres the vessel should still be kept on the starboard tack, as W'ly winds will probably be sooner found.

From November to February, a vessel should pass about 50 miles W of Ilha das Flores and Ilha do Corvo; but from June to August, at about 250 miles W of these islands. At other times of the year, at intermediate positions.

9.40.02. For Bordeaux, proceed as for the English Channel but begin to make easting on reaching the parallel of 30° N, passing between Ilha Terceira and Ilha de São Miguel and rounding the NW point of Spain at from 60 to 80 miles distance.

9.41. Cape Town or Cape of Good Hope to North and Central America and West Indies

9.41.01. To cross the equator, follow the route to the English Channel (9.40.01) as far as 5° E and then steer with a fair Trade Wind towards Isla Fernando de Noronha. On reaching 10° S, at about 30° W, stand more to the N, so as to cross the equator between 31° and 34 °W, and as soon as the North-east Trade has been picked up, steer through it, and thence as follows:—

9.41.02. For New York, try to reach 30° N, 70° W, and thence steer as directly as possible to New York.

9.41.03. For the Caribbean coast, Trinidad and the Guianas, proceed towards New York as in 9.21.02; leave that route when clear of the Equatorial Counter-current and proceed to destination as described in article 9.06.04.

9.41.04. For Leeward Islands, Jamaica, Belize, or ports in the Gulf of Mexico. Proceed as in 9.41.03, making W as described in article 9.06.03.

9.41.05. For Cuba, proceed as above, but make W as directed in article 9.06.02.

9.42. Cape Town to South American ports

9.42.01. General directions. Follow the directions in article 9.41.01 as far as 20° S; then run along this parallel with a fair South-east Trade wind as far as 30° W, whence steer direct for Río de Janeiro, or if for ports to the S, pick up, at 35° W, the outward route from the English Channel (9.07.06, 9.07,07. 9.08.) to the required destination.

9.43. Cape Town to west coast of Africa

9.43.01. General directions. First obtain a good offing to the NW, as squalls from NW or WNW are not infrequent near the coast, and have been experienced in all seasons. Steer to the N in the South-east Trade, taking advantage of the Benguela Current.

Bound to ports on the coast E of Cape Palmas, proceed as directly as navigation permits after first obtaining the offing described above.

ROUTES FROM PORTS ON WESTERN SIDE OF ATLANTIC OCEAN

9.44. From Canada and east coast of United States

9.44.01. For English Channel, owing to the prevailing fair winds and favourable currents, great circle or rhumb line courses may be steered as desired, provided that care is taken to avoid ice.

9.44.02. For Cape Town or Cape of Good Hope, make for 35° N, 45° W. It is better to be about 60 miles N of this position in midsummer and the same amount S in midwinter. From this position there are two main routes according to the time of year, each offering the quickest passage through the Doldrums.

From May to September, steer from about 36° N, 45° W to 25° N, 30° W, and thence through the North-east Trade Wind until meeting the South-east Trade Wind between the parallels of 1° N and 5° N. Then proceed on the starboard tack, crossing the parallel of 5° N between 17° and 20° W—the more E'ly longitude in July and August—and then put the vessel about, so as to cross the equator between 25° and 23° W. Thence stand S through the South-east Trade Wind, and begin to make easting from 25° S, 30° W, running due E along the parallel of 35° S as soon as it is reached, direct to destination.

October to April. From the position in about 34° N, 45° W, take a direct track through the North-east Trade Wind, so as to cross the parallel of 5° N between 20° W and 23° W. The S'ly winds will be met with in about 7° N; and on doing so, put the ship on whichever tack gives the most southing, and cross the equator between 20° W and 24° W.

Directions for crossing the equator are also given in article 9.07.03.

After crossing it, stand through the South-east Trade Wind, and when it is lost, steer SE so as to cross the parallel of 30° S in about 30° W, and thence so as to cross the meridian of Greenwich in 40° S. From this point, steer direct for Cape Town, taking care not to be set N by the Southern Ocean and Benguela Currents, which make NE'ly somewhat across the track.

For general directions for rounding the Cape of Good Hope when bound to the Indian Ocean or to Australia, see 9.70.01.

9.44.03. For South American ports, proceed as for Cape Town (9.44.02) as far as 5° S, and then follow the directions given in articles 9.07.04 to 9.08.02, as required by the destination.

9.44.04. For Río Amazonas, stand E to about 33° N, 50° W. Then turn S, and make as directly as possible to destination, but nothing to the W of 43° W until reaching 5° N, on account of strong W-going North Equatorial Current.

In July and August it will be advisable to make for 20° N, 37° W, and then to stand S until the South-east Trade Wind is picked up, between 5° N and 10° N, thus approaching Río Amazonas from well to the E.

9.44.05. For Caribbean Sea and Gulf of Mexico. Bound for **Barbados** or **Trinidad,** make good easting, passing either side of Bermuda, but steering so as to cross the meridian of 60° W or even 56° W, according to the season, before entering the tropics and steering to the S, always allowing for the current to leeward.

If bound for **Antigua** or **Leeward Islands** it will not be necessary to go so far E as 60° W. For **Mona Passage,** 66° W will give enough easting.

If bound for **Jamaica** or **Colon** make good easting as for Barbados, and then take Turks Island Passage and Windward Passage, which is the shortest route.

If bound for **Puerto La Guaira** (*10° 37′ N, 66° 56′ W*) or ports to the E, make good easting as for Trinidad, and use Mona Passage if required. A vessel making the South American coast W of her port will have considerable difficulty and lose much time working to windward to gain it.

If bound for the **Gulf of Mexico,** proceed as above by Turks Island Passage and Windward Passage to pass S of Cuba and through Yucatan Channel.

Further to the directions for approaching Mississippi River, given in Admiralty Sailing Directions, it may be said that the currents near the mouth of the river are uncertain, and fog and haze are prevalent, especially in summer and autumn. The mud banks are low, and the wind is generally from the E; soundings should therefore be obtained well to windward. If approaching from S or SW great attention should be paid to checking the latitude, for the bank is steep-to.

If bound for the S shores of the Gulf of Mexico, a vessel should strike the E edge of Banco de Campeche between the parallels of 22° N and 22½° N, and a knowledge of the exact point made is of great importance to check the longitude, especially during the rainy season, March to September, when observations can seldom be obtained. Sounding therefore must be used early and constantly. In this season it is best to take the inshore track across the bank as regular land and sea breezes then prevail; but if bound to Vera Cruz in the "Norther" season it is best to pursue the outer track, which runs between Arrecife Sisal and the outer cays, and into the open between the Trinagulo Oeste and Cayo Nuevo.

9.45. New Orleans to east coast of North America, or English Channel

9.45.01. General directions. Pass through Florida Strait, taking full advantage of the Gulf Stream, proceeding in it up the coast of the United States, if N-bound; but if for the English Channel standing NE for 40° N, 60° W, and thence continue as directly as possible, with a favourable current and with prevailing W'ly winds, to destination.

9.46. New Orleans to Colon or Mosquito coast

9.46.01. For Colon, pass between 5 and 10 miles off Cabo San Antonio, to a position 25 miles ENE of Farrall rock, and from thence pass between 5 and 10 miles W of Isla de Providencia, and direct to Colon.

9.46.02. For Mosquito coast, after passing Cabo San Antonio steer to pass W of Swan Islands and Vivario Cays and thence through Mosquito Channel (*14° 21′ N, 83° 10′ W*).

9.47. South-west part of Gulf of Mexico to Atlantic Ocean

9.47.01. General directions. From the SW ports in the Gulf of Mexico take the passage inshore along the coast of Yucatan, where the adverse current is weak. Bound E, pass over Banco de Campeche within the shoals, but the passage between Arrecife Sisal and the coast should only be taken by daylight. In passing through Florida Strait from any part of the Gulf, and in proceeding N off the Atlantic coast of the United States, take all possible advantage of the Gulf Stream.
For English Channel, stand NE for 40° N, 60° W, and then proceed direct, see 9.45.01.

9.48. Belize to English Channel or coast of North America

9.48.01. For the English Channel, proceed via Yucatan Channel, thence through Florida Strait with the Gulf Stream to a position midway between Bermuda and Halifax; thence after crossing the meridian of 40° W in about 45° N, continue direct to destination.

9.48.02. For east coast of North America, proceed as directed in 9.45.01.

9.48.03. For the north coast of the Gulf of Mexico, pass 35 miles E of Isla Mujeres (*21° 12′ N, 86° 43′ W*), and thence continue as directly as possible to destination.

9.49. Colon or Colombian ports to English Channel, New York or New Orleans

9.49.01. For English Channel, steer to pass through Windward Passage, between Haiti and Cuba, and thence make northing on the starboard tack. When in the westerlies, steer to cross the meridian of 40° W in about 44° N in summer, and about 40° N in winter. Thence continue as directly as possible.

9.49.02. For east coast of United States, pass through Windward Passage as in 9.49.01 and, having cleared Turks Island, stand NW in the Antilles Current, until picking up the Gulf Stream N of the Bahamas, and thence proceed as directly as possible along the Atlantic coast of the United States.

9.49.03. For north shore of the Gulf of Mexico, take the reverse of the New Orleans to Colon route (9.46.01) as far as the position off Farrall Rock, after which a course can be shaped to pass 30 to 40 miles W of Cabo San Antonio.

9.50. From the southern shores of the Caribbean Sea northward

9.50.01. General directions. From any of the ports along the Venezuelan coast and along the S shores of the Caribbean Sea, work E coastwise in the eddies or counter current, until able to fetch the desired port on the starboard tack. At times, however, off Venezuela, the W'ly current is so far inshore, that vessels have to cross it and work up to the N of it, as mentioned for Curaçao in 9.52.01. In winter, when the wind is well NE, it is necessary to make more easting than in summer, when the wind is in places E of S.
From any of the Venezuelan ports, Mona Passage gives the best route for sailing vessels bound to any United States Atlantic port, or to English Channel.

9.51. Jamaica to New York, Halifax, or English Channel

9.51.01. General directions. From April to September, run to leeward round the W end of Cuba, and then through Florida Strait, thus getting full benefit of the Gulf Stream. Thence proceed as described in article 9.45.01.

From October to March, N'ly winds prevail in Florida Strait, and Windward Passage should be preferred, although ships are frequently opposed there by contrary winds and currents. These may to some extent be overcome by keeping nearer the coast of Santo Domingo, Haiti, as there a windward current is frequently found.

When through Windward Passage, use either Crooked Island, Mayaguana, or Caicos Passages according as the wind may favour, and from thence proceed direct to New York or Halifax. If bound to the English Channel, see 9.49.01 onward from Windward Passage.

9.52. Jamaica to Curaçao and southern shores of Caribbean Sea

9.52.01. General directions. Work to windward along the S coast of Haiti, where at full and change of the moon, and also near the time of the autumnal equinox, there is often a counter or E'ly set, until on, or to windward of, the meridian of Curaçao; then stand across for that port when certain of fetching well to windward to allow for the prevailing W'ly current. In summer more easting is necessary than in winter, as the wind has more southing in it and the current in the summer is stronger.

A vessel which makes a landfall to leeward of her port will usually find a counter or E'ly set near the shore in which she can work up; failing to do this, if E of the meridian of 70° W, she may possibly have again to cross the prevailing W'ly set, and work up to the N of 14° N or 15° N.

9.53. West Indies to United States ports, to Canadian ports or to English Channel

9.53.01. General directions. The great object for sailing vessels is to get N into the W'ly winds as speedily as possible, and Bermuda lies in the track (or near the best track) for this purpose, though a course E or W of it may be taken according to the direction of the wind met with and the season. A more N'ly route is followed in summer than in winter.

From Barbados, fetch to windward of all the islands, but from the other Windward Islands pass close to leeward of Antigua, taking care not to come within a depth of 20 m.

Having cleared the other islands, and when steering directly for Bermuda, vessels sometimes fall to the E of the course, and find it very difficult to make the latter island when W'ly winds prevail; in this case take advantage of the Trade Wind to reach the meridians of 68° or 70° W before going N of the parallel of 25° N.

When bound to the English Channel, or to Western Europe, it is seldom advisable to pass E of Arquipélago dos Açôres but a passage between Ilha do Corvo and Ilha das Flores and the other islands of the Arquipélago is recommended by some navigators. If E'ly winds are met with after passing Arquipélago dôs Açôres, still keep on the starboard tack, as by so doing W'ly winds will probably be sooner found.

9.50. Barbados to north-east coast of South America

9.54.01. General directions. Work SE until abreast the destination before attempting to cross the prevailing W'ly current, particularly during and near the months of August and September when the current is strong and the wind well to the S of E. It has been recommended at this season that sailing vessels should not come S of 8° N until they are certain of fetching their destination on the port tack.

9.55. Río Amazonas to Recife

9.55.01. The normal route is close inshore out of the influence of the W'ly current, and by taking advantage of the current, tidal stream, and every slant of wind, a sailing vessel will generally perform the voyage from Río Amazonas to Recife in about 30 days. During the prevalence of ENE'ly and NE'ly winds a current sets ESE along and near the coast; this fact is well known to the masters of the coasting craft and is taken advantage of by them.

When the weather will permit, a vessel may anchor off any part of the coast without danger. In working along shore, the dry season (July to December) is considered preferable, as the winds are then fresh and steady. Stand off during the day, and in towards the land at night, so as to be near the coast in the morning to take advantage of the land breeze, by which a good sailing vessel will make from 40 to 50 miles a day.

In the rainy season (January to June), working to windward is more tedious, as calms, light variable winds, squalls and rain prevail. In this case stand on the tack that is most favourable, and, as a general rule, do not go outside a depth of 55 m. If the wind is steady, tack as in the dry season, but do not lose sight of the coast.

9.55.02. Alternative route. Stand directly N across the equator into about 10° N, and then tack. This will save wear of sails and rigging, and will probably take no longer than working along the inshore route.

9.56. Río Amazonas to New York or English Channel

9.56.01. General directions. After getting a good offing, stand N, so as to pick up the main Atlantic routes to the N; that to New York (9.41.02) in about 10° N to 15° N, and that to the English Channel (9.40.01) between 25° and 30° N, passing W of Arquipélago dos Açôres as directed in that article.

9.57. Recife and north-east coast of South America to English Channel or New York

9.57.01. For English Channel, after obtaining a good offing, stand N, and after crossing the doldrums, stand through the North-east Trade Wind into the Westerlies, passing W of Arquipélago dos Açôres as directed in article 9.40.01.

9.57.02. For New York and ports northward, proceed as in 9.57.01, and when the doldrums are crossed, and the North-east Trade Wind is reached, stand direct for the required destination by the main route from the Cape of Good Hope (9.41.02) from about 10° N.

9.58. Pôrto do Salvador to Europe or North America

9.58.01. General directions. In leaving the ports immediately S of Recife for Europe, the NE winds sometimes compel sailing vessels to keep on the port tack for 10 or 15 days, and to stand SSE or even SE to the parallels of 28° S or 32° S; and as far E as the meridian of Ilha da Trindade. Then on the starboard tack it should be possible to weather the E part of the coast, and also Arquipélago de Fernando de Noronha. As northing is made the wind will veer from E to SE, and the equator should be crossed in 27° W to 29° W.

9.59. Río de Janeiro to Pôrto do Salvador or Recife

9.59.01. General directions. N-bound along the E coast of Brazil, it is preferable first to make a stretch to the SE. Working along the coast, bordered by reefs, subject to currents, and light winds at night, is not recommended.

The Brazil Monsoons do not extend more than 120 or 150 miles out to sea. Beyond this limit the Trade Wind is found, generally blowing from between SE and E.

From November to February, while fresh NE winds and a S'ly current of 1 or 1½ knots extend along the coast, especially in the vicinity of Cabo de São Tomé, the wind being also more N'ly than in the offing, it is necessary to stand for 450 to 600 miles to the ESE before tacking. This season, particularly December and January, is the most unfavourable time of year for the N-bound passage. In October and March, do not stand farther E than actually necessary for weathering Arquipélago dos Abrolhos, as N of their latitude the winds will be about E or E by S.

From March to September, close the coast as near as possible, taking advantage of the land and sea breezes, and making short tacks to the E on meeting the fresh NE winds which are common off Cabo Frio and Cabo São Tomé. Then continue along the coast at distances of from 30 to 90 miles. A more E'ly route is generally used, but if bound for Pôrto do Salvador it does not appear advantageous to stand too far off the land.

9.60. Río de Janeiro to Europe or North America

9.60.01. General directions. Make first a stretch to the SE to about 35° W, and then stand N, in the South-east Trade, crossing the equator between 27° W and 32° W; and after passing through the doldrums, steer direct for American ports, or to the NW and W of Arquipélago dos Açôres, as directed in article 9.40.01, if bound to European ports.

9.61. Río de Janeiro to Cape of Good Hope

9.61.01. General directions. Stand to the SE to about 32° S, 30° W; thence through 35½° S, 20° W; 37° S, 10° W; 37½° S, 0°; and 37° S, 10° E; making the Cape of Good Hope from SW.

If bound to the Indian Ocean, without calling at Cape Town, cross the meridian of Greenwich in about 40° S, and run E on that parallel, or, from November to March, on 45° S, see 9.70.01.

9.62. Río de La Plata to Europe or North America

9.62.01. General directions. From May to September proceed direct to Cabo Frio, and thence across the equator in 27° W to 29° W, as from Río de Janeiro (9.60.01).

From October to April stand E to beyond 30° W, and thence N into and through the South-east Trade Wind, as from Río de Janeiro (9.10.01).

9.63. Río de La Plata to Cape of Good Hope

9.63.01. General directions. Pick up the parallel of 40° S in 30° W. Thence, keep along that parallel as far as the meridian of Greenwich, whence steer directly for Cape Town, or, if bound to the Indian Ocean without calling at that port, continue E along, or, in the summer, a few degrees S of, the parallel of 40° S. See 9.70.01.

5

9.64. Río de La Plata to Falkland Islands

9.64.01. General directions. Keep well W of the direct route until nearing the islands.

10

9.65. Río de La Plata to round Cabo de Hornos

9.65.01. Routes. Two routes are recommended, either to steer SE and pick up the route from Río de Janeiro (9.08.02) or to sail coastwise (9.07.07). In either case Estrecho de le Maire offers the alternative to passage E of Isla de los Estados (9.08.02).

15

9.66. Cabo de Hornos to English Channel

20

9.66.01. Rounding the Horn from W to E is a comparatively easy matter, for the prevailing winds are favourable and the current near Cabo de Hornos sets strongly E. The passage is usually made between 56° S and 57° 30′ S, to the N of the W-bound route. December and January are the most favourable months; June and July, when E'ly winds are not unusual, are the least favourable. Heavy W'ly gales, with snow and hail, may be expected in August and September; in winter, a track about 80 miles S of Cabo de Hornos is recommended.

25

9.66.02. The best landfall after rounding Cabo de Hornos is W of Estrecho de le Maire, where the coast is free of outlying dangers. The islands make a lee during SW'ly and W'ly winds. Keep in mid-channel in Estrecho de le Maire, avoiding the overfalls off Cabo San Diego.

A vessel in trouble should run boldly through Estrecho de le Maire and round up under the land if necessary.

30

9.66.03. Cabo de Hornos to Equator. The usual route is about 80 miles S of Falkland Islands and to a position in about 35° S, 30° W; making W of that position between April and August, and E of it from September to March. Continue, according to season, from April to August standing N as far as 10° S, 25° W, keeping as much as possible to the W of 25° W throughout, and cross the equator between 25° W and 28° W. It might even be possible to pass W of Ilha de Trinidade at this time of year. From September to March, stand NNE from 35° S, 30° W to about 25° S, 20° W, and then run N with the South-east Trade Wind, to cross the equator between 22° W and 25° W.

35

40

9.66.04. Alternative routes to the equator. If ice is prevalent, particularly between October and February, steer so as to cross 50° S in about 51° W and 40° S in about 45° W. Then make northing until the South-east Trade Wind is met, joining the route from Río de La Plata (9.62.01) in about 35° S.

Alternatively, some navigators recommend passage W of Falkland Islands from October to February on account of the greater freedom from ice in that region, after which a NE'ly course should be steered to join the N-bound route in about 35° S, 41° W. If unable to pass W of Falkland Islands, pass as close E as the wind will allow.

45

Caution: If meeting with a foul wind whilst S of 40° S, it would be better to stand NW than to the E, as ice is likely not far E of Falkland Islands.

50

9.66.05. From Equator to English Channel, join the route from Cape Town (9.40.01) on meeting the North-east Trade Wind.

9.67. Cabo de Hornos to east coast of North America

55

9.67.01. General directions. From April to August, follow the directions in 9.66.03 to 10° S, 25° W, where the track from the Cape of Good Hope to North America crosses that from Cabo de Hornos; follow it to destination.

From September to March, follow the directions in 9.66.03 for these months to 15° S, 20° W, where the route meets the track from the Cape of Good Hope to North America (9.41.01); follow this route to destination.

60

9.68. Cabo de Hornos to east coast of South America

65

9.68.01. General directions. At all times of the year, after rounding Cabo de Hornos, stand N with the Falkland Current between Falkland Islands and Tierra del Fuego, and carry it up the coast, with the prevailing W'ly winds, to Bahia Blanca or Río de La Plata.

From Río de La Plata onwards to Cabo Frio or Río de Janeiro, see 9.62.01, and from Río de Janeiro to Pôrto do Salvador, or Recife, see 9.59.01.

70

F

9.69. Cabo de Hornos to Cape Town

9.69.01. General directions. Follow the directions given in articles 9.66.03 and 9.66.04 taking particular notice of the remarks as to ice, as far as about 50° S, 45° W, and from this position, at all seasons steer a direct course with the prevailing W'ly wind, and a favouring current to 40° S, on the meridian of Greenwich; thence steer in a NE'ly direction for Cape Town. See the relevant part of article 9.10.01 on the route from the English Channel; the portions dealing with the voyage after passing the meridian of Greenwich are equally applicable to the route from Cabo de Hornos, as regards winds, currents, and the making of Cape Town itself.

9.70. Cabo de Hornos eastward to Indian Ocean and Australian ports

9.70.01. General directions. Follow the directions given in article 9.69.01 as far as 40° S, on the meridian of Greenwich, and from this position continue due E along that parallel, but from November to March a quicker passage will probably be made in about 45° S, though better weather will be found in 40° S.

For continuation onward through the Indian Ocean see the appropriate routes from Cape Town, articles 10.01—10.08.

CHAPTER 10

INDIAN OCEAN, RED SEA, AND EASTERN ARCHIPELAGO
SAILING ROUTES

CONTENTS   *Page*

ROUTES THROUGH RED SEA

ROUTES FROM ADEN

ROUTES FROM WEST COAST OF INDIA AND CEYLON

ROUTES FROM PORTS IN BAY OF BENGAL

ROUTES FROM PORTS IN BURMA

ROUTES SOUTHWARD OR WESTWARD FROM SINGAPORE OR EASTERN ARCHIPELAGO

NORTHERN AUSTRALIA TO SYDNEY, INDIAN OCEAN, AND CHINA SEA

ROUTES FROM SOUTH-WEST AND SOUTH AUSTRALIA

ROUTES FROM SYDNEY TO PORTS IN INDIAN OCEAN

ROUTES FROM CAPE TOWN OR CAPE OF GOOD HOPE

10.01. Cape Town or Cape of Good Hope to Australia and New Zealand

10.01.01. Icebergs are most numerous SE of the Cape of Good Hope and midway between Kerguelen Island and the meridian of Cape Leeuwin. The periods of frequency vary greatly. It may happen that while ships are passing ice in lower latitudes, others, in higher latitudes, find the ocean free of it.

The lengths of many of the Southern Ocean icebergs are remarkable; bergs of 5 to 20 miles in length are frequently sighted S of the 40th parallel, and bergs of from 20 to 50 miles in length are far from uncommon.

It may be gathered from numerous observations that bergs may be found anywhere S of the 30th parallel, that as many as 4500 bergs have been observed in a run of 2000 miles, that estimated heights of from 240 m to 520 m are not uncommon, and that bergs of from 6 to 82 miles in length are numerous.

10.01.02. Rounding Cape of Good Hope. From Cape Town, vessels are recommended to pick up the E-bound track from Cabo de Hornos (9.70) at the point where it is met by the track from the North Atlantic (9.10) bound to the Indian ocean, namely in about 40° S, 20° E. There is but little difficulty in passing the Cape of Good Hope E-bound at any time, though a greater proportion of gales will be met with from April to September, the winter season.

From October to April, E'ly winds prevail as far S as the tail of Agulhas Bank (about 37° S), with variable but chiefly W'ly winds beyond it. In May and September, at the tail of the bank, E'ly and W'ly winds are in equal proportion, but between these months W'ly winds prevail, extending sometimes close in to the coast. Should a SE'ly wind be blowing on leaving Table Bay or Simons Bay, stand boldly to the SW until the W'ly winds are reached or the wind changes to a more favourable direction. In all cases when making for the 40th parallel S of the Cape of Good Hope, steer nothing E of S, so as to avoid the area SE of the tail of Agulhas Bank, where gales are frequent, and heavy and dangerous breaking cross seas prevail.

10.01.03. Crossing the Indian Ocean. Having crossed to the S of the (W-going) Agulhas current, and picked up the W'ly winds, the best latitude in which to cross the ocean must to some extent depend on circumstances.

45

50

55

60

65

70

Vessels bound to Australian ports would make the passage at about the parallel of 39° or 40° S, but those bound to Tasmania or New Zealand, would do so at between 42° or 43° S, especially from October to March. Between 39° S and 43° S the winds generally blow from a W'ly direction, and seldom with more strength than will admit of carrying sail. In a higher latitude the weather is frequently more boisterous and stormy; sudden
5 changes of wind with squally wet weather are almost constantly to be expected, especially in winter. Île Amsterdam may be seen from a distance of 60 miles in clear weather.

In summer, many vessels take a more S'ly route, some going as far S as 52° S, but the steadiness and comparatively moderate strength of the winds, with the smoother seas and more genial climate north of 40° S, compensate by comfort and security for the time presumed to be saved by taking a shorter route.
10 Tempestuous gales, sudden violent and fitful shifts of wind, accompanied by hail or snow, and terrific and irregular seas are often encountered in the higher latitudes; moreover the islands in the higher latitudes are so frequently shrouded in fog that often the first sign of their vicinity is the sound of the surf beating against them.

15 **10.01.04. Approaching Bass Strait,** passage N of King Island is recommended. In this approach, when making the land at Moonlight Head or Cape Otway, the currents must be carefully watched, particularly during SW'ly or S'ly winds; vessels have been wrecked on King Islands by not steering for Cape Otway. In normal weather, it is desirable to round Cape Otway at a distance of not less than 3 or 4 miles. When approaching Bass Strait in thick weather, or when uncertain of the vessel's position, do not reduce the soundings to less than 70 m. Soundings
20 of 110 m to 130 m will be found 25 or 30 miles W of King Island. Outside this limit the soundings deepen rapidly to over 180 m.

Caution: In approaching King Island from the W, especially during thick or hazy weather, caution is required on account of the variable strength of the current, which sets SE at a rate which varies from $\frac{1}{2}$ knot to $2\frac{1}{2}$ knots, according to the strength and duration of the W'ly winds, and sounding is recommended.
25 The entrance to Bass Strait between King Island and Hunter Group is not recommended on account of Bell Reef and Reid Rocks which lie in it. If, from necessity or choice, entering Bass Strait by this passage, keep S of Reid Rocks and Bell Reef, the latter being passed at a distance of $2\frac{1}{2}$ miles S of it by steering for Black Pyramid on a bearing of 098°. With a commanding breeze the passage between King Island and Reid Rocks may be taken without danger by paying attention to the tidal streams, which set somewhat across the channel at times.
30 From Black Pyramid pass about one mile N of Albatross Islet, whence, if bound to Port Dalrymple, round the sunken danger Mermaid rock, off Three Hummock island, and then make a direct course.

10.01.05. Passage to Fremantle. Leave the trans-ocean route (10.01.03) in about 90° E, and thence make direct for destination. Some navigators, however, recommend continuing eastward as far as 100° E before
35 turning NE.

During summer, from October to March, to avoid being set to the N of Rottnest Island, it is advisable to make the land about Cape Naturaliste, see 6.131.

10.01.06. Passage to Adelaide. Leave the trans-ocean route (10.01.03) on the meridian of Cape Leeuwin, or
40 about 115° E. Thence proceed direct for Cape Borda.

10.01.07. Passage to Melbourne. Leave the trans-ocean route (10.01.02) in 135° E and proceed direct for Bass Strait (10.01.03). If Cape Otway is rounded early in the evening, with a fresh S'ly wind, beware of over-running the distance, as a strong current after a prevalence of S'ly gales, often sets NE along the land; bearings of Split
45 Point light give a good check. When abreast of Split Point, if there is not enough daylight to get into pilot waters, stand off and on shore till daylight, keeping in more than 35 m of water. Do not heave to.

10.01.08. Passage to Sydney. In summer, leave the trans-ocean route (10.01.03) in about 120° E, and steer to pass S of Tasmania.
50 After rounding South Cape, give a berth of 20 or 30 miles to Cape Pillar and the E coast of Tasmania, to escape the baffling winds and calms which frequently perplex vessels inshore, while a steady breeze is blowing in the offing. This is more desirable from December to March, when E'ly winds prevail, and a current is said to be experienced off the SE coast at 20 to 60 miles from the shore, running N at the rate of $\frac{3}{4}$ knot, while inshore it is running in the opposite direction, with nearly double that rate. From a position about 30 miles E of Cape
55 Pillar, proceed on a course of about 012° for about 350 miles to a position 15 miles E of Cape Howe, whence continue as directly as possible to make Sydney, but keeping at first at a distance from the coast, in order to lessen the strength of the S-going Australian Coast Current, not closing the land till N of South head, Port Jackson.

Some navigators prefer to stand E as far as 155° E before turning N for Port Jackson, and thus escape almost
60 altogether the S'ly set.

In winter follow the route for Melbourne (10.01.07) as far as Cape Otway and then steer to pass through Bass Strait about 2 miles S of Anser Group, 3 miles N of Rodondo Island and 2 miles S of South East Point Wilson Promontory. Then steer to pass about 5 miles SE of Rame Head and Gabo Island. Occasionally and especially during and after E'ly gales the current sets strongly towards the land; in thick weather sounding must
65 not be neglected. See Navigational Notes on Bass Strait in 10.01.04. and 10.160.

From Rame Head stand on to the E to about 154° E, before turning to the N in order to escape from the S'ly set of current along the coast of New South Wales, and approach Port Jackson from a point slightly to the N. During E'ly gales (June to August), an offing may be maintained by watching the shifts of wind, and keeping on the starboard tack as long as prudent, thus bringing the prevailing S-going current on the lee
70 bow.

10.01.09. Passage to Hobart. Leave the trans-ocean route (10.01.03) in about 120° E; then steer for a position 10 miles S of South West Cape, Tasmania; or in any case far enough to the S to ensure avoiding the rocky W coast at night through any error in the reckoning, or being caught on a lee shore by a SW gale. In fine weather, from 10 miles S of South West Cape, pass between Maatsuyker Group and Mewstone Islet, then steer to pass 3 miles S of South Cape. When blowing heavily from SW or S, especially if unable to obtain observations before making the land, it is desirable to keep more to the S, passing S of Mewstone Islet and on either side of Pedra Blanca and Eddystone, taking care to avoid Sidmouth Rock. Proceed to Hobart through Storm Bay.

10.01.10. Passage W of Tasmania and to New Zealand ports. It is often necessary, and in heavy W'ly weather desirable, to make the passage down the W coast of Tasmania at from 120 to 250 miles from the coast, and often at the same distance round the S end of the island.

From the Indian Ocean, for New Zealand ports, it is normal in summer to leave the trans-ocean route (10.01.03) in about 110° E and to proceed S of Tasmania in 45° S to 47° S, whence the main route is also taken across the Pacific Ocean (11.02). In winter, take the winter route for Sydney (10.01.08) through Bass Strait.

Both in summer and winter, if bound to Auckland proceed round the N point of New Zealand; if for Wellington, through Cook Strait, and if for Otago or Lyttleton, S of New Zealand through Foveaux Strait or S of Stewart Island.

See also 11.03.04, 11.03.05.

10.02. Cape Town or Cape of Good Hope to Singapore or China Sea

10.02.01. General notes. Although this voyage takes a vessel out of Indian Ocean waters, properly so termed, into the Eastern Archipelago and China Sea (which should be considered as "Pacific Ocean" waters), it is treated more conveniently as a continuous voyage, and will so be considered. As the voyage is complicated not only by different routes due to monsoons, but also by several alternative channels and straits among the islands of the Eastern Archipelago the following procedure has been adopted.

The routes below give, in detail, the passage from the Cape of Good Hope as far as the S entrances to the Eastern Archipelago, and thence a summary of the various straits and passages to be navigated on the continuation of the voyage to Singapore or the China Sea. Directions for passages through the Eastern Archipelago are given in articles 10.30 to 10.51.

Vessels passing the Cape of Good Hope in September have taken, with great success, a route passing S and E of Australia, W of New Caledonia, through Pioneer Channel (*5° S. 154° E*), across the equator in about 156° E, and thence direct. This route is known as the **Great Eastern Route.**

The monsoon periods, on which these routes depend are from May to September, when a SE'ly or E'ly Monsoon prevails in the Eastern Archipelago, and a SW'ly Monsoon (usually not strong) in the China Sea; and from October to March, when a NW'ly or W'ly Monsoon prevails in the Eastern Archipelago, and a NE'ly Monsoon (the latter usually strong) in the China Sea.

The object of a vessel bound to the China Sea being to get as far to windward as possible in the Indian Ocean before arriving in the monsoon area, she would make for the W end of the island chain during the SW'ly Monsoon period of the China Sea (May to September); and for the more E'ly passages of the chain during the NE'ly Monsoon period of the China Sea (October to March). The alternative route to the China Sea, above referred to, is suitable only in October and November, and passes through the central part of the island chain.

The following variations to the above are not infrequently taken though they do not appear to possess any particular advantage.

Though the October to March route to the China Sea is usually made by the more E'ly passages through the islands, it is possible to make it by passing through Sunda Strait; and then proceeding N through the China Sea along the N coast of Borneo by Palawan Passage (11.33); or else, after passing Sunda Strait, to stand E through the Java Sea to the E passages.

Vessels bound only to Singapore use Sunda Strait at all times.

Vessels bound to ports on the E coast of Borneo, or in Makassar Strait, etc., use either Sunda Strait, Bali Strait, Lombok Strait or Alas Strait. These straits could also be used, during the local North-west Monsoon period, instead of the passage through the islands farther E; and then standing E to pick up the regular Eastern route.

10.02.02. For Singapore, from May to September take route across the Indian Ocean described in 10.01.02, along the parallel of 39° S or 40° S, as far as about 75° E. From thence edge away to the NE crossing 30° S in about 100° E; and 20° S in 105° E, passing close W of Christmas Island, and up to Tandjung Gedeh (the E entrance point of Sunda Strait from the Indian Ocean). Care must be taken to keep well to the E, especially in June, July, and August, when the South-east Monsoon and the W-going current are at their strongest, or the vessel may fall to leeward of Tandjung Gedeh and find great difficulty in recovering it against wind and current.

From October to March, take the trans-ocean route, as above, as far as about 75° E; thence steer to pass through 25° S, 98° E and thence directly N for Sunda Strait, passing midway between Christmas Island and Cocos or Keeling Islands, and steering for Balimbing Pamantjasa on the W side of Sunda Strait, as in this season the E-going current is strong, and W'ly winds blow at times with considerable strength. If contary winds are met with after passing Île Saint-Paul (*38° 43' S, 77° 33' E*), stand N, through the South-east Trade, into the North-west Monsoon, and from thence direct to Sunda Strait.

During the changes of monsoon, March, April, and September-October, it is advisable to make easting until due S of the entrance to Sunda Strait, and then steer directly for it.

In continuation of the route for Singapore there are three alternatives from Sunda Strait, as summarised below. For directions see 10.32–10.42.

The usual route is through Selat Bangka and Riouw Strait (10.34–10.37).

The first alternative route is through Selat Gelasa and then either by Riouw Strait to Singapore; or else from Selat Gelasa continue N to the E of Bintan Island and through Singapore Strait, from the E entrance to Singapore road. See 10.39–10.42.

The second alternative route, known as the Inner Route, should be taken between October and March only, when the North-east Monsoon is blowing strong in the China Sea, when, having passed either through Selat Bangka or Selat Gelasa a vessel is confronted by a head wind, a heavy sea, and an adverse current in attempting to make the southern entrance to Riouw Strait. This route is described in article 10.38.

10.02.03. For China Sea, from May to September, proceed to Sunda Strait as directed in 10.02.02 for that season, and thence by one of the three alternative routes which follow.

The most direct route from Sunda Strait is to pass through Selat Bangka or Selat Gelasa and thence between Anambas Kepulauan and Natuna Kepulauan into the China Sea; thence between Paracel Islands and Macclesfield Bank to Hong Kong. Selat Gelasa offers a more direct route than Selat Bangka, but in thick weather Selat Bangka can be navigated without risk, and should be taken rather than Selat Gelasa, which cannot then be approached with safety.

The first alternative, by Palawan Passage, should be taken when the North-east Monsoon is likely to begin before reaching Hong Kong. The route passes through Selat Gelasa and Palawan Passage; thence along the coast of Luzon as far as Cape Bolinao; thence to Hong Kong.

The second alternative route passes through Karimata Strait into the China Sea direct.

Although much broader than Selat Bangka or Selat Gelasa, Karimata Strait is not much frequented except by sailing vessels returning from China, or by vessels making E through the Java Sea, as, from the effects of winds or currents, it is difficult to get through it to the W. The great breadth of Karimata Strait in comparison with the others is of advantage to vessels working to windward; but this is partly counterbalanced by the several shoals which lie in or near the fairway and out of sight of land, as well as irregular currents, necessitating a dependence being placed on the reckoning.

If having passed through Sunda Strait into the Java sea, the North-east Monsoon in the China Sea has already begun to blow, do not attempt to make farther to the N, but at once turn E and pass through the Java Sea S of Borneo to Saleier Strait (between the S point of Sulawesi and Saleier Island); and thence by the passage between Buton Island, off the SE point of Sulawesi and the islands S of it, into the Banda Sea; and thence through the Ceram Sea into the open Pacific Ocean either by Djailolo Passage or Dampier Strait (between Halmahera Island and the W extreme of New Guinea).

When in the Pacific pass E of Palau Islands and into the China Sea through one of the channels between Luzon and T'ai-wan.

10.02.04. For China Sea, leaving Cape of Good Hope in September, proceed as directed for Sydney in 10.01.07 and pass S of Australia or Tasmania. Thence continue by the Great Eastern Route (10.02.01).

10.02.05. For China Sea, from October to March, the route is taken via Ombai Strait and the Second Eastern Passage, as directed below.

Cross the Indian Ocean as directed in 10.01.03 as far as 75° E and then steer for 20° S, 110° E. (Some navigators recommend making easting to the 90th meridian instead of the 75th before turning N to make for the above position). From 20° S course may be directed to Ombai Strait.

The usual and the best recommended passage through the islands, after crossing the Indian Ocean, is through Ombai Strait, between the NW point of Timor and Alor Islands; thence either W of Buru Island into the Ceram Sea or (more usually) through Manipa Strait, between Buru Island and Manipa Island (passing near Ambon) and into the Ceram Sea. Thence through Djailolo Passage or Dampier Strait into the open Pacific Ocean. This route is known as the **Second Eastern Passage.** When in the Pacific Ocean, make easting between 1° 30′ N and 3° 00′ N, till able to pass E of Palau Islands; but after February pass W of this group.

Having passed Palau Islands make to the NW to pass through Surigao Strait (N of Mindanao, in the Philippine Islands) into the Sulu Sea, and having passed through those waters, W into the China Sea by Mindoro Strait, or Verde Island Passage (S of Luzon Island), and on to Manila or to Hong Kong.

A more usual route, however, after passing Palau Islands, is to proceed NNW, keeping E of the Philippine Islands, and then pass N of Luzon, through Balintang Channel to Hong Kong or, if bound to Shang-hai, to continue N to pass between Okinawa Guntō and Sakishima Guntō towards the mouth of the Ch'ang Chiang; or to proceed NNE in the full strength of the NE-going Kuro Shio to Yokohama and Japan.

For directions, see 10.46.

In October and November (only) the passage from the Indian Ocean to the China Sea may be made via the central passages of the Eastern Archipelago by a route known as the **First Eastern Passage,** as follows.

From 20° S, 110° E make Bali Strait, Lombok Strait, or Alas Strait. Thence pass through Makassar Strait into the Sulawesi Sea and through Basilan Strait into the Sulu Sea at its SE end. Pass then along the W coasts of Mindanao, Negros, and Panay Islands in the Philippine Islands, and enter the China Sea by Mindoro Strait, or Verde Island Passage. Thence, work along the coast of Luzon to Cape Bojeador, before crossing the China Sea to Hong Kong.

This route to China, though often used in former days, has little to recommend it, on account of the adverse current, setting to the S through Makassar Strait, often strongly, at all seasons. The winds are boisterous and uncertain at the S end of Makassar strait, and light and variable at the N end, while the navigation is anxious throughout almost the whole voyage to the open China Sea.

The First Eastern Passage, described in detail in article 10.47 is more suitable for S-bound traffic, but in the case of vessels from the Cape of Good Hope wishing to reach ports on either side of Makassar Strait, it is mentioned here.

10.03. Cape Town or Cape of Good Hope to Bay of Bengal

10.03.01. General notes. There are three principal routes, two of which are appropriate to the South-west Monsoon and one to the North-east Monsoon.

The choice of route rests, not so much on the month in which departure is made from the Cape of Good Hope, as on the month in which a vessel may be expected to arrive in the region affected by monsoons, (6.02–6.05), comprising the Arabian Sea, the Bay of Bengal, and the Indian Ocean N of the equator. The month references given below for the varying routes refer, therefore, to the months of a vessel's arrival in Indian waters.

10.03.02. From May to September by the Inner Route. This route via Moçambique Channel is the most direct for vessels to any port of India during the South-west Monsoon, but it must not be taken unless there is a certainty of reaching the port before the close of the monsoon.

On leaving the Cape of Good Hope, if with SE'ly winds, stand S and run down the easting in 39° to 40° S to about 30° E; if with W'ly winds, run along the coast, guarding against any indraught, keeping S of 35° S until in 37° E; then steer for Moçambique Channel, passing E of Île Europa and on either side of Île Juan de Nova; pass through Îles Comores, cross the equator in about 54° E, thence steer direct for Eight Degree Channel, and pass S of Ceylon into the Bay of Bengal, see 10.03.05 and 10.05.02.

10.03.03. From May to September by the First Outer Route, which is more usually preferred to the Inner Route on account of ease of navigation, but it must only be used if certain of reaching port before the end of the South-west Monsoon.

From the Cape of Good Hope cross the Indian Ocean as directed in 10.01.03, between the parallels of 39° and 40° S, as far as about 60° E. From this position proceed NE to cross 30° S in about 80° E, and then stand N as directly as possible for destination, as summarised below.

Bound for Madras, or adjacent ports, cross the equator in 82° E.

Bound for Calcutta, cross the equator in 88° E.

Bound for Rangoon, cross the equator as for Calcutta, but leave that route at 10° N, and steer for Rangoon N of Andaman Islands in about 15° N.

See 10.03.05.

Note: On the voyage N from 30° S, it is advisable to gain easting, to counteract the W'ly current, and to be prepared for the wind shifting to the N, for in the South-east Trade it often happens, particularly in April and May, that the wind is more from E and ENE than from SE. The South-east Trade at this season extends to the equator; and from 1° N to 2° N the South-west Monsoon, between May and September, is a fair wind to Calcutta or any part of the Bay of Bengal.

10.03.04. From October to March by the Second Outer Route, which is taken when it is likely that the Bay of Bengal will not be reached before the South-west Monsoon is over (September) or when expecting to arrive in the Bay of Bengal in November, when the North-east Monsoon has set in.

From the Cape of Good Hope, cross the Indian Ocean as directed in 10.01.03, between the parallels of 39° and 40° S, as far as about 70° E. From this position, steer ENE, so as to cross 35° S in about 82° E, and thence proceed NNE through the Trade Winds, to cross the equator in 92° E.

From this position, steer to pass 150 miles W of the NW extreme of Sumatra, and about 60 miles W of Nicobar Islands and Andaman Islands, and thence as directed below.

If the wind is W'ly, give the islands a good berth, but if NW'ly, steer up the Bay close-hauled. In about 16° N to 17° N the wind often shifts to the N, when favourable tacks may be made to the E.

If bound to Calcutta do not approach either shore, but work to windward in the middle of the Bay of Bengal, where there is smooth water and moderate wind; from close W of Nicobar Islands, the entrance to Hooghly River has often been reached without tacking. If the equator is crossed late in February or in March, keep well to the W side of the Bay of Bengal.

If bound to Madras, shape direct course from the position off Nicobar Islands.

If bound to Rangoon, leave the route at about 3° N, and steer to the NE, passing between Pulau Wé and Nicobar Islands as directly as possible to destination, keeping midway between the coast of the Malay Peninsula and Andaman Islands.

10.03.05. General directions for vessels northbound or southbound in Bay of Bengal. From 15th January to 31st May, N-bound keep to the W side of the bay; S-bound keep to the E side. In June, July, and August, N-bound keep in the middle of the bay; S-bound keep in the middle, or E of Andaman Islands. In September, October, and November, N-bound and S-bound take the E side and the W side respectively. From 1st December to 14th January, all ships keep in the middle of the bay.

10.03.06. General remarks as to cyclones in Bay of Bengal. When in the Bay of Bengal with a strong SW wind, occasional squalls and rain, and a slowly-falling barometer, bad weather prevails somewhere to the N.

Between early June and the middle of September the storm centre is probably N of 16° N, and in July or August still farther to the N, and a sailing vessel should steer to the E to take advantage of the S'ly and SE'ly winds on the E side of the storm as it moves NW. But should the weather get rapidly bad, and the barometer continue to fall, then heave-to, and determine the position with regard to the movement of the storm before proceeding.

In May, October, or November the storm travels in some direction from W, through N, to NE; and its course should be definitely ascertained before any attempt is made to round its E side, as if it is moving NE such a proceeding would be attended with danger.

See also 6.16 and 10.90.

10.04. Cape Town or Cape of Good Hope to Colombo

10.04.01. From May to September by the Inner Route, proceed as directed for the Bay of Bengal in 10.03.02, and after passing through Eight Degree Channel steer as directly as possible for Colombo. Notes on Moçambique Channel are given in 10.05.02.

10.04.02. From May to September, east of Madagascar, there are two alternatives. Firstly, follow the directions given for passage to Bombay in 10.05.03 until across the equator in about 62° E, after which steer direct for Colombo. Secondly, in April and October only, take the route for Bombay given in 10.05.04 until the equator is crossed, and steer thence direct to Colombo.

10.04.03. From November to March, proceed as far as the equator as directed for the Bombay route in 10.05.05, thence steering direct.

Alternatively take the Second Outer Route for the Bay of Bengal (10.03.02) as far as 20° S; after that parallel is crossed steer direct for Colombo.

10.05. Cape Town or Cape of Good Hope to Bombay

10.05.01. General notes. There are six routes; three are available during the South-west Monsoon, two of them during the North-east Monsoon and one in the periods between the Monsoons. The month references given below for the different periods refer to the expected time of arrival in Indian waters, and not necessarily to the months in which the Cape of Good Hope is left.

10.05.02. From May to September, the Inner Route through Moçambique Channel is the most direct route for vessels bound to any part of India but it must not be taken unless there is certainty of reaching India before the close of the Monsoon (September).

On leaving Cape of Good Hope, if a SE'ly wind prevail, stand S and run down the easting in 39° to 40° S to about 30° E; if a W'ly wind prevail, run along the coast, guarding against any indraught, and keep S of about 35° S until in 37° E; when, in either case, a course may be shaped for Moçambique Channel, passing E of Île Europa and on either side of Île Juan de Nova. From thence pass through Îles Comores, cross the equator in 53° or 54° E, and steer direct for Bombay. In the height of the South-west Monsoon, June, July and August, when the weather is thick and heavy, and observations very uncertain, vessels should sound frequently when making the land.

By using this track through Moçambique Channel, vessels will avoid the strongest part of the SW'ly current, and will be nearly sure of a fair wind until about half-way through the channel, when adverse winds may be expected; should such occur, it is better to make easting on the port tack rather than westing; thus avoiding the African coast with its prevailing S'ly current. The passage on the E side of Île Europa is recommended, but vessels should not approach that island nor Bassas da India at night, the currents in their vicinity being very strong and uncertain.

The winds in Moçambique Channel do not blow with the same regularity that is found farther N, and are generally stronger in the middle of the channel. The North-east Monsoon sets in between mid-September and mid-October, and the change is usually accompanied by squally weather. When near the Madagascar coast, advantage may be taken of the alternating land and sea breezes.

10.05.03. From May to September, passage east of Madagascar is often preferred to the Moçambique Channel route, as it is less dangerous and the winds are more steady, particularly in August and September, when light variable winds are found in Moçambique Channel. This passage also must only be used when there is a certainty of reaching port before the South-west Monsoon is over (September).

On leaving the Cape of Good Hope, make easting in 39° S to 40° S until in about 45° E, and thence stand to the NE, crossing 30° S in about 53° E. From thence run through the South-east Trade, passing W of Île de la Réunion, Farquhar Islands, and Amirante Islands; then cross the equator in 53° E or 54° E, and steer direct for Bombay.

If arrival at Bombay before the start of the North-east Monsoon is uncertain, make easting, as before directed, in 39° S to 40° S but stand NE on reaching 40° E. Cross 30° S in about 59° E, and then run N, passing between Mauritius and Île de la Réunion. After passing these islands, there are two courses; one being to join with the route from Moçambique Channel, described above, at about 15° S and to continue on it to destination; the other is to stand on directly N, through the Trade Wind, passing W of Saya de Malha Bank. Cross the equator in about 62° E and steer direct for Bombay.

In case the North-east Monsoon has started, keep towards the coast of India after passing Maldive Islands.

10.05.04. In April and October, a W'ly wind is often experienced on leaving the Cape of Good Hope. If this happens, during these months, run along the coast as directed for a W'ly wind in 10.05.02, but stand on to the ENE past Madagascar into the Indian Ocean, making directly for a position in about 15° S, 70° E, passing either between the islands of Mauritius and Rodriguez, or E of the latter. From this point, steer to cross the equator in 75° E, passing E of Chagos Archipelago, and thence on a N'ly track, to the E of Maldive Islands and Laccadive Islands, parallel with the coast of India, to Bombay, working the land and sea breezes.

10.05.05. From November to March, two routes from Cape Town to Bombay are available, both making use of the W portion of the route for Australia described in 10.01.03, and making easting between the parallels of 39° S and 40° S. The more W'ly of the two routes leaves that latitude in 60° E, and a vessel using it should stand NE to 35° S, 70° E, and then stand due N through the South-east Trades to 10° S. She should then make NNE so as to cross the equator in 80° E, and make northing into the North-east Monsoon, standing for Cape Comorin and finally working the land and sea breezes along the Malabar coast.

Alternatively, for the more E'ly route, proceed as above to 35° S, 70° E, after which some authorities consider it more prudent to make further easting, so as to be well to windward on reaching the North-east Monsoon, and make first for a position in about 25° S, 80° E. From this point turn N, run through the Trade and the North-west Monsoon, cross the equator in 82° E to 85° E and the track onward is as above, making northing into the North-east Monsoon. Then stand for Cape Comorin, and work up the Malabar coast with the land and sea breezes.

10.06. Cape Town or Cape of Good Hope to Mauritius

10.06.01. General directions. At all times of the year, make easting in 39° S to 40° S as far as 40° E. Then stand NE, crossing 30° S in about 59° E, as far as 25° S, and then steer direct for destination in the South-east Trade wind.

Note: Vessels from this direction bound for Port Louis should pass E of Mauritius and round its N end, in order to avoid the calms caused by the high land near the SW extreme of the island.

It may sometimes be possible to follow the route given in 10.05.04, leaving it when abreast Mauritius, which it passes at about 100 miles to the S.

10.07. Cape Town or Cape of Good Hope to Aden

10.07.01. General notes. There are three routes available from April to September, and one from November to March. In October either route may be taken.

10.07.02. From April to September or October, take the Inner route for Bombay, as directed in 10.05.02, as far as the equator, crossing it in 53° E; and thence continue to destination, passing between Ras Asir and Socotra. Work along the African coast as far as Mait Island before standing across the Gulf of Aden.

Alternatively, pass E of Madagascar as directed in 10.05.03, standing direct for Ras Asir after passing Amirante Islands and Seychelles Group. Round Ras Asir closely and then proceed as directly as possible. Alternatively, pass between Mauritius and Île de la Réunion to join this route in about 15° S.

10.07.03. From October or November to March, follow the directions given in 10.01.02 and 10.01.03 from the Cape of Good Hope, continuing the route, between the parallels of 39° S and 40° S, as far as 60° E. From this position, stand N to pass about 200 miles E of Rodriguez Island, and to cross the equator in 68° E. At this point, turn to the NW, steering so as to cross the meridian of 60° E at 10° N and thence, N of Socotra, which should be given a berth of from 40 to 60 miles, to destination.

10.08. Cape Town or Cape of Good Hope to Mombasa and adjacent ports

10.08.01. Routes. The shortest route is through Moçambique Channel, as directed in 10.05.02 but passing W of Îles Comores, and steering thence as directly as possible. The preferable route, for all seasons, is E of Madagascar. Follow the directions given in 10.05.03 as far as the N end of Madagascar, from which point both wind and current are favourable for Mombasa and adjacent ports.

ROUTES FROM EAST COAST OF AFRICA AND MAURITIUS

10.09. Durban to Australia, New Zealand, India, Singapore, and China Sea

10.09.01. Durban to Australia, and New Zealand. Stand SE, and pick up the main route across the Indian Ocean (10.01.02) in 50° E, and from that position follow the directions in 10.01.03 to 10.01.10.

10.09.02. Durban to India, Singapore, and China Sea. Stand SE, and make easting in about 35° S until picking up the route to pass through the Eastern Archipelago, to the Bay of Bengal, or to Bombay, according to the season, as directed in 10.02 to 10.05.

10.10. Durban to Mauritius, East Africa, and Aden

10.10.01. Durban to Mauritius. Stand SE, and make easting in about 35° S. From about 50° E, keep gradually more to the N, crossing the parallel of 30° S in 58° E or 59° E, and then steer direct through the Trade Winds to Mauritius.

10.10.02. Durban to Mombasa and adjacent ports. The shortest route is by Moçambique Channel, steering first to the SE across the Moçambique Current until picking up the route from Cape Town to Bombay (10.05.02), and passing W of Îles Comores; but the preferable route is to proceed as directed in 10.10.01 to Mauritius, and taking the route either W or E of Île de la Réunion, around the N end of Madagascar to destination, with a favourable wind and current.

10.10.03. Durban to Aden. The routes are the same as from Cape Town (10.07) according to season, making easting to pick up those routes that pass E of Madagascar on about the parallel of 35° S.

10.11. Durban to Cape Town

Proceed as directly as possible, at 20 miles or more from the coast. A favourable current will be carried throughout the passage. See note under 10.17.02 and relevant part of 10.54.05.

10.12. Mauritius to Australia and New Zealand

10.12.01. Mauritius to Fremantle, southern Australia, and New Zealand. Make southing to pick up the main track across the Indian Ocean (10.01.03). Follow the appropriate part of that route to destination.

10.12.02. Mauritius to northern Australia. From April to October, during the South-east Monsoon on the N coast of Australia, stand S, as in 10.12.01, and proceed by Bass Strait, and to destination via the E coast of Australia and Torres Strait. See directions from Sydney to Torres Strait (11.09). From November to April, during the North-west Monsoon, stand N into that Monsoon and then proceed as directly as possible.

10.13. Mauritius to Singapore or China Sea

10.13.01. Stand SE or E to pick up the route from Cape Town (10.02) according to destination and season.

10.14. Mauritius to Indian ports

10.14.01. From April to October, the route given in 10.05.03 passes Mauritius closely, and may be followed to Bombay. For the Bay of Bengal, leave that route in 5° N and pass through Eight Degree Channel and round the S end of Ceylon. For Colombo, steer direct from Eight Degree Channel. From November to March, stand E or SE to pick up the routes given in 10.03.04 for Bay of Bengal, 10.04.03 for Colombo, or 10.05.05 for Bombay.

10.15. Mauritius to Aden

10.15.01. From April to October, join the route from Cape Town in about 15° S (10.07.02), which passes E of Madagascar.
From November to March, run N through the South-east Trade and the North-west Monsoon, to pick up the route described in 10.07.03, crossing the equator in about 68° E.

10.16. Mauritius to Mombasa and adjacent ports

10.16.01. Proceed as directly as possible, passing N of Madagascar.

10.17. Mauritius to Durban or Cape Town

10.17.01. Mauritius to Durban. Proceed as directly as possible, passing about 100 miles S of Madagascar, and making the African coast well N of Durban.

10.17.02. Mauritius to Cape Town. Pass about 200 miles S of Madagascar and make the African coast about 200 miles SW of Durban, afterwards keeping in the strength of the Agulhas Current until abreast Mossel Bay; from thence, steer direct to round Cape Agulhas at a prudent distance.
Note: When nearing the Cape of Good Hope with strong W'ly winds, keep on Agulhas Bank, not more than 40 or 50 miles from the coast, where will be found smoother water than elsewhere. See 10.74.

10.18. Mombasa and adjacent ports to Aden

10.18.01. From April to October, keep coastwise in the strength of the current and pick up the route from Cape Town or Cape of Good Hope to Aden, as described in 10.07.02, in about 10° N.

10.18.02. From November to March, work to the E into the North-west Monsoon keeping as far N as the wind will permit until that Monsoon is reached; then run E, edging to the N at the latter part, as far as about 68° E, when stand N into the North-east Monsoon, and from thence direct for the Gulf of Aden. The same route may be taken from Seychelles Group.

Socotra should be weathered if possible. If efforts are only made to pass S of it, and the monsoon happens to be fresh, there is a great chance of being swept to leeward of Ras Asir. If leaving Mombasa in March, do not go E of Seychelles Group before standing N, as S'ly winds might be expected before reaching Ras Asir.

10.19. Mombasa and adjacent ports to Bombay

10.19.01. From April to October, keep coastwise in the strength of the current to about 5° N and then steer directly as possible to Bombay, making the landfall on the parallel of Khanderi Island if the weather is thick, see 10.05.02.

10.19.02. From November to March, work E into the North-west Monsoon, then run E on about the parallel of 5° S until in 82° E or 84° E, when stand N across the equator into the North-east Monsoon, and make the S end of Ceylon, and then Cape Comorin; thence work up the Malabar coast with the land and sea breezes.

In March it would perhaps be better to go direct when the North-west Monsoon is met with as NW'ly winds are prevalent in the Arabian Sea at the end of the North-east Monsoon.

10.20. Mombasa and adjacent ports to Colombo or Calcutta

10.20.01. From May to September, stand E on the starboard tack, and make for Eight Degree Channel if bound to Colombo, or pass through the more direct route offered by Kardiva Channel; but not at night, unless the entrance has been made before dark, or the latitude of the vessel is accurately known. If bound to Calcutta, pass S of Ceylon and pick up the Bay of Bengal route from the Cape of Good Hope (10.03.03). See also 10.03.05.

10.20.02. From October to April, the route passes close S of Seychelles Group. On leaving Mombasa, keep N of the direct route to Seychelles Group, while working to the E until the North-west Monsoon is picked up, which may be expected after passing the meridian of 45° E, although this is very uncertain. Light winds and calms render this generally a tedious passage.

After passing Seychelles Group, and if bound to Colombo, run E in about 5° S, cross the equator in from 82° E to 84° E, and stand N into the North-east Monsoon, then making for the SW end of Ceylon; then work up the coast, taking advantage of the land and sea breezes. If bound to Calcutta, continue to make easting until the route from the Cape of Good Hope to Calcutta (10.03.04, 10.03.05, and 10.03.06) is picked up in about 92° E, and follow it to destination.

10.21. Mombasa and adjacent ports to Mauritius and Australia

10.21.01. General notes. In all seasons the route to Australia is taken via, or passing close to, Mauritius.

10.21.02. For Mauritius, from April to October, stand E, regardless of crossing the equator in so doing, until E of Chagos Archipelago, when southing should be made into the Trade Wind, and then a direct course should be steered for Mauritius.

10.21.03. For Mauritius, from November to March, the recommended route is to make easting with the North-east and North-west Monsoons and cross 10° S in about 70° E, and from thence steer direct through the Trade Wind for Mauritius. Vessels should keep N of a line drawn from Zanzibar to Seychelles Group until in the North-west Monsoon.

The alternative route from November to March is to stand down through Moçambique Channel, taking advantage of the current on the African coast. Then, from the S end of the channel, stand SE into the W'ly winds and make easting S of the 35th parallel. Recross 30° S in about 58° or 59° E, and then make direct for Mauritius through the Trade.

Caution: The cyclone season is from November to March, and the first route is therefore the safer as the path of these cyclones is then more easily avoided.

10.21.04. For Australia, follow the directions given in 10.12 after calling at, or passing close to Mauritius as described in 10.21.03.

10.22. Mombasa and adjacent ports to Durban or Cape Town

10.22.01. At all seasons proceed as directly as possible, keeping in the strength of the Moçambique and Agulhas Currents. See 10.54.05.

ROUTES NORTHWARD AND SOUTHWARD THROUGH EASTERN ARCHIPELAGO

10.30. General notes on presentation

This section (10.30–10.51) contains directions for the routes through the Eastern Archipelago, which constitute an important linking system between the Indian Ocean and the Pacific Ocean.

Since each particular route passes through a number of straits or channels, a list of the seas and straits of the Archipelago is given in 10.31, where the directions are indexed. The routes themselves are outlined in 10.32, and references are given to the paragraphs which contain the relevant directions.

10.31. Alphabetical list of seas and straits

Name	Directions N-bound	Directions S-bound
Selat Abang	10.36.03	—
Alas Strait	10.47.04	10.50.04
Bali Strait	10.47.02	10.50.04
Balintang Channel	10.46.06	10.50.02
Selat Bangka	10.35.04	10.49.03
Balabac Strait	Admiralty Sailing Directions	Admiralty Sailing Directions
Bashi Channel	10.46.06	10.50.02
Basilan Strait	10.47.06	10.47.06
Selat Baur	10.40.03	10.49.06
Berhala Strait	10.36.03, 10.38.02	10.49.01
Buton Passage	—	—
Ceram Sea	10.46.03	—
Dampier Strait	10.46.03	10.50.03
Djailolo Passage	10.46.03	10.50.03
Durian Strait	10.38.04	10.49.01
Selat Gelasa	10.40.01, 10.41.01	10.49.04
Karimata Strait	10.44.03, 10.44.04	10.49.07
Selat Leplia	10.40.02	10.49.05
Selat Limendo	10.40.04	10.49.06
Lombok Strait	10.47.03	10.50.04
Makassar Strait	10.47.05	10.51.01
Manipa Strait	10.46.02	10.50.04
Mindoro Strait	10.51.02	10.51.02
Molukka Sea	10.46.03	10.50.03
Ombai Strait	10.46.02	10.50.04
Selat Pengelap	10.36.03	—
Riouw Strait	10.37	10.49.02
Saleier Strait	—	—
San Bernardino Strait	10.46.05	—
Sapudi Strait	—	—
Sibutu Passage	—	10.51.03
Singapore Strait	10.39	10.39
Sunda Strait	10.33	10.49.09
Sulu Sea	10.47.06	10.47.06
Surigao Strait	10.46.04	—
Verde Island Passage	10.46.05	—

10.32. Routes through Eastern Archipelago

10.32.01. General remarks. The following paragraphs are intended as a guide to the selection of the best route through the Eastern Archipelago and the season for which it is recommended. Articles 10.02.01 10.30, and 10.48 are also relevant.

10.32.02. Sunda Strait to Singapore. There are six possible routes. The usual route, though principally for the period May to September, is via Selat Bangka and Riouw Strait. References for this passage are 10.33, 10.34, 10.35, 10.36, 10.37, 10.39 .

From October to March, a route known as the Inner Route, via Selat Bangka, Berhala Strait and Durian Strait, may be used. References are 10.33, 10.34, 10.35, 10.38, 10.39.

In December, January, and February, a route via Selat Bangka, Berhala Strait, Selat Pengelap or Selat Abang, and Riouw Strait, is recommended. References are 10.33, 10.34, 10.35, 10.36, 10.38, 10.39.

As an alternative, from May to September, proceed via Selat Bangka and E of Bintan. References are 10.33, 10.34, 10.35, 10.39, 10.42.

A second alternative from May to September is via Selat Gelasa and Riouw Strait. A vessel which, having chosen this route, finds that the North-east Monsoon is blowing strongly in the China Sea, should steer for Berhala Strait and continue through Durian Strait. References are 10.33, 10.40, 10.41.

A third alternative from May to September is via Selat Gelasa and E of Bintan. References are 10.33, 10.34, 10.40, 10.42.

10.32.03. Sunda Strait to China Sea. From May to September, proceed either via Selat Bangka (10.33, 10.34, 10.43); or via Selat Gelasa (10.33, 10.40, 10.43); or via Karimata Strait (10.33, 10.44).

From November to February, or, if on entering the Java Sea it is found that the North-west Monsoon of the Java Sea or the North-east Monsoon in the China Sea have begun, proceed E through the Java Sea and join the Second Eastern Passage (10.33, 10.45, 10.46). Alternatively, join the First Eastern Passage (10.33, 10.45, 10.46.05, 10.51.02) in Makassar Strait.

10.32.04. Ombai Strait to China Sea. This route, known as the Second Eastern Passage, is for use from October to March. Main references for the route are in 10.46.

The Second Eastern Passage passes through Ombai Strait, Banda Sea, and Manipa Strait (10.46.02), Ceram Sea, Djailolo Passage, Dampier Strait or the Molukka Sea to the Pacific Ocean (10.46.03), and to the China Sea via Surigao Strait (10.46.04) or by San Bernardino Strait and Verde Island Passage (10.46.05) or E of the Philippine Islands and through Balintang Channel or Bashi Channel (10.46.06) to the China Sea.

10.32.05. Bali Strait, Lombok Strait, or Alas Strait to China Sea. This route, known as the First Eastern Passage, is for use in October and November only. From the approach Strait (10.47.02) it passes through the Java Sea, and Makassar Strait to the Sulawesi Sea (10.47.05). It continues through Basilan Strait, the Sulu Sea, and Mindoro Strait (10.47.06) to the China Sea.

10.32.06. Northern Australia to Singapore. Either N of Timor and through the Java Sea or S of all the islands and through Sunda Strait. See 10.135.

10.32.07. Singapore to Sunda Strait. From November to April, proceed via Riouw Strait and Selat Bangka (10.49.02, 10.49.03, 10.49.08), or, from October to April, Selat Gelasa (10.49.04) may be used instead of Selat Bangka.

Also from October to April, passage may be made through Durian Strait, Berhala Strait, and Bangka Strait. This is known as the Inner Route (10.39.03, 10.38.04, 10.38.03, 10.38.02, reversed, and 10.49.03, 10.49.08, 10.49.09).

From May to September a route known as the Outer Route should be taken, passing E of Bintan and through either Karimata Strait or Selat Gelasa (10.39.02, reversed, 10.49.07 or 10.49.04, 10.49.08, 10.49.09).

10.32.08. China Sea to Sunda Strait. This route between the China Sea and the Indian Ocean is known as the Western Route. From October to April, ships having used the North-east Monsoon route through the China Sea, which passes between Anambas Kepulauan and Natuna Kepulauan (11.42) should use Selat Gelasa (10.49.04) or, from November to April, Selat Bangka (10.49.03).

From May to September, Palawan Passage and the coastwise route off Borneo are used in the China Sea, and either Selat Gelasa or Karimata Strait should be taken in continuing for Sunda Strait. See 10.49 and 11.04.03.

10.32.09. China Sea to Indian Ocean. From mid-May till the end of July the Indian Ocean should be approached through Ombai Strait, or by either Alas Strait, Lombok Strait, or Bali Strait. The Eastern Route from the China Sea is used, passing through either Balintang Channel or Bashi Channel into the Pacific Ocean and thence through the Archipelago via Djailolo Passage, Dampier Strait, or the Molucca Sea to the Ceram Sea, and thence through Manipa Strait and the chosen entrance channel to the Indian Ocean. See 10.50.

In May only the Central Route from the China Sea may be used: it enters the Sulu Sea via Mindoro Strait or Verde Island Passage, and leads thence through either Basilan Strait or Sibutu Passage to the Sulawesi Sea and Makassar Strait. Either Alas Strait, Lombok Strait, or Bali Strait are then used in the approach to the Indian Ocean, or a route through the Java Sea and Sunda Strait may be taken. See 10.51.

10.33. Approaches to, and northbound passage through Sunda Strait

10.33.01. General remarks. Sunda Strait and its approaches are described in Admiralty Sailing Directions, which should be read in conjunction with the following remarks.

10.33.02. Landfall. Coming from the S in the South-east Monsoon, keep well to the E, especially in June, July and August, when the Monsoon and the W-going current are at their strongest, or the vessel may fall to leeward of Tandjung Gedeh and find great difficulty in recovering it against wind and current.

In December, January and February, considerable swell rolls into the strait, and the sea is heaviest when the tidal stream, combining with the prevailing SW-going current, runs contrary to the wind. The sea is said to be calmest in March, July and November.

Having made a landfall, shape course to pass between Rakata Island and the Java shore, or between Sebesi Island and Sebuku Island; the former is recommended except for those with local knowledge, and then only in daylight.

10.33.03. Selat Panaitan, between the NW side of Udjung Kulon and Panaitan Island, possesses the great advantage of affording anchorage to sailing vessels becalmed, which the channel N of that island does not; light baffling winds and calms are experienced about the entrances to Sunda Strait, occurring even in the strength of the East Monsoon, and sailing vessels when unable to anchor are liable to be set back by adverse currents.

Selat Panaitan is entirely clear, but the Panaitan Island side must not be approached within one mile on account of Karang Djadjar and the coastal reef which extends from the S side of Legon Semadang; these dangers are always marked by surf.

Working through the passage keep nearer to the Java coast than to Panaitan Island, especially in the South-east Monsoon.

10.33.04. Channel N of Panaitan Island. This channel, sometimes known as "Great Channel," although the widest into Sunda Strait, and much frequented, being considered free from dangers, has the disadvantage of being too deep for anchoring if becalmed; in which case a vessel may drift out of the strait with the W-going stream.

Entering Sunda Strait by this channel, keep nearer Panaitan Island, and when farther in, borrow on the same, or Java, side.

The channel is recommended for the later part of the West Monsoon period, and for the transition period.

10.33.05. Passage through Sunda Strait. In this note it is presumed that a sailing-vessel will make her way through Sunda Strait along the Java side, whether she has approached from the Indian Ocean to make Tandjung Gedeh, or Balimbing Pamantjasa, or half way between the two; in the two latter cases a vessel is presumed to have passed S of Rakata Island.

10.33.06. Passage with a favourable wind. There is not much difficulty in proceeding through the strait in the North-west Monsoon period; the Java side of the strait and the channel S of Sangian Island being recommended. Pass about 2 miles off Karang Tjikoneng and between Pulau Tempurang and Palau Merak Besar. Facilities for anchoring, if becalmed, are available on this route, while the channel N of Sangian Island is not favourable for this purpose, due to the deeper water; the two dangers, Terumbu Kalihat and Terumbu Gosal, also lie in or near the most N'ly, or W'ly channel.

10.33.07. Passage during the South-east Monsoon. During the South-east Monsoon the winds may be E'ly and variable, and sometimes strong from the NE towards midday. This, combined with the adverse current, possibly from 2 to 3 knots in mid-stream, renders the passage more tedious, and it may become necessary to anchor to avoid losing ground; and therefore the coast of Java should be kept, where anchorage may be had in many places, and where the current is much weaker, and at times nil, when the S-going tidal stream is at its strongest.

A vessel having to work up may stand into Teluk Miskam, when N of Pasir Gundul, to a depth of about 15 m but when near Popolé Island into not less than 18 m to avoid Gosong Panjang, and into not less than 27 m or 2 miles off Tjaringin to avoid Karang Kebua. To the N of it the shore may be approached closer, by sounding. Approaching Pasang Tenang, stand into not less than 22 m, or one mile from the shore. Karang Tjikoneng and the coast E is fringed by reef to the distance of 1 to 2 cables, but is steep-to. There is good anchorage S of Karang Tjikoneng in about 11 m, and also off Anjer Lor, to the E of the point, but it is not so good off Karang Tjikoneng itself.

Passing between Sangian Island and Java it is advisable to keep outside a depth of 36 m unless seeking anchorage.

10.34. Sunda Strait to Selat Bangka

10.34.01. Directions. From a position to the N of Pulau Tempurang and with a favourable wind, steer direct for Kepulauan Segama, keeping the S islet bearing less than 010° to lead E of Djankat Lajang; the islets can be passed on either side, during daylight, W of Lynn reef, and Brouwers Banks. Sjahbandar Bank must not be approached into depths of less than 13 m.

Working to the N, it will be prudent to keep on the Sumatra side and when N of Sybrandi Reef, and standing towards the shore, to tack when in a depth of between 11 m and 15 m; the directions for clearing Djankat Lajang, described in the preceding paragraph must be noted.

After passing Kepulauan Segama, a safe guide is to keep in depths of about 18 m; approaching the coast when the depths increase to between 22 m and 24 m, and holding out when they decrease to 17 m. Vessels working up must give the Sumatra coast a wide berth when N of Kepulauan Segama.

While power vessels are advised to pass to the E of Five Fathom Banks (7.111), some authorities consider that a sailing vessel, working up the coast, may pass between those banks and Arend Shoal and, after passing the latter, may stand on the inshore tack to a depth of 9 m. It should be noted, however, that the 5 m line is some 14 to 15 miles from the coast in places. If making for Stanton Passage a vessels should always pass E of Five Fathom Banks.

Note: The trees between Tandjung Bungin and Tandjung Serdang and the groups of trees NW of Tandjung Mendjangan are the highest landmarks on this coast, but they should not be in sight from the deck, as abreast both points the banks extend about 14 miles offshore. These trees afford some guide from aloft during the

North-west Monsoon, which is the clear season, but would not be visible during the South-east Monsoon, except on rare occasions; if this land is sighted from on deck it is a definite warning that a vessel is too far W of her safe course.

10.35. Approaches to, and northbound passage through Selat Bangka

10.35.01. Winds. The winds in Selat Bangka follow the direction of the coast, though with slight variations from the influence of the land and sea breezes; and fresh breezes may always be expected when working against the Monsoon. During the latter part of the South-east Monsoon, it frequently blows hard from SW. Land breezes occur at night.

10.35.02. Tidal streams. A full description is given in Admiralty Sailing Directions, but it can be noted here that, due to the variations in the predominant streams in the two monsoonal seasons, it is preferable to work N on the Bangka side of the strait during the North-west Monsoon, and on the Sumatra side during the South-east Monsoon.

10.35.03. Directions for Maspari Passage and Stanton Passage. The navigation of Stanton Passage is difficult for sailing vessels working N at night; there are not enough marks for fixing the vessel's position, sounding is not a trustworthy guide, and the usually strong tidal streams make the position uncertain. Maspari Passage should never be attempted at night, except in clear weather and with local knowledge, and it is not possible with adverse winds; if Maspari Island is not visible at a distance of 4 miles it is advisable to anchor.

Sailing vessels working N through Maspari Passage by day can safely approach the bank extending from the Sumatra coast by sounding, but they must not stand into a depth of less than 11 m when 5 miles southward of Tandjung Djati, and must keep in depths of 18 m or more when off that point.

Maspari Island (3° 13′ S, 106° 13′ E) can be approached to within 3½ miles on the S side, about 4 miles on the SE side, and to within 1 mile on the W side. Sounding generally gives enough warning when standing towards the banks on the E side of the channel.

In Stanton Passage, sailing vessels with a fair wind can follow the directions given for power vessels in Admiralty Sailing Directions. Working N through Stanton Passage by day, they can approach Dapur Islands within about ¾ mile. The summit of Permisan range bearing about 323° and open NE of Besar light-structure leads NE of Melvill Bank. As soon as Tandjung Labu bears more than 035°, vessels will remain clear of the banks on either side of the channel by keeping in depths of not less than 20 m.

10.35.04. Directions northbound in Selat Bangka. After rounding Tandjung Panggung, work up under the Bangka side of the strait; the landmarks here are more conspicuous, and vessels can derive more advantage from the land winds, which are somewhat stronger and more regular under the Bangka shore than in the middle of the strait.

Some sailing vessels, and even power vessels, make use of the narrow channel between Karang Tembaga and the Bangka coast, when this is feasible, as the tidal streams are more favourable there. Farther N, the coastal bank extending from Bangka is fairly steep-to, and nearing Nangka Islands vessels must keep in depths of not less than 13 m in order to clear the bank which surrounds these islands.

Standing over to the Sumatra side, the bights in the coast may be approached by sounding, but the points must never be approached in depths of less than 20 m, as within this the depths decrease very suddenly. From about 5 miles E to 6 miles W of Tandjung Katima Bongko, the coastal bank is steep-to and is very hard W of this point. Farther W, the depths decrease regularly towards the shore, and vessels can approach it into depths of 9 m.

The passage between the Sumatra coast and Kolepon Rocks can be easily negotiated by sounding; the coast there can be approached into depths of 8 m, but vessels should tack away from the E side of the passage immediately the depths increase to more than 16 m. If taking the channel E of Kolepon Rocks, vessels must not stand over too far towards the Bangka shore, on account of the reefs lying as much as 2½ miles offshore between Tandjung Kelian and Tandjung Ular.

10.36. Selat Bangka to Riouw Strait

10.36.01. General notes. There are two routes, one direct and the other via Berhala Strait and Selat Pengelap or Selat Abang. The latter is recommended for the months of December, January and February; see also 10.38, Selat Bangka to Singapore Strait via Berhala Strait and Durian Strait.

The route from Selat Bangka to Singapore, E of Kepulauan Lingga and through Riouw Strait, is the one commonly adopted by vessels proceeding either way between Sunda Strait and Singapore, as being safe, sheltered, and easily navigable; whereas the route E of Bintan Island is exposed in both monsoons, and the fairway is encumbered with many dangers, which render it necessary for vessels to keep at a considerable distance from the land. Riouw Strait is suitable for all classes of vessels, both by day and by night. The swept channels and their depths are detailed in Admiralty Sailing Directions.

10.36.02. The direct route, ordinarily used by sailing vessels N-bound from Selat Bangka, is between Tudju Islands and Saja; they may, however, pass on either side of Saja, which, being high and bold, is very convenient to make in thick weather or at night.

At night, or in thick weather, sounding may be very useful in detecting the drift caused by cross currents between Tudju Islands and the coast of Sumatra, for the depth decreases generally towards Sumatra, and increases towards those islands, but care should be taken in approaching them, as the remarkable irregularities of the currents have brought many vessels into danger. Near Sumatra a mud bottom, mixed with sand, prevails, and near the islands mud only.

From Saja keep NE to a position some 12 or 13 miles NE of Tandjung Djang, the SE extreme of Lingga, and from thence as follows:

By day, with a fair wind, steer directly for the fairway into Riouw Strait, taking particular note of the tidal stream, especially when setting strongly to the SE.

At night, steer a little more to the N to give more clearance to the shoals, and haul in for Riouw Strait when the bank extending NE from Mesanak has been crossed.

When working northward, it is seldom necessary to work along near the islands from Mesanak to Korek Rapat; it is generally found advantageous to stand to the N, in case of meeting with a NW'ly wind. But it may occasionally happen that advantage will be derived by standing towards them; in which case, when standing towards the N side of Mesanak, keep the summit of Benan bearing less than 275°, which will lead N of the extensive shoal with a least depth of 4 m 6, NE of the E point of Mesanak. To clear Rifleman Reef, E of Benan, keep the E extreme of Mesanak bearing more than 133°, and the N extreme of Katang Lingga Island less than 285°.

If working in towards Selat Dempo, do not get S of lines joining the N point of Katang Lingga Island and Selanga Islets, and the latter and Udiep.

When standing to the westward towards Pulau Galang Baru, tack before Karas Ketjil is shut in by Korek Rapat; or, farther N, to clear the shoal water between Tandjung Tjakang and Korek Rapat, when reaching a depth of 18 m; Dempo bearing 214° is a safe turning mark. Between Korek Rapat and Karas Ketjil it is possible to stand into depths of 15 m before tacking, but care must be taken to give Karang Segutji a good berth. Karas Ketjil and Karas Besar should be given a berth of ½ mile.

From this point continue as directed in 10.37.02.

When standing to the eastward towards Telang Ketjil, at the S entrance to Riouw Strait, be careful to give the SE side of that island a berth of 2 miles, and to keep the conspicuous hill on Tandjung Punggung, the SW extremity of Pulau Mantang, well open of Telang Ketjil, bearing 304°, to avoid Karang Sandara. Tandjung Punggung Islet and Ranggas may be approached to a prudent distance.

For continuation through Riouw Strait, see 10.37.02.

For passage to Singapore Strait from Selat Bangka passing E of Bintan, see 10.42.

For passage from Selat Bangka to China Sea, see 10.43.

10.36.03. The alternative route, via Berhala Strait and Selat Pengelap or Selat Abang, is in fact an alternative to the "Inner route" from Selat Bangka to Singapore Strait, via Berhala Strait and Durian Strait, described in article 10.38, but it is described briefly here as it is also an alternative route to Riouw Strait. The passage through Berhala Strait which is given in article 10.38, is usually taken in December, January and February, when strong N'ly winds prevail; there is then smooth water, good anchorage, and but little tidal stream.

To either Selat Pengelap or Selat Abang follow the directions given in 10.38.04 towards Durian Strait, as far as necessary.

Selat Pengelap is the wider of the two straits mentioned above. Owing to the uneven nature of the bottom the tidal streams, near spring tides, cause whirls and overfalls which are somewhat alarming to strangers; the strait is, however, clear except for the sand patch and rock on the W side of the fairway, and is easy to navigate. Approaching the strait, steer to pass about one mile or less from Alor Islets, passing preferably N of Batu Belajar. Batu Belajar bearing 224°, and well open SE of Alor Islets, leads through Selat Pengelap.

Selat Abang, between Dedap Island and Pengelap Island on the SE side, and Abang Ketjil on the NW side, is reduced to a breadth of about ¾ mile by the reefs on either side, but is clear and deep in the fairway.

Having passed through either of the above straits, the directions for approaching Riouw Strait are the same as those given in the relative part of 10.36.02.

10.37. Passage through Riouw Strait to Singapore Strait

10.37.01. With a fair wind, Riouw Strait offers no difficulties, and no directions are necessary other than to keep in the main fairway.

10.37.02. When working through Riouw Strait from southward, continuing the directions given in 10.36.02 for standing to the W towards Pualu Galang Baru, when between Pulau Karas Besar and Pulau Mubut Laut, stand in to a depth of 15 m; Pulau Karas Ketjil well open of Pulau Karas Besar is a good turning point to avoid the bank off the latter; Pulau Lobam Ketjil to the N, open E of Pulau Mubut Laut, leads E of the bank extending S of the latter island.

The main channel passes E of a 7 m patch lying 2¼ miles E of Tandjung Sembulang, and when working N keep the E extreme of Mubut Laut bearing more than 163°, in order that the bank which extends NW from the island may be cleared; if intending to pass W of the 7 m patch do not cross this W limit until Tandjung Sembulang bears 287°.

N of Tandjung Sembulang, stand farther W, but keep the W extreme of Mubut Laut well open of Tandjung Sembulang, to clear Gosong Tjemara. Give Pulau Tundjuk a berth of about ½ mile, and, when to the N, keep Tandjung Sembulang well open of it, to avoid the bank E of Pulau Subang Mas, and the reef E of Pentjaras.

To avoid the reef about ¼ mile E of the S extremity of Pulau Nginang, keep Tandjung Sau light-structure well open of Nginang; and to clear the reef fringing that island, keep the E point of Pulau Sau well open of the point under the light-structure. After passing Sau, in standing to the W, keep Tandjung Sau light-structure open of Pulau Sau; this will clear Pulau Tubu and shoals, as well as the 7 m patch about ¾ mile SE of Karang Malang Orang.

Vessels are recommended to pass out of Riouw Strait into Singapore Strait E of Karang Galang. If, however, it is decided to pass W of this reef, keep Kalang Malang Orang bearing more than 180° until able to pass between Terumbu Betata and Karang Galang.

Continuing the directions given in 10.36.02 for standing to the E towards Kelang Ketjil, when nearing Tapai Islands, the hill on Tandjung Punggung kept open of the S point of Ranggas, bearing 098°, leads S of them in a depth of about 8 m and of Karang Kata in about 7 m; the SW extreme of Pangkil kept bearing more than 325° leads W of Karang Kata and other shoals SE of Pangkil. To clear the 7 m bank extending 2½ miles S of Tapai Islands keep the prominent hill on Pulau Siulung open of the hill on Tandjung Punggung bearing less than 077°, until the summit of Lobam Island is open W of Pangkil, bearing 327°, or more.

The SW end of Pangkil Island should not be approached nearer than ⅓ mile, as its reef is steep-to; the W side may be approached to a depth of 13 m, but off its N end keep Karas Ketjil light-structure open of Pangkil Island, bearing 167°, or less, to avoid the fringing reefs.

Between Pangkil Island and Gosong Tulo, stand to the E into depths of 15 m, or until Terkulai light-structure bears 000°, but do not bring the NE extreme of Pangkil Island to bear more than 158°, or Terkulai light-structure less than 355°, to avoid Soreh reefs. Terkulai light-structure bearing 087° leads S of Gosong Tulo, and the light-structure on the E point of Tandjung Sau in line with the W side of Lobam Ketjil bearing 329°, leads W of it; the SE extreme of the Lobam group, bearing less than 090° until Tandjung Sau light-structure bears more than 338°, leads W of Karang Lolo. When N of Karang Lolo do not bring the W extreme of Lobam Ketjil to bear more than 160° until Tandjung Taloh bears 090°, which will avoid the dangers near Karang Plasit. Tandjung Taloh is steep-to, and both it and Buau Island may be approached to about 3 cables, except near the extremes of that island. Tandjung Uban is bold, but do not approach the shore N of it, to Malang Djarum, nearer than ⅓ mile. The rocks above water on the edge of the shore reef are useful guides.

To the N of Malang Djarum there are depths of 7 m close to the edge of the shallow bank which fronts this part of the coast to the distance of nearly 1 mile. This bank, as well as Netscher Shoal and Crocodile Shoal, and the shoal between them, will be avoided by keeping Tandjung Sau light-structure bearing less than 205°. If the weather is hazy and Tandjung Sau light-structure cannot be made out at this distance, Malang Djaru Islet, which will be seen well clear of the extreme of the land as Netscher Shoal is neared, must be kept bearing less than 200° until Karang Galang light-structure bears 248° or Tandjung Sebung north extreme bears 095°; a vessel will then be N of those dangers and in Singapore Strait.

10.38. Inner Route from Selat Bangka to Singapore Strait

10.38.01. General notes. The Inner Route is suitable between October and March.

Berhala Strait forms the S part of the Inner Route to Singapore, and Durian Strait the N part; the intermediate part, between the W side of Kepulauan Lingga and the E side of Sumatra, has no specific denomination. The total distance from Berhala Island to Singapore is about 120 miles.

The Inner Route is lighted and buoyed, and is suitable for all classes of vessels. The least depth in the fairway, from 10 m to 11 m, is in the S part, SW of Mutji.

Sailing vessels, bound from Selat Bangka to Singpore during the strength of the North-east Monsoon, frequently adopt this inner route. During the prevalence of strong N'ly winds in December, January and February, they will save much time doing so, for these straits have smooth water, good anchorage, and but little tidal stream, whereas on the E side of Lingga, at this season, there is generally a heavy sea and a S'ly current sometimes running at the rate of 3 knots. In Berhala Strait, sailing vessels will also be greatly assisted by the squalls from the Sumatra coast.

In order to avoid the difficulty and delay sometimes experienced in getting from the N part of Durian Strait to Singapore Strait, many sailing vessels have preferred the alternative of passing from the Inner Route by Selat Abang or Selat Pengelap into Riouw Strait. It seems probable that the best passages might be made in this way, for the great depth of water in the W part of Singapore Strait is often embarrassing in light winds, as there is no anchorage ground on which to bring up in case of the wind failing. See 10.36.04.

10.38.02. Selat Bangka to Berhala Strait. Having passed Kolepon Rocks (10.35.04), shape course for the light-structure on Berhala, distant about 74 miles, avoiding the shoal area extending SE from Tandjung Djabung. The bank along the Sumatra coast being shelving, sounding will be the best guide, and the rule is to keep in depths of from 10 m to 13 m. In working, the coast may be approached with care to a depth of 9 m, observing that the bank with less depths than 9 m extends nearly 13 miles SE of Tandjung Djabung.

Pass through Berhala Strait, using the passage S of Berhala Island; the channel between Berhala and Singkep Laut is not safe as there are several rocks in it, and uncharted dangers may exist. In Berhala Strait keep in depths of from 18 m to 22 m, to be well clear of the bank projecting from the shore W of Tandjung Djabung; thence, in working along the coast to the W the bank is steep-to, and may only be approached occasionally, with care, to a least depth of 13 m.

10.38.03. Berhala Strait to Durian Strait. From abreast Berhala Island with a favourable wind, shape course to pass 2 to 3 miles W of Mutji Islet light-structure. With a working breeze, the Sumatra coast may be approached to depths of from 11 m to 13 m, but the vessel's position must be fixed frequently, as the tidal streams are very irregular off Sungai Djambi. The mudbank W of Tandjung Djabung for a distance of 14 to 15 miles, is nearly dry at low water, spring tides, and extends 4 to 5 miles seaward.

There is no difficulty in standing E in the vicinity of Speke Reef and Mutji, both of which are lighted, but, when nearing Mutji, tack when it bears 000°, to avoid Atkin Reef; it is best, however, to pass Mutji at a distance of about 2 miles, as mentioned above.

With a fair wind, having passed Mutji steer for Padri Selatan Island, passing either side of it, but preferably to the E, which is the main channel; Djora, the summit of Moro Besar, which is visible from a considerable distance, bearing 344°, is a good mark for making towards Padri Selatan.

In working, be careful not to stand nearer to Tandjung Bakau or Tandjung Dato, the entrance points of Teluk Kuala Tjenaku, than 2 miles; and when between them, off that bay, remember that the bank, which extends beyond a line joining these points, is steep-to, and sounding will give no warning. Excepting abreast the S part of Kateman Island, at about 12 miles N of Tandjung Dato, the depths decrease more regularly towards the bank, which may from thence be approached by sounding into depths of 13 m towards Durai and the other nearby islands. In standing to the E, when abreast Tandjung Dato, do not deepen above 35 m, for the ground on that side is foul and unsuitable for anchorage.

Cameleon Rock is out of the fairway track, but if standing over so far to the E, Petong Island summit bearing 350° or more leads well W of it.

10.38.04. Durian Strait and to Singapore Strait. The initial part of this passage may be taken either E or W of Rukan Islands. If taking the E side, having passed E of Rukan Tengah, and standing towards Eastern Banks, tack while Djora, the summit of Moro Besar, still bears more than 308°, to avoid the banks. Having passed Rukan Utara, steer to pass between Perasi Besar Islet and Pelangkat Island; in working, by keeping Perasi Island open W of Pulau Durian Ketjil, bearing more than 318°, Carnbee Reef, 1 mile S of Moro Besar, will be avoided.

If taking the route W of Rukan Islands, pass about 1½ miles W of these islands in depths of from 18 m to 25 m, but do not enter Durian Strait until Perasi is well open E of Perasi Besar, bearing 322°, to avoid Richardson Reef. When in the strait, steer to pass between Perasi Besar and Pelangkat, as above.

Continuing N, the peak of Sanglang Besar Island, astern, in line with the apex of Perasi Island, bearing 159°, leads between Melvill Reef and Middleburg Reef. Thence steer to pass through Phillip Channel if bound to Singapore, or to the N and NW if bound into Malacca Strait.

If the channel W of Middelburg Reef is taken, the water will be found to shoal gradually towards the W shore over a bottom of soft mud, suitable for anchorage. The E point of Degong Island bearing 180° leads E of the dangers extending off Buru Island and the islands N of it. Little Karimun Island bearing less than 325° also leads E of the dangers which project 3 miles from Great Karimun Island.

When working to the N after passing Perasi Island, and standing E, keep W of the alignment of Manjilang, the summit of Sanglang Besar, with the NW extremity of Pulau Durian Ketjil bearing about 168°; this will avoid the reef about 1¼ miles W of the southern extremity of Belukar Island.

10.39. Singapore Strait

10.39.01. General remarks. Heavy rain squalls, during which visibility is moderate or poor, are frequently experienced in Singapore Strait; the colours and topmarks of the various beacons are then useful guides.

In the following directions, the Strait is considered in two parts, the E part for vessels coming from, or going to, the China Sea or the Eastern Archipelago via Riouw Strait or E of Bintan; the W part for vessels coming from, or going to, Malacca Strait or Durian Strait.

Of the three channels into which the E entrance to Singapore Strait is divided, Middle Channel is recommended. North Channel has no advantage except perhaps to vessels bound N along the coast; it should be used only by those possessing local knowledge. South Channel is not recommended for vessels of deep draught; the bottom is generally rocky and uneven, and the channel is encumbered with shoals.

10.39.02. Passage westward through the eastern part of Singapore Strait. If approaching from E of Bintan Island, South Channel may be used, but, in view of the remarks in 10.39.01, vessels are recommended to stand on and pass through Middle Channel.

There is no difficulty in identifying Singapore Strait when coming from the E, in clear weather; both Groote Bintanberg and Gunong Pelali are good marks and Horsburgh Light marks the S side of Middle Channel.

Sailing vessels will experience no difficulty in working in either direction through Middle Channel and the E part of the strait. The best plan is to keep towards the N shore, in case of having to anchor, as the depths are more convenient on that side. The shore may be approached to depths of 20 m; Pulau Mungging, kept open of Tanjong Ayam, bearing 075°, leads S of Johore Shoal and, when standing towards this danger, if these objects cannot be seen, preserve the depths mentioned, for the shoal is steep-to.

When E of Tanjong Ayam keep Tanjong Stapa in line with, or open of Tanjong Ayam, bearing 274°, until Pulau Mungging bears less than 360°; and, when standing towards Falloden Hall Shoal, keep Tanjong Ayam bearing more than 266°, and when standing towards Congalton Skar and the shoals N of it, keep Tanjong Punggai bearing less than 337°. A vessel may stand towards Remunia Shoals until the S extremity of Pulau Mungging bears 256°.

There are no dangers on the S side of the strait, excepting those fronting the coast of Pulau Bintan and Crocodile Shoal, Terumbu Betata, and Karang Galang, in the entrance to Riouw Strait. But do not stand so far over as to get near these dangers, for no advantage will be gained by doing so, and the depths there are inconveniently great for anchorage.

Small vessels bound to Singapore Road from the E will have no difficulty, as they have merely to proceed to a convenient anchorage. Vessels of less than 4 m 6 draught may pass within the banks off Tangjong Katong, by keeping in the run of deep water, fairly close to the end of the lines of fishing stakes which extend from that point. It is the usual custom for sailing vessels belonging to the port, to keep these banks well aboard when proceeding to the anchorage from the E, when the wind is off the land and the tidal stream setting to the W. *5*

10.39.03. Passage eastward through Main Strait. Owing to the strong tidal streams in the W part of Singapore Strait, sailing vessels are frequently obliged to anchor, for which purpose the N side of the channel is to be preferred. Between Sultan Shoal and Raffles Lighthouse on that side, there is convenient anchorage in depths from 11 m to 22m, while to the S the water is deep, and the bottom rocky; the S side of this part of the strait is, *10* therefore, unsuitable for anchorage, especially as violent squalls are common.

Abreast the S end of St. John's Islands, vessels ought not to anchor if it can be avoided, for the water is deep, and the tidal streams and eddies run with greater strength than in any other part of the strait.

There is fair anchorage between Buffalo Rock and Helen Mar Reef, as well as about 1 mile to the N and W of the latter dangers; also from 1 mile to 2 miles E of Buffalo Rock, in depths of from 22 m to 27 m, or between *15* it and Pulau Subar. Vessels may stand closer inshore and anchor near the edge of the charted 10 fm (18 m 3) line, SW and NE of Pulau Subar; it is inadvisable to go closer in, on account of the strong tidal streams, sometimes rendering it difficult to get underway again, especially in the light winds which prevail here.

When working to the E between St. John's Islands and Raffles lighthouse, it is usual to keep on the N side of the channel, making short tacks if necessary, as that part of the strait affords tolerably convenient anchorage *20* along the greater portion of it, and vessels are liable to meet with light baffling airs which would render it necessary to anchor. It is important to remember this when E of Buffalo Rock, for on that part of the S side of the strait the water is deep, and the bottom rocky and unsafe for anchoring, the danger being much increased by rapid tidal streams with eddies and overfalls. There is also much power vessel traffic in both directions, including many long vessels of very deep draught. *25*

Continuing E towards the China Sea, follow generally the directions in 10.39.02, in reverse.

10.40. Sunda Strait to, and through Selat Gelasa
30

10.40.01. General remarks. Of the three principal passages through Selat Gelasa, namely from W to E, Selat Leplia, Selat Limendo, and Selat Baur, the latter is preferable for sailing vessels N'bound with a fair wind, being the broadest and having no dangers in the fairway. Sailing vessels working through, and vessels of low power, should use Selat Leplia during the North-west Monsoon (but see 10.40.02,) and Selat Baur during the South-east Monsoon, the currents thus being less unfavourable. Selat Limendo is seldom used. *35*

10.40.02. Sunda Strait to, and through, Selat Leplia. After leaving Sunda Strait, pass between Djankat Lajang and Jason Rock. Thereafter, with a fair wind, steer to sight and pass Djaga Utara and then make for a position about 4 miles W of Hippogriffe Reefs; then steer to make good 005°, passing W of Kait Rock and Medang, when land will soon be sighted; Pulau Simedang should on no account be sighted by day. When past *40* Medang steer to pass midway between Karang Baginda and Drievadems Bank, taking care to avoid the shoals lying about 6 miles S of the former, and thence N between Discovery Rocks and Tjelaka, giving the latter a berth of about 2 miles; care must be taken to avoid the 8 m 8 patch lying 2¾ miles E of Tandjung Labu, and the other dangers in this vicinity. When the N extremity of Liat bears 090° steer to pass E of Pulau Gelasa, or E of Tandjung Berikat, according to destination. *45*

Note: In thick weather it is advisable to anchor on the bank, around Hippogriffe Reefs, in depths of from 12 m to 18 m, and await more favourable conditions. Vessels coming from the Java sea, and uncertain of their position, can approach the coast of Sumatra to a depth of 17 m.

Vessels proceeding through Selat Leplia at night should take care that they sight Tandjung Murung during daylight, if coming from the S; if approaching from the N, Tandjung Berikat should be sighted during daylight. *50*

Working through Selat Leplia from the southward. During the strength of the North-west Monsoon it is almost impossible to work through Selat Gelasa; even in the latter part of the monsoon, about March, when the winds are light, sailing vessels often are obliged to anchor on account of the strength of the S-going current. In the South-east Monsoon also, vessels will often meet with light variable winds, rendering it impossible for them to preserve a direct course. *55*

The approach to Selat Leplia does not afford convenient clearing marks, but the following directions are given as being, so far as can be judged, the best for that purpose. As, however, some of the objects are at a considerable distance from the dangers, navigators are cautioned not to depend too implicitly upon being able to recognise such distant objects. Particular attention should be paid to the set of the tidal streams and currents, and to sounding. *60*

Coming from Sunda Strait a sailing vessel is advised to work up the coast of Sumatra, see 10.34.01. Approaching Selat Leplia proceed as follows.

If standing E, to the N of Hippogriffe Reefs, stand towards Karang Pasir, which does not quite cover at high water, until it is but 4 miles distant, or within half a mile of Haaien Reef, giving Medang and Kait Rock a wide berth. Pulau Simedang bearing 028° leads 1 mile W of Branding Reefs. This island should not be approached *65* nearer than 3 miles, on account of the dangers lying W of it.

Tandjung Murung kept bearing more than 318° leads SW of Karang Baginda, and Kalangbahu summit, bearing 054°, leads NW of the S and central portions of those reefs; Keladi, on Pulau Liat, which is not easily recognised, kept bearing more than 005°, leads W of the most W'ly shoal, which is awash at low water, and the N end of Aur Island open N of Bakau Islet, bearing 064°, leads N of the reefs. *70*

When N of Karang Baginda, keep Bakau Islet bearing less than 108°, and Selemar Islet more than 360°, to avoid the shoals between them; and to clear the reef extending 3 miles S of Pulau Liat, keep Kueël Islet bearing less than 108° if Keladi bears less than 349°.

To clear the reefs and shoals lying SW and W of Pulau Liat, Bakau Islet must be kept bearing less than 134° until Tjelaka Islet bears 090°; and to clear Discovery Rocks, keep Tandjung Labu bearing more than 220° until Tjelaka bears 090°, which bearing also clears the rocks to the N.

To clear the reefs extending off the NW side of Pulau Liat, keep Tandjung Labu bearing less than 215° until the S extreme of Kelapan Island bears 247°.

When standing to the W, to clear the banks between Medang and Tandjung Murung keep Bakung, a hill 2 miles W of Tandjung Labu, open E of Tandjung Murung, bearing 344° until Baginda, a hill 167 m high, about one mile NW of Tanjong Baginda (Besar), bears 276°; after which it is possible to stand W until Tandjung Murung bears 017°.

To clear the shoals off the E side of Pulau Lepar, Tandjung Murung must be kept bearing more than 219° until the NE extreme of Kelapan bears 308°. To clear Discovery Rocks, see above.

To avoid Wilson Bank, Bakung must be kept bearing more than 186°, or Tandjung Labu less than 180°, until Tandjung Berikat bears less than 322°.

10.40.03. Northbound through Selat Baur. For sailing vessels with a fair wind, Selat Baur is preferable to the others, and should present no difficulties; the land is, in the fine weather of the North-west Monsoon, visible from the outer dangers. The greater breadth of Selat Baur enables sailing vessels to make longer boards, and as most of the islands can be seen at night the vessel's position is more easily fixed.

The shoals that lie within the strait appear to form the only drawback to the adoption of this channel, and in clear weather even this drawback would almost disappear, for good hill peaks, by which to fix the ship's position, are visible on all sides, distant from 20 to 35 miles.

With a fair wind, making for Selat Baur from the S, from Djaga Utara shape course for Larabe Shoal during the North-west Monsoon, and for Carnbee Reefs in the South-east Monsoon. In clear weather the mountains in the SW part of Belitung will be sighted some distance S of these dangers; Ludai, which may be visible from about 12 miles S of Carnbee Reefs, first comes into sight, and shortly afterwards Beluru (*3° 10′ S, 107° 40′ E*) will be sighted. When near Larabe Shoal other mountains on Belitung as well as Pulau Simedang should be sighted, so that in clear weather there is no difficulty in making the strait. If a vessel is far to the E of the track, Kebatu, about 25 miles SE of Carnbee Reefs, will be a useful mark for fixing the position.

When the landfall has been made, steer a N'ly course, passing about 6 miles E of Pulau Simedang, midway between Kasenga and Geresik and not less than 2 miles W of Tandjung Ajer Lantjur.

With bad visibility or in thick weather, sounding must be depended upon entirely; in such cases it is advisable to make the S edge of the bank, with depths of from 13 m, to 18 m, clay with sand, which extends about 25 miles S from Pulau Simedang, by sounding, and then immediately steer E until in depths of more than 18 m; then steer N, taking care to keep in depths of more than 18 m, and when passing E of Pulau Simedang, keeping in depths of not less than 29 m. If however, depths of over 36 m have been obtained when making for the S entrance, it may be presumed that the vessel is well over on the E side of the channel, and a NW'ly course may then be steered, taking care to keep in these depths. In unfavourable conditions, or if any doubt as to which side of the strait the vessel may be, it is advisable to anchor; bad visibility does not usually last for any length of time.

At night, Selat Baur can be approached from S without danger in clear weather, as the light on Pulau Simedang is visible up to 3 miles S of Hancock Shoal, the most S'ly danger on the W side of the approach. When this light is sighted steer to pass about 2 miles E of Pulau Simedang, and thence proceed N until in the arc of visibility of the light on Tandjung Ajer Lantjur, which must be kept between the bearings of 003° and 022°. When Geresik Island is sighted, the position can be fixed by bearings of this island and Tandjung Ajer Lantjur light, and course may be shaped to pass either E or W of Akbar Shoal, according to destination; vessels passing E of this shoal have the advantage of being able to fix their position by bearings of Langkuas Island light in addition to Tandjung Ajer Lantjur light; passing W, vessels make for Pulau Gelasa.

Working through Selat Baur, and standing E towards Carnbee Reef, keep Beluru, a mountain 360 m high, 6½ miles NE of Tandjung Genting, bearing more than 011°; and to clear Naga reef, Gosong Awal, and Cooper Reef, keep Marang Bolo, a hillock on the S point of Seliu, bearing more than 350°. To avoid the dangers N of Cooper Reef, keep farther W, Marang Bolo bearing more than 010°.

Pass Batu Malang at a distance of at least 1 mile, the approach from S being on a bearing of more than 001°, but to the N it should not bear more than 112°, until the N point of Seliu bears 073°, to clear Karang Tiga; after passing which, Batu Malang must not bear more than 146°, or Marang Bolo more than 124°, until Karang Njera and the 11 m patch NW of it are cleared.

After passing these dangers, Marang Bolo bearing less than 132° will lead S and SW, and Tandjung Ajer Lantjur bearing more than 003° to the W, of all dangers until N of Lima Islands. After Geresik bears 270° stand a little farther to the E but keeping Tandjung Ajer Lantjur bearing more than 355° until within about 2 miles.

Give the lighthouse on Tandjung Ajer Lantjur a berth of about 1½ miles, and keep it bearing less than 158° until Langir bears 046° to clear the reef round Pulau Kembung; to the N, the latter in line with the lighthouse bearing about 180° leads a full mile W of Malang Wankang and will clear all the reefs between Pulau Kembung and Langir.

Give the coast between Mendanau and Langkuas a berth of 6 to 7 miles keeping Langir bearing less than 214° and Langkuas bearing more than 046°.

When standing to the westward, Pulau Simedang, if not brought to bear more than 000°, will lead E of all the shoals S of it, and sounding will also give good warning when standing towards them, as they lie some 4 or 5 miles within the charted 10 fm (18 m 3) line. Pulau Simedang and Pulau Simedang Ketjil must be approached with caution, as sounding does not give much warning when nearing their outlying reefs; they should on no account be approached within a distance of 2½ miles. Pulau Simedang Ketjil bearing 183°, astern, leads E of Bliss Reef, between which and Aur Island a vessel may stand to the W until the summit of that island bears 023°, which will lead E of Karang Baginda. Kalangbahu bearing 265° leads S of the dangers extending from Aur and Geresik. The E side of Geresik may be approached to a distance of 1 mile; but the E side of Kelemar has a rock lying 1 mile off, which will be avoided if Geresik is not brought to bear less than 160°. The summit of Aur, in line with the E extreme of Kelemar, bearing 180°, leads 1½ miles E of Hewitt Reef.

Having passed Hewitt Reef, stand farther W towards Liat, but the SE extreme of that island must bear more than 200° to clear the reefs off its NE side. When N of all the reefs off the N side of Liat (at night the light on Tandjung Ajer Lantjur or, by day, the rounded summit of Sagoweel, about 2 miles SE, bearing more than 111°) stand W towards Bangka.

10.40.04. Selat Limendo, E of Liat, is narrower and more encumbered with dangers than either Selat Leplia or Selat Baur, between which it lies, but it is easily navigable by sailing vessels with a fair wind, during daylight. No vessel would from choice attempt to work through Selat Limendo, as Selat Leplia and Selat Baur are much better adapted for that purpose; but it is possible that a vessel, embarrassed by light baffling winds, may find it convenient to proceed through some part of it. The numerous islets afford every facility for fixing the position of the vessel from time to time.

10.41. Selat Gelasa to Riouw Strait

10.41.01. General remarks. Most vessels, N-bound from Selat Gelasa, prefer passing E of Gelasa, which is the safer route; but some, especially when bound to Singapore by Riouw Strait, prefer the less safe, but more direct, route between the shoals W of that island, or as an alternative to pass between Tandjung Berikat and Pulau Berikat. During the strength of the North-west Monsoon, N'ly winds will be met along the coast of Bangka and the adverse current off and W of Tandjung Berikat will make it difficult to beat up.

10.41.02. Passage east of Gelasa. With a fair wind, pass about 3 miles E of Gelasa. Continue N, keeping Gelasa bearing more than 180° to clear Belvedere Rock, Magdalena Reef and Lanrick Reef. As the summit of Gelasa is visible from a distance of 30 miles in clear weather, a vessel should be nearly abreast of Lanrick Reef before losing it.

After clearing Lanrick Reef pass E of Severn Reef and between that reef and the group of reefs about 27 miles to the NNE. Soundings give no warning of the approach to any of the above, as they are steep-to, but in the vicinity of Severn Reef, in fine weather, the highest hill on Tandjung Tuing and Radja, a hill close W of Tandjung Radja, are visible.

If the wind should prevent a direct course from being steered from abreast Pulau Liat, Gelasa should be kept bearing more than 338° until the vessel is N of Akbar Shoal. After passing about 3 miles E of Gelasa proceed as above.

Having passed Severn Reef steer E of Toty (*0° 55′ S, 105° 46′ E*) and continue NW to join the route described in 10.36.02 NE of Tandjung Djang.

10.41.03. Passage west of Gelasa. Proceed N, as in 10.41.02, to clear Akbar Shoal, but noting that the direct course required passes about 1 mile W of Gelasa Rock. After passing Gelasa Rock steer 000° until the summit of Gelasa bears 135°, which bearing if retained, leads about 4½ miles NE of Van Sittard Reefs, passing between Warren Hastings Reefs and Tiung Reef; Gelasa bearing 135° will also assist in passing E of Keuchenius Reef, although it will be lost to sight a few miles before reaching the reef.

There should be no difficulty in avoiding Iwan Reef and Severn Reef as the Bangka Island coast can generally be seen from the former, and mountains from the latter as described in 10.41.02, the directions in which can be followed from this point.

If circumstances prevent a straight course from being steered when N of Gelasa, keep its summit bearing between 130° and 146° until Tandjung Berikat bears 195° to clear Warren Hastings Reef and Tiung Reef; thence keep the summit between the bearings of 135° and 157° to pass between Van Sittard Reef and Keuchenius Reef to the W and Magdalena Reef and Lanrick Reef to the E. Thence as before.

10.41.04. Passage between Tandjung Berikat and Pulau Berikat. Having passed about 1 mile off either and proceeding to the NNW, keep Pulau Berikat bearing less than 146° to clear the SW extreme of Warren Hastings Reefs; thence keep Tandjung Berikat bearing between 175° and 195° to lead W of Warren Hastings Reefs and Tiung Reef, and E of Van Sittard Reefs. After Gelasa bears more than 135° proceed as in the last paragraph of 10.41.03.

10.42. Selat Bangka or Selat Gelasa to Singapore Strait, passing eastward of Bintan

10.42.01. General remarks. These routes are alternative to those described in 10.36 to 10.41. They are not recommended for use during the season of N'ly and NW'ly winds, from November to March.

10.42.02. Selat Bangka to Singapore Strait. Having passed E of Saja as described in 10.36, a vessel should steer a N'ly course so as to pass E of Admiral Stellingwerf Reef, crossing the equator in depths of about 37 m. At night it is advisable to keep in depths of not less than 43 m when between the parallels of 0° 30′ N and

0° 50′ N. Merapas bearing 315° or less leads NE of Admiral Stellingwerf Reef and Gosong Ara. Having rounded the NE point of Bintan, proceed as directed in 10.39.02, preferably using Middle Channel.

10.42.03. Selat Gelasa to Singapore Strait. First proceed as directed in paragraph 10.41.02 as far as Lanrick Reef. Then continue on a course 000° until Pedjantan is sighted. Thence shape course for Singapore Strait. See 10.39.02.

10.43. Selat Bangka or Selat Gelasa to China Sea, May to September

10.43.01. General remarks. In either case the route N into the China Sea is as direct as possible. When the North-east Monsoon is likely to develop before Hong Kong is reached, pass through Api Passage and Palawan Passage. See 11.32, 11.33.

10.43.02. From Selat Bangka (10.36), after clearing Saja, steer to pass between Anambas Kepulauan and Natuna Kepulauan, but see 11.32, 11.33, 11.38.

10.43.03. From Selat Gelasa, either proceed N as directed in 10.42.03 to sight Pedjantan, and thence E of Tambelan Kepulauan, and between those islands and the coast of Borneo; or steer directly to pass W of Pengibu Kepulauan. In either case continue N between Anambas Kepulauan and Natuna Kepulauan (10.43.01).

10.44. Sunda Strait to Karimata Strait and China Sea

10.44.01. General remarks. Karimata Strait is the passage between Belitung and Momparang Islands on the W side, and Karimata Island and the Borneo coast on the E side. It is the customary route taken by vessels bound for Singapore or China from the E part of the Java Sea. Such vessels pass well outside all the dangers lying off the E side of Belitung, and hardly ever sight either Belitung or the Borneo coast; the direct route to Pontianak from the Java Sea is E of Karimata Island.

The main route lies E of Discovery East Bank (*3° 35′ S, 109° 11′ E*) and Cirencester Shoal. The lines joining Discovery East Bank, a position 20 miles E of Cirencester Shoal, Catherine Reef, and Ontario Reef must be considered as the W limit of safe navigation for large vessels passing through Karimata Strait.

Besides the main channel, there are several other channels between the numerous islands lying E and NE of Karimata Island, and between it and the Borneo coast. The most E'ly of these, known as Greig Channel and the Inner Route, have a regular tide, and convenient depths for anchoring, and are therefore much frequented by vessels working through the strait; it being quite impossible to work through the main channel against a strong monsoon, and a continuous current setting to leeward.

10.44.02. Sunda Strait to Karimata Strait. Pass E of Djangkat Lajang and W of Jason Rock. Thence, having passed within sight of Djaga Utara, shape course to pass S of Discovery East Bank.

10.44.03. Passage northbound through Karimata Strait. With a fair wind, having passed E of Discovery East Bank, steer N approximately on its meridian until past Momparang Islands; then alter course to the NW so as to pass between Ontario Reef and Serutu Island, steering so as to pass the light-structure near the W end of Serutu at a distance of about 5 miles. Proceeding N to the China Sea, after passing between Ontario Reef and Serutu, keep approximately on the meridian of 108° E, taking care to avoid the 5 m reef, lying about 28 miles NW of North Grieg Shoal, and then pass E of Pengiki Besar. A vessel may pass through Greig Channel as an alternative to the main strait, see 10.44.04.

If making for Karimata Strait from East Java make for the E side of the S entrance to the strait, passing W of Fox Banks, Aruba Bank and Clemencia Bank, and then steer NW so as to pass between Ontario Reef and Serutu Island.

10.44.04. Working through Inner Route and Greig Channel. Vessels working through Karimata Strait have to take either the Inner Route, which is suitable for small vessels only, or Greig Channel (10.44.01). In these channels the sea is smoother and the current not so strong, it being wholly or in part overcome by the tidal stream and the indraught into the rivers on the W coast of Borneo; vessels also have the advantage of the change of wind at night and in the morning caused by the land breeze, and which often brings it several points more to the E in both Monsoons.

These channels have a convenient depth for anchoring, with a bottom of soft mud, but working through them is slow and tedious. Sounding gives good warning when approaching the Borneo side; vessels can pass fairly close to Karimata Islands.

Less water than charted has been reported between Aur and the SE coast of Panebangan.

Coming from SW, note the W limit of safe navigation described in 10.44.01. When N of the dangers off Mangkut and off Tandjung Pagar Antimun, the Borneo coast may be approached to a depth of 15 m, and to 11 m in Van Sukadana Bight. The S group of Kepulauan Lajah should not be approached nearer than 1 mile. Pass on either side of the N group of Kepulauan Lajah, observing that the depth quickly shoals to 9 m at 3 miles NE of Meledang, the most E'ly of this group, and at less than 2 miles N of Bulat, the most NE'ly.

Between Krawang and the N group of Kepulauan Lajah the depths are from 22 m to 27 m, decreasing fairly regularly towards the Borneo coast. Greig channel is deep and bold towards either side.

10.44.05. Passage northbound from Karimata Strait. Between Panebangan and Masa Tiga the Borneo coast may be approached to a depth of 11 m, but when about 8 miles NW of Masa Tiga do not bring it to bear more than 135°, or stand into depths of less than 15 m, until off Sungai Padang Tikar, N of which the coast may be approached to within 4 miles. Masa Tiga can usually be seen from a distance of 20 miles.

A vessel may stand off to, or W of, Leman Islands, observing that those islands (in sight from aloft) kept bearing more than 140° lead E of Twilight Reef, China Reef, and Greig Shoals.

Having cleared dangers as above, make good a course towards Datu or Pengiki Besar.

10.45. Sunda Strait eastward to Banda Sea and Second Eastern Passage

10.45.01. General remarks. From November to February, vessels which have passed through Sunda Strait into the Java Sea, and find that the North-west Monsoon in those waters, and the North-east Monsoon in the China Sea, have already set in, are advised to make E at once, and to pick up the Second Eastern Passage in the Ceram Sea N of the South Molukka Archipelago.

Alternatively, a vessel can join the First Eastern Passage off the entrance to Makassar Strait in November, but there is no advantage in so doing.

10.45.02. Directions. To join the Second Eastern Passage, the better recommended and more usual route is to stand NE from Sunda Strait and, having passed through the Java Sea, to pass through Saleier Strait and Buton Passage into the Banda Sea. With W'ly winds, when coming from Saleier Strait, close Tandjung Batu Toro, the SE point of Buton, to about 3 miles, and keep along the coast as far as Tandjung Kassolanatumbi to prevent being set over towards Wakatohi Kepulauan, in the light airs and S'ly currents which frequently prevail in the offing.

Alternatively, passage may be made N of Java, through Sapudi Strait, N of Bali, Lombok, and Sumbawa, and through the Flores Sea and Banda Sea to the Ceram Sea.

Directions for Ceram Sea, Manipa Strait, Djailolo Passage, and Dampier Strait are given in 10.46.02, 10.46.03.

10.46. Second Eastern Passage

10.46.01. General remarks. See 10.32.04. The passage from the South Indian Ocean to the China Sea through Ombai Strait is usually made during the season October to March. When proceeding to Singapore, the routes via Sunda Strait, previously described, should be taken.

An alternative route in October and November is to pass through one of the central passages, Bali Strait, Lombok Strait or Alas Strait, joining the route from Ombai Strait in the Ceram Sea. See 10.47.

December to April is the season of the tropical storms known as Willy-Willies. They may occur occasionally in November. See 6.16.

From Ombai Strait, the route is either W of Buru or more usually, through Manipa Strait between Buru and Manipa into the Ceram Sea. Thence pass through Djailolo Passage or Dampier Strait into the open Pacific Ocean. When in the Pacific Ocean, make easting between the parallels of 1° 30' N and 3° 00' N until able to pass E of Palau Islands; but between March and September pass W of these islands.

Having passed Palau Islands, a variety of routes is available, either through Surigao Strait and to the China Sea via Mindoro Strait or Verde Island Passage, or through San Bernardino Strait and Verde Island Passage, or, perhaps more usually, to keep E of the Philippine Islands and to Hong Kong via Balintang Channel or Bashi Channel; to Shang-hai between Sakishima Guntō and Okinawa Guntō and to Japan by a more N'ly route in the full strength of Kuro Shio.

For the sake of convenience in directions, the Second Eastern Passage may be divided into three parts; firstly from Ombai Strait to the Ceram Sea (10.46.02); secondly from the Ceram Sea through Djailolo Passage or Dampier Strait (10.46.03); and, thirdly, the continuation to the China Sea (10.46.04).

10.46.02. Ombai Strait and to Ceram Sea. Ombai Strait is the broad deep passage separating the NW coast of Timor from Alor Islands; from October to March it was frequently used by sailing vessels proceeding from Europe to China and Japan, and it was also used by sailing vessels bound for East Java from the China Sea from the middle of May to the end of June.

In the partially enclosed region N of Sawu Islands and Timor, known as the Sawu Sea, especially in the E portion, where it is continued E by Ombai Strait, the percentage of bright sky is greater than in any other part of the archipelago, and the haziness is equally great whenever E'ly winds blow; the rainfall is heaviest in December and January, but showers may fall with all W'ly winds.

The South-east Monsoon blows steadily between the middle of April and the end of September, from ESE to SE, the land breezes from Timor increasing the force of the wind at night, and the sea breezes diminishing it by day, similarly in the other season the wind will be most steady by day and unreliable at night.

In October and November the winds are from SE to SSW, and in December from the SW quarter, accompanied by thunderstorms, but the North-west Monsoon does not reach its full development, from W to WNW, until January, and begins to abate in February. Variable winds will then blow until April.

Proceeding NE through Ombai Strait, make the E point of Sumba (*10° 08' S, 120° 51' E*) and pass between it and Sawu Islands or between Sawu Islands and Roti, if falling to leeward with NW'ly wind. Under the exceptional conditions of a strong NW wind and lee current, it may be desirable to pass W of Sumba and S of Flores.

Passage from Ombai Strait to the Ceram Sea may be made either W of Buru or through Manipa Strait, which is the more usual route. If attempting to weather the W side of Buru, and falling to leeward, it is better to abandon the attempt and pass through Manipa Strait. Manipa Strait is a good and safe channel, conveniently situated for a call at Ambon.

During the North-west Monsoon vessels making N should do so along the E coast of Buru, where the adverse tidal stream is not so strong, and the favourable tidal stream runs strongly. In the strength of the monsoons, there may be a high sea running in Manipa Strait; if so, consideration must be given to the use of Kelang Strait, between Manipa and Kelang, but an adverse current prevails here during the North-west Monsoon season.

10.46.03. Through Ceram Sea to, and through Djailolo Passage or Dampier Strait, or through Molukka Sea to Pacific Ocean. Having entered the Ceram Sea as in 10.46.02, steer as directly as possible to pass through one of the channels between the chain of islands between Obi Major and Kofiau into the Halmahera Sea. The channel between Tobalai and Kekek is recommended in the North-west Monsoon so as to keep well to windward.

Continue N through the Halmahera Sea and pass into the Pacific Ocean through Djailolo Passage or Dampier Strait. Sagewin Strait, between Batanta and Salawati, should not be taken by sailing vessels, as there are frequent calms on account of the high land on either side, and the rapid tidal streams with strong eddies are liable to make the vessel unmanageable. The only difficulty in Djailolo Passage arises from the strong tidal streams which cause whirlpools and tide rips. The general directions for the passage of a sailing vessel through Dampier Strait are the same as those for a power vessel, see Admiralty Sailing Directions. If the wind is from the N, a sailing vessel, having passed through the narrows, should keep over towards Waigeo rather than Irian Barat, to avoid being driven on to the Irian Barat coast by the swell from the N. Great attention must be paid to the set of the currents.

Although the Molukka Sea is the principal passage for power vessels proceeding between the Sulawesi, Ceram, Banda and Arafura Seas, it is not recommended for a sailing vessel working through to the N during the North-west Monsoon season, the period dealt with in this article, as the current sets with the wind at a rate of 16 to 24 miles a day. If obliged to pass through it, a sailing vessel would find it best to enter through Peleng Strait, keeping along the Sulawesi coast.

10.46.04. Pacific Ocean to China Sea by Surigao Strait. Surigao Strait is less frequented by sailing vessels than is San Bernardino Strait, which is more to windward in the North-east Monsoon. It is, however, more direct and safer than San Bernadino Strait, but it obliges sailing vessels that take it, if they are making for Manila, to work up the W coast of Negros and Panay and the E coast of Mindoro. It is of advantage to vessels going to the more S'ly parts of the Philippine Islands or to the Sulu Sea. Surigao Strait is safe and deep throughout its length, and the shores of the islands that border it are steep-to.

At the entrance to Surigao Strait the North-east Monsoon sets in towards the end of September, and blows throughout October and November; in December NE winds alternate with N'ly gales. In January, winds blow from NE to ENE accompanied by heavy rain. In February and March, E'ly winds prevail. In April, May and June, the prevailing wind is SE, with occasional gales called "collas" from the S. In July, August and September, collas from SW are frequent.

The NE winds, though strong, cease during the night; but winds from SE, S, and SW will continue to blow. It generally rains with NNE and ENE winds; the rain ceases and the weather clears with E winds, and more so with SE winds. With SW winds it remains clear unless a gale arises, which sometimes brings rain.

In general there is no very bad weather in this part of the archipelago, except when a typhoon occurs. The season when a typhoon might occur is from the end of October to the beginning of January. They begin to blow from the NW, and finish from the SE, having passed through either NE or SW; when they shift through NE they blow the stronger, and more rain falls.

10.46.05. Pacific Ocean to China Sea by San Bernardino Strait and Verde Island Passage. When entering San Bernardino Strait from the E in the South-west Monsoon, work to windward with the flood stream, and when this loses its strength, make for the banks NW or W of Biri Island, where anchorage can be had on a sandy bottom until the tide makes again.

On weighing, work according to the direction of the stream, so as to pass through Kapul Pass, between Kapul and Dalupiri or through Dalupiri Pass, between Dalupiri and Samar. The latter is probably the safer, especially coming from a S'ly direction. If the tide should turn before a vessel has entered these passages, make for the open bay off Quinaguitman, S of Lipata point, in Samar Island. Anchorage can also be had, if necessary, in the channel on either side of Dalupiri Island, on a sandy bottom strewn with big stones.

The only danger to guard against at this part is Diamante Rock; this once passed, take either the passage between Naranjo Islands and Kapul or between Naranjo Islands and Destacado. This latter route is the better; shaping the course then to pass round the N end of Ticao.

For information respecting winds, currents, and passages with a fair wind through the strait (which is the same as for power vessels, see Admiralty Sailing Directions.

Verde Island Passage lies between the SW part of Luzon and the N coast of Mindoro. Verde Island divides the channel into N and S passages. Both are safe, but the more N'ly, or North Pass, is preferred, as the more S'ly, or South Pass, is interfered with by Bako Islands. It is a favourite route during the North-east Monsoon for vessels coming from a S'ly direction. Get to the N under the lee of Negros and Panay and from the NW point of Panay proceed between Mindoro and Tablas to Dumali Point, and then on through Verde Island Passage and up the W coast of Luzon, thus ecsaping the strong monsoon that is generally felt on clearing Lubang Islands.

10.46.06. Pacific Ocean to China Sea, passing north of Philippine Islands. Referring to 10.46.01, a vessel on passage from Djailolo Passage or Dampier Strait will have benefited by the gradually increasing effect of

Kuro Shio as far as Balintang Channel or Bashi Channel, one of which must be used. These channels are described in Admiralty Sailing Directions.

10.47. First Eastern Passage

10.47.01. General remarks. As outlined in 10.32.05, the First Eastern Passage should be taken N-bound in October and November only. It is more suitable for S-bound vessels, but then only in May and from the China Sea. It has little to recommend it on account of the adverse current setting to the S through Makassar Strait, often strongly, at all seasons. The winds are boisterous and uncertain at the S end of Makassar Strait, and light and variable at the N end, while the navigation is difficult throughout almost the whole voyage to the open China Sea.

The route runs from either Bali Strait, Lombok Strait, or Alas Strait across the Java Sea into, then through Makassar Strait into the Sulawesi Sea, and thence to the Sulu Sea through Basilan Strait. It then passes up the W coast of Mindanao, Negros, and Panay, and enters the China Sea through Mindoro Strait or Verde Island Passage.

10.47.02. Notes on Bali Strait, Lombok Strait, and Alas Strait. Of these three straits, Bali Strait is the narrowest and most difficult for sailing vessels. It was formerly preferred by them, due to the anchoring facilities it offered. Lombok Strait is the widest, but Alas Strait is probably preferable as there are no dangers and anchorage can be obtained if necessary during the calms to which all these straits are more or less subject.

In Bali Strait, which is only one mile wide at its N end, the chief difficulty lies in the currents, and sailing vessels should only navigate the strait by day.

During the South-east Monsoon, N of the area of the Trade Winds, the wind is mostly SSW and SSE to SE, with a W-going stream; from July to September the wind can be very strong. In the North-west Monsoon, a vessel N of the Trade Wind area may be set strongly to the E, both by wind and stream.

Lombok Strait is the most important passage between the Indian Ocean and Makassar Strait, mainly on account of its width and the ease with which it can be navigated. During the North-west Monsoon sailing vessels average one day to make the N-bound passage; during the South-east Monsoon the time taken on the passage usually varies from one to three days. Making the S-bound passage during the North-west Monsoon takes at least one day, but usually more; in the South-east Monsoon this passage is quick, averaging 16 or 17 hours, but in April and October sailing vessels have experienced great difficulty in getting through the strait S-bound. February and March are the best months for navigating the strait.

In Lombok Strait, during the South-east Monsoon, calms are frequent from sunrise to noon, when a fresh S'ly wind arises, turning to SE on the Bali side, and to SSW on the Lombok side, blowing strong during the night. In the North-west Monsoon the winds are generally from NW, sometimes with violent squalls, and a high sea in the N approach.

10.47.03. Directions for Lombok Strait. During the South-east Monsoon the South-east Trade Wind continues through the strait. When nearing the strait, keep E of the entrance and sight Lombok Island, taking into consideration that the vessel may be set W by the monsoon drift. Sail into the entrance close along the SW point of Lombok, and then hold the Lombok side. At this season Nusa Besar must never be approached, as in the event of calms, especially with a S-going stream, there is danger of being set on to it.

In the transition months (March, and the end of October and beginning of November), if W'ly winds predominate hold the Bali side, passing through Badung Strait; if E'ly winds predominate hold the Lombok side. Badung Strait is always preferable, as anchorage may be obtained there.

During the North-west Monsoon, make for Bukit Badung and proceed through Badung Strait under the Bali shore.

10.47.04. Directions for Alas Strait. In the South-east Monsoon the wind blows strongly from S during the greater part of the day, but subsides towards evening, when the land breeze from Lombok Island begins. In the North-west Monsoon variable and baffling S'ly winds are often experienced in Alas Strait.

Approaching from the S, Alas Strait may be identified by the high, rugged land of the SW part of Sumbawa, and the plateau forming the SE part of Lombok. From the N, Mount Rindjani and the high NW part of Sumbawa are conspicuous, and the islands lying under the coasts of Lombok and Sumbawa will also be visible.

As all the straits E of Java are more or less subject to calms, sailing vessels proceeding through Alas Strait may find it necessary to anchor; it is therefore, advisable to hold the Lombok side of the strait, where conditions for anchoring are more favourable.

10.47.05. Notes on passage through Java Sea and Makassar Strait to Sulawesi Sea. Having passed through Bali Strait, Alas Strait, or Lombok Strait as directed, steer to pass between Kepulauan Kangean and Kepulauan Tengah, and thence to enter Makassar Strait by one of the three channels into which the S entrance is divided. The middle one of these three channels is to be preferred for entering the strait, though the most E'ly channel is also frequently used, especially by vessels bound for Makassar. In the latter case Spermonde Kepulauan and its associated bank rises so steeply from depths greater than 180 m that sounding will give no indication of a vessel's approach. The most W'ly of these three channels is seldom used, partly owing to the fact that no land is visible, which makes it difficult for a vessel to determine its position, and partly because no saving of distance is effected.

Some 150 miles to the N of the above channels the strait is again divided into two channels by Balabalagan Island and Little Paternoster Islands. The width of the W channel is 20 miles, and of that on the E side of the islands 45 miles. There are some dangers in the W channel, but it is nevertheless much frequented, and for some reasons preferred to the E, on account of the more moderate depths off the coast of Borneo, which permit anchoring in case of necessity, while the Sulawesi coast is steep-to in many places, and destitute of anchorage.

Having passed N of Little Paternoster Islands there is no difficulty in navigating through the remainder of Makassar strait into the Sulawesi Sea.

10.47.06. Sulawesi Sea to China Sea. This section of the First Eastern Passage passes frrom the Sulawesi Sea, through Basilan Strait into the Sulu Sea, and thence by Mindoro Strait or Verde Island Passage to the China Sea. Verde Island Passage, see 10.46.05, is a favourite N-bound route during the North-east Monsoon.

In Basilan Strait, the channel N of Santa Cruz Islands, although narrower than that on the S side of them, is generally preferred by sailing vessels for its better anchorage facilities.

The Sulu Sea is of great depth and offers no particular problems. For winds and currents in this sea area and its vicinity, see Admiralty Sailing Directions.

10.48. Routes southbound through Eastern Archipelago

10.48.01. General remarks. There are three principal routes for vessels S-bound from the China Sea through the Eastern Archipelago.

The Western route (10.49) passes through the China Sea W of the Philippine Islands and Borneo to Sunda Strait, either direct or via Singapore.

The Eastern route (10.50) passes through the China Sea, E of the Philippine Islands to Djailolo Passage, and thence to Ombai Strait or to one of the central passages (Alas Strait, Lombok Strait, or Bali Strait).

The Central route (10.51) passes W of the Philippine Islands and E of Borneo, through Makassar Strait to one of the central passages.

Of these three routes the Western and Central are those used by vessels from ports in S China; the Central Route is also used from Manila and ports in the S parts of the Philippine Islands or on the E side of Borneo; the Eastern Route is used by vessels from ports in N China or from Japan. In the strength of the South-west Monsoon vessels from ports in S China sometimes use the Eastern Route.

10.49. Western Route southbound from China Sea

10.49.01. General remarks. Passage may be taken either direct or via Singapore, the latter being best made during the North-west Monsoon period (October to April), and there are then two principal passages, one by Riouw Strait and Selat Bangka or Selat Gelasa, but in October by Selat Gelasa only, because light and baffling winds prevail in that month between Riouw Strait and Selat Bangka; and the other, known as the Inner Route, by Durian Strait, Berhala Strait, and Selat Bangka. Riouw Strait and Berhala Strait are particularly convenient for sailing vessels leaving Singapore for Europe in the North-west Monsoon (North-east Monsoon of the China Sea). By using these routes, the difficulties of beating E out of Singapore Strait into the North-east Monsoon of the China Sea are avoided.

During the South-east Monsoon, the ordinary route would be to beat out through Singapore Strait to the E, and work S by Karimata Strait or Selat Gelasa to Sunda Strait. At the same time, vessels are frequently able to proceed much more quickly to the S by the Inner Routes than by the outer one. Convenient anchorage is always available in the straits for sailing vessels held up by wind, or tidal streams.

To make the passage from the China Sea to Sunda Strait during the North-east Monsoon of the China Sea, a vessel having passed either E or W of Anambas Kepulauan would proceed S through Selat Bangka or Selat Gelasa; but during October the former should not be attempted, owing to the calms and baffling winds which occur during that month in its N approaches.

During the South-west Monsoon, a vessel from Palawan Passage or one that has crossed to the Borneo coast from Mui Dinh should proceed by Karimata Strait or Selat Gelasa.

Directions for vessels S-bound through Durian Strait and Berhala Strait are the reverse of those given for the N-bound passage by the Inner Route in paragraphs 10.38.04 and 10.38.02. Directions for the other straits and channels follow.

10.49.02. Passage southward through Riouw Strait. Vessels having a fair wind leaving Singapore at high water, or about the first quarter of the ebb or E-going stream, and taking about 4 hours to reach the entrance to Riouw Strait, will probably carry a fair tidal stream through both straits, but no dependence can be placed on it. See Admiralty Sailing Directions.

The directions given in paragraph 10.37.02 for coming N through Riouw Strait, if reversed, will suffice for proceeding S. Vessels of deep draught should pass E of Karang Galang.

At night, steer to pass ¾ mile E of the light on Karang Galang, from which position Tundjuk leading lights will be in line bearing 180°. When Terkulai light is open S of Lobam Island bearing 100°, and the vessel is S of Karang Lolo, shape course about 135°, allowing for tide, until the light on Karas Ketjil bears 154°, when it may be steered for on that bearing. Pass about half a mile or more E of it, and then keep it astern, bearing about 320° or less, as long as it is in sight, to lead in the fairway S of the strait.

10.49.03. Approach to, and passage southward through Selat Bangka. With a fair wind, when coming from the N, and having passed Tudju Islands and steering to the S to pass through Selat Bangka, there will be no difficulty in clear weather in determining a position; in such circumstances enter the strait E of Kolepon Rocks.

In thick weather it often happens that no land can be seen until the vessel has arrived very near to the entrance to the strait, and at such times it is important to get hold of the bank extending from the Sumatra coast, and then proceed along its edge in low water depths of from 15 m to 11 m, carefully attending to sounding. Sometimes Menumbing will be seen, but no other land, and in such case it will be prudent to proceed as before, keeping along the edge of the bank.

When working through Selat Bangka from the N, the passage W of Kolepon Rocks is much to be preferred when the land is obscured and reliable bearings cannot be obtained; at other times the E channel is preferable. By reversing the directions given in 10.35.03 and 10.35.04 for working through from the southward, no difficulty will be experienced in navigating Selat Bangka.

10.49.04. Approach to, and passage southward through Selat Gelasa.
Although the navigation of this strait is complicated by the many dangers in it, yet, as, the course by it is more direct, and the prevailing winds are more favourable, and the distance less than by perhaps the safer route through Selat Bangka, many seamen prefer it, especially when S-bound from China late in the North-east Monsoon.

In consequence of the N entrance to Selat Gelasa being so near the equator, the winds, even in the strength of the monsoons, are very uncertain, producing a corresponding uncertainty in the direction and force of the tidal streams and currents. A sailing vessel approaching the strait from N will, therefore, have to be principally guided by the winds and currents which may have been encountered rather than by relying upon those which are mentioned to have been experienced at certain seasons and described in Admiralty Sailing Directions.

In thick weather the greatest caution is necessary when approaching Selat Gelasa, for unless good observations can be obtained there is no means of ascertaining an exact position, and, in such circumstances, it is advisable to steer for Selat Bangka, where the soundings, on the edge of the bank extending from the Sumatra coast, may be a useful guide, although the land may not be distinguished. See 10.49.03.

When approaching the NE coast of Bangka use every precaution not to get entangled among the outlying dangers when running S for Selat Gelasa in thick weather. Some of these dangers are over 40 miles from the shore, between Tandjung Berikat and Tandjung Tuing, which are about 75 miles apart.

Early in the North-east Monsoon, when the wind is generally from N or NW, and intending to go through Selat Gelasa, pass between Toty and Dokan, which lie off the N coast of Bangka; a little later in the monsoon the wind is more E'ly, and it is then better to pass from 10 to 20 miles E of Toty.

Cross bearings of the mountains on Bangka, in clear weather, will enable a vessel to clear Iwan Reef and Severn Reef, which lie in the track to Selat Gelasa. If passing N of Severn Reef, steer so as to get on the meridian of Pulau Gelasa before reaching the parallel of 1° 50′ S. Pulau Gelasa is visible in clear weather at a distance of over 30 miles, but it is not visible from Lanrick Reef, the most N'ly danger, for which a careful lookout is necessary. When Pulau Gelasa comes in sight, bring it to bear 180° which leads clear of all dangers lying to the W. Then pass E of Pulau Gelasa and shape course for Selat Leplia, which is the passage usually taken.

The above directions apply only to sailing vessels coming from China early in the North-east Monsoon. Late in the monsoon, SE'ly and E'ly winds are often met with between Bangka and Belitung, and it will be better to pass from 10 to 12 miles W of Pedjantan (*0° 08′ N, 107° 12′ E*), and try as soon as possible to get on the meridian of Pulau Gelasa. When that island is seen, bring it to bear 180°, and proceed as above.

Late in the North-east Monsoon also, SSW winds are often met in the S part of the China Sea, obliging vessels to keep farther E towards the islands off Borneo. If this should happen in May or June, it would be tedious work getting to Selat Leplia, and therefore steer for Langkuas Island off the NW point of Belitung, and pass through Selat Baur.

Selat Gelasa can only be approached from the N at night by passing E of all the dangers lying N of it. Having passed well to the W of Florence Adelaide Reef, shape course for the light on Langkuas, and when it comes in sight, alter course to pass about 4 miles W of Langir Islet.

10.49.05. Passage southward through Selat Leplia.
In the early part of the North-east Monsoon, N'ly and NW'ly winds prevail about the N entrance to Selat Gelasa, and strong SE'ly currents will generally be experienced between Pulau Gelasa and Pulau Liat, especially near the N extremity of Pulau Liat. Neglect to guard against the effect of this current has been a frequent cause of accidents.

Vessels intending to proceed S-bound through Selat Leplia by night should take care to sight Tandjung Berikat during daylight.

Having passed from 1 mile to 2 miles E of Pulau Gelasa, steer to the SW until that island bears 014°, and then keep it on that bearing, astern, until the SE extreme of Pulau Kelapan bears 236° and the N point of Pulau Liat bears 125°. From this position keep in the fairway of the channel, steering about 185° to pass between the dangers off Tjelaka and Discovery Rocks. carefully guarding against the effects of tidal streams or currents by frequently fixing the position.

10.49.06. For passage southward through Selat Baur and Selat Limendo,
the directions given in 10.40.03 and 10.40.04 should be applied in reverse.

Selat Baur is the best channel to use for working through against the South-east Monsoon, since the currents in it are weaker than elsewhere.

10.49.07. Approach to, and passage southward through, Karimata Strait.
If using the Main Channel during the North-west Monsoon, take the channel E of Ontario Reef. Approach Serutu with its summit bearing less than 152°, and thence pass 4 or 5 miles W of the lighthouse, observing that the W extreme of the island kept bearing less than 354° leads E of Ontario Reef. Thence gradually bring the summit of Serutu to bear 335° astern, until lost sight of, which direction being preserved leads well to the E of Catherine Reef. From a position 10 miles

E of Catherine Reef, steer 170° through the fairway, and about 5 miles E of Discovery East Bank lighthouse, clear of all dangers.

If using Greig Channel or Inner Channel, the directions given in 10.44.04 are generally applicable. When the South-east Monsoon is strong, smoother water, with less current, will be found in these channels than in the main part of the strait.

10.49.08. General directions for passages from Selat Bangka, Selat Gelasa, or Karimata Strait to Sunda Strait. Dangerous shoals extend for about 35 miles to the S of Selat Gelasa rendering great caution necessary when leaving it and making for Sunda Strait.

Having cleared the shoals S of Selat Gelasa and Karimata Strait, the route to Sunda Strait is the same as that from Selat Bangka, described below.

With a fair wind, after passing E of Five Fathom Banks, in depths of from 18 m to 22 m, steer to pass a prudent distance W of Djaga Utara and E of Brouwers Banks and Lynn Reef; from thence reverse the directions given in 10.34.01 for proceeding N.

When working S from a position W of Five Fathom Banks, reverse the directions for working N as given in 10.34.01, and observe the caution for anchoring at night when the position is at all doubtful. Clifton Bank, with a least depth of 5 m, E of Tandjung Sekopong, will be avoided by keeping Kepulauan Segama bearing more than 180°, and when S of them, the islands bearing less than 360° will lead E of Djangkat Lajang, which has a depth of 8 m over it.

In the South-east Monsoon, when the atmosphere is hazy and the coast rarely visible, great care is necessary in passing Kepulauan Segama, which from N appear as one.

10.49.09. Passage southward through Sunda Strait. The general description of Sunda Strait, together with the winds, sea and tidal streams to be expected therein, is given in Admiralty Sailing Directions. See also 10.33.01.

During the South-east Monsoon, from April to September, keep in the main fairway when the wind is favourable; but if proceeding through Selat Panaitan keep closer to the Java coast than to Panaitan. This route may be taken also at the beginning of the North-west Monsoon, up to about the end of December if conditions are favourable.

The monsoon is generally supposed to shift at about the beginning of October, but often is delayed for a month; the interval being filled with calms, light S'ly winds, and frequent heavy Sumatra squalls, or south-westers. These squalls at this season generally take place at night, accompanied by heavy rain, thunder and lightning, and are of short duration.

During the North-west Monsoon, from October to April, the alternative is offered between routes on the N and S sides of Sunda Strait.

By the **Northern Route,** during the strength of the North-west Monsoon in January and February, the W channel, between Sangian and Kepulauan Sumur is recommended, giving the latter a berth of 1½ miles and thence working NW when winds are from W.

If it is late in the day when Kepulauan Sumur are sighted, with strong SW winds and an adverse stream, a vessel will do well to seek anchoarge off the Sumatra coast or Tandjung Sumur Batu at the N end of the islands, or off Sindu Islet, inshore of Kandang Balak, the SW island of Kepulauan Sumur. The vessel should be got aweigh immediately the stream turns, to take advantage of the morning land breeze.

Working through the passage between Sebuku and Sumatra, pass on whichever side of Pulau Tiga the strong currents and hard squalls will allow, and thence N of Serdang, and between it and Siuntjal; or, alternatively, pass N of Legundi and out through Selat Legundi avoiding Medusa Reef, which lies NE of Seserot, passing on either side of that island in mid-channel. In this manner a quick passage may be made through the strait if the wind be not too variable, besides having the advantage of anchorage being available on the E side of Sebuku or on the W side of Lampung Bay if the current or wind prove too strong.

Note: Legundi Strait, between the Sumatra coast and Legundi, is 2 miles wide, and is recommended to sailing vessels working out of Lampung Bay in the North-west Monsoon. The passages on either side of Seserot are equally good, and, with contrary winds or current, there is anchorage on the E side of the island in depths of from 18 m to 22 m, sand. Vessels drifting through the strait in a calm will be carried past the island by the off-set of the current. To the W of Legundi Strait is Teluk Kiluan, where safe anchorage may be found, if required, by vessels with local knowledge only. Sailing vessels may run out with the land wind, which blows here from the N, but it is recommended to have a boat in attendance to tow, lest they should get becalmed under the high land; it is advisable to pass close W of Tandjung Tuntungkalik.

The **Southern Route** through Sunda Strait takes a vessel to the Indian Ocean along the Java coast and through Selat Panaitan. There are on record many instances of vessels having worked out of the strait during the North-west Monsoon by taking this course, with more ease and celerity than could have been effected by stretching into Lampung Bay, in consequence of the SW'ly current from the Java sea having then developed its chief strength along the E side of the strait. This is, however, a lee shore and therefore dangerous, at this season.

In spite of this, cases are on record in which vessels have worked through Selat Panaitan in a remarkably short time during a W'ly gale, by carrying a heavy press of sail and tacking between the squalls, when it was impossible for any vessel in Great Channel to beat against the current and heavy sea. In this monsoon, particularly when working out, it is advisable to keep nearer the island shore, to obtain the help of a current sometimes running to the W, and to avoid being set upon the rocks about Tandjung Gedeh by the heavy swell. Near the Java shore, when outside anchorage depths in a calm, vessels would be in considerable danger.

10.50. Eastern Route south-bound from China Sea

10.50.01. General remarks. The Eastern Route passes from the China Sea to Ombai Strait, or to Alas Strait, Lombok Strait or Bali Strait. It is useful from the middle of May to the end of July.

During the strength of the South-west Monsoon, the best route from Hong Kong and adjacent coast ports is to pass N of the Philippine Islands, through Bashi Channel or Balintang Channel, and then steer, either along the E side of the Philippines, or to the SE towards Palau Islands.

When the E'ly monsoon is encountered, shape course to pass E of Halmahera Island, through Djailolo Passage or Dampier Strait to the Halmahera Sea and thence to the Ceram Sea; alternatively a vessel may pass to the Ceram Sea from the Pacific Ocean through the Molukka Sea.

From the Ceram Sea pass to the Banda Sea either through Manipa Strait, E of Buru Island, or by passing W of Buru; then continue through the Banda Sea to Ombai Strait, or through the Flores Sea to Alas Strait, Lombok Strait, or Bali Strait; if bound to Bali Strait, the usual route is via Sapudi Strait.

10.50.02. China Sea to Pacific Ocean via Balintang Channel or Bashi Channel. Balintang Channel is reputed to be free of danger, and is frequently used by sailing vessels S-bound from ports in China. Bashi Channel is also used. See Admiralty Sailing Directions.

10.50.03. Pacific Ocean to Ceram Sea. As mentioned in 10.50.01, this part of the Eastern Route can be taken via Djailolo Passage, or Dampier Strait, or through the Molukka Sea.

In Djailolo passage, the deep channel lying between Pulau Muor and Pulau Gébé presents no difficulty except from the strong tidal streams, often accompanied by whirlpools and tide rips, particularly off the NW extremity of Pulau Gébé.

Having passed through Djailolo Passage steer through the Halmahera Sea to enter the Ceram Sea through one of the channels between the chain of islands about 70 miles S of Djailolo Passage. The channel between Pisang Island and Boo Islands is recommended for sailing vessels during the South-east Monsoon.

When approaching Dampier Strait from an E'ly direction, Tandjung Momfafa should be made out, a good berth being given to the shoals, which extend about 7 miles ENE, and which may be avoided by keeping Wajam Island bearing more than 245°; then proceed, reversing the directions given in 10.46.03 and in Admiralty Sailing Directions.

Having passed through Dampier Strait proceed direct to the Ceram Sea.

As for N-bound vessels (10.46.03), the Molukka Sea cannot be strongly recommended S-bound between the Pacific Ocean and Ceram Sea. It is sometimes used by sailing vessels S-bound from China, and, after September, with advantage: but it is a tedious passage to beat through, as the currents set with the wind at the rate of from 16 to 24 miles a day. When it is difficult to get to the S by the channel between Sula Islands and Obi Major, sailing vessels might try to do so, by keeping near the W coast of Halmahera and passing through Patientie Strait, between Halmahera and Batjan, and thence through Obi Strait and Tobalai Strait to the Ceram Sea.

10.50.04. Ceram Sea to Indian Ocean via Ombai Strait, Alas Strait, Lombok Strait, or Bali Strait. The recommended route is to pass through Manipa Strait into the Banda Sea and thence proceed as directly as possible to Ombai Strait or to Alas Strait, Lombok Strait, or Bali Strait.

In passing through Manipa Strait, S-bound in the South-east Monsoon, keep towards the W side of Manipa Island, where the N-going current will not be so strongly felt. See 10.46.02 and Admiralty Sailing Directions.

Approaching Alas Strait from the N, Mount Rindjani and the high NW part of Sumbawa are conspicuous. The 180 m depth contour line from the S terminates about a mile from Tandjung Ringgit; from the N it penetrates as far as a line running W from Belang Island. The soundings between are deep but irregular. Alas Strait, as are all straits E of Java, is more or less subject to calms; it is therefore advisable in a sailing vessel to keep within soundings on the Lombok side, the more so as the currents are not so strong there as in the middle and on the E side.

When S-bound, it is advisable to get under weigh very early in the morning, in order to clear the strait, if possible, before the sea breeze sets in.

In Lombok Strait, S-bound during the South-east Monsoon, with predominating SE winds, it is advisable to work up under the Bali shore with a N-going stream until Mount Agung bears 270°; under these conditions, working to the S under the NW coast of Lombok is difficult, and the same applies to the Bali shore S of the parallel of Mount Agung.

During the North-west Monsoon and in the transition months, Lombok Strait from the N affords no particular difficulties; the remarks on the tidal streams in Admiralty Sailing Directions should be studied.

Bali Strait (10.47.02) offers a safe passage to S-bound vessels during the North-west Monsoon, and with the exception of Alas Strait, E of Lombok Island, is to be preferred to all the passages E of Java, as there is anchorage on both sides of the narrows in case they should not be passed through in a single tide. For vessels coming from the N, the chief difficulty to contend with is the great strength of the currents. Sailing vessels should only navigate this strait by day. During the North-west Monsoon, the water in the Strait is smooth, and the passage easy.

It is well to have boats ready for towing the vessel, when near the shore, in calms.

10.51. Central Route south-bound from China Sea

10.51.01. General remarks. The Central Route runs from the China Sea, through Makassar Strait, to Alas Strait, Lombok Strait, or Bali Strait. It is, in fact, the reverse of the First Eastern Passage (10.47). It is intended for vessels leaving China at the end of April or the beginning of May.

Summarising the route, a vessel should steer from the vicinity of Macclesfield Bank, to pass through Mindoro Strait, and thence across the Sulu Sea to the Sulawesi Sea via Basilan Strait or Sibutu Passage; Basilan Strait is recommended for sailing vessels, though Sibutu Passage is sometimes used. The voyage now continues through the Sulawesi Sea and Makassar Strait into the Java Sea, through which either of two routes may be taken, namely to Sunda Strait or to one of the central passages, Alas Strait, Lombok Strait, or Bali Strait. Vessels bound to the last named usually pass through Sapudi Strait.

If an alternative to Makassar Strait is desired, a vessel may pass from the Sulawesi Sea to the Banda Sea via the Molukka Sea, Ceram Sea and Manipa Strait.

10.51.02. Passage through Mindoro Strait into Sulu Sea. The wide Mindoro strait, separating the Calamian Islands from Mindoro Island, is one of the most frequented channels for sailing vessels which leave Manila for the Indian Ocean towards the end of April, and throughout the South-west Monsoon period; and by other vessels at all times of the year from the ports of China to Australia. Land and sea breezes are felt on the coasts of the larger islands in Mindoro Strait, mostly during the South-west Monsoon and in the periods between the monsoons; they are not so regular during the North-east Monsoon.

For further information, see Admiralty Sailing Directions.

10.51.03. Passage through Sulu Sea to Makassar Strait. Making to the S through the Sulu Sea, it is best to keep on the E side along the coast of Panay Island, and through Basilan Strait. The more direct route from Mindoro Strait S through Sibutu Passage is not recommended and no special directions are available for it. For the Sulu Sea and Basilan Strait, see 10.47.06.

The passage from Basilan Strait or Sibutu Passage, across the Sulawesi Sea to Makassar Strait, is as direct as possible.

10.51.04. Passage southbound through Makassar Strait and Java Sea. In Makassar Strait, the Borneo side provides anchorage in case of need; the coast of Sulawesi is steep-to. Although there are some dangers in the channel W of Little Paternoster Islands, it is nevertheless much frequented for the same reason.

On leaving Makassar Strait, and entering the Java Sea, course must be shaped for Sunda Strait or for the N entrance to one of the three passages between the islands immediately E of Java, namely Alas Strait, Lombok Strait, and Bali Strait. See 10.47.02.

If bound for Alas Strait or Lombok Strait, steer to pass about 20 miles E of the dangers on that side of Kangean Kepulauan. If bound for Bali Strait the usual route is through Sapudi Strait, which is a good and safe channel with no dangers other than Tembaga Reefs, which dry, and Jacoba Elizabeth Rock, with a depth of 11 m 9, lying on the W side; it is preferable to both the channels W of Gili Jang and the channel E of Sapudi.

In Sapudi Strait and the passages farther E, including Kangean Kepulauan, the South-east Monsoon prevails from April to October, and the North-west Monsoon from November to March. In April and May all winds are southerly, in June the monsoon becomes dominant from SSE to SE, and blows with greatest strength during July, August and September. In November winds are N'ly, alternating with rain squalls from all points; in December N and NW winds last longer and squalls come from NW or WNW; January and February are marked by very squally weather from NW to N, and in March it often continues to blow stiffly from W to WNW.

ROUTES THROUGH RED SEA

10.55. General note. Sailing vessels, whether N-bound or S-bound, at times experience great difficulties when working against the strong winds, which, in the winter season, blowing from either end of the Red Sea towards its centre, produce a short hollow sea, and, combined with the strong current that often runs with the wind, renders the progress of such vessels very slow. In working to windward in the central channel, a vessel cannot do wrong by keeping towards the Arabian shore, but should not stand close in with a light wind or heavy swell. After dark she ought only to stand towards the shore half the distance she stands out, and should never come nearer than 10 miles to the reefs at night, to guard against the possibility of mischance from the unexpected existence of a cross current.

10.56. Southbound through Red Sea. For sailing vessels, the most favourable part of the year for the S-bound passage is from June to September, or the period of the South-west Monsoon in the Arabian Sea, as N'ly winds of variable strength then prevail throughout the whole length of the Red Sea. Particular attention should be paid to the description of the currents in the Red Sea; this is especially necessary for the narrower portions of the passage, and the approaches thereto. See 6.51–6.53 and Admiralty Sailing Directions.

On approaching the Straits of Bāb-al Mandab, choice must be made between using Large Strait, or Small Strait. For ease of navigation the former is recommended, numerous accidents having occurred in the latter; at the same time consideration must be given to the fact that anchorage, in case of need, is possible in any part of Small Strait. The circumstances prevailing at the time must determine the course to be followed.

10.57. Northbound through Red Sea. For the N-bound voyage by the same route as the S-bound (10.56), December, January and February are the best months, as the S'ly winds often carry a vessel as far as the parallel of Jiddah, and sometimes as far as that of Quseir, or even, at times, to Suez itself. After losing the S'ly wind, a vessel will have the N'ly wind to beat against.

If as far N as Quseir, and bound for Suez, and a strong N'ly wind is encountered, a vessel in the central channel of the Red Sea, or even on the W shore, ought to stand over to the Arabian coast, where she will probably fetch

Al Muwailih (*27° 40′ N, 35° 27′ E*). Having worked up 30 miles N of that place, she may stand over to Ras Muhammad, leaving the Arabian coast at night. As she proceeds, the N'ly winds will veer to NNE out of the Gulf of 'Aqaba; by sailing as close as possible, these will enable her to fetch Ras Muhammad.

ROUTES FROM ADEN

10.60. Aden to Bombay. During the South-west Monsoon from April to September, take as direct a route as possible. Keep in the centre, or rather towards the Arabian shore of the Gulf of Aden, to avoid the W'ly current on the African coast. During the strength of the South-west Monsoon, in June, July and August, when the weather is thick and heavy, and observations very uncertain, steer direct for Khānderi Island, and watch the soundings carefully.

When steering for Bombay Harbour, from the middle of May till August, steady gales and clear weather will be experienced at times, until within 70 or 90 miles of the coast, but cloudy weather with rain and squalls may be expected on the bank of soundings, as the land is approached.

If not certain of the latitude it will be prudent to keep between the parallels of 18° 15′ N and 18° 25′ N, and endeavour to get soundings on Direction Bank, after passing over Fifty Fathoms Flat.

During the early part and strength of the South-west Monsoon, great care must be observed not to get N of the entrance to the harbour, for then the N-going tidal stream, as well as the heave of the S'ly swell, frequently sets vessels along the bank towards the Gulf of Cambay, and late in May, June and July it would be found difficult at times to work round Prongs Reef. Therefore, in these months a vessel should steer direct for Khānderi Island, allowing for a N'ly set of the tidal stream—though the prevailing current outside the depth of 55 m off the harbour, after the burst of the monsoon, is S-going—and endeavour should be made to make the island bearing between 090° and 135°, borrowing a little either way, as circumstances require, to carry a fair wind in entering the harbour.

If the wind is inclined to blow in squalls from W to WNW, a vessel should not run too close inshore S of Khānderi Island, not even approaching that island very close, as there might be difficulty in weathering it with these winds, which are sometimes experienced in June and July, but are more frequent in August.

During the interval between the land and sea breezes in the forenoon, a heavy smoky haze frequently hangs over the land, obscuring everything from view, so that great care should be exercised when approaching the land shortly after daylight between May and August. Occasionally this also occurs during the calm hours of the evening.

During the North-east Monsoon, from October to March, the passage from the Red Sea to India or the Persian Gulf is very tedious for sailing vessels, and is seldom attempted. In former times, the passage between Aden and Bombay, when unavoidably taken at this season, frequently occupied from 60 to 90 days.

If it is necessary to make the passage, work along the coast of Arabia, taking advantage of every shift of wind. Should the W-going current be strong inshore, stand out 60 or 80 miles from the land; if the wind be light, take advantage of the tides and land winds inshore, anchoring when requisite. When off Kuria Muria Islands, stretch over for Bombay, and as easting is made, the wind will draw to N or even W of N.

10.61. Aden to Ceylon and Bay of Bengal. From April to October, during the South-west Monsoon, invariably pass N of Socotra to avoid the heavy cross seas S of that island. It is at all times desirable to avoid passing S of Socotra if this means making Abd-al-Kuri at night, as the currents often set strongly N.

For Ceylon, proceed direct and thence to the Bay of Bengal, see 10.03, where directions for the Bay of Bengal will be found.

From October to March, keep along the coast of Arabia to about 52° E; pass through Eight Degree Channel or Nine Degree Channel; then steer to round Ceylon, and having cleared that island, make easting on the parallel of 5° N as far as the middle of the Bay of Bengal, and then work N. From the meridian of 87° E, a vessel will probably fetch Madras. After mid-February, round Ceylon at a distance of about 50 miles and then proceed direct.

The currents off the coast of Ceylon are strong and variable, see Admiralty Sailing Directions.

10.62. Aden to Malacca Strait. From April to October, pass N of Socotra, and thence direct round the S end of Ceylon and across the Bay of Bengal, entering Malacca Strait S of Great Nicobar Island.

From October to March, work along the Arabian coast as far as Ras Fartak, or just beyond it, and thence stand across the Arabian Sea, passing S of Minicoy Island, and round the S end of Ceylon, and across the Bay of Bengal. Pass close S of Great Nicobar Island, if the wind permit, and thence keep on the Malay side of Malacca Strait, see 10.83.

10.63. Eight Degree Channel and Nine Degree Channel are separated by the island of Minicoy. In Nine Degree Channel, the practice of steering to pass a few miles N of Minicoy, especially by night, is a dangerous one, because the island is over 4 miles long in a N and S direction, the light is on the SW side, and the current at times sets strongly to the S. On the other hand, in Eight Degree Channel, a vessel should keep in the N part of the channel, nearer to Minicoy than to the Maldive Islands.

10.64. Aden to Fremantle, Cape Leeuwin, and southern Australia or New Zealand. During the South-west Monsoon, from April to October, when W'ly winds prevail in the Gulf of Aden, proceed to the S of Ceylon, as directed in 10.62. After rounding the S extreme of Ceylon steer to the SE to cross the equator in about 95° E; thence continue S across the South-east Trade into the W'ly winds and round Cape Leeuwin if, not bound to Fremantle.

G

From November to March, proceed towards Ceylon, as directed for that season in 10.62; and thence, with the North-east Monsoon, cross the equator in about 90° E into the North-west Monsoon. Then make easting in that monsoon as far as the E end of Java; thence stand S across the South-east Trade into the westerlies, and thence continue to Cape Leeuwin and Fremantle.

At all seasons, if bound to ports on the S or SE side of Australia, to Tasmania, or to New Zealand, continue S and SE in the westerlies to join the appropriate part of the route from the Cape of Good Hope, see 10.01.03.

10.65. Aden to Mauritius. During the South-west Monsoon, from April to October, pass N of Socotra, run through the South-west Monsoon; cross the equator in about 72° E or even run through One and half degree Channel, and make southing into the South-east Trade, passing E of Chagos Archipelago. From thence proceed direct to Mauritius.

From November to March, work along the Arabian coast until able to weather Ras Asir, run through the North-east and North-west Monsoons, crossing the equator in about 64° E, and the parallel of 10° S in about 70° E; when in the South-east Trade steer direct for Mauritius.

10.66. Aden to Cape of Good Hope. From April to October, pass N of Socotra, run through the South-west Monsoon, cross the equator in about 72° E, or even run through One and half degree Channel and then cross the equator; thence making southing into the South-east Trade Wind, passing E of Chagos Archipelago. Run through the South-east Trade, passing S of Mauritius and about 100 miles S of Madagascar, and make the African coast about 200 miles S of Durban. From thence keep in the strength of the Agulhas Current until abreast of Mossel Bay, and thence proceed direct round Cape Agulhas. With W'ly winds after passing Algoa Bay, keep within 40 or 50 miles of the shore. See 10.74.

From November to March, work along the Arabian coast until able to weather Ras Asir, then run down the coast of Africa and through Moçambique Channel, taking advantage of the full strength of the Moçambique and Agulhas Currents as before.

See 10.05.02 and 10.74.

10.67. Aden to Mombasa or Seychelles Group. From April to October the route is via Seychelles Group. Having passed N of Socotra, stand away to the SE on the starboard tack and cross the equator in about 70° E, or as far W as the monsoon permits.

The South-east Trade will be met with, after crossing the doldrums, in from 2° S to 4° S, and having picked it up, steer direct for Seychelles, if calling there, or towards Mombasa; but allowance must be made for the probability of the wind heading, and for the strong N-going current which will be entered on nearing the African coast.

From November to March, proceed as directed in 10.66 for that season, but heading for the desired port when it can be reached in the South-east Trade wind.

ROUTES FROM WEST COAST OF INDIA AND CEYLON

10.70. Karāchi to Bombay. Proceed direct, but in June, July and August first get an offing into depths of from 27 m to 36 m before standing S; Bombay should be made on the parallel of Khānderi Island, and the soundings should be carefully attended to. There is considerable indraught into the Gulf of Kutch from March to September.

10.71 Bombay to Karāchi. In May and early in June, on leaving Bombay, make westing so as to be able to weather Diu Head by 100 miles if bound into Gulf of Kutch, or by 200 miles if for Karāchi. During June, July and August when bound for Karāchi be careful not to make the coasts of Sind and Kutch before sighting Manora Lighthouse, as there is a SE'ly set, and the wind is liable to lull occasionally inshore, leaving the vessel with a heavy swell and lee current.

In the first part of the South-west Monsoon (May and June), the stream during the flood, setting into the Gulf of Kutch, is greatly accelerated.

In September and October, also in March and April, when NW'ly winds are general, work direct for Diu Head, and thence along the coast. In November, December, January and February work along the coast with the land and sea breezes, making due allowance for the tides, sighting High Land of Saint John (*20° 03′ N, 72° 49′ W*), or reaching the parallel of 20° N, before crossing to Diu Head, as the wind hangs much to N and NNE across the Gulf of Cambay.

November is a calm month along the S coast of Kāthiāwar, and it is frequently necessary to anchor on the flood to avoid being swept into Gulf of Cambay.

From November to January, when fresh NE'ly winds blow outside the Gulf of Kutch, and when working into it, anchor during the ebb off Dwārka or Kachigadh, and start with the flood across the mouth of the gulf to make the Kutch coast, where the water is smoother and a vessel can work to the E.

10.72. Bombay, or Cochin, Calicut and Malabar Coast to Aden. From May to September, during the South-west Monsoon, this passage is seldom taken; but in case of necessity it is given as follows, by what is known as the "Southern Passage".

After gaining an offing from the Indian coast into depths between 27 m and 36 m (or even to 75 m in the first part of the South-west Monsoon, as the wind then hangs much in a S'ly quarter) steer down the coast, keeping in soundings of from 73 m to 91 m; this is advisable to keep clear of Laccadive Islands in the thick overcast rainy weather that may be expected, when observations may not be obtainable for days together. After passing these islands make as little easting as possible. The wind will be from SW to WSW with hard W'ly squalls; a SSE'ly current of 20 to 30 miles a day will be experienced.

Cross the equator, and when fairly in the South-east Trade run to the W, passing S of Chagos Archipelago and NE of Seychelles Group; recross the equator in 53° E or 54° E. Run through the South-west Monsoon, and make the African coast between Ras Hafun and Ras Asir, due consideration being given to the strong NE'ly current which will be experienced on nearing the land. Pass close round Ras Asir, and keep along the African coast up to Mait Island, and then stand across the Gulf of Aden. The utmost caution is necessary when rounding Ras Asir from S or SE during the South-west Monsoon, see 10.73.

From October to April, during the North-east Monsoon, proceed direct, but towards the end of the North-east Monsoon, in March and April, the winds are less constant in the Arabian Sea than in the four preceding months, and there are calms at times. In these months, steer to pass S of Socotra; for, early in April, the North-east Monsoon is nearly expended about this island and on the coast of Arabia, and is succeeded by light breezes from SW and W, with frequent calms. The current also begins to set strongly to the N about Socotra, and between it and the coast of Africa. About and from the latter end of March, therefore, it is advisable to pass about 50 miles S of that island, in order to fetch Ras Asir with the SW'ly winds which may then be expected.

Leaving Bombay late in April, shape a course to pass well S of Socotra, in order to make the coast of Africa S of Ras Asir with the SW'ly wind, which will probably be met with long before that shore is approached. The land may then be made anywhere between Ras Hafun and Ras Asir, and the remainder of the passage may be made as directed above for the South-west Monsoon.

In November, December, January or February, sailing vessels bound to the Red Sea from Cochin, Calicut, or other ports on the S part of the Malabar coast, may steer directly W through the most convenient channel through Laccadive Islands. Those from Cochin should pass through Nine Degree Channel, but vessels from Mangalore or Cannanore should pass N of all the islands. In March and April, the prevailing winds between the Malabar coast and the African coast being from N to NW, it is better to keep near the Malabar coast until N of Mount Delly and to pass N of the islands; or if Nine Degree Channel is adopted, vessels should pass near Kalpeni and Suheli Par as the current sets S towards Maldive Islands in these months.

When W of Laccadive Islands in November, December, January or February, a course may be shaped to pass N of Socotra; but late in March or early in April, it is prudent to keep farther S, in 9° N or 10° N as the wind may admit; and, in May, when the South-west Monsoon may be expected, it is advisable to keep well to the S.

10.73. Caution when approaching Ras Asir. As many vessels have been wrecked on the coast to the S of Ras Asir, the utmost caution is necessary when rounding this headland from the S or SE, during the South-west Monsoon, when the weather is stormy, accompanied by a heavy sea and strong current, and the land is generally obscured by a thick haze. By day there is usually a gradual change in the colour of the water from blue to dark green as the land is approached; the sea decreases and the swell alters its direction to the E of S when N and W of Ras Hafun. When the land cannot be clearly seen and recognised, extreme caution is necessary.

After rounding Ras Asir keep towards the African shore until Mait Island is reached, then steer for Aden. Beating along the African shore against strong W'ly and WSW'ly winds is sometimes tedious, but perseverance is more likely to succeed here than in the middle of the gulf or on the Arabian shore.

Good sails and rigging are essential, for the wind frequently blows in severe gusts along the African coast.

10.74. Bombay to Cape of Good Hope. From May to September, stand down the coast of India (see 10.54.06, 10.54.07) and across the equator into the South-east Trades; then steer to pass S of Mauritius and about 100 miles S of Madagascar, and make the African coast about 200 miles SW of Durban. From thence, keep in the strength of the Agulhas Current until abreast of Mossel Bay, and then proceed direct round Cape Agulhas.

In the early part of the monsoon (June and July) when the wind is more S'ly than later on, get an offing from Bombay into about 90 m of water before standing down the coast, and then keep in a depth of between 73 m and 90 m to ensure being well inshore of Laccadive Islands.

In April and October the route is similar but somewhat to the W, and in April a considerable shortening can usually be effected by making a direct course from 15° S, 70° E to 30° S, 40° E, where the former route is again picked up.

From November to March, there are two routes for the first part of this passage, one leading E, and one W, of Îles Comores; the two routes rejoin in about 20° S and thence continue to the Cape of Good Hope.

To follow the route E of Îles Comores, proceed direct from Bombay, W of Seychelles Group and Amirante Islands, and between Madagascar and Îles Comores, on a rhumb line towards the African coast at Durban. Thence keep in the strength of the Moçambique Current and Agulhas Current. In rounding the Cape of Good Hope if W'ly winds prevail, keep over Agulhas Bank not more than 40 or 50 miles from the coast; here the sea will be smoother than elsewhere.

A route passing W of Îles Comores is recommended by some navigators on account of the rather better current on the African side of Moçambique Channel. A vessel using this route would sail direct from Bombay as above and, keeping on the African side of the channel, proceed S as directed above.

When approaching Moçambique Channel from N, keep well off the land until up to Cabo Delgado, as the wind sometimes hangs to the E and even S of E; from thence, stand down the coast, inside Saint Lazarus Bank, keeping in the strength of the Moçambique Current and the Agulhas Current and making Cape Agulhas. A vessel will probably have to work to windward in the S part of Moçambique Channel, the prevailing winds there being S'ly.

June, July and August are the worst months, and January and February the best months for sailing vessels proceeding W-bound round the Cape of Good Hope, and it should be borne in mind that there is much less sea over Agulhas Bank in depths of from 110 m to 130 m, or less, during heavy gales, than there is near its edge and

S of it. If it is found necessary to heave-to, the port tack should be chosen, as, with the exception of SE'ly gales beginning with SE'ly winds, the shift of wind is almost invariably against the hands of a watch, and the vessel will come up to the sea.

From October to April, E'ly winds prevail as far S as the tail of Agulhas Bank, in about 37° S, with variable, but chiefly W'ly winds beyond.

Mariners should remember that off all parts of the S coast of Africa, and especially off salient points, sunken wrecks or uncharted dangers may lie close inshore; and that it is not adviable to approach this surf-beaten coast, even in full-powered steam-vessels, within a distance of 3 or 4 miles; sailing vessels should give Cape Agulhas a berth of 7 or 8 miles.

10.75. Bombay to Colombo. At the onset of the South-west Monsoon, when the wind hangs to the SW, first get a good offing into depths of from 70 m to 90 m off Bombay, and keep on the edge of the bank in those depths to keep clear of Laccadive Islands. On proceeding S the wind will generally become more favourable, veering to W and WNW. Between Cochin and Cape Comorin S'ly currents and WNW'ly winds prevail from mid-July to mid-October.

October to May is the period of the North-east Monsoon and of the land and sea breezes along the W coast of India. A summary of the weather that may be expected, and advice to sailing vessels desirous of making full use of the land and sea breezes is given in 10.76.

10.76. Land and sea breezes off west coast of India. Except during the South-west Monsoon, land and sea breeze effects are usually well developed near the coast, but the strength and duration of the land winds may be modified by the mountainous nature of the hinterland.

Off the Konkan coast, the South-west Monsoon fails after the middle of September, and is followed by light variable breezes, frequent calms, cloudy weather, and occasional showers. This unsettled weather lasts for 6 or 8 weeks, with prevailing winds from the NW; but occasionally from SW and S. On the Kanara, Malabar and Travancore coast there are occasional off-shore squalls.

Late in October, or early in November, a breaking-up storm may take place, with a high wind suddenly coming up from the S and blowing hard for several hours, accompanied by thunder and lightning. After this, the North-east Monsoon sets in, with fine weather; and land and sea breezes are experienced within 10 or 20 miles of the coast, which continue until March or April.

The sea breezes of the Malabar coast are fairly established throughout October, while as yet the land winds are only occasional, light and uncertain; the former seldom fail, till they are merged in the South-west Monsoon. Thus the navigator may calculate on sea breezes for eight months of the year, but on regular land winds for only half that period.

When the land and sea breezes are regular, the sea breeze fails in the evening about sunset, and is generally followed by a calm which continues until the land wind comes off at between 2000 and 2200; at first, it comes in fluctuating gentle breezes, but it soon steadies from between NE and ESE, continuing so till 0900 or 1000; it then begins to fail, decreasing to a calm about mid-day. About this time, or soon after, the sea breeze sets in from WSW, W, or NW, and generally veers towards N in the evening, decreasing in strength.

In March and April, off the coast of Maharashtra, the land breezes are very light and uncertain, seldom coming off till morning, and continuing so short a time that little advantage is gained by them; it is therefore necessary to keep an offing, to be ready for the sea breeze, which may at this time, between Bombay and Cape Comorin, be termed NW winds; they usually set in about noon at WNW veering gradually to NW and NNW, in the evening, from which direction they continue during the first part of the night, declining afterwards to a calm about mid-night, or early in the morning. A faint land breeze sometimes follows; but more frequently light airs from N or calms may be expected, nearly from midnight until the NW wind sets in about noon on the following day.

In April the weather is mostly hazy, and at times cloudy over the Ghats in the evenings, with light showers.

In May the prevailing winds along the coast S of Bombay are from NW and W, but often variable and uncertain, with cloudy threatening weather and light showers at times, accompanied by lightning from SE. A gale from SW or S is liable to occur in this month, and several ships have speedily run along the coast to Bombay; but it is prudent to keep well out from the land, and to be prepared for bad weather, in order to avoid being driven on a lee shore if a storm should set in from W. When NW winds prevail, the weather is settled and clear of clouds, though a little hazy; but it is cloudy and threatening when they blow between SE and SW. It sometimes happens that heavy clouds collect over the land in the evenings, producing a hard squall with rain about mid-night; this has frequently been experienced between Mangalore and Hog island in May and early in June, when these land squalls blow in sudden gusts through the gaps between the mountains.

The land and sea breezes described above require attention for sailing vessels to benefit by them to the full extent. During the night, with the land breeze, it is prudent to keep well inshore, if the wind admit, without tacking, for there it is strong and steadier than farther out; but in the morning it is advisable to edge more out, to get an offing of 15 or 20 miles, or soundings of from 50 m to 55 m, before noon, ready for the sea breeze. In the evening it is desirable to be near the shore, before the land breeze comes off; the coast may be approached to a depth of 18 m in most places from Bombay to Quilon, and if close inshore before the land breeze starts, short tack should be made near the shore until it comes off; when calm, its approach is frequently indicated by the noise of the surf on the beach, which is heard at a considerable distance.

During the period of change, before the South-west Monsoon has set in, the small coasting vessels run into the nearest river or place of shelter S of Bombay in the afternoon, but large vessels should have sea-room.

10.77. Bombay to Bay of Bengal. Proceed first as for Colombo, but so as to round the S side of Ceylon. From June to mid-January, make easting to the middle of the Bay of Bengal, but during the other half of the year keep on the W side, to destination. See 10.03.05, 10.03.06.

10.78. Colombo to Bombay and west coast of India. During the height of the South-west Monsoon, do not attempt to work N along this coast. At other times between May and September, opportunities may present themselves, see 10.76 and Admiralty Sailing Directions.

In September and October, the N-bound passage is very tedious; on the S part of the coast a strong current sets constantly to the S, and the wind is NW and variable, with frequent light airs; vessels often anchor to avoid being drifted back. The weather is threatening at times, with heavy showers. The land winds begin to blow about the beginning of October, S of Calicut, but do not extend far off-shore until November.

In December, January, and February regular land and sea breezes render the navigation N-bound near the coast easy, as the sea is remarkably smooth and the sea breeze is at its strongest.

Where there are gaps in the mountain chain, as at Pālghāt, on the parallel of 10° 45′ N, the land winds in December and January continue sometimes to blow for more than a day without any intervening sea breeze. This occurs, also, but in a rather less degree, off Kārwār Head, where the valley of Kālinadi River assumes a straight funnel shape in an E–W direction. In these months a sailing passage may sometimes be made from Cape Comorin to Bombay in six to eight days, and the return voyage in four or five days. In November and early in December the sea breezes are weak, but become stronger afterwards. As February advances, the land breezes decrease in strength and duration, and are not always regular.

In March and April, the land breezes will generally fail in strength and duration N of Mount Delly; make certain, therefore, particularly in April, of being well to seaward, in depths of from 65 m to 75 m, about noon, so that a long stretch to the NNE or NE with the NW'ly winds may be made. If near the shore early in the evening, with the wind at NW, make short tacks, until the breeze veers to the N, which may be expected early in the night; then stretch off to the NW or WNW to be ready for the sea breeze of the following day.

When a strong NW'ly wind sets in, it is liable to continue for two or three days, or longer, rendering it impracticable to gain any ground when working near the coast. At such times keep about 60 miles or more from the land, where the winds are generally moderate and the sea smooth.

Late in April, or during May, keep a good offing towards Laccadive Islands, and when to the N of those islands keep a greater offing still, in case of a gale coming on.

On the S part of the coast, S of Mount Delly and meeting with NW winds in this month, stretch off to the W of the islands, passing between Suheli Par and Minicoy or between any of the Laccadive Islands, to benefit by the approaching W'ly winds.

10.79. Colombo to Aden. The passage is hardly ever undertaken against the South-west Monsoon, from April to September. In case of necessity, however, the directions are to stand at once across the equator into the South-east Trade, thence run W passing S of the Chagos Archipelago, and NE of Seychelles Group; recross the equator in about 53° E or 54° E, and shape course to make the African coast at Ras Hafun; round Ras Asir and work along the African coast as far as Mait Island, before standing across the Gulf of Aden. Caution is necessary when making the African coast, see 10.73.

From October to March, pass through Nine Degree Channel, and then proceed direct for Aden. After the middle of March, pass S of Socotra, as light SW'ly and W'ly breezes may then be expected near this island. See 6.59.

10.80. Colombo to Cape of Good Hope. Pick up the route from Bombay described in 10.74, according to time of year, at the nearest available point, passing through Nine Degree Channel from November to March (North-east Monsoon), but directly to meet the May-to-September route at about the equator, during the South-west Monsoon.

10.81. Colombo to Fremantle and south and south-east Australia, or to New Zealand.

From April to October, having rounded the S extreme of Ceylon steer to the SE to cross the equator in about 95° E; thence proceed S across the South-east Trade into the W'ly winds for a direct passage to Fremantle or round Cape Leeuwin. To the E of Cape Leeuwin, proceed as directed in 10.64.

From November to March, make as much easting as possible in the North-west Monsoon, and then proceed S across the Trades as above.

10.82. Colombo to Malacca Strait. In the South-west Monsoon proceed direct to pass S of Great Nicobar Island.

In the North-east Monsoon, stand S as far as about 3° N, and then work NE towards the NW end of Sumatra, entering Malacca Strait S of Great Nicobar Island.

10.83. Malacca Strait. Directions are as given in Admiralty Sailing Directions. From April to October, after passing the NW end of Sumatra the South-west Monsoon will probably fail and it is advisable then to keep to the Malay side of the channel for better breeze and tidal streams. Sometimes a brisk W'ly wind will be carried as far as Pulau Penang, and, once the islands off the Malay coast are sighted, there will be no difficulty in making to the S.

The winds on the E side of the Strait tend to be more favourable for a S-bound passage from October to March also.

From October to March, during the North-east Monsoon, a sailing vessel N-bound should, after passing Pulau Pangkor, keep near the edge of the mud flat that fronts the coast in order to avoid the strong wind and short sea likely in the offing near Pulau Penang.

Directions for making Singapore are given in 10.39.03.

ROUTES FROM PORTS IN BAY OF BENGAL
(except from Rangoon southward)

10.90. Notes on navigation under sail in Bay of Bengal. There is no difficulty in proceeding from S to N or from W to E in the Bay of Bengal during the South-west Monsoon, nor from N to S or from E to W during the North-east Monsoon. See 10.03.05.

When the monsoon is contrary, a sailing vessel must work as necessary for the passage. At the change of the monsoon, voyages are usually tedious, for the light and variable winds, then prevalent, are as often adverse as favourable, every slant should be taken advantage of, and the NE part of the bay avoided, unless bound to, or from, one of the ports on that side of the bay.

As stated in 6.16, **cyclones** occur from May to November, with November as the month of greatest frequency. They occur very occasionally in March, April, and December, and are almost unknown in January and entirely so in February. See *The Mariner's Handbook* and Admiralty Sailing Directions.

If warning of a storm in the N part of the bay is given by E'ly winds and a falling barometer between June and September, or by a squally E'ly or NE'ly wind driving low, long-drawn masses of cloud before it, or a strong W'ly current at the head of the bay, in May, October, or November, a vessel in Hooghly River or a port at the head of the bay should remain in harbour till the weather moderates.

If at sea in the right-hand semicircle, the vessel should be hove-to on the starboard tack until the storm has passed, and if undoubtedly in the left-hand semicircle she should heave-to on the port tack if the wind is E of N, or run to the S, keeping the wind on the starboard quarter, when the wind is N, or W of N.

Vessels lying in the roadsteads of the Coromandel coast on the approach of a cyclonic storm usually run in a S'ly direction round the SW quadrant, and this is probably the only course open to sailing vessels.

10.91. Madras to Calcutta. From April to August, proceed as directly as possible, making the land about Bāvanapādu (*18° 34′ N, 84° 21′ E*).

In September and October, stretch over to North Andaman Island or Cape Negrais; when 100 miles W of either tack to the NW.

From November to January, make easting across the bay, and then northing on the E side or in the middle.

In February and March, steer direct, if possible; otherwise stand to the E across the bay as from November to January.

10.92. Madras to Rangoon, Moulmein or Mergui. During the South-west Monsoon, sight Landfall Island of the Andaman Islands if with S'ly wind, or Great Coco Island with W'ly wind. Pass through Coco Channel, and thence to the E, sighting Narcondam Island; then as directed by Admiralty Sailing Directions for Rangoon or Moulmein. If bound for Mergui, pass S of Little Andaman Island, and thence steer for Tenasserim Island.

During the North-east Monsoon, make northing in the middle of the Bay, pass through Preparis North Channel or Preparis South Channel, and then as directed by Admiralty Sailing Directions for Rangoon or Moulmein, sounding continuously and allowing for tidal streams. If bound for Mergui, pass N of Andaman Islands, and thence work to the E and pass Tavoy Island on either side. See 10.03.04, 10.03.05.

10.93. Bay of Bengal to Bombay. This passage is seldom undertaken in the South-west Monsoon. A vessel should first stand S across the equator into the South-east Trade and then run W between 8° S and 9° S, passing S of Chagos Archipelago. From 70° E, steer to re-cross the equator in 62° E or 63° E, and sail thence direct.

During the North-east Monsoon, steer as directed in 10.03.05 and round Ceylon at a convenient distance. After passing Cape Comorin keep the W coast of India in sight, so as to profit from the sea breezes (10.76).

10.94. Bay of Bengal to Aden. This passage is seldom undertaken during the South-west Monsoon. A vessel should run S across the equator into the South-east Trades. Then run W, passing S of Chagos Archipelago and NE of Seychelles Group; cross the equator in about 53° E or 54° E, and make the African coast at Ras Hafun; great caution is necessary in making the land. Round Ras Asir and work along the African coast as far as Mait Island before standing across for Aden.

In the North-east Monsoon, pass round Ceylon and through Nine Degree Channel; thence steer to pass N of Socotra. After the middle of March keep S of Socotra.

For crossing the Arabian Sea and landfall, see 10.72, 10.73.

10.95. Bay of Bengal to Cape of Good Hope. From May to September, vessels from Sandheads should make for the Orissa coast, sighting the land south of False Point (*20° 20′ N, 86° 44′ E*) and working to the SW along the shore; make short tacks during the day and long boards off-shore during the night, bringing Kalingapatam (*18° 19′ N, 84° 08′ E*) abeam before leaving the coast and standing down the bay. A comparatively smooth sea and a favourable current will be found near the shore, and advantage may be taken of a veering wind in the squalls off the land.

When standing down the Bay of Bengal in the South-west Monsoon, keep well W of the Andaman Islands, in order not to be on a lee shore should a strong W'ly gale set in; or, which is better, pass through Preparis North Channel or Preparis South Channel, and then work S in the comparatively smooth water E (or to leeward) of Andaman Islands and Nicobar Islands.

Note: Fast sailing vessels from Calcutta, in the South-west Monsoon, do beat down the Bay of Bengal, reaching 100 miles W of Andaman Islands; but the wear and tear is great and the saving in time slight.

From Madras or the Coromandel coast, stand at once across the equator into the South-east Trade.

In either of the above cases, and from all parts of the Bay, stand S so as to cross the equator in about 95° E, keeping on the tack which makes most southing into the South-east Trade.

Cross the meridian of 90° E in 10° S, and from this position, steer a direct course for Cape Agulhas, passing about 200 miles S of Rodriguez Island, and the same distance S of Madagascar. Make the African coast in about 33° S, and keep in the strength of the Agulhas Current to abreast Mossel Bay, and then round Cape Agulhas. See 10.74.

From November to March, run straight down the Bay of Bengal, cross the equator in 86° E to 87° E, and pick up the May to September route at about 15° S, and run thence direct to Cape Agulhas, as described above.

During October and April, run down the bay on a line just E of the 90th meridian; cross the equator at 90° E, and pick up the May to September route at 15° S, continuing to destination thence, as described above.

10.96. Bay of Bengal to Fremantle, Cape Leeuwin and south and south-east Australia, and to New Zealand. From March to October, having worked along the W shore of the Bay of Bengal, see 10.95, far enough to weather Nicobar Islands and the islands fronting the SW coast of Sumatra, stand out of the Bay on the starboard tack, cross the South-east Monsoon and South-east Trade; and having got into the prevailing W'ly winds S of the Trades, proceed E for Fremantle or Cape Leeuwin. The doldrum belt will be found to extend to about 4° S.

From November to April, stand down the middle of the Bay of Bengal, and across the equator into the North-west Monsoon. Thence make easting in the North-west Monsoon as far as Christmas Island; then stand S across the South-east Trade into the westerlies, and so to Fremantle or Cape Leeuwin.

To the E of Cape Leeuwin, proceed as directed in 10.64.

10.97. Calcutta to Madras or Ceylon. During the South-west Monsoon, make southing without closing the E side of the Bay, as directed in 10.95. Steer for port when 60 miles S of it.

If unable to work S, pass E of Andaman Islands and Nicobar Islands and through Selat Bengalla. Thence work across the Bay of Bengal; but in June, July and August, stand across the equator into the South-east Trade, make westing, and recross the equator in about 83° E, if bound for Madras; then proceed direct. Bound for Colombo, recross the equator in about 77° E.

During the North-east Monsoon, steer direct. In September, with light S winds, work SW, keeping in soundings, or stand out to sea. Give the coast a berth in February and March as the current then runs to the N.

10.98. Calcutta to Rangoon, Moulmein, or Mergui. During the South-west Monsoon, steer to pass through Preparis South Channel, and thence as directed in Admiralty Sailing Directions, for Rangoon or Moulmein. If bound for Mergui, pass on either side of Coco Islands.

During the North-east Monsoon, steer to pass round Alguada Reef and then work E, sounding frequently and making full allowance for tidal streams.

10.99. Calcutta to Singapore. During the South-west Monsoon, proceed direct through Preparis South Channel and Malacca Strait.

During the North-east Monsoon, proceed through one of the Preparis Channels, and thence direct through Malacca Strait.

See 10.39 for directions for Singapore Strait.

ROUTES FROM PORTS IN BURMA

10.105. Rangoon or Moulmein to Calcutta. During the South-west Monsoon, pass through one of the Preparis Channels, and then proceed as directly as possible.

During the North-east Monsoon, pass S of Alguada Reef, and thence proceed N, about 30 miles off the Burma coast before stretching across; but after January, from Alguada Reef stand first into the middle of the Bay of Bengal before working N.

Vessels intending to leave Rangoon or Moulmein in periods of strong NE'ly winds, with a falling barometer, denoting the existence of a cyclonic storm E of Andaman Islands, should wait until the storm has passed. This is indicated by a rising barometer, and the wind shifting to E or S of E. See 10.90.

10.106. Rangoon or Moulmein to Madras. During the South-west Monsoon, keep well out to sea if the wind becomes W'ly and endeavour to sight Narcondam Island.

In working S, keep W of and at a moderate distance from the Mergui Archipelago. Pass S of Great Nicobar Island and thence work W to destination.

During the North-east Monsoon, pass through Preparis North Channel and thence proceed as directly as possible. After January, however, make the land S of destination on account of the N'ly sets which occur off this coast after that month.

10.107. Rangoon or Moulmein to Malacca Strait and Singapore. In the South-west Monsoon, proceed as directed in 10.106, passing the S point of Salang Island; thence proceed direct through Malacca Strait.

In the North-east Monsoon, keep outside Mergui Archipelago, sight the S point of Salang Island and proceed thence direct through Malacca Strait.

Directions for passage through Singapore Strait to Singapore will be found in 10.39.03.

10.108. Rangoon or Moulmein to Cape of Good Hope. In both monsoons, stand S, to the E of Andaman Islands and Nicobar Islands, and pick up the May to September route from the Bay of Bengal given in 10.95 at 15° S, continuing to destination as described in that article.

10.109. Mergui to Calcutta. During the South-west Monsoon, work to the W and pass through Coco Channel or one of the Preparis Channels.

During the North-east Monsoon, pass through any channel N of Andaman Islands and then proceed direct.

10.110. Mergui to Madras. During the South-west Monsoon, after clearing the islands, work S to the N end of Sumatra; pass through Selat Benggala or S of Great Nicobar Island and proceed thence direct.

During the North-east Monsoon, until the end of January, pass through any channel N of Andaman Islands; after that date, steer to pass S of Little Andaman Island.

ROUTES SOUTHWARD OR WESTWARD FROM SINGAPORE OR EASTERN ARCHIPELAGO

10.115. Singapore to Madras. During the South-west Monsoon, keep along the N coast of Sumatra, pass through Selat Benggala, and work across the Bay of Bengal; but in the height of the South-west Monsoon (in June, July and August), from off Udjung Masam Muka cross the equator, and make westing in the South-east Trade, recrossing the equator in about 83° E.

During the North-east Monsoon, keep on the Malay coast until Salang Island is reached; thence pass through either Ten Degrees Channel or Sombrero Channel. In December and January make the land N of destination on account of the S'ly set on the Coromandel and Ceylon coasts.

10.116. Singapore to Colombo. During the South-west Monsoon, keep along the N coast of Sumatra and pass through Selat Benggala; from off Udjung Masam Muka cross the equator and make westing in the South-east Trade. Recross the equator in 77° E, and proceed as directly as possible to Colombo.

During the North-east Monsoon, pass on either side of Pulau Perak and between Pulau Rondo and Great Nicobar Island; thence proceed direct, but if W'ly winds are experienced near the N end of Sumatra, which is probable in October and November, keep to the N before altering course.

10.117. Singapore to Calcutta. During the South-west Monsoon, pass to the S of Nicobar Islands, and thence steer direct for the Orissa coast.

During the North-east Monsoon, up to mid-January pass E of Andaman Islands. After mid-January pass S of those islands, or through Duncan Passage, and work to the N in the middle of the Bay of Bengal, as NW'ly and W'ly winds are then found N of Andaman Islands.

10.118. Singapore to Rangoon or Moulmein, During the South-west Monsoon, sight Narcondam Island. During the North-east Monsoon, sight Great Western Torres islands, and thence proceed as directed by Admiralty Sailing Directions.

10.119. Singapore to Port Darwin. From April to October, in the South-west Monsoon in the China Sea, and the E'ly monsoon on the N coast of Australia, when bound from Singapore to Port Darwin, proceed through Balabac Strait across Sulu Sea, through Basilan Strait and Bangka Strait, and thence through Manipa Strait for Port Darwin.

From November to April, during the North-east Monsoon of the China Sea, proceed through Sunda Strait and thence for Port Darwin with the North-west Monsoon. Alternatively, go through Karimata Strait and Sapudi Strait, and into the Indian Ocean by Lombok Strait or Alas Strait.

10.120. Singapore to Torres Strait. From April to October, follow the route given above for that season for Port Darwin, as far as the Ceram Sea, to join the route from Hong Kong to Torres Strait described in 11.44.01, or its alternative.

From November to April, proceed via Karimata Strait and thence to the Arafura Sea either via Lombok Strait or Alas Strait, or through the Java Sea and Flores Sea to join the April–October route, described above.

10.121. Singapore to Fremantle or southern Australia. From April to October, proceed S through Selat Bangka and Sunda Strait, and thence across the South-east Trade until in the region of W'ly winds, whence a course may be shaped for Fremantle or Cape Leeuwin. See also 11.30.01.

From November to April, if bound to one of the W or S ports of Australia proceed through Selat Bangka, N of Java, and through Bali Strait or Lombok Strait, and thence steer to the S into the South-east Trade. Keep the ship close hauled on the port tack in the Trade Wind, and on losing the Trade steer to the S and SE into the W'ly winds, whence proceed as directed in paragraph 10.01, Cape of Good Hope to Australia.

10.122. Singapore to Sunda Strait and Cape of Good Hope. First proceed to the Indian Ocean via Sunda Strait by one of the routes in 10.49.

From April to September, having cleared Sunda Strait, steer directly for a position 200 miles S of Rodriguez Island, in about 23° S, 63° E; thence pass 200 miles S of Madagascar and as directed in 10.17.02.

From October to April, after clearing Sunda Strait, stand S into the South-east Trade Wind, passing through 16° S, 90° E; steer thence for a position 200 miles S of Rodriguez Island and as above. This period is the cyclone season of the South Indian Ocean.

10.123. Singapore or Sunda Strait to Aden. The route from Singapore may be taken either via Malacca Strait or via Sunda Strait.

Having passed through Malacca Strait and taken departure as directed in 10.57.02, from April to September follow that route into the South-east Trade and then make westing to pass S of Chagos Archipelago, there to join the Colombo–Aden route (10.79).

From October to March proceed S of Ceylon and through Nine Degree Channel (10.79).

If the route is taken via Sunda Strait a similar procedure should be adopted, namely to join the Colombo–Aden route S of Chago Archipelago or in Nine Degree Channel, according to season.

10.124. Sunda Strait northward along west coast of Sumatra. The three routes, Outer, Middle, and Inner, are described in detail in Admiralty Sailing Directions.

For a sailing vessel, the voyage in either direction and at all seasons is long and wearisome on account of frequent calms, but it is generally more difficult to work N than S, owing to the prevalence of SE'ly currents, which continue to set even with and after a S'ly wind. January and February are the best months for going N, while in September, October and November vessels will often be compelled to keep far out to sea in order to make even a little northing; working in-shore during these months is almost impracticable.

The Outer Route, to the W of all the islands, is the best of the three, more especially for sailing vessels. SW'ly and S'ly winds often prevail here, when NW'ly squalls, variable baffling winds, calms and S'ly currents, may be experienced close to the land.

The Middle Route, between the chain of large islands, in the offing, and those small islands adjacent to, and interspersed along the coast, should not be followed by a sailing vessel when N-bound, nor at any time, if it can be avoided without inconvenience. Although it is wide, and may be adopted by night or day in vessels of light draught when the weather is clear and favourable, vessels are more at the mercy of the currents when the winds are light and baffling, and there is no anchorage; in some parts there are dangerous coral shoals, of the approach to which sounding will give no warning.

The Inner Route, close along the coast, and between some of the islands and dangers off it, like the Middle Route, should seldom be chosen by N-bound sailing vessels in either monsoon; but as there are, in many places, moderate depths for anchoring, it is preferable in that respect to the Middle Route.

10.125. Bali Strait, Lombok Strait, Alas Strait, or Ombai Strait to Cape of Good Hope. From Bali Strait, Lombok Strait, or Alas Strait, stand to the SW, during the South-east Monsoon, or direct to the S during the North-west Monsoon, to pick up the South-east Trade Wind at the nearest point, then make to cross the meridian of 90° E, at 22° S to 23° S. From this position stand W along the parallel to join the route from Singapore to the Cape of Good Hope (10.122) in about 23° S, 63° E.

From Ombai Strait, pass through the Sawu Sea and into the Indian Ocean between Timor and Sumba. Thence steer to join the above route at the most convenient point, having regard to the prevailing wind at the time.

NORTHERN AUSTRALIA TO SYDNEY, INDIAN OCEAN AND CHINA SEA

10.130. Northern Australia to Sydney. From April to October, in the South-east Monsoon, stand W to make North West Cape (*21° 47′ S, 114° 10′ E*) and beat S to round Cape Leeuwin and proceed by Bass Strait to Sydney. See 10.01.04, 10.01.08.

From November to April, in the North-west Monsoon, proceed through Torres Strait and stand into the Pacific Ocean until enough easting has been made to enable the port to be reached with the South-east Trade. See 11.29, Thursday Island to Sydney.

10.131. Northern Australia to Fremantle. From November to April, in the North-west Monsoon period, short boards along the coast S of North-west Cape will enable advantage to be taken of the land breezes. Only during the strength of the North-west Monsoon should a sailing vessel proceed E-about via Torres Strait, Bass Strait, and Cape Leeuwin.

10.132. Northern Australia to Cape of Good Hope. From April to October, during the South-east Monsoon, shape course through the Arafura Sea to join the route from the S part of the Eastern Archipelago (10.125).

During the strength of the North-west Monsoon proceed via Torres Strait and Bass Strait. See 11.29, Torres Strait to Sydney and 10.164, Sydney to Cape of Good Hope.

10.133. Northern Australia to Colombo. From April to October, proceed W with the Monsoon, crossing the equator in about 75° E, and thence steer as directly as possible to Colombo in the South-west Monsoon.

From November to April, make to the N through Banda Sea and Molukka Sea, see 10.46.03, and round the N of Sulawesi, through Basilan Strait into the Sulu Sea; cross it and pass into the China Sea through Balabac Strait, and thence to Singapore. Thence proceed through Malacca Strait, and S of Great Nicobar Island to destination, in the North-east Monsoon, see 10.116.

For passages through the Eastern Archipelago and the approach to Singapore, see 10.30.

10.134. Northern Australia to Calcutta. From April to October, during the South-east Monsoon on the N coast of Australia and South-west Monsoon in the Bay of Bengal, proceed as in 10.133 for Colombo, but crossing the equator in about 82° E; thence steer E of Ceylon for the mouth of Hooghly River.

Enough westing should be made in the South-east Monsoon before proceeding N to enter the limits of the South-west Monsoon of the Indian seas.

From November to April, during the North-west Monsoon, follow the directions in 10.133 as far as Singapore, then 10.117 to Calcutta.

10.135. Northern Australia to Singapore. From April to October, two routes are recommended, the usual route passing N of Timor, through Wètar Strait and Wètar Passage into the Flores Sea, continuing W along the N side of all the islands and through Sapudi Strait to Selat Bangka or Selat Gelasa (10.35–10.42).

An alternative route passes either N or S of Timor and along the S side of all the islands, entering the Java Sea through Sunda Strait (10.33); thence as directed in 10.32.02.

From November to April take the Colombo route for that season, see 10.133.

10.136. Northern Australia to Hong Kong. From April to October, proceed as directed for Singapore for that season, see 10.135, but pass through Selat Gelasa or Karimata Strait and thence between Anambas Kepulauan and Natuna Kepulauan into the China Sea; thence steer between Paracel Group and Macclesfield Bank to Hong Kong. In thick weather proceed through Selat Bangka in preference to Karimata Strait or Selat Gelasa.

From November to April, the route is either by Bougainville Strait or by the Second Eastern Passage (10.46). For the Bougainville Strait route, proceed E through Torres Strait, thence E of Treasury Islands, through Bougainville Strait and N of Philippine Islands.

ROUTES FROM SOUTH-WEST AND SOUTH AUSTRALIA

10.140. Fremantle to Mauritius. In all seasons, steer NW from Fremantle into the strength of the South-east Trade Wind, which is generally found between the parallels of 15° and 20° S, and where the Equatorial Current sets to the W. Having reached the parallel of 20° S, and the meridian of 90° E, in summer, and two or three degrees nearer the equator in the winter of the S hemisphere, continue W for Mauritius, passing about 50 miles S of Rodriguez; though from November until April it is advisable to keep at a greater distance, as cyclones sometimes occur at this season, not only in this locality, but also in the space between these islands and the NW coast of Australia. After passing Rodriguez steer as directly as possible for Mauritius.

10.141. Fremantle to Cape of Good Hope. There are two routes to the Cape of Good Hope, Northern and Southern; of which the Northern is available all the year round, and the Southern only during the summer, from December to March; the Southern Route is rather more direct.

For the Northern Route, proceed as for Mauritius (10.140), but pass 100 to 200 miles S of Rodriguez, and thence about the same distance S of Madagascar, to make the African coast about 200 miles S of Durban. From thence, keep in the strength of the Agulhas Current until abreast Mossel Bay, and then proceed direct round Cape Agulhas. See 10.74.

For the Southern Route, steer for 30° S, 100° E, and thenceforward make a nearly W'ly course across the ocean to the meridian of 40° E, keeping between the parallels of 27° S and 29° S; being farthest to the S in December, and to the N in March. From the meridian of 40° E, steer towards the African coast to join the Northern Route E of Algoa Bay. See notes on rounding the Cape of Good Hope in 10.17.01 and 10.74.

10.142. Fremantle to Aden. From April to October, proceed direct to pass S of Chagos Archipelago to join the route from the Indian coast as directed in 10.72 and 10.73.

From November to April, follow a great circle track to 4° 00′ S, 73° 30′ E; then proceed by rhumb line to round Ras Asir.

10.143. Fremantle to Colombo. From April to October, with the South-east Trade in the South Indian Ocean and the South-west Monsoon N of the equator, cross the equator in 80° E, and thence proceed to Colombo.

From November to April, with the North-west Monsoon in the South Indian Ocean and the North-east Monsoon in the Bay of Bengal, steer across the South-east Trade to enter the North-west Monsoon in about 10° S, 90° E. Thence continue N with the North-west Monsoon across the equator in about 87° E, and with the North-east Monsoon to Colombo.

10.144. Fremantle to Calcutta. From April to October, with the South-east Trade in the South Indian Ocean, and the South-west Monsoon in the Bay of Bengal, proceed direct for the E-coast of Ceylon, and thence for Hooghly river. See 10.03.06 and 10.90.

From November to April, during the North-west Monsoon in the South Indian Ocean, proceed direct to the equator, crossing it in about 93° E; and thence to make the land about Udjung Masam Muka, the NW point of Sumatra. From Udjung Masam Muka steer to pass to the W of Nicobar Islands, and thence to the N, close-hauled, and W of all the islands.

If the equator is crossed as late as March, keep well to the W in the Bay of Bengal, as the current at that time runs N along the E coast of India, and the winds will be found between SW and SE. In the middle of the Bay they are light and variable from NW to NE.

10.145. Fremantle to Singapore. From April to October, steer on a direct course for Sunda Strait, taking care to make the land to the E of the strait as the W-going current is often strong near the S coast of Java. Continue from Sunda Strait as indicated in 10.32.02.

From November to April, steer for 12° S, 102° E, and then pass midway between Christmas Island and Cocos or Keeling Island, there joining the route from Cape Town to Singapore via Sunda Strait (10.02.02). Alternatively, cross 20° S in about 110° E and then follow the Second Eastern Passage (10.46) as far as Manipa Strait. From this point pass through Molukka Sea, Bangka Strait, Sulawesi Sea, Basilan Strait, Sulu Sea and Balabac Strait into the China Sea. Thence proceed to Singapore in the North-east Monsoon. This alternative route, though longer, will probably give a better passage.

10.146. Fremantle to Hong Kong. From April to October, proceed to Sunda Strait as directed in 10.145 and continue to the China Sea as indicated in 10.32.03.

From November to April a vessel may either follow the seasonal directions in 10.145 and pick up the Second Eastern Passage, or proceed to Singapore via Sunda Strait as directed in that article and thence through Palawan Passage and along the coast of Luzon until able to stand across to Hong Kong.

A vessel which, having passed through Sunda Strait, finds that the North-west Monsoon in the Java Sea and the North-east Monsoon in the China Sea have already begun, is advised to make to the E to pick up the Second Eastern Passage, a route which is available only from November to February, see 10.45.

10.147. Fremantle to south-east Australia, or to New Zealand. Stand S, and act as directed in 10.01.06–10.01.10, for the voyage from the Cape of Good Hope.

10.148. South-east Australia to Cape of Good Hope. There are two routes according to season.

The Northern Route is available from April to October, at the time of year when the South-east Monsoon of the Arafura Sea connects with the South-east Trade of the Pacific Ocean, and with the South-east Trade of the Indian Ocean. Vessels using it should proceed first to the N, along the E coast of Australia, and through Torres Strait (10.164), and from thence through the Arafura Sea into the Indian Ocean and to the Cape of Good Hope as directed in 10.132.

Note: Directions for the passage through Bass Strait are given in 11.03.07.

The Southern Route should be used from December to April, when E'ly winds are prevalent off the S coast of Australia. First proceed as directly as possible to round Cape Leeuwin at a safe distance, having regard to the weather prevailing at the time and the danger of being caught on a lee shore. From Cape Leeuwin stand to the NW into the South-east Trades and join the route from Fremantle as directed in 10.141.

Note: It is reported that masters of vessels bound for European ports from Adelaide would often defer decision whether to make the passage E-about or W-about until they had ascertained the wind direction in the Australian Bight. Thus, with a W'ly wind, they would sail E-about (11.03), and with an E'ly wind they would take the Southern Route, as above, for the Cape of Good Hope.

10.149. South-east Australia to Aden. From April to October, proceed as directed for the Northern Route (10.148) to Torres Strait, and thence through the Arafura Sea, see 10.132. Having cleared all dangers in the Arafura Sea, steer to pass S of Chagos Archipelago and as directed in 10.72.

From November to April, pass round Cape Leeuwin as directed for the Southern Route in 10.59.09 and then steer NW to join the route from Fremantle to Aden (10.142). See 6.167.

10.150. South-east Australia to Colombo. From April to November, take the Northern Route as for Cape of Good Hope (10.148) to Torres Strait and the Arafura Sea, whence departure should be taken for Colombo (10.132).

From December to April, when E'ly winds are prevalent off the S coast of Australia, the Southern Route, round Cape Leeuwin, is taken. When round Cape Leeuwin stand to the NW into the South-east Trade and enter the North-west Monsoon in about 10° S, 90° E. Thence steer a N'ly course with the North-west Monsoon across the equator in about 87° E, and with the North-east Monsoon to Colombo, remembering that this is the cyclone season in the South Indian Ocean.

10.151. South-east Australia to Bay of Bengal. From April to November, proceed through Torres Strait as directed in 10.148 and thence through the Arafura Sea. Keep in the South-east Trade until the meridian of 85° E is reached, and then stand NW to cross the equator in about 80° E. From this point proceed direct allowing for the strong E'ly current.

From December to April, pass round Cape Leeuwin, and steer NW through the South-east Trade so as to enter the North-west Monsoon in about 85° E; then shape course towards Udjung Masam Muka, and proceed W of Nicobar and Andaman Islands to destination.

10.152. South-east Australia to Singapore. From April to November, three routes are available; N-about through Torres Strait, thence N of Timor and through the Java Sea; or S of the islands and through Sunda Strait (10.135); or S-about round Cape Leeuwin. The N-about routes are probably the best.

From December to April, in spite of the prevailing E'ly winds to the S of Australia, a route S-about round Cape Leeuwin is not recommended for Singapore on account of the N'ly winds and S-going currents prevalent between November and March in Sunda Strait, Selat Bangka, Selat Gelasa, and Karimata Strait. A vessel has been known to take 30 days from Sunda Strait to Singapore, at this time of year, a distance of 500 miles. It is therefore advisable to proceed by the Outer Route (11.09.03), to the E of Australia and through Torres Strait, and as directed in 10.133, or to take the route E of New Guinea through Bougainville Strait, and through Surigao Strait into the China Sea.

ROUTES FROM SYDNEY TO PORTS IN INDIAN OCEAN

10.160. From Sydney to and through Bass Strait, there are two main routes, direct, and through Banks Strait. By the direct route, in order to take advantage of the current as far as Cape Howe, which appears to run strongest from November to March, keep along the outer edge of the charted 100 fm (182 m 9) line of soundings, or at a distance of 15 to 18 miles from the coast, where the current runs stronger and with more regularity than elsewhere.

From about 15 miles E of Cape Howe, if the wind is S'ly, do not steer a more W'ly course than 212° until in 39° 30′ S on account of the danger to be apprehended from SE'ly or S'ly gales upon Ninety Mile Beach between Cape Howe and Corner Inlet. On reaching the parallel of 39° 30′ S, steer to pass about 3 miles N of Wright Rock, and the same distance S of the S point of Deal Island, the SE of Kent Group. Having passed Kent Group, steer to pass 2 or 3 miles S of Sugarloaf Rock, and S of Judgment Rocks.

From Sugarloaf Rock steer 15 or 20 miles to the N of King Island, if the wind permits; but should the wind hang to the W of N, a course may be safely directed for the N extreme of Three Hummock Island, taking care to avoid Mermaid Rock and Taniwha Rock, passing afterwards N or S of King Island, as may be most favourable; the former is preferable.

Navigational Notes: Local experience has shown that with W'ly and SW'ly winds smoother water is found inshore off Ninety Mile Beach; and as SW'ly winds are the prevailing ones, mariners bound to the W may often take advantage of the smoother water and an absence of danger to approach the beach, instead of avoiding it. A vessel inshore when an easterly gale is threatened should at once get an offing; these gales give signs of warning.

Between December and March, as W'ly gales veer to the S, it is advisable to stand toward the Tasmanian coast, and so be ready to take advantage of the shift of wind.

Between April and November, and more particularly in September, October and November, the same course cannot be recommended, as in these months the wind tends to back to WNW.

The alternative route is via Banks Strait, which lies between Cape Barren Island and the N coast of Tasmania, and offers an alternative entrance to Bass Strait. The chief dangers to be avoided on the S shore are the reef and rocks off Swan Island, and the foul ground and rocks N of Foster Islets.

When working through to the W in the summer, when W'ly gales are of short duration, it is advisable to stand towards the Tasmanian coast, to take advantage of the shift of wind.

10.161. Sydney to Melbourne. Proceed as directed in 10.160 as far as Sugarloaf Rock, and then to Port Phillip as directly as circumstances permit.

10.162. From Bass Strait to Adelaide, in fine weather, from off Cape Otway steer to pass about 5 miles S of Cape Nelson, 10 miles SW of Cape Northumberland and Cape Banks, thence make a direct course to Cape Willoughby. Care must at all times be taken to guard against a set towards the land, but with S'ly and W'ly winds the coast should be given a much greater berth, as a current of 1 knot sometimes sets towards it between Cape Otway and Cape Willoughby.

In entering the Gulf of St. Vincent by Backstairs Passage, Young Rocks must be given a wide berth at night, but, since they are above-water, they are not dangerous by day in clear weather. At times the sea breaks heavily in the offing S of Cape Willoughby, see Admiralty Sailing Directions.

10.163. From Bass Strait to Spencer Gulf, proceed as directed in 10.162 to Cape Northumberland.

Thence to Spencer Gulf, give a good berth to South-west Young Rock, which is only 1 m 5 high; and except with strong SE'ly winds, make allowance for the E'ly set which usually prevails. From December to March, with SE'ly winds, a current runs at about 1 knot to the NW.

In the event of threatening weather from the S and W, care must be taken to secure a good offing.

10.164. Sydney to Cape of Good Hope and to all ports in Indian Ocean. October and November are unsuitable months in which to start a passage from Sydney to the W, either by Torres Strait or to the S of Australia.

From March to September, a route to the N of Australia should be taken, since the prevalence of strong W'ly gales renders the S-about route very difficult, indeed, generally impracticable, for sailing vessels during the whole period from April to November. The worst months for making this W-bound passage N of Australia are September, October and November, for W'ly gales are then of frequent occurrence, the wind sometimes being from WSW to WNW for more than a week at a time, and blowing very strong. From December to August, N'ly winds are very common.

In these circumstances, the best W-bound route is via Torres Strait and the Arafura Sea, taking (by preference) the Outer Route (11.09.03) from Sydney through the Coral Sea to Torres Strait.

From Torres Strait, directions are given as follows:

To Calcutta	10.134
To Cape of Good Hope	10.132
To Colombo	10.133
To Fremantle	10.131
To Hong Kong	10.136
To Singapore	10.135

From December to March, a route S of Australia may be taken. During these months, proceed through Bass Strait, or round Tasmania; E'ly winds prevail in the strait and along the S coast of Australia at that season, and good passages have been made by keeping N of 40° S, and passing round Cape Leeuwin into the South-east

Trade Wind, which then extends well to the S. A vessel from Bass Strait bound round Cape Leeuwin is recommended, with a favourable wind, to shape a course which will lead about 150 miles S of that cape.

In adopting this route advantage must be taken of every favourable change of wind, in order to make westing; and it is advisable not to approach too near the land, as it would become with SW gales, which are often experienced, even from December to March, a most dangerous lee shore, and the contrary currents run strongest near the land.   5

After rounding Cape Leeuwin, stand to the NW into the South-east Trades, and follow the directions given below:

To Aden	10.142
To Calcutta	10.144
To Cape of Good Hope	10.141
To Colombo	10.143
To Mauritius	10.140

10

15

CHAPTER 11

PACIFIC OCEAN SAILING ROUTES

CONTENTS

ROUTES FROM BANGKOK OR SAIGON

ROUTES FROM PORTS IN CHINA

ROUTES FROM MANILA

ROUTES FROM JAPAN

ROUTES FROM ISLANDS IN NORTH PACIFIC OCEAN

ROUTES FROM PRINCE RUPERT, VANCOUVER, OR COLUMBIA RIVER

ROUTES FROM SAN FRANCISCO

ROUTES FROM LOWER CALIFORNIA AND PANAMA

ROUTES FROM SOUTH AMERICAN PORTS

ROUTES FROM CABO DE HORNOS

NAVIGATIONAL NOTES FOR PACIFIC OCEAN

11.01.01. Soundings and dangers. Very large areas of the Pacific Ocean are imperfectly surveyed and many dangers are steep-to from the ocean bed. See 7.48.

11.01.02. Currents call for particular attention when navigating amongst the islands. See 7.49.

11.01.03. Navigation between the islands. Within the region of the Trade Winds, there is no difficulty in travelling from E to W, the winds being fair.

From W to E for short distances, a vessel may beat, but for long distances, as for instance from Fiji to Tahiti, or from Tahiti to Pitcairn Island, a vessel should stand S through the Trade Winds into the W'ly winds; then run down her easting and re-enter the Trade Winds in about the meridian of her destination.

SOUTH AFRICA AND SOUTHERN AUSTRALIA TO PACIFIC OCEAN PORTS

11.02. South Africa to Cabo de Hornos

11.02.01. In the Indian Ocean, the route (10.01.03) passes S of Tasmania between the parallels of 45° S and 47° S.

10.02.02. Icebergs are most numerous near this route midway between New Zealand and Cabo de Hornos, but the periods of frequency vary greatly, and it may happen that while ships are meeting ice in lower latitudes, higher latitudes will be free of it. See 10.01.

11.02.03. The usual route in the Pacific Ocean, all the year round, passes S of New Zealand in about 48° 30′ S, or about 30 miles S of Snares Island (*48° 01′ S, 166° 36′ E*). From this position a vessel should steer to the E between Bounty Islands (*47° 41′ S, 179° 03′ E*) and Antipodes Islands, whence, inclining slightly to the S, the route assumes, as a mean track, the parallel of 51° S from the meridian of 150° W, across the ocean to 120° W; keeping at about 60 miles N of this parallel from December to February (so as to be more clear of ice), and at 60 miles S of it from June to August; but in this case, also, dependent on ice conditions. From the meridian of 115° W, incline gradually to the S, to round Islas Diego Ramirez and Cabo de Hornos, see 11.101, 11.125.

11.02.04. The alternative route, which is only recommended from December to February, runs on a more S'ly track from the position S of Tasmania (11.02.01) to pass between Auckland Islands and Campbell Island in about 52° S, and to cross the Pacific Ocean between 54° S and 55° S.

This course would, clear of ice, and with favourable weather, doubtless ensure the quickest passage, as being the shorter distance, but experience has proved that at nearly all times of year so much time is lost at night and in thick weather, and even serious danger is incurred on account of the great quantities of ice normally met with in these higher latitudes, that a parallel even as far N as 47° S has been adopted with advantage.

It is believed that a passage made between 47° S and 50° S will provide steadier winds, smoother water, and less ice; and that a quicker passage may be expected in better weather, and with more security than in a higher latitude.

11.03. South-east Australia to Pacific Ocean

11.03.01. Adelaide to Cabo de Hornos. Steer SE to join the main route (11.02) in about 46° S, 146° E.

11.03.02. Melbourne to Cabo de Hornos. In summer (December to February) shape course to pass about 60 miles W of King Island and thence W of Tasmania to join the main route (11.02) in about 46° S, 146° E It is often necessary, and in heavy weather desirable, to make this passage at a considerable distance from the coast of Tasmania; namely at from 120 to 250 miles from the W coast, and round the S end of the island.

For the rest of the year, and as alternative to the summer route, pass through Bass Strait and steer to join the main route S of Snares Island (11.02.03).

11.03.03. Hobart to Cabo de Hornos. Either join the main route S of Snares Islands (11.02.03) or the alternative route (11.02.04) between Auckland Islands and Campbell Island.

11.03.04. Adelaide, Melbourne or Hobart to Chilean ports. Proceed to 48° 30′ S, 166° 30′ E, S of Snares Islands as directed in 11.02.02, 11.02.03, 11.03.01, 11.03.02, or 11.03.03, and thence make easting across the Pacific Ocean between the parallels of 46° S and 48° S, being towards the more S'ly of these latitudes in March, and towards the more N'ly in August, as far as 112° W; from which position steer as directly as possible for destination, bearing in mind the N-going current running up the whole W coast of South America.

11.03.05. Adelaide, Melbourne or Hobart to San Francisco or British Columbia. Proceed to 48° 30′ S, 166° 30′ E, S of Snares Islands (11.03.04) and thence make for 41° S, 138° W, keeping about 60 miles N of the direct line to this position in September, and 60 miles S of it in March. From 41° S, 138° W, proceed to 30° S, 124° W, and from this position make nearly N through the South-east Trades, crossing the equator in 116° W.

After picking up the North-east Trades in about 10° N, steer for 30° N, 131° W, in November and December, and in June and July for 30° N, 136° W. At other times, cross 30° N between these positions.

From the parallel of 30° N, proceed as direct to destination as the prevailing W'ly winds and the SE-going current, which crosses the track at a rate of 20 to 30 miles a day, will allow. See also 11.129, which joins this route soon after crossing the equator.

11.03.06. Melbourne to New Zealand. If the wind is W'ly on departure, steer to pass Rodondo Island and then N of Kent Group. Then, for ports on the E side of South Island, steer S of Snares Islands and thence to destination.

For Wellington, steer, direct for Cook Strait.

For Auckland, steer for Three Kings Islands, and thence round the N point of New Zealand to Auckland.

If, on leaving Port Philip, the wind should blow from the E it may be desirable to run to the S, passing W of King Island, and then proceed along the W coast of Tasmania, being prepared for the prevailing W'ly or SW'ly winds, when this coast becomes a dangerous lee shore, see 11.03.02. Having rounded the outlying dangers off the S coast of Tasmania, proceed to destination as above.

11.03.07. Adelaide or Melbourne to Sydney. If the wind is favourable for Bass Strait, first steer for Rodondo Island, passing about 20 miles S of Cape Otway if bound from Adelaide.

Having passed Rodondo Island and Kent Group, steer for a position about 20 miles SE of Rame Head and make Gabo Island or the land in the vicinity of Cape Howe; but if it is blowing hard from the S, a more E'ly course should be steered to avoid Ninety Mile Beach, from Corner Inlet for 150 miles, or nearly to Cape Howe, which would then be a dangerous lee shore. From a position E of Cape Howe, steer to the N along the E coast for Port Jackson at such distance from the land as the wind and weather would suggest, bearing in mind that the current generally sets to the S at a distance of 20 to 60 miles from the land.

If on leaving Adelaide or Melbourne, there should be an E'ly wind, it might be desirable to run to the S, instead of taking Bass Strait; if from Melbourne, passing between Cape Otway and King Island. Thence proceed down the W coast of Tasmania, giving it a good berth, see 11.03.02. Having rounded the outlying dangers S of Tasmania, steer a N'ly course, following the directions given above.

ROUTES FROM SYDNEY

11.04. Sydney to southern Australia and New Zealand

11.04.01. Sydney to Melbourne or Adelaide. When proceeding S from Sydney, keep at between 20 and 60 miles from the coast, so as to derive the full benefit of the S-going current.

To make the passage via Bass Strait, follow the directions in 10.160. if the wind permits.

To make the passage S of Tasmania, reverse the directions for that route given in 11.03.07.

11.04.02. Sydney to Hobart. On entering Storm Bay from the E, stand over towards Cape Frederick Hendrick, and steer thence along the NE coast of Bruny Island for the entrance to River Derwent. In working against a NW wind work up along the same coast, to avoid the strong outset from Frederick Henry Bay.

If, when off Betsey Island, the wind should blow from the NW so as to prevent a vessel from working into River Derwent, good anchorage may be obtained either in Adventure Bay or Frederick Henry Bay. In calms or light winds vessels may, if necessary, anchor with a stream or kedge in Storm Bay until they get a breeze.

11.04.03. Sydney to Auckland. There are two routes, according to time of year, though it is sometimes possible to make a direct course to sight and to pass 10 miles N of Three Kings Islands, and thence around North Cape. Sailing ships not having a commanding breeze, should not attempt to pass S of Three Kings Islands.

From September to April proceed to 30° S, 170° E and thence to Auckland.

From May to August, take a more S'ly route, through 35° S, 170° E.

11.04.04. Sydney to Wellington. Take as direct a route as possible to Cook Strait, noting that the best time of year for this passage is October to February.

11.04.05. Sydney to Port Chalmers or adjacent ports. Steer S of Snares Islands, as described in 11.05.01, and then proceed as directly as possible to destination.

The passage round the SW end of South Island and through Foveaux Strait is also possible, but it is not recommended.

11.05. Sydney to west coasts of the Americas

11.05.01. Sydney to Cabo de Hornos. At all seasons and from whatever quarter the wind may blow, it is advisable on leaving Port Jackson to proceed to the S rather than to the N of New Zealand. Advantage therefore should be taken of the most favourable winds for either passing S of Snares Islands and Auckland Islands, to join the route described in 11.02.03 or, if baffled by S'ly winds and favoured by fine weather, the passage through Cook Strait may be taken with advantage, especially from October to February, joining the route (11.14) from Wellington off that port.

See also 11.02.04 for an alternative route if passing S of New Zealand.

11.05.02. Sydney to ports on west coast of South America. Follow the directions in 11.04.03 according to season as far as the meridian of 170° E, and from thence proceed to destination.

11.05.03. Sydney to ports between Talcahuano and Iquique. After crossing 170° E (11.05.02), steer to cross the 180th meridian in about 35° S, and the meridian of 150° W between the parallels of 39° S and 43° S, being to the N in November and December, and to the S in April and May. Keep between these two parallels as far as 106° W, and from that position curve the track gradually N for the port of destination, making due allowance for the N-going current along the coast of South America. The winds will be usually from some S'ly direction.

11.05.04. Sydney to ports between Iquique and Panama. After crossing 170° E (11.05.02), steer to cross the 180th meridian between the parallels of 33° S and 34° S, and cross the ocean on a nearly E'ly course, not going S of 36° S. On reaching the meridian of 100° W, begin to make to the NE through the South-east Trades to destination, making allowance for the N-going set along the coast as far as the equator.

11.05.05. Sydney to San Francisco or British Columbia. There are two routes, via Tahiti and via Fiji. To make the passage via Tahiti, pass either N or S of New Zealand, or through Cook Strait, according to the direction of the wind on leaving; but preferably through Cook Strait. Thence make to the NE so as to cross 30° S in about 160° W, and then N through the South-east Trades, passing closely W of Îles de la Société.

In June, July and August, cross the equator in 148° W, but from October to February in 151° W, steering through the doldrums to 10° N, 143° W, where the North-east Trade Wind should be picked up. Stand through the Trade Wind towards 30° N, 152° W, and from this position, where the W'ly winds should begin to be felt, make as directly as possible for destination. From November to February, the turn to the E can usually be made in about 33° N, but in August stand N to 40° N before turning towards the land. Allowance must be made for a current setting SE and S more and more strongly as the United States coast is approached. It is also felt off the coast of British Columbia, but is there complicated by tidal streams. See 11.64.

To make the passage via Fiji, take the Auckland route (11.04.03) as far as the meridian of 170° E; thence continue E (nothing to the N) as far as 176° E, when course may be altered towards Fiji Islands.

If not calling at Fiji, pass E of the group and thence steer due N to cross the equator and the parallel of 18° N on the 180th meridian; thence stand more to the E, to 30° N, 172° W, and then proceed as directly as possible to destination.

11.06. Sydney to, and among, South Pacific islands

11.06.01. Sydney to Tahiti. Follow the directions for the Tahiti route in 11.05.05.

11.06.02. Sydney to Fiji. Follow the directions for the Fiji route in 11.05.05.

11.06.03. Sydney to other Pacific islands, and amongst them. When bound from the coasts of Australia to islands in the South Pacific Ocean, precise directions cannot be given on account of the irregularity of wind; but, as a general rule, easting must be made S of the Trade Wind limits, *i.e.*, in about 32° S. This is, however, liable to interruption, especially between January and April. When on the meridian of the island to which bound, the trade wind may be entered, and the ship sailed well free, as the current will be found setting to windward until near the islands.

For all practical purposes of navigation between the various groups of islands, it is important to draw attention to the fact that they lie within the limits of the South-east Trade Wind and of the Equatorial Current. For sailing vessels this means a favourable wind and current when proceeding from E to W, excepting with regard to currents when within the limits of the Equatorial Counter-current; and a beat to windward against the current and a choppy sea, when bound in the opposite direction.

11.06.04. Sydney to Noumea. Pass between Lord Howe Island and Elizabeth Reef and thence direct. The passage in a sailing vessel varies from 5 to 28 days, and it is seldom made without encountering a gale.

11.07. Sydney to Yokohama

11.07.01. General notes. The route changes seasonally both N and S of the equator, the two seasonal routes, changing with the Monsoons, being preferred S of the equator, see 11.07.02 and 11.07.03. N of the equator, the route changes seasonally as directed in 11.07.04.

Alternative routes known as the Eastern, Middle, and Western Routes may be taken, see 11.07.05. They do not differ greatly from the other routes.

11.07.02. During the North-west Monsoon, S of the equator, from November to March, pass between Lord Howe Island and Elizabeth Reef and thence to the N between Recifs d' Entrecasteaux on the E, and Bellona Reef and Chesterfield Reef on the W; thence between Solomon Islands and Santa Cruz Islands, crossing the equator in about 166° E at about 60 miles W of Nauru.

11.07.03. During the South-east Monsoon, S of the equator, from April to October, on leaving Port Jackson, steer directly to the NE, as far as 157° E; then to the N, between Kenn Reef and Bellona Reef, E of Pocklington Reef, and either through Bougainville Strait or through Pioneer Channel, between Solomon Islands and New Ireland, crossing the equator in about 155° E.

11.07.04. North of the equator, from January to June steer direct for Yokohama, passing E of Caroline Islands. In July and August, take a more E'ly track, passing about 100 miles W of Marshall Islands, and crossing the meridian of 160° E in 18° N, and steering thence direct to destination. From September to December, a track midway between these two is recommended.

11.07.05. Alternative routes. The Eastern Route is to Norfolk Island, thence to Matthew Island, and N along the meridian of 171° E to the parallel of 11° S, across the equator in 166° E and through the E part of Caroline Islands.

The Middle Route is midway between Lord Howe Island and Elizabeth Reef, W of New Caledonia, between Solomon Islands and Santa Cruz Islands, across the equator in 159° E, and through the middle of Caroline Islands.

The Western Route is along the meridian of 157° E, as far as 11° S; thence through Bougainville Strait, and across the equator in 153° E, when a direct course may be steered for Yokohama.

11.08. Sydney to Hong Kong

11.08.01. General notes. There are three routes, appropriate to the monsoon periods.

11.08.02. During the North-west Monsoon, from October to March, steer midway between Lord Howe Island and Elizabeth Reef. From this position pass N between Bellona Reefs and New Caledonia, and thence between Solomon Islands and Santa Cruz Islands, to the equator in 159° E. Thence steer through the middle of Caroline Islands and pass N of Philippine Islands.

The passage may be expected to be made in from 40 to 44 days.

11.08.03. During the first part of the South-east Monsoon, from April to June, steer NE as far as the meridian of 157° E and then due N as far as the parallel of 11° S; thence continue through Pioneer Channel, between New Ireland and Bougainville Island, or through Bougainville Strait, crossing the equator in about 153° E. From this position steer to pass through the most W'ly Caroline Islands, and through Balintang Channel to the China Sea.

11.08.04. The Torres Strait Route, appropriate to the second part of the South-east Monsoon, and to the South-west Monsoon of the China Sea, may be taken provided the vessel is through Torres Strait before the end of September; if not follow the directions in 11.08.02 or 11.08.03. The Torres Strait Route may be expected to occupy 40 days, and although not free from danger, may be navigated in safety by those with experience amongst coral reefs.

The passage from Sydney to Torres Strait is described in 11.09. Directions for the straits and routes in the Eastern Archipelago are given in Chapter 9. In this area, there are several alternative routes between Torres Strait and Hong Kong, the first being to pass through Wètar Strait and into the Flores Sea, and thence along the N side of the islands and through Sapudi Strait. From Sapudi Strait stand N to pass through Karimata Strait and thence to Hong Kong.

The second alternative is to pass round the N end of Timor, through Ombai Strait, Savu Sea and Sumba Strait to Alas Strait; thence steer N to pass through Karimata Strait and to the China Sea. Otherwise, a vessel may pass S of Timor and Sumba to Alas Strait, but this route leads through a part of the Arafura Sea in which there are many known, and probably many undiscovered, dangers.

The third alternative is to steer between Pulau-pulau Aru and Tanimbar Islands to Manipa Strait. Thence pass round the N end of Sulawesi and across the Sulawesi Sea, through Basilan Strait into the Sulu Sea. Pass through Mindoro Strait into the China Sea and Hong Kong.

11.09. Sydney to Torres Strait

11.09.01. General remarks. There are two routes; the Inner Route, which passes inshore of Great Barrier Reefs, and the Outer Route, to seaward of the reefs and through the Coral Sea. The proper time for making either passage under sail is from March to September, during the South-east Monsoon. Large sailing vessels seldom take the Inner route, but small vessels can do so without difficulty.

It is not desirable to reach the entrance to Torres Strait before the beginning of April, in order to avoid the chance of an equinoctial gale, as well as to make sure that the South-east Monsoon has begun in the Arafura Sea. Vessels have left Sydney as late as October, and made their passages; yet, generally speaking, it is much too late; for although the North-west Monsoon does not blow until November, and sometimes later, the calms and light variable winds that precede it protract the passage very much.

11.09.02. Inner Route. Proceed as directly as possible N along coast to Sandy Cape.

The prevailing wind off the coast to Sandy Cape being NE'ly from October to April, and W'ly from May to September, the seaman will use his own discretion in getting to the N against the strong S-going current generally running along the coast. The strength of this current is found on the edge of the charted 100 fm (182 m 9) line, from 10 to 30 miles from the coast, and will be avoided by keeping well outside this line.

Curtis Channel and Capricorn Channel are the only entrances to the Inner Route from SE; the latter is recommended. For details of these channels and of the Inner Route, see Admiralty Sailing Directions.

11.09.03. Outer Route. On leaving Port Jackson, avoid the S-going current by keeping within about 2 miles of the land until a direct course can reasonably be made to 24° S, 157° E. Thence, passing clear E of Cato Bank and Wreck Reef, proceed to 21° 10′ S, 156° 35′ E and continue on a NW'ly course, to pass NE of Eastern Fields and Portlock Reefs to Bligh Entrance.

11.10. Sydney to Singapore

11.10.01. Routes. From March to September, the South-east Monsoon period, Torres Strait is used, see 11.09.03. After passing through the strait, proceed by one of the two routes given in 11.08.04 to Karimata Strait, and thence through Riouw Strait to Singapore. This passage may also be made through Selat Gelasa or Selat Bangka instead of Karimata Strait.

A third route for March to September, from Torres Strait, is by the third alternative mentioned in 11.08.04, to Basilan Strait and the Sulu Sea; thence through Balabac Strait to the China Sea and Singapore.

From November to February, during the North-west Monsoon, steer to the N to pass E of New Guinea, and after meeting NE'ly winds in about 5° N, pass S of Mindanao, through Basilan Strait, Sulu Sea, and Balabac Strait to the China Sea and Singapore.

For routes in the Eastern Archipelago, see Chapter 9.

ROUTES FROM NEW ZEALAND

11.11. New Zealand to Australia. In all cases steer to pass through Cook Strait or round the N end of North Island. These passages are always more favourable than round the S end of South Island where W'ly winds prevail.

11.12. New Zealand to Sydney and ports northward. Having cleared Cook Strait or the N end of North Island, proceed as directly as possible if bound for Sydney or Brisbane; if bound for Torres Strait join the Outer Route (11.09.03) in 24° S, 157° E. To ports N of Brisbane join the Inner Route (11.09.02) in Capricorn Channel.

11.13. New Zealand to southern Australia. Pass through Bass Strait if wind permits; otherwise S of Tasmania. Then join the routes from Sydney (10.60.02, 10.60.03, 11.04.01).

11.14. New Zealand to Cabo de Hornos. From Auckland, join the trans-ocean route (11.02.03) in about 51° S, 148° W. From Cook Strait, join it in 170° W; from South Island ports, join at the 180th meridian.

11.15. New Zealand to South America. From Auckland, see 11.05.03 and 11.05.04; from other departures see 11.03.04. These trans-ocean routes should be joined at the nearest position.

11.16. New Zealand to San Francisco or British Columbia. Steer N so as to get through the Equatorial Trough (7.02 and 7.15) as quickly as possible; this particularly applies in July, August, and September. At all times join the appropriate route from Sydney (11.05.05) as soon as possible.

11.17. New Zealand to South Pacific islands. Make easting S of 40° S to about 165° W if bound for Rarotonga, or to 155° W if bound for Tahiti; haul gradually N into the South-east Trade, and then proceed direct.

The South-east Trade is tolerably regular among the Samoan, Tonga, Fiji and New Caledonia Islands, from April to October, but from December to March it is very light and uncertain, and NW'ly winds are frequent.

Cyclones sometimes pass over these localities from January to March, inclusive.

11.18. New Zealand to China Sea or Japan. Steer N to pick up, on the parallel of 30° S, the appropriate route from Sydney. References are for Yokohama, 11.07; for Hong Kong 11.08; for Torres Strait 11.09; for Singapore 11.10.

ROUTES FROM ISLAND GROUPS BETWEEN NEW CALEDONIA AND ÎLES DE LA SOCIÉTÉ

11.19. Islands (as above) to Sydney or southern Australia. Proceed W on about the parallel of the islands, taking full advantage of the Trade Wind and the favourable current; pass about 150 miles S of New Caledonia and then proceed as directly as possible to port, or to Bass Strait if bound to South Australia. For passage through Bass Strait and to Melbourne and Adelaide, see 10.160–10.163; and for passage from Bass Strait to Cape Leeuwin, see 10.164. For route from Tahiti, see 11.28.

11.20. Islands (as above) to New Zealand. From islands E of the meridian of 170° W steer W in the Trade Wind until that meridian is reached, and thence proceed as directly as possible to destination, bearing in mind that approaching New Zealand a sailing vessel should, especially in winter, keep W, rather than E of the direct route; W'ly winds are likely to be experienced S of the Trade.

11.21. Islands (as above) to Cabo de Hornos or Estrecho de Magallanes. From any of the Pacific islands stand through the Trades to the S and then into the W'ly winds of the S hemisphere; from thence, proceed by great circle to Estrecho de Magallanes or to round Cabo de Hornos, but do not get to the S of the route from South Africa (11.02).

11.22. Islands (as above) to ports between Talcahuano and Panama. Stand through the Trades into the westerlies to pick up the routes from Australia to the required destination in 160° W, or W of that meridian, according to starting point. See 11.03.04, 11.05.03, 11.05.04. From July to October, however, a direct passage S of Archipel des Tuamotu can usually be made, passing Pitcairn Island.

11.23. Islands (as above) to San Francisco and British Columbia. Stand S (except from Tahiti) and pick up the route from Sydney via Tahiti (11.05.05).

11.24. Fiji to Honolulu. Stand N through both Trades and into the W'ly winds N of the North-east Trade, from thence making easting to about 155° W, thence proceeding direct.

11.25. Fiji to Tahiti. Stand through the South-east Trade Wind into the westerlies, then run down the easting, re-entering the Trade Wind in 150° W.

11.26. Samoa eastward. When sailing to the E it will be found an advantage to keep on the S side of the group, where there is not only a favourable current, but the winds will be found more regular and calms less frequent.

11.27. Tahiti to Honolulu. Steer to the N to cross the equator in about 147° W, and thence to make the Hawaiian Islands from E, to ensure the breeze.

The channel between Moorea and Tahiti should never be used by sailing ships except with steady winds from NE or SW, as these are the only winds that blow through the channel. When there is a fresh breeze from the E to the N of Tahiti it is generally calm in this channel, and vessels have remained becalmed here for days, whilst a fresh breeze prevailed to seaward.

11.28. Tahiti to Australia and New Zealand. For Sydney, run with the Trade Wind, steering to pass about 150 miles S of New Caledonia; thence proceed as directly as possible to destination. See 11.19.

For Wellington, run with the Trade Wind to about 170° W, and thence proceed as directly as possible to destination. See 11.20.

11.29. Torres Strait to Sydney. The ocean passage appears not to have been made very often, and like that from Torres Strait to Sydney by the Inner Route, was formerly considered only practicable in the North-west Monsoon—from November to February or March. The first object after clearing Torres Strait, in the North-west Monsoon, will be to take advantage of W'ly winds for making easting, looking upon immediate progress to the S as of secondary importance.

In the North-west Monsoon, leave Torres Strait by Great North East Channel, and having cleared Eastern Fields, take every advantage of W'ly breezes and try to reach a position in about 15° S, 156° E, keeping an especial look-out when proceeding E of the route, into the unexplored area N of Mellish Reef (*17° 25′ S, 155° 51′ E*).

Having attained the meridian of 156° E, and thus probably far enough to the E to take advantage of the South-east Trade, haul on a wind on the port tack and try to fetch Mellish Reef; great caution is necessary when in the neighbourhood of this reef, and there is generally a strong W-going set to guard against. Pass, if the wind permit, between Kenn Reef and Wreck Reef on the E side, and Frederick Reef and Saumarez Reef on the W side.

If there is too much southing in the prevailing South-east Trade Wind to weather Frederick Reef, pass W of it, and between Saumarez Reef and Swain Reefs, when a S-going current will probably enable a vessel to weather Sandy Cape, care being taken to avoid Breaksea Spit and the shoal near its E edge.

As a rule a vessel should be so sailed as to close the intermediate passage reefs in the day-time, to take a fresh departure, as the current between Saumarez Reef and Swain Reef may otherwise seriously affect the vessel's reckoning.

From Sandy Cape proceed for Sydney by keeping the mainland in sight, to take advantage of the S-going current.

ROUTES FROM SINGAPORE AND EASTERN ARCHIPELAGO

11.30. Singapore to Sydney

11.30.01. General remarks. From Singapore, near and during the period of change from the South-east Monsoon to the North-west Monsoon (about October), sailing vessels may be five and six weeks in making the passage from Singapore to Selat Bangka.

11.30.02. Directions. From November to February the route is taken through Torres Strait. Leaving Singapore in the North-west Monsoon, between mid-November and mid-February, proceed through Selat Bangka or Karimata Strait, and enter the Indian Ocean by Lombok Strait or Alas Strait, after passing through Sapudi Strait. Having reached the Indian Ocean, steer to pass N or S of Timor and thence to Torres Strait. See also 10.120. Continue as directed in 11.29.

From April to October, follow the directions in 10.57.07 through Sunda Strait into the W'ly winds, and then pass S of Australia and through Bass Strait to Sydney. See 10.01.03, 10.01.07, 11.03.07.

11.31. Singapore to Molukka Archipelago

11.31.01. General remarks. The passage should be made S of Borneo in the North-east Monsoon and N of Borneo in the South-west Monsoon.

11.31.02. From October to May, when the North-east Monsoon blows N of the equator, and the North-west Monsoon S of it, proceed through Karimata Strait passing E of Ontario Reef (*2° 00' S, 108° 39' E*). On leaving the strait, steer to pass 10 to 15 miles S of Karang Mian and about 10 miles S of Masalembo Besar; thence proceed to Saleier Strait as directly as possible.

After clearing Saleier Strait, Ambon is easily reached by passing S of Batu Ata and Binongko; if bound to the Ceram Sea, first round the S point of Buton and then, after skirting the shore of that island, and having passed Wangi Wangi Islands, steer N as far as Wowoni Island. Thence run for the S point of Sanana (*2° 28' S, 126° 03' E*) and thence into the Ceram Sea.

The currents in this locality set to the S and are very strong. If a vessel has been set to leeward of the N point of Buru Island, it is best to pass to the S of that island, and then through Manipa Strait to the Ceram Sea.

11.31.03. From May to September, when the South-west Monsoon blows N of the equator, and the South-east Monsoon S of it, run S of Anambas Kepulauan and then between Royal Charlotte Reef and Louisa Reef, taking care to avoid the dangerous shoals bordering the Borneo coast, and also of being set to leeward of Pulau Balambangan by the N-going current which prevails in the South-west Monsoon. Having made Pulau Balambangan, haul round its N point, and steer through Balabac Strait into the Sulu Sea, then through Sibutu Passage or one of the passages of the Sulu Archipelago, cross the Sulawesi Sea for the N point of Sulawesi, and then work S through the Molukka Sea.

For an alternative route as far as Balabac Strait during the South-west Monsoon, see 11.32.03.

Directions for the straits and channels in the Eastern Archipelago are given in Chapter 10. See 7.113 for currents in Palawan Passage.

11.32. Singapore to Sulu Sea

11.32.01. General remarks. In Singapore Strait, E-bound, follow in reverse the directions given in 10.39. The main route is via Balabac Strait, to which the passage is varied according to season; the passage may also be made by proceeding S through Karimata Strait or Selat Gelasa, through the Java Sea, and to the N through Makassar Strait, but this is not recommended except in October and November.

11.32.02. From October to May, during the North-east Monsoon, the route is via Balabac Strait. In December, January, and February, do not leave Singapore Strait in strong NE winds, but anchor on the N shore, under Pulau Che Kamat. In those months gales often occur with thick weather, the rain lasting two or three days and the SSE-going current outside attains a rate of 2½ or 3 knots. A vessel leaving the strait then, instead of fetching Pedjantan, would fall bodily to leeward, and have to work up the W coast of Borneo. Fine weather follows, with the wind backing round to N and NW; and the current in the offing decreases in strength to about 1¼ knots.

Having obtained the fine weather, the first object should be to pass through the channel between Natuna Kepulauan and Subi Kepulauan (*3° 03' N, 108° 51' E*) or, if this proves impossible or difficult, to use one of the passages to the S.

To pass through the channel between Natuna Kepulauan and Subi Kepulauan a vessel should leave the anchorage off Pulau Che Kamat with the first of the ebb, and keep clean full. She should then steer to the NE to go through the channel between Subi Ketjil, which is lighted, and Bunguran, passing S of Midai Island, a passage that may be made in these months without much difficulty, especially at full and change, when, it is stated, the wind, after a few hours calm, frequently shifts to the W with squalls and rain, and then hauls round to SW and S, blowing moderately for 24 hours. By taking advantage of these changes Subi Kepulauan may be easily weathered.

If after arriving in the vicinity of Midai Island, nearly in the fairway SW of Bunguran, the wind continues E'ly, steer to the N on the starboard tack, passing W of Midai Island, and keeping not less than 3 miles from its SW side to avoid the shoal water extending 2½ miles from it. Pass about 5 miles W of Timau (*3° 18' N, 107° 34' E*), as the coral reefs about that island extend fully 3 miles from its SW side, with least known depths of 7 m. Vessels are not recommended to pass between Timau and Midai Island, on account of Diana Reefs, which extend some 14 miles N of Midai. There would be no danger, however if the wind permits of a vessel laying through, and passing 4 or 5 miles S of Timau and Karang Sedimin (*3° 24' N, 107° 50' E*), thus giving a wide berth to Diana Reefs, provided those objects are available for cross bearings. The channel S of Midai Island is preferable if a vessel can lay through.

If bearing up, after passing Timau there will be no difficulty in working towards the S point of Bunguran, as that island, when approached from the SW, shelters against the strong SW-going current of the Monsoon. Off its S coast at night, in fine weather, the wind is off the land, but the S and SE coasts should not be approached nearer than 6 or 7 miles, on account of the off-lying dangers.

If fetching to leeward of Subi Kepulauan with a N'ly wind take Koti Passage, between Pulau Pandjang and Serasan Group. Serasan Passage is also safe when either side is kept aboard, to avoid Haynes Shoal, the 6 m 4 patch in the fairway. The current among these islands is more regular than in Api Passage, where it sets in various directions, and with considerable velocity to the SW from 16 to 19 hours at a time; for large vessels any of the other passages are preferable to this, as great caution and perseverance are requisite in working through. When using it, keep the Borneo coast aboard, in depths of from 18 m to 20 m, to avoid the current and to profit by the land winds. See directions for Api passage, below.

In taking Koti Passage give Pulau Pandjang a good berth to avoid the reef which surrounds it, and extending off its SW end. The winds amongst these islands and as far E as the meridian of Tanjong Sirik are generally from N to NNW. The passage cleared, proceed to the NE; endeavouring, if not certain of the longitude, to make Royal Charlotte Reef or Luisa Reef, whichever is the weathermost, by running on its parallel of latitude; and as the currents appear to be influenced by the prevailing winds, a set in the direction in which it is blowing should be anticipated, the velocity of the current being proportionate to the force of the wind. Having made either Royal Charlotte Reef or Louisa Reef, or passing in mid-channel between them, steer to the E for about 100 miles towards Balabac Strait, and through it to the Sulu Sea. See Admiralty Sailing Directions for the W approaches to, and passage through Balabac Strait.

When approaching Api Passage from W, especially when working against the North-east Monsoon, a vessel may gain by keeping close to the Borneo coast, as favourable tidal streams may be found near the shore when a strong current is running S in the offing. For directions, see Admiralty Sailing Directions.

Burung Kepulauan may be boldly approached from W; large sailing vessels had better pass outside them, but smaller craft may often, with advantage, pass between them.

11.32.03. From May to September, during the South-west Monsoon, first proceed to Api Passage as described below and thence, with a fair wind, parallel with the Borneo coast, as far as Balabac Strait, and thence into the Sulu Sea.

Directions from Singapore to Tandjung Api are as follows: As far as the E entrance to Singapore Strait, the tidal streams are tolerably regular, but some miles off-shore a current will be found setting about NNW in the South-west Monsoon; its greatest strength will be experienced between Pulau Tioman and Anambas Kepulauan.

In order to obviate the effect of this set or current, it is considered prudent to make good the course for Pulau Mendarik (1° 20′ N, 107° 02′ E) from Singapore Strait, by which, should light airs prevail, the option will be afforded of steering either between Pengibu and Kaju Ara, or S of Kaju Ara, thus avoiding Acasta Rock. On leaving Kaju Ara, shape course, allowing for a N'ly set, to pass well S of Muri Islets and then keep Saint Pierre Light, whilst in sight, bearing 255°, which will lead about 2 miles S of Merundung Rock.

Banggi South Channel and Malawali Channel between Banggi and Borneo are sometimes used by vessels navigating to the ports on the NE coast of Borneo; they are somewhat intricate and demand careful navigation, being for the greater part bounded by dangers. Balabac Main Channel is recommended in preference to either of these channels, being considered much safer. See Admiralty Sailing Directions for a description and directions for these channels.

In October and November, only, an alternative route via Makassar Strait may be taken. A vessel should proceed S to pass through Selat Gelasa or Karimata Strait, and thence E through the Java Sea to Makassar Strait, there joining the "First Eastern Passage" (10.47) and following it to the Sulu Sea.

11.33. Singapore to Manila

11.33.01. From October to May, during the North-east Monsoon, follow the directions given in 11.32.02 as far as the entrance to Balabac Strait, and continue thence to the N by Palawan Passage, between the charted 100 fathom (182 m 9) line W of Palawan Island and that of the off-lying foul ground; a channel about 40 miles in width, except towards the S end, where, between Royal Captain Shoal and the edge of Palawan Bank, it is 28 miles wide. This is the most dangerous part of the channel. From the N end of Palawan Passage, in about 11° N, work to the N to Manila, hugging the coast by short boards when possible. See 7.113 for currents in Palawan Passage.

11.33.02. From June to October, during the South-west Monsoon, follow the directions given in 11.32.03 to Tandjung Api, and then proceed directly along the coast and through Palawan Passage with a fair wind to destination. Or as an alternative route, pass S of Anambas Kepulauan and Bunguran and between Royal Charlotte Reef and Louisa Reef, to pick up the Palawan route off Balabac Strait.

When working through Palawan Passage and having conformed with the directions given for making the SW end of Palawan, in fine weather try to make in-shore boards in the afternoon, for the sun then being astern of the vessel, the patches lying near the edge of the bank will generally be distinguished from the masthead in ample time to tack. In squally weather, also during heavy rains, these patches have been observed imparting a very distinct yellowish hue to the surface of the water. It is most desirable to get soundings before dark in order that a good departure may be made for the night. On making the inshore board, be prepared to tack immediately on getting the first indication of the shore bank, on which a vessel is likely to come suddenly into soundings. See 7.113 for currents in Palawan Passage.

When approaching the islands in the vicinity of Balabac and Palawan, if the wind be well to the S and the weather thick, Balabac Island may be approached near enough to obtain a good observation of the land; but caution is necessary not to go within 12 miles of it, as soundings of 48 m and 37 m extend that distance off, in a W'ly direction from the peak, having shoal patches immediately inside them. If the wind be to the W, with thick cloudy weather, Balabac Island should not be approached nearer than 30 miles, as W'ly winds usually force a strong E-going current through the passages.

Off the SW end of Palawan, it is not unusual, particularly in squalls, for the wind to veer to WNW, and sometimes NW, blowing with violence, and placing the vessel on a lee shore with respect to the shoals inside the edge of the bank. This weather generally prevails off Palawan about September and October, rendering it uncertain and difficult to make the narrowest part of the channel, owing to the land being obscured.

11.34. Singapore to Hong Kong

11.34.01. During the North-east Monsoon, a route similar to the Main Route for powered vessels (7.113), except that it passes initially between Anambas Kepulauan and Bunguran, may be used, although it is not strongly recommended.

During the strength of the North-east Monsoon, use Palawan Passage (11.33.01) as far as the N end of Palawan Island; then work up the coast of Luzon as far as Cape Bolinao or even Cape Bojeador. Among the island groups N of Luzon no continuous strong breezes will be experienced at all comparable, either in force or consequent high seas, with those which prevail between Cape Bolinao and Hong Kong. But see notes on Pratas Reefs (11.47.01) and T'ai-wan Strait (11.50.01).

A route through Selat Gelasa or Karimata Strait, the Java Sea, Saleier Strait, and the Banda Sea, to join the Second Eastern Passage (10.46), affords a leading or fair wind and favourable currents nearly throughout.

11.34.02. Between the Monsoons, a route on the W side of the China Sea is recommended, passing along the Malay coast to Pulau Redang; thence along the coast of Vietnam to 16° N; coastwise off the E side of Hai-nan and inshore of Ch'i-chou tao (*19° 58' N, 111° 16' E*) to make the mainland coast about Tien-pai (*21° 30' N, 111° 14' E*).

Approaching Hong Kong, try to make Ta-wan shan bearing about 000°, then steer between it and Wen-wei chou, of Chia-peng ch'ün-tao; thence between Wai-ling-ting and Li-ma ch'ün-tao, and through Lema Channel into West Lamma Channel. After the middle of August, when E'ly winds are likely to prevail for several days together (as also at other times of the year), it will be necessary to make the NE end of Li-ma ch'ün-tao and proceed in by Lema Channel to West Lamma Channel. East Lamma Channel is also safe in both monsoons.

Note that NE'ly and W'ly gales blowing out of the Gulf of Tong King, with dark weather and rain, have been experienced on this route, causing danger of being driven among the Paracel Islands, but such gales are not frequent and the land should be kept in sight, for smoother seas and the availability of anchorage.

11.34.03. During the South-west Monsoon (May to September) the Main Route for powered vessels (7.113) is appropriate except that the vessel should be taken between Anambas Kepulauan and Bunguran if the monsoon has not settled in.

The route on the W side of the China Sea (11.34.02) may also be used during the earlier part of the South-west Monsoon.

During the latter part of the South-west Monsoon, a route through Palawan Passage is recommended, observing that at this time of year a N-bound route in the W part of the China Sea is hampered by strong S-going currents in the vicinity of Îles Catwick (*9° 59' N, 109° 05' E*), with light N'ly winds, variable airs, or calms.

Steer N of Pengibu (*1° 35' N, 106° 35' E*) and between Bunguran and Subi Kepulauan, and thence as directed for Palawan Passage in 11.33.01.

11.35. Singapore to ports north of Hong Kong

11.35.01. During the North-east Monsoon, proceed by the Palawan Passage Route (11.34.01) as far as Cape Bolinao; then continue to work up the coast of Luzon and through Balintang Channel. Proceed thence off the E coast of Tai-wan and to destination.

The alternative route during the North-east Monsoon is via Karimata Strait and the Second Eastern Passage, as directed in 11.34.01.

11.35.02. Near the change of Monsoon, the inner route (11.34.02) may be taken as far as Hong Kong, except during the latter part of the South-west Monsoon; and thence along the coast of China to destination.

11.35.03. During the South-west Monsoon (except the latter part) take one of the routes advised in 11.34.03 as far as Hong Kong, and thence continue along the China coast to destination. In the latter part of this Monsoon, use the Palawan Passage route.

11.36. Singapore to Saïgon

11.36.01. During the South-west Monsoon, the winds in Singapore Strait are between SE and W, and sailing vessels will have no difficulty in getting through to the E.

Having cleared the strait, steer to pass W of Archipel de Poulo Condore, and thence along the edge of the bank fronting the mouths of Le Mé Kong, extending to the mouth of Rivière de Saïgon.

Strong freshets run out of these rivers during the South-west Monsoon, and join the NE-going current, whereby vessels are obliged to keep the edge of the bank aboard to prevent being set to leeward of Mui Vung Tou (*10° 19′ N, 107° 05′ E*). Keep sounding continuously while steering along the edge of the bank, so as to remain in depths of not less than 18 m. If the water begins to shoal, haul off to the E, when it will soon deepen, as the depths are fairly regular. Continue along the edge of the bank in these depths until Mui Vung Tou bears less than 030°, when course may be steered as requisite for the Saïgon pilot.

11.36.02. During the North-east Monsoon, steer as directed in 11.32.02 until clear of Natuna Kepulauan, and then steer NE until reaching the meridian of 112° E; after which stand across the China Sea to make Mui Vung Tou, or preferably the land to windward of that cape, to avoid being set to leeward by the prevailing current.

From 7° N until about 70 miles E of the mouths of Le Mé Kong, a strong current will be found setting to the SW governed considerably by the prevailing winds, for when strong gales blow in the early part of this monsoon, the SW-going current is stronger, and often runs at a rate of 3 knots. The tidal streams are regular, and set strong near the Vietnam coast during both monsoons.

In the latter part of March and April an E'ly wind is often found E of Anambas Kepulauan that will take a vessel to Archipel de Poulo Condore; thence work to Mui Vung Tou, W of that island, keeping towards the Vietnam coast, which is very low, and can seldom be seen at night.

From abreast the mouths of Le Mé Kong, the ebb stream will be found setting to windward, greatly assisting vessels standing inshore; but they should not stand near these mouths during the flood stream, and on no account shoal the water to less than 22 m in the night. Sounding should never be neglected when standing towards this low land, which may be seen from a distance of about 10 miles in clear weather.

The North-east Monsoon often blows very strong on the parallel of Iles Catwick, and between them and the Vietnam coast, in December, January, February and sometimes in March, continuing for two or three days with a heavy sea and strong current, the sky being generally thick and hazy throughout. A gradual rise in the barometer is a sure indication of an increase in the strength of the monsoon. If the monsoon proves too strong to contend with bear up for Archipel de Poulo Condore, where good shelter will be found, and anchor.

At about 90 miles from the coast, the wind in settled weather usually hauls to ENE and E at about 1600, continuing all night fresh and puffy. This is the time to stand inshore, and although as far to leeward as the meridian of Mui Vung Tou, with the ebb tide under the lee, the vessel will be to windward of Muy Ky Van (*10° 22′ N, 107° 16′ E*) in the morning.

11.37. Singapore to Bangkok

11.37.01. During the South-west Monsoon, winds between SE and W prevail in Singapore Strait, and therefore sailing vessels will have no difficulty in making to the E.

Having cleared the strait, shape course for Pulau Redang, and thence keep the W shore of the Gulf of Thailand aboard, passing inside Ko Losin and Koh Krah.

11.37.02. During the North-east Monsoon, follow the directions given in 11.32.02 until clear of Natuna Kepulauan, and then proceed NE to the meridian of 111° or 112° E. This can be done easily, as the wind is invariably from N to NNW as far as the meridian of Tanjong Sirik, when it generally veers to the NE. Then stand across the China Sea to Hon Khoai. Little or no current will be experienced until the parallel of 6° N or 7° N is gained; then it will be found setting strongly to the SW, governed to a large extent by the prevailing winds.

In April and May the best passages to the Gulf of Thailand are made by keeping the Malay coast aboard; but expect squalls, calms and rain; a weak current begins to set to the NE about this period.

11.38. Eastern Archipelago to China. Generally, the various routes, according to season, are described in articles 10.30–10.51.

Passing N, through the straits to the W of Borneo, usually May to September, take the Main Route, or the route on the W side of the China Sea (11.34.03).

Between November and April, the Second Eastern Passage (10.46) is recommended. The First Eastern Passage (10.47) can be considered but the disadvantages outweigh the advantages.

ROUTES FROM BANGKOK OR SAÏGON

11.39. Bangkok or Saïgon to Hong Kong and northward

11.39.01. During the North-east Monsoon (November to April), to attempt to work N, especially in the full strength of the monsoon, is so certain to be tedious that vessels are advised to stand S to Natuna Kepulauan to join the Palawan Passage route (11.35.01); or, near the change of monsoon, to take the coastwise route (11.34.02) if bound to Hong Kong; if bound to ports N of Hong Kong either of these routes is possible but consideration should be given to a route embodying the Second Eastern Passage, see 11.34.01.

11.39.02. During the South-west Monsoon, if from Bangkok, follow generally the directions given in 11.34.03 or 11.35.03.

11.40. Bangkok to Singapore

11.40.01. During the North-east Monsoon (November to April), the passage from Bangkok S through the Gulf of Thailand will often be shortened by sighting Îlot Kusrovie (*11° 07′ N, 102° 46′ E*) and passing inshore of Koh Tang. Thence keep well E of Poulo Panjang, and if bound to Singapore steer well out to sea for a quick passage. Pass about 20 miles E of Pulau Tenggol and E of Pulau Aur; see also 11.43.01.

11.40.02. During the South-west Monsoon (May to September), keep the W shore of the Gulf of Thailand aboard, passing inside Perhentian Islands and Pulau Redang, Pulau Kapas and Pulau Tenggol. S of Pulau Kapas, keep inshore to avoid the current, passing inside Pulau Tioman, Pulau Sribuat, and Pulau Sibu; thence proceed to Singapore Strait, taking advantage of the tidal streams and the land and sea breezes which prevail during settled weather in this monsoon.

The inshore channel extending from Pulau Sibu to Pulau Sribuat, and formed by a chain of islands and rocks parallel with the mainland, is a good and safe one, having but few hidden dangers, and good anchorage all the way through.

11.41. Saïgon to Singapore

11.41.01. During the North-east Monsoon, from a position off Mui Vung Tou, shape a course to pass E of Archipel de Poulo Condore, and thence direct to make Pulau Aur. From Pulau Aur to Singapore proceed according to directions as from Hong Kong (11.43.01).

11.41.02. During the South-west Monsoon (May to September), either the direct route or a route E of Natunas Kepulauan may be taken. The latter is probably the better.

On the direct route, many good passages have been made by keeping the Vietnam coast aboard as far as Les Deux Frères, W of Archipel de Poulo Condore, or Hon Khoai, and then crossing the Gulf of Thailand with a strong NW'ly wind until the Malay coast is reached. From Pulau Kapas (*5° 10′ N*) follow the directions given in 11.40.02, Bangkok to Singapore, in this monsoon.

Alternatively, the passage E of Bunguran is considered, generally speaking, to be better, especially for large vessels.

After making departure from Mui Vung Tou, steer to the SW until the South-west Monsoon forces the vessel off to a more SE'ly course. This may be accomplished by taking every advantage of the N and NE winds, which frequently blow at night, and in some parts of the day, within a short distance of the coast. These local winds often carry vessels 40 or 50 miles SW of Archipel de Poulo Condore without any interruption.

While standing to the SE the full strength of the NE-going current will be met with in the neighbourhood of Charlotte Bank; it gradually decreases and becomes slightly favourable when NE of Bunguran. In this locality SE'ly and E'ly winds will generally be met with, and fast sailing vessels frequently pass through the channel between Subi Kepulauan and Midai Islands, and into Singapore Strait. There is a light on Subi Kechil, on the S side of the channel between Subi Kepulauan and Bunguran; this channel is safe for all classes of vessel.

Strong W'ly winds, with rain, frequently blow during the early part of this monsoon, and may force vessels E to about 111° 30′ E. When this is the case, make for Api Passage (11.32.02) keeping the NW coast of Borneo aboard from Tandjung Api to the S until Burung Kepulauan are reached. This will be accomplished without difficulty, for strong land and sea breezes prevail, and the current is weaker near the coast. (Many vessels, through leaving the coast of Borneo too soon, have fetched no higher than Pulau Aur or Pulau Tioman).

Leaving Burung Kepulauan, pass either N or S of Tambelan Kepulauan. If the wind is scant from the SW after leaving these islands, try to make Mapor Island, off the E side of Bintan Island.

The current in the offing runs strongly to the N and through Api Passage. Vessels coming through this passage should keep the N side, when possible, towards Merundung Island, and should keep in depths of more than 24 m on the S side between Tandjung Datu and Tandjung Api; the latter point has shoals steep-to at 1½ miles off, but beyond that distance there is not less than 9 m between it and Tandjung Datu. Vessels should be ready to anchor in the passage or off any other part of the coast, as the tidal streams are greatly influenced by the current, which often changes without warning.

ROUTES FROM PORTS IN CHINA

11.42. China or Japan to Indian Ocean

11.42.01. Summary. Directions for the principal passages most frequently used by sailing vessels are given elsewhere in this book. References are as follows:

Main route, 10.49, 10.50, 10.51.
Eastern Archipelago to Indian Ocean, 10.115–10.125.
Hong Kong to Singapore, 11.42.06 and 11.43.
Shang-hai to the S, 11.53.
Manila to Saïgon, 11.59.

Manila to Hong Kong, 11.60.
Manila to Indian Ocean and Australia, 11.63.

11.42.02. The Western Route (10.49) passes through the China Sea to the W of the Philippine Islands and of Borneo to Sunda Strait through the Eastern Archipelago either direct, or via Singapore; the selection of which alternative to follow depends to a great degree on the final destination to be reached.

11.42.03. The Eastern Route (10.50) passes E of the Philippine Islands, and then via Djailolo Passage, or the Molukka Sea into the Ceram Sea and the Banda Sea. Thence it continues to Ombai Strait, or to one of the central passages (Alas Strait, Lombok Strait, or Bali Strait). If bound to Torres Strait the passage from the Banda Sea would be as described in 11.44, Hong Kong to Torres Strait, and Port Darwin.

11.42.04. The Central Route (10.51) passes W of the Philippine Islands through Sulu Sea and Basilan Strait, E of Borneo through Makassar Strait, and thence to one of the central passages (Alas Strait, Lombok Strait, or Bali Strait). Alternatively a vessel, after leaving Makassar Strait, may stand W through the Java Sea to enter the Indian Ocean through Sunda Strait.

11.42.05. Choice of route. Of the three principal routes, Western, Eastern, and Central, the Western and Central are used by vessels from ports on the S coast of China; the Central Route also for vessels S-bound from Manila and the S part of the Philippine Islands, or the E part of Borneo. The Eastern Route is used by vessels from ports in the N part of China, or from Japan, also from ports in the S part of China during the South-west Monsoon.

11.42.06. Seasonal variation of routes from ports in southern China. From September to February, during the North-east Monsoon, pass between Macclesfield Bank and Paracel Islands, then about 60 miles E of Îles Catwick (borrowing to the E where the winds are more favourable), and between Anambas Kepulauan and Natuna Kepulauan to Selat Bangka or Selat Gelasa; thence continue to Sunda Strait.

In March, April, and early May, after leaving the coast of China, stand over to the coast of Luzon and proceed through Palawan Passage, along the coast of Borneo, through Api Passage, past Pengiki Besar Island and through Karimata Strait; then close round Djaga Utara and direct to Sunda Strait. On this route E'ly winds, without calms, but with fine weather, and a smooth sea are likely to be experienced.

Alternatively, at the end of April or the beginning of May, stand towards Macclesfield Bank and then follow the Central Route (11.42.04) by standing SE to join it at Verde Island Passage or Mindoro Strait.

From the middle of May till the end of July, cross the China Sea and pass through Balintang Channel to join the Eastern Route (11.42.03).

In August, stand towards Hai-nan tao, cross the Gulf of Tongking, and work down the coast of Vietnam with the land and sea breezes, as far as Cap Varella or Mui Dinh. Then cross to the coast of Borneo, tacking as necessary to clear any reefs, and work along that coast and through Karimata Strait or Selat Gelasa to Sunda Strait.

11.43. Hong Kong to Singapore

11.43.01. In the North-east Monsoon, from October to March, steer to pass between Macclesfield Bank and Paracel Islands, and thence to pass E or W of Poulo Cecir de Mer and Îles Catwick. Thence, passing W of Charlotte Bank and Anambas Kepulauan, steer to make Pulau Aur.

Departing from Pulau Aur, bring it to bear about 360°, and steer S until Horsburgh Light is sighted.

When making the entrance to Singapore Strait, steer for Horsburgh Light, making allowance for the set of the stream, so as to pass from 1 to 2 miles N of it.

In slightly hazy weather, with Pulau Aur disappearing astern, bearing 360° or less, steer a course between 192° and 204° which may be requisite if the NE-going stream is setting out of Singapore Strait. The depths will decrease regularly in steering to the S, and the low land will probably be seen to the W when in depths of from 33 m to 37 m; if so, coast along it at a distance of about 13 miles, until Bukit Tautau is sighted. If in any doubt about the position, or if a depth of from 18 m to 22 m is obtained, either haul off the land or anchor.

Having made the entrance to Singapore Strait, proceed as directed in 10.39.02.

In March, during the latter part of this monsoon, the winds are steady from the E, the weather is settled and the current is weak. In April, the prevailing winds are also from the E, but are much lighter and accompanied by calms and squally weather; from the latter end of this month to about the middle of May the monsoon gradually breaks up.

Caution is necessary if the weather is thick, with a fresh breeze, when near Pulau Aur. In these circumstances, round to under its lee, and wait a convenient time to bear up for the strait. The current between this island and the E point of Bintan sets about SSE, by which it often happens that vessels leaving Pulau Aur steer too much to the S, and are swept with the current and the E-going stream coming out of Singapore Strait so far to the leeward of Bintan Island that they have been obliged to proceed round it, and come up through Riouw Strait. See 10.37.

11.43.02. In the South-west Monsoon, on leaving the S ports of China, or Manila, in March, April, and May, make for the passage between Palawan Island and the off-lying reefs, at a point in about 11° 30′ N, 118° 30′ E, and thence make SW through Palawan Passage, and then on a mean course roughly parallel with the coast of Borneo.

Pass through one of the passages through the S group of Natuna Kepulauan, and stand across to the entrance to Singapore Strait. Thence proceed as directed in 10.39.02.

When approaching Singapore Strait make sure of the landfall. Keep well to the S before closing Bintan Island, so as to allow for the current which sometimes runs to the N at the rate of 2 knots.

During the early part of the South-west Monsoon, if the wind is in the SW on leaving Hong Kong, a good passage may occasionally be made by standing to the SE as far as 15° 00′ N, 115° 30′ E. Thence pass SW of Macclesfield Bank, to Îles Catwick or Mui Dinh, and cross the Gulf of Thailand to Pulau Aur and thence to Singapore, as above.

From August to October, after leaving Hong Kong stand toward Hai-nan tao, which will be often fetched without tacking, as the wind frequently blows for days together from SE or E in that part of the China Sea; from thence cross the Gulf of Tongking to the Vietnam coast. Land and sea breezes and smooth water generally prevail close to that coast, for which reason work down as close to the shore as possible, taking advantage of every slant of wind, but being careful not to get too far off the land. It is sometimes possible to get as far to the S as Mui Dinh, in this way, but generally after passing Cap Varella the monsoon is found blowing very fresh, with frequent hard squalls out of the Gulf of Thailand rendering it impossible to work much to windward. From Cap Varella, or from Mui Dinh if a vessel has been able to fetch it, stretch away to the S, making a tack if necessary, to weather West Reef (*8° 51′ N, 112° 13′ E*) of London Reefs or other shoals, till the coast of Borneo is reached; work along this coast and proceed W through the S group of Natuna Kepulauan and to Singapore as directed for March, April, and May.

11.44. Hong Kong to Torres Strait

11.44.01. The usual route passes across the China Sea to make Lubang Island or Cape Calavite, and enters the Sulu Sea through Mindoro Strait (11.42 and 10.51) or, by passing E of Lubang Island, through Verde Island Passage (10.46.05) and Tablas Strait.

In either case, having passed through Cuyo East Pass, E of Sombrero Rocks, proceed S through the Sulu Sea to and through Basilan Strait into the Sulawesi Sea (10.47.06). Cross the Sulawesi Sea to Bangka Strait off the NE point of Sulawesi, passing through it into the Molukka Sea, and continue S, to enter the Ceram Sea between Sula Islands and Obi Major Island.

Cross the Ceram Sea and pass through Manipa Strait (10.50.04), into the Banda Sea. Having cleared Manipa Strait, steer SE to pass between Pulau-pulau Ewab and Tanimbar Islands, leaving Pulau Manuk to N or S as convenient.

Having passed Tanimbar Islands, the direct route to Torres Strait passes S of Pulau-pulau Aru and past False Cape, but this is not recommended owing to the dangers SW and S of Pulau-pulau Aru, and to the chain of known and unexamined dangers lying W from False Cape almost as far as 134° E. Instead, a vessel is recommended to keep to the SE from Tanimbar Islands to cross the meridian of 134° E in about 9° S, and proceed thence to Torres Strait.

In July and August, the alternative route for power vessels given in 7.161 may prove useful to sailing ships, after passing Obi Major.

11.44.02. An alternative route for the whole passage, which can be used from April to October, is given in 11.45.02.

11.45. Hong Kong to Port Darwin

11.45.01. From November to April, follow the directions given in 11.44.01 as far as Manipa Strait and then steer to the SSE to pass E of Pulau-pulau Penju (*5° 23′ S, 127° 47′ E*) and between Pulau Damar and Teun Island; thence pass between Sermata Island and Babar into the Arafura Sea. Proceed across the Arafura Sea to make Cape Fourcroy, the SW extremity of Bathurst Island, avoiding Flinders and other shoals near the route; thence proceed to Port Darwin. See Admiralty Sailing Directions for a description of the dangers in the approaches.

11.45.02. From April to October, steer across the China Sea and pass through Balintang Channel into the Pacific Ocean. Thence proceed SE to pass either side of Palau Islands, and make easting in the Equatorial Counter-current between 4° N, 8° N, until able to fetch through Solomon Islands with the South-east Trade, crossing the equator in about 158° E. After passing through Solomon Islands, steer to the W to Torres Strait via Great North-east Channel (11.09.03) and thence to Port Darwin.

From Palau Islands some navigators take St. George's Channel, between New Ireland and New Britain, see Admiralty Sailing Directions, instead of passing through Solomon Islands, or again. Pioneer Channel, between New Ireland and Solomon Islands, may be used.

11.46. Hong Kong to Sydney

11.46.01. In the South-west Monsoon, from April to September, four routes are available. Two pass into the Pacific Ocean and run E of Australia; the other two lead through the Eastern Archipelago and W and S of Australia.

Directions for the route which passes into the Pacific Ocean N of the Philippine Islands are given in 11.45 as far as the Coral Sea. Thence, steer S to join the route from Thursday Island (11.29) in about 15° S, 156° E.

For the Pacific Ocean route which passes S of the Philippine Islands, follow the directions given in 11.45 as far as the Sulawesi Sea, and thence enter the Pacific Ocean S of Mindanao, between Sarangani Islands and Kawio Islands. Thence make easting in the Equatorial Counter-current as directed in 11.45.02, and join the route, described above, S of Solomon Islands or St. George's Channel.

For the routes passing W and S of Australia, pass through the Eastern Archipelago either by the Eastern Route (10.50) or by the Central Route (10.51). On reaching the Indian Ocean proceed as directed in 10.121 to round Cape Leeuwin, and then as directed in 10.01.

11.46.02. In the North-east Monsoon, from October to February, proceed either via Torres Strait (11.44.01) or via Sunda Strait and a passage W and S of Australia (11.42.06 and 10.121).

11.47. Hong Kong to Manila

11.47.01. In the North-east Monsoon (October to April), make for the coast of Luzon at about Piedra Point, Cape Bolinao. The current sets strongly to leeward, but decreases near Luzon. From the latitude of Piedra Point, steer S for Manila Bay, giving the coast dangers a wide berth.

11.47.02. In the South-west Monsoon (May to September), take every advantage of the wind shifting to make southing towards Macclesfield Bank; then steer direct for Manila Bay.

11.47.03. Pratas Reef, lying in the route between Manila and Hong Kong, is a serious danger, especially in the North-east Monsoon, when strong gales and thick clouds are sometimes prevalent for weeks together; and as, in this monsoon, vessels generally approach the reef from SE, the greater number of wrecks have occurred on this side. See Admiralty Sailing Directions.

11.48. Hong Kong to Yokohama

11.48.01. During the North-east Monsoon (October to April) work up the coast of China as far as Lien-hua-feng-chiao, taking advantage of the fact that the wind hauls to the N at night and to the E during the day. From Lien-hua-feng-chiao (*22° 56′ N, 116° 30′ E*) stand across for the S end of T'ai-wan and work up on the E side of that island; a S'ly set will be felt until reaching O'luan pi, after passing which Kuro Shio will be experienced setting N. Continue N, to the W of Nansei Shotō as described below.

Towards the end of the North-east Monsoon, stand across the China Sea until near the coast of Luzon, where the wind will be more E'ly or even SE'ly, when tack and stand NNE along the E coast of T'ai-wan, and W of all the groups of Nansei Shotō, with generally a favourable current. Thence pass through one of the channels S of Ōsumi Kaikyō, and from 50 to 80 miles off the S coast of Japan in the strength of Kuro Shio, making the land about Omae Saki, to enter Uraga Suidō.

11.48.02. During the South-west Monsoon, run up the China coast as far as Tung-yin Shan (*26° 23′ N, 120° 32′ E*), thence steer to pass through Tokara Guntō S of Akuseki Shima (in preference to Ōsumi Kaikyō, where dense fogs will probably be found, whilst farther seaward in the warm waters of Kuro Shio the atmosphere is bright and clear). The course along the S coast of Japan is the same as in the North-east Monsoon.

11.49. Hong Kong to Nagasaki

11.49.01. During the North-east Monsoon, follow the directions for the Yokohama route (11.48.01) until N of T'ai-wan, after which continue as direct as navigation permits.

11.49.02. During the South-west Monsoon, follow the directions in 11.48.02 as far as Tung-yin Shan and thence take a direct course to Nagasaki.

11.50. Hong Kong northward, to ports on the coast of China

11.50.01. General remarks. Except in crossing T'ai-wan Strait, there is no difficulty in making this passage in the South-west Monsoon, but in the North-east Monsoon a sailing vessel should be in good condition for meeting rough weather and for carrying sail.

The crossing of T'ai-wan Strait is attended with considerable trouble at all times of the year, on account of the strong, variable, and sometimes opposite currents setting across the track. This is particularly noticeable at the change of monsoons. In the S and W parts of the strait, a strong drift current setting to leeward (in both monsoons) must be allowed for. See Admiralty Sailing Directions.

11.50.02. During the North-east Monsoon, make the passage either E of T'ai-wan so as to benefit from Kuro Shio and the diminished strength of the monsoon, and to avoid the heavy short sea of T'ai-wan Strait; or work up the coast of China taking advantage of every favourable change of wind and tidal stream, and anchor whenever possible, if conditions are unfavourable.

For the route E of T'ai-wan, work along the China coast as far as Lien-hua-feng chiao (*22° 56′ N, 116° 30′ E*) to maintain as long as practicable the advantage of the land wind at night, of smoother water, and of the E-going tidal stream out of the deep bays, which will generally be under the lee when on the starboard tack. There are numerous convenient anchorages should the wind blow too hard to make way. Keep within 10 miles of the land, to avoid being carried S by the monsoon drift current whilst standing off-shore; but as this cannot be done at night without risk, anchor, if possible, in the evening, and weigh between midnight and 0400, when the wind, generally being more off the land, allows a good board on the off-shore tack. From Lien-hua-feng chiao stand across to the S end of T'ai-wan, as by passing E of that island the heavy short sea of T'ai-wan Strait is avoided, as well as the constant S-going current.

After rounding the S end of T'ai-wan, off which there is generally a troublesome sea, make short tacks, if requisite, and keep within the influence of Kuro Shio.

The North-east Monsoon does not blow with its full strength on the E coast of T'ai-wan, but strong gales are often experienced 20 miles to the E. If the wind declines in strength, with less sea on the W'ly board (particularly between 0900 and 1500 or up to sunset), it is advantageous to hug the coast as close as prudent; but caution is requisite, for the coast is mountainous and steep-to, and sudden loss of wind accompanied by swell might be attended, if followed by calm, with imminent danger, as there are no harbours. Stronger winds, with much rain, are met as advance is made to the E during the North-east Monsoon. If an off-shore course is maintained whilst E of T'ai-wan a constant succession of bad weather may be expected, with strong winds and a heavy sea.

Towards the close of the North-east Monsoon, and still later, it is preferable to cross over towards Luzon than to beat up to Lien-hua-feng chiao (*22° 56′ N, 116° 30′ E*) against fresh NE breezes; therefore stand off on the port tack, clean full to the SE and pass through the SW-going current quickly, and on nearing Luzon, as the wind becomes more E'ly (sometimes even from SE), tack NNE with a strong favourable current and arrive E of T'ai-wan in less time than it would have taken to fetch Lien-hua-feng chiao by keeping along the coast of China.

Having weathered the N end of T'ai-wan, it is still advisable to keep well to the E, and not approach the coast of China until the parallel of 30° 30′ N is gained. In case of being driven to the W, take cautious advantage of the tidal streams through the S part of Chou-shan chün-tao.

Bound for Shan-t'ou chiang, Hsia-men, or the ports between that place and Min chiang, there is generally difficulty in getting round Lien-hua-feng chiao, for the tidal stream there is of no assistance. Advantage must therefore be taken of the wind, which will probably draw off the land after midnight, when, by being inshore, a good board can be made, and possibly Hao-wang chiao (*23° 14′ N, 116° 48′ E*) reached. For Hai-men wan and Ch'i-wang wan anchorages, see Admiralty Sailing Directions.

Having reached Hao wang chiao, the NE-going stream assists a vessel to round it, and the ebb out of Han chiang is a weather tide; if not going inside Nan-ao tao (*23° 24′ N, 117° 07′ E*) try to get along the S side of the island, and anchor in Yün-ao Wan, should the weather be too bad to proceed. Both streams are strong off Yen-tun yen, and also off Chou k'o-k'o Chiao (*23° 36′ N, 117° 27′ E*) in rounding which take the first of the NE-going stream and the port tack.

Farther N, about Li-shih liei-tao (*23° 46′ N, 117° 43′ E*), the NE-going stream with strong winds causes a very uneasy sea. Chiang chun-ao and Ting t'ai wan are good stopping places for small vessels; the latter should be preferred, though at the loss of 2 or 3 miles, to anchoring in an exposed position in Hsia-men harbour entrance, as when NE winds freshen there during the rising tide they are generally accompanied by a mist, which obscures the entrance, and the tidal stream makes it difficult to get to sea.

Wei-t'ou ao (*24° 30′ N, 118° 34′ E*), N of Hsia-men, affords good shelter; Shen-hu-wan is not so good. The current in the monsoon overcomes the tidal streams; and advantage must be taken of every slant of wind, bearing in mind that it is likely to draw off the land after midnight, and in the event of anchoring for shelter this is the time to start, should the wind moderate; by waiting for daylight vessels lose their offing, and have to make an off-shore board at a loss. The fog is at times thick and soundings must be taken, the bottom generally changing from sand to mud as the shore is approached. There is fair anchorage under Ta-tso chiao (*24° 53′ N, 118° 59′ E*), but not so good as that under South Yit (*25° 09′ N, 119° 30′ E*), and if the vessel is heading N or anything E of it, the ebb from Mei-chow wan is of assistance.

The most difficult part of the passage to Min Chiang is from Nan-jih tao, or the S end of Hai-t'an Hsia to Pai chuan lieh tao (*25° 58′ N, 119° 59′ E*); sailing vessels should keep outside Hai-t'an Hsia, and stretch over to the NW coast of T'ai-wan, where they have the advantage of a weather tidal stream.

Off the coast of China N of Min Chiang, the indraught during the rising tide must be considered.

There is good anchorage in a cove in the W island of Tung-yin shan (*26° 22′ N, 119° 29′ E*), but N of this sailing vessels (unless under 3 m 7 draught) must keep off the coast in deep water. The tidal streams afford but little assistance until Chuo-shan chün-tao is reached; the NE going stream causes an uneasy sea in the shallow water, while the SW-going stream has too much southing, unless the wind is well from E. Nan-chi Shan (*27° 28′ N, 121° 04′ E*), and Pei-chi-shan lieh-tao, about 10 miles to the NE, afford good shelter.

The route through the more S'ly channels of Chou-shan chün-tao is not usually taken by sailing ships. In working through the N part of this archipelago, advantage can be taken of the tidal streams.

The eddy tidal streams generally carry vessels clear of the large islands, but caution is required to prevent being set in amongst detached rocks.

11.50.03. During the South-west Monsoon, there is no difficulty in making the N-bound coastwise passage from Hong Kong, but the currents may be variable, see Admiralty Sailing Directions.

11.51. Hong Kong or Manila to North America and Panama

11.51.01. Routes. In all cases follow the Yokohama route (11.48) and then take the routes given from Yokohama onwards. References are 11.64 for Columbia River, Vancouver, or Prince Rupert, 11.65 for San Francisco, and, for Panama, 11.65 as far as 150° W; thence direct.

11.52. Hong Kong or Manila to west coast of South America

11.52.01. During the South-west Monsoon, (May to September), the passage may be made either through Bashi Channel or San Bernardino Strait.

If proceeding via Bashi Channel, continue as directed in 11.48 past Yokohama and make easting thence before standing S, joining a suitable route from Sydney (11.05) as convenient.

The Pacific Ocean may also be reached in the South-west Monsoon by San Bernardino Strait as described below. When clear of the strait, make easting to join the route from Bashi Channel as convenient; or steer to the NE until in the westerlies and then make easting as above.

A vessel intending the passage of San Bernardino Strait should approach it through Verde Island Passage and thence proceed to a position S of Marinduque Island. From this position steer to make the NW point of Masbate Island, to avoid being embayed with a SW wind in Nabasagan Bay on the W coast of Burias Island. A mid-channel course should be steered between Burias and Masbate, and when the SE point of Burias Island is passed steer a NE'ly course to pass N of Tikao Island, giving San Miguel Island, off the N point of Tikao a good berth on account of the strength of the tidal stream near it.

If the wind is settled, steer for Naranjo Islands, and thence pass midway between Kapul Island and the islands off the SE point of Luzon, proceeding out of the strait by the channel S of San Bernardino Islets.

If the SW wind is not settled, it is well to wait at anchor at San Jacinto, on the E side of Tikao, lest calms or light winds should leave the vessel at the mercy of the tides in the strait. The best time for leaving the port is at half-flood, for then a vessel is likely to get the first of the ebb when she is near Naranjo Islands.

If in danger of being carried near Kalantas Rock, it would be well to make for the coast of Luzon, where anchorage may be had, or to anchor on the bank in good time. The navigation of the strait requires great care, and an anchor should always be ready to let go.

11.52.02. During the North-east Monsoon (October to April), proceed as directed in 11.44.01 as far as the Sulawesi Sea, and then either take a route direct to the Pacific Ocean or to the Coral Sea by Torres Strait.

For the Pacific Ocean Route, cross the Sulawesi Sea to enter the Pacific S of Mindanao, and then steer to pass N of New Guinea and continue E between the parallels of 2° N and 4° N as far as Gilbert Islands. Thence steer SE into the westerlies to join a route from Sydney, see 11.05.

For the Torres Strait route, continue from the Sulawesi Sea as directed in 11.44.01, Hong Kong to Torres Strait. After clearing Torres Strait continue along the S coast of New Guinea and Louisade Archipelago until far enough E to cross the Trades into the westerlies to join a route from Sydney, see 11.05.

11.53. Shang-hai coastwise to the southward

11.53.01. During the North-east Monsoon (October to April) after passing Ma-an lieh-tao and Tung-fu shan (the most E'ly island of Chou-shan chün-tao), steer a good offshore course, passing outside the outer islands, giving them a good berth at night, and closing the land for a fix by day, if necessary; for thick, hazy or rainy weather may always be expected.

11.53.02. During the South-west Monsoon, (May to September), although the constant adverse current makes this a tedious passage, a vessel of moderate sailing qualities can do it, as this monsoon is not steady in its direction, and land and sea breezes prevail.

Fog is frequent in the early part of the season, and renders caution necessary; it sometimes lifts near the land.

11.54. Shang-hai to Indian Ocean

11.54.01. During the North-east Monsoon, take the coastwise route towards Hong Kong (11.53.01) and pick up a route to the Indian Ocean (11.42), proceeding either via Singapore or direct through the Eastern Archipelago.

11.54.02. During the South-west Monsoon, steer direct for a position in 15° N, 132° E, to the E of the Philippine Islands, to pick up the route described in 11.68.02, Yokohama to the Indian Ocean.

11.55. Shang-hai to Nagasaki

11.55.01. Caution is necessary in the vicinity of Socotra Rock (*32° 07′ N, 125° 11′ E*), which lies on the route. See Admiralty Sailing Directions.

11.55.02. During the North-east Monsoon (October to March), with the wind E of N, make northing at once, taking advantage of the tidal streams. As advance is made to the N, the wind usually draws round through N to NW. Make allowance for the current, which then sets to the SE or E.

11.55.03. In the South-west Monsoon (March to September), during the E'ly and SE'ly winds which prevail from March to June, make easting or southing, even when a fair wind occurs, for it is sure to be of short duration; and the tendency of the prevailing wind being to keep a vessel on the starboard tack, there is always a probability, during these months, when the current sets to the NE, of being set towards the Korean Archipelago. If uncertain of the position when near Me Shima, in Danjo Guntō, Tori Shima, or Gotō Rettō, make these islands in daylight.

After June, with a steady South-west Monsoon and a fair wind, steer from the estuary of Ch'ang Chiang a course to pass between Danjo Guntō and Tori Shima.

The direct course from Chiku Chiao leads midway between Tori Shima and Gotō Rettō; but it should not be taken, as the branch of Kuro Shio, which sets through Korea Strait, has to be crossed, and vessels have been carried by it even N of the S end of Gotō Rettō.

11.56. Shang-hai to Yokohama

11.56.01. During the North-east Monsoon (October to March), if the wind on departure is to the E of N, as it frequently is in the monsoon, make northing; and when the wind draws round to the NW, steer as directly as possible round the S end of Japan; and thence in the strength of Kuro Shio.

11.56.02. In the South-west Monsoon (May to September), make easting or southing as directed in 11.55.02, and then proceed direct round the S end of Japan and in the strength of Kuro Shio.

11.57. Shang-hai to ports in North America

11.57.01. Routes. Proceed as directed in 11.56 to Yokohama, and then as directed in 11.64 to Columbia River, Vancouver, or Prince Rupert; or 11.65 to San Francisco.

ROUTES FROM MANILA

For routes from Manila to ports in North or South America, see 11.51, 11.52.

11.58. Manila to Singapore

11.58.01. Route. In all seasons, steer to pass N of the central dangers of the China Sea for Îles Catwick, thence proceed direct to Pulau Aur and to Singapore. See directions for Hong Kong to Singapore, in 11.43.01.

11.59. Manila to Saïgon

11.59.01 In the North-east Monsoon (October to March) take a direct passage across the China Sea, allowing for the current which sets with the wind.

11.59.02. In the South-west Monsoon (April to September), sailing vessels will find the voyage long and trying whichever route they adopt. The following route has been recommended:—On leaving Manila Bay take Verde Island Passage, pass down the E side of Mindoro Island and the W coast of Panay Island, cross the Sulu Sea passing out by Balabac Strait, and work down the NW coast of Borneo to make westing; then cross the China Sea passing E of Natuna Kepulauan.

11.60. Manila to Hong Kong or Hsia-men

11.60.01. In the North-east Monsoon, there is a choice between two routes, W or E of T'ai-wan, if bound for Hsia-men; to Hong Kong proceed as directed in 11.34.02.

For the passage W of T'ai-wan, keep near the coast to Cape Bojeador, and then work N to O-luan Pi (*21° 54' N, 120° 51' E*), and thence along the SW and W coasts of T'ai-wan until able to stand across T'ai-wan Strait to Hsia-men.

For the passage E of T'ai-wan, if the monsoon is well set in, it might be advisable to stand to the E, N of Luzon, and work to the N with the benefit of Kuro Shio, passing E of, and round the N of, T'ai-wan. Thence, allowing for current, steer to make the China coast N of the destination.

11.60.02. In the South-west Monsoon, proceed direct, making allowance for a lee current.

11.61. Manila to Iloilo

11.61.01. In the North-east Monsoon (October to March), pass through Verde Island Passage and Tablas Strait, and continue S along the W coast and round the S end of Panay Island to Iloilo.

H

11.61.02. In the South-west Monsoon (April to September), proceed as above as far Dumali point (*13° 07′ N, 121° 34′ E*), and then steer to pass S of Simara Island and between Tablas Island and Romblon Island. Thence pass through Jintotolo Channel between Jintotolo Island and Zapatos Islands, and then, turning S, proceed along the E coast of Panay to Iloilo.

11.62. Manila to Cebu

11.62.01. Route. In both monsoons, take the South-west Monsoon route for Iloilo (11.61.02) as far as Jintotolo Island, and then proceed to Malapascua Island and thence S to Cebu.

11.63. Manila to Indian Ocean and Australia

11.63.01. In the North-east Monsoon (October to March), follow the directions in 11.58 to Singapore, and then take the appropriate route onward, see Chapter 10.

If not calling at Singapore and bound to the S through the Eastern Archipelago, proceed, after passing Îles Catwick (11.41.01) between Anambas Kepulauan and Natuna Kepulauan, and thence as directed in Chapter 10, joining the route from Singapore for the passage onward through the Indian Ocean.

11.63.02. In the South-west Monsoon (April to September), proceed as directed in 11.44.01 as far as the Sulawesi Sea, and thence either continue on the Central Route from the China Sea to the Indian Ocean, see 11.42.04, or cross the Sulawesi Sea to pass through Bangka Strait, off the NE end of Sulawesi, into the Molukka Sea. Thence continue S to the Ceram Sea, Manipa Strait and Banda Sea, to Ombai Strait and the Indian Ocean.

In both cases join the route described in 10.57.11 if bound to the Cape of Good Hope; or if bound to other ports join, or steer to join as directly as possible the appropriate route from Singapore.

To Torres Strait follow the directions given in 11.44.01 from Verde Island Passage onwards.

An alternative route to the E coast of Australia is to pass into the Pacific Ocean through San Bernardino Strait (11.52.01). Thence proceed SE, making easting until able to cross the equator in about 158° E, and pass through Solomon Islands; thence continue onward to the S to join the route from Thursday Island to Sydney (11.29) in about 15° S, 156° E.

ROUTES FROM JAPAN

11.64. Yokohama to Columbia River, Vancouver, or Prince Rupert

11.64.01. Route. Cross 167° E in about 42° N, being about 30 miles N of that position in August and the same distance S of it in January. From this position, steer almost due E, with a fair wind and favourable current, so as to cross the meridian of 150° W in about 44° N, keeping a little to the N throughout the voyage during the summer, and to the S in the winter. From 150° W proceed direct to destination, still with a fair wind.

11.64.02. The tidal streams, on the approach to the coast of Vancouver Island, cause a general set towards the land, and an indraught on the flood into all sounds. Sailing vessels, therefore, when making Juan de Fuca Strait during the winter especially during November and December, and experiencing E'ly and SE'ly winds, which then prevail, should try to hold a position SW of Tatoosh Island, and on no account to open up the entrance to the strait until an opportunity occurs of getting well inside. See Admiralty Sailing Directions.

11.65. Yokohama to San Francisco

11.65.01. From April to September, follow the directions in 11.64 as far as 44° N, 150° W, and thence proceed as directly as possible to San Francisco.

11.65.02. From October to March, winter conditions demand a more S'ly though rather longer route. First steer to cross the meridian of 165° E in 40° N, and thence along that parallel as far as 140° W or 135° W; thence proceed direct to San Francisco.

11.66. Yokohama to Honolulu

11.66.01. Route. Steer to cross the meridian of 160° E in 41° 30′ N, of 180° in 43° 30′ N, and of 160° W in 40° N; thence keep to the SE to a position in 35° N, 153° W, and thence proceed direct to Honolulu, making allowance, on approaching the land, for a W-going current running at the rate of about 1 knot.

11.67. Yokohama to Singapore

11.67.01. From October to April, proceed first to pass S of Tanega Shima and through Tokara Kaikyō, between the N end of Tokara Guntō and the S end of Osumi Guntō; thence steer to the SW to join the coastwise route from Shang-hai to the S (11.53), in about 28° N.

11.67.02. From May to September, two routes are appropriate, W and E of the Philippine Islands. For the former, pass E of all the groups of Nansei Shotō, and thence through Bashi Channel. From Bashi Channel make for Îles Catwick and thence to Pulau Aur.

The passage from Pulau Aur to Singapore is described in 11.43.01, Hong Kong to Singapore.

For the passage E of the Philippine Islands, first steer to the S passing to the E of Nanpō Shotō, the chain of islands lying S of the SE point of Honshū. Thence make to the SSW for Djailolo Passage, passing about 300 miles E of the Philippine Islands. Then pass S through the Ceram Sea and Manipa Strait into the Banda Sea; thence W through the Flores Sea and the Java Sea; and finally N through one of the straits between Sumatra and Borneo to Singapore.

Directions for the straits and seas of the Eastern Archipelago are given in Chapter 10.

11.68. Yokohama to Indian Ocean

11.68.01. From October to April, follow the directions in 11.67.01 to Singapore; then proceed to the Indian Ocean through either Malacca Strait or Sunda Strait.

If not calling at Singapore, proceed as above, but after passing Îles Catwick, pass between Anambas Kepulauan and Natuna Kepulauan to Selat Gelasa or Karimata Strait and thence to Sunda Strait. See Chapter 10.

11.68.02. From May to September, either take the route W of the Philippine Islands described in 11.67.01, calling at Singapore or otherwise, as for October to April; or follow the route E of the Philippine Islands (11.67.02), leaving it as necessary to enter the Indian Ocean through one of the straits between Ombai Strait and Sunda Strait. See Chapter 10.

11.69. Yokohama to Sydney

11.69.01. Direct route in North-east Monsoon. Steer to cross 160° E in 20° N, and thence to cross the equator in 168° E. Thence steer to pass E of the New Hebrides and New Caledonia, and thence direct to Sydney, passing N of Middleton Reef.

Alternatively, after crossing the equator, pass between the Solomon Islands and Santa Cruz Islands, and then W of Bampton Reefs; and thence proceed to Sydney, making the Australian coast S of Sandy Cape and thence continue S along the coast.

11.69.02. Direct route in South-west Monsoon. First make easting N of 35° N until in about 170° E; thence stand S through the North-east Trade to cross the equator in 173° E. Thence pass E of the New Hebrides and of New Caledonia, and thence to Sydney as in 11.69.01.

11.69.03. Routes via Guam. If intending to call at Guam, steer to the S, passing E of Nanpō Shotō, and E or W of the Marianas, according to conditions prevailing at the time.

From Guam proceed as follows according to Monsoon.

In the North-east Monsoon, make southing with the North-east Trade, and pass through Bougainville Strait, or between Solomon Islands and Santa Cruz Islands.

From Bougainville Strait proceed to a position in about 15° S, 156° E to join the route from Thursday Island to Sydney described in 11.29. From the position E of Solomon Islands, proceed as in the alternative route in 11.69.01.

In the South-east Monsoon, pass Solomon Islands as above and make enough easting to ensure a long board across the Coral Sea; make, and keep along the Australian coast S of Sandy Cape, where the prevailing wind will be found to be W'ly at this time of the year.

11.70. Yokohama to Hong Kong, Hsia-men, etc.

11.70.01. During the North-east Monsoon (October to March), stand to the SW across Kuro Shio as far as 28° N, 135° E, thence N of Tokuno Shima (27° 45' N, 129° 00' E), one of Amami Guntō, and after passing Tori Shima (27° 50' N, 128° 15' E) steer for Tung-yin Shan (26° 22' N, 119° 29' E) and down the coast of China.

11.70.02. During the South-west Monsoon (April to September), steer SE from Uraga Suidō to cross the parallel of 30° N in about 145° E. Thence passing E of Ogasawara Guntō and E and S of Kazan Rettō, cross the meridian of 140° E in 21° N. Thence shape a direct course to pass N of Luzon and straight to Hong Kong, making allowance for the NE-going set in the China Sea.

11.71. Yokohama to Shang-hai

11.71.01. Routes. It was formerly recommended that the best sailing route was through Naikai (Inland Sea), avoiding the strength of Kuro Shio by keeping near the coast between Yokohama and Kü Suidō, and sailing as direct as possible after passing through Kanmon Kaikyō and Korea Strait.

H*

Owing to traffic and other factors, the route through Naikai is probably no longer feasible without detailed local knowledge. Either a coastwise route S of Japan and through Osumi Kaikyō, taking advantage of local counter-currents, see Admiralty Sailing Directions, or an ocean route S of the strongest part Kuro Shio, seem preferable.

11.72. Yokohama to Hakodate

11.72.01. Winter route. In winter (November to March) make the passage as close inshore as safety will allow, as the wind is usually off the land and there is smooth water near the coast. In the event of encountering a NE gale, the best course is to make for the nearest sheltered anchorage, if any such is available. The frequent snow-storms often obscuring the land, and the irregularity of the currents, render it necessary to use every precaution when navigating this part of the coast.

11.72.02. Summer route. In summer (May to September) keep offshore and take advantage of Kuro Shio. Fogs will usually be met with when as far N as Kinkasan. Close the land to the S of Shiriya Saki and round that promontory at a distance of not less than 2 miles to avoid Ō Ne. (41° 26′ N, 141° 27′ E).

In thick weather, when the land about Shiriya Saki has not been seen, a rise in the temperature of the water, the presence of floating debris such as plants, trees and driftwood in the sea, or heavy tide rips, may assist in determining that the vessel is to the N of Shiriya Saki and in the influence of the E-going current through Tsugaru Kaikyō.

If proceeding direct for Hakodate from the E entrance to Tsugaru Kaikyō, a vessel may, after passing 5 miles off Shiriya Saki steer for Esan Misaki, so as to take advantage of the cold W-going stream along the S coast of Hokkaidō, remembering that the NE-going current is sometimes found close inshore near Shiokubi Saki.

11.72.03. Directions for Tsugaru Kaikyō. Approaching Tsugaru Kaikyō from E, the adverse current will be avoided by keeping near the shore, giving Ō Ne and the dangers off Ōma Saki a berth.

Make Shiriya Saki bearing about 310°, and pass it at a distance of not less than 2 miles; when N of it, keep towards the S shore to avoid the current and to be in a position to anchor if becalmed. By keeping towards this shore, a vessel may possibly be drifted for a considerable distance by the W-going stream, while the NE-going current is running strongly in the middle of the strait.

Wait at anchor SE of Ōma Saki for a favourable opportunity to cross the strait, and as the winds during summer are generally light from the SW for a considerable period, freshening a little when the W-going stream makes, this is the proper time to weigh.

Proceeding from Hakodate to the W, against SW'ly winds, keep near the shore when N of Yagoshi Misaki, and if unable to round it, anchor with a kedge about 2 miles NE of it, weighing again when the next W-going stream makes.

With a light wind a sailing vessel might not clear the strait in one tide, in which case it would be better to wait at anchor, E of Shirakami Misaki, and take the whole of the following tide to get sufficiently to the W rather than run any risk of being swept back through the strait by the current.

Approaching Tsugaru Kaikyō from SW during foggy weather, guard against being carried by the current to the N past the entrance; if the weather is clear when nearing Nyūdō Saki, it might be as well to sight it.

If the weather thickens when nearing Nyūdō Saki, good though open anchorage over a sandy bottom will be found to the S of it; but to the N the bottom is rocky though anchorage is still possible.

For currents, tidal streams, and ice, see Admiralty Sailing Directions.

Sailing vessels, passing through Tsugaru Kaikyō, particularly to the W, should have a kedge anchor and 300 metres of hawser ready for immediate use, and keep the shore close aboard.

11.73. Nagasaki to China coast

11.73.01. Routes. For Shang-hai, steer as direct a course as circumstances will allow, keeping rather to windward of the course as, except near the coast of Japan, the drift of the current is usually to leeward. Give Socotra Rock (11.55.01) a good berth.

For Hong Kong, Hsia-men, Swatow and ports in the vicinity, in the North-east Monsoon (October to April), steer to make the coast of China a little S of Chou-shan chün-tao, and thence sail coastwise. In the South-west Monsoon (May to September), first stand across to the coast of China and thence make to the S, coastwise.

ROUTES FROM ISLANDS IN NORTH PACIFIC OCEAN

11.74. General notes and cautions. When navigating in the Pacific Ocean, particularly amongst the islands, attention is directed to the notes and cautions in 11.01.01 and 11.01.02, as well as to the notes on navigation in coral waters in *The Mariner's Handbook*.

The notes on Winds, Weather, Currents, and Ice in Chapter 7 and in Admiralty Sailing Directions should be consulted.

In this sub-section only the routes from Honolulu are given in detail. From other islands of the North Pacific Ocean, the most favourable route to be taken can be ascertained by consulting World Climatic Charts (5301, 5302); charts of Sailing Ship Routes (5308), and Tracks followed by sailing and auxiliary powered vessels (5309); as well as the Routeing Charts (5127–5128).

11.75. North Pacific islands (except Hawaii), to Asia or North and South America. Chart 5308 shows that little difficulty will be experienced in deciding on the most profitable route for a vessel W-bound to any port in Asia, the Eastern Archipelago, the Indian Ocean, or Japan; a number of routes from North or South America and from Australia pass near the islands and can be joined at a convenient position.

For a vessel bound to the E, the general principle is to stand N, or S, through the Trade Winds to reach the belt of W'ly winds as quickly as possible; a favourable current may be expected in the area of W'ly winds. E-bound passages across the Pacific Ocean that may conveniently be joined are given in 11.64 and 11.65 from Yokohama, and 11.05 from Sydney; or, by making to the S across the routes from Sydney, to join the route across the South Pacific described in 11.02.

11.76. North Pacific islands (except Hawaii) to other North Pacific islands. W-bound, no difficulty should be experienced as a fair wind should be carried and, except in the Equatorial Counter-current (*4° N to 8° N*), a favourable current should assist the passage.

Proceeding E-bound to Honolulu, stand N through the Trade Winds as far as about 40° N or until the W'ly winds are met. Cross the 180th meridian in about 43° N, and 160° W in 40° N; thence keep SE to a position in about 35° N, 153° W, and thence proceed direct to Honolulu. See the directions from Yokohama given in 11.66.

To other North Pacific islands the direct mean course can be steered over short distances, but this usually means working E against the North Equatorial Current.

In most cases, it is probably best to stand S or SE into the Equatorial Counter-current, and thence work E until able to fetch the destination, making allowance for a W-going set as the vessel makes to the N.

11.77. North Pacific islands to South Pacific islands or to Sydney. The longitude of most of the principal island groups of the South Pacific Ocean is E, or little or nothing to the W, of that of similar groups of the North Pacific Ocean (except the Hawaii Islands). Therefore the first objective, in all passages, must be to make easting while still N of the equator which is usually crossed between 168° E and 173° E. Probably the most advantageous passage to reach this objective is to stand S, or as much to the SE as can be made on the port tack, until the region of the Equatorial Counter-current is reached (between 4° N, and 8° N); then work E until able to stand across the equator as stated above. From the equator proceed S as follows:

Bound to Solomon islands, New Hebrides or New Caledonia proceed direct.

Bound to Sydney, follow the relevant directions in 11.69 from Yokohama.

Bound to Fiji, pass down the W side of Ellice Islands and then direct.

Bound to Samoa, stand S as far as the latitude of the Fijian Islands if necessary, weathering them if possible until able to make Samoa on the starboard tack.

Bound to islands E of Samoa, it is best to stand S through the Trade Winds into the westerlies; then run down easting until the meridian of the island to which bound is reached. Then re-enter the Trades and proceed to destination.

11.78. North Pacific islands to Torres Strait. At all times of the year the route E of New Guinea may be taken, following generally the directions in 11.45.02 modified as necessary, as far as the equator, in accordance with the position of the island of departure, e.g., from the E or W groups of islands.

In the North-east Monsoon season (October to April) as good, or even a better passage may be made by steering direct to pass through Djailolo Passage and joining the route from Hong Kong (11.44.01) in the Ceram Sea.

11.79. General remarks on winds, currents, and sailing passages around Hawaiian Islands. With regard to winds, the E'ly Trade Winds seem to divide at Cape Kumukahi, part following the coast to the NW around Upolu Point, where it loses its force, the other part following the SE coast around Cape Ka Lae, where it also loses its force.

On the W coast of Hawaii the sea breeze sets in about 0900 and continues until after sunset, when the land breeze springs up.

Sailing vessels coming from the W, bound to ports on the windward or SE side of Hawaii, should pass close to Upolu Point and keep near the coast, as the wind is generally much lighter than offshore. Those from the W, bound to ports on the E side of Hawaii should keep well to the N until clear of Alenuihaha Channel.

On account of the current, which nearly always sets to the N along the W coast of Hawaii, it is advisable for sailing vessels to make the land S of their port, as during calms and light airs a vessel is liable to drift to the N.

With regard to navigation, Alenuihaha Channel, between Hawaii and Maui and Kahoolawe Islands, is 26 miles wide and clear of dangers. The North-east Trade Wind, which predominates throughout the year, frequently blows through the channel with great strength, and there is also a strong current setting W; but, during calms, there is at times an E-going set of about 1 knot which during "kona" winds (reversals of the Trade Wind) may increase to 2 or 3 knots.

Vessels from any of the W'ly ports of Hawaii are therefore recommended to keep close in under the lee of the island until reaching Upolu Point, when they will be enabled to fetch across to Alalakeiki Channel on the W side of Maui. Those from the N, bound to Hilo, will probably find it impossible to weather Upolu Point from the W side of Maui, but on getting under the lee of Hawaii the Trade Wind fails until reaching the S point of the island, when they will have to beat against wind and current along the SE coast.

11.80. Honolulu to Tahiti. Stand first to the N of the Hawaiian Islands, and then make easting in the North-east Trade, cross the equator well to the E, and then proceed SW in the South-east Trade to Tahiti.

11.81. Honolulu to Fiji, Australia, and New Zealand. For Fiji, proceed as directly as navigation permits, with a fair Trade Wind.

For Australia and New Zealand, take the above route to Fiji, and then follow the directions in 11.19 and 11.20 to Australia or New Zealand, but leave the route to Fiji in about 170° W to 175° W, and proceed direct in the latter case.

Except when bound to Auckland, owing to the prevalence of W'ly winds off the New Zealand coast, it is best to pass down the W coast of New Zealand, and through Cook Strait for ports in North Island (if conditions are favourable) or round South Island and N along the E coast.

11.82. Honolulu to China, Japan, or Philippine Islands. The routes described in articles 11.92 to 11.95, from San Francisco to these destinations, pass close S of Hawaii, and should be picked up at any convenient position between 160° W and 170° W.

11.83. Honolulu to San Francisco. Throughout the year, first steer due N before turning E on reaching the steady W'ly winds. The turning point varies in latitude, being farthest N in August and farthest S in November and December. The ensuing routes are roughly as follows:

In August, turn E in approximately 40° N, and steer along that parallel to 150° W. Thence proceed direct to destination.

In June and July, turn to the NE in 35° N to 36° N, and steer on a slightly curving course to cross 150° W in approximately 39° N, and then proceed direct.

In May, September, and October, turn to the NE in about 30° N, and steer on a curving course to cross 150° W in 37½° N to 38° N, and then proceed direct.

In March and April, turn to the NE in 26° N to 27° N, and steer on a curving course to cross 150° W in about 36½° N, and then proceed direct.

In January and February, turn to the NE in 25° N to 26° N, and steer on a curving course to cross 150° W in about 33° N, and then proceed direct.

In November and December, turn to the NE in about 24° N, and steer on a curving course to cross 150° W in 32° N to 32½° N, and then proceed direct.

Note: The curving course referred to above can best be understood by referring to Chart 5308.

11.84. Honolulu to North and Central America between San Francisco and Panama. Proceed N as directed in 11.83, but turn E instead of NE. Make easting as directly as possible, gradually altering course to ESE after reaching 150° W to 140° W, depending on destination, the latter to the more S'ly ports. Join the route from San Francisco (11.98) at a convenient position.

11.85. Honolulu to west coast of South America or to Cabo de Hornos. The most important objective must be to make easting as soon as possible so as to be able to stand SE to join one of the routes from San Francisco to South American ports (11.99 or 11.100) or the route from San Francisco to Cabo de Hornos (11.101). In any case it appears advisable to join these routes N of the equator, where the Equatorial Counter-current is available if getting too far W on the passage S.

ROUTES FROM PRINCE RUPERT, VANCOUVER, OR COLUMBIA RIVER

11.86. Prince Rupert, Vancouver or Columbia River to Honolulu and Yokohama. From Prince Rupert, stand S through Hecate Strait, and from Juan de Fuca Strait or Astoria, Columbia River, stand seaward to make a safe offing, but keeping as close inshore as prudence dictates, to avoid the heavy seas experienced farther out. Proceed S until within about 300 miles NW of San Francisco, and thence proceed direct to Honolulu. W of Honolulu, the route is seasonal.

From May to November, get on to the parallel of 20° N, and run W on it as far as the meridian of 180°. Thence steer to cross the meridian of 160° E in 25° N, and thence for Yokohama, allowing for the NE-going set of Kuro Shio.

During the winter, from December to April, a vessel may have to keep farther S to get the strength of the Trade Wind for the run to the W after leaving Honolulu. The directions given in 11.92, from San Francisco, should be followed, according to date, after running to the W.

An alternative route for all seasons is to make SW from Honolulu to join one of the seasonal routes from San Francisco to Yokohama. See 11.92.

11.87. Prince Rupert, Vancouver or Columbia River to Sydney. From Prince Rupert, stand S until reaching the North-east Trade Wind, passing on either side of Queen Charlotte Group.

From Juan de Fuca Strait, or from Astoria, Columbia River, stand SW at once to pick up the Trade Wind.

Then proceed as directly as possible, crossing the equator in about 170° W, and passing W of the Fiji Islands and SE of New Caledonia, from June to August, but at other times of the year, crossing the equator between 150° W and 155° W, and passing S of the Tongan and Fijian island groups. Make the Australian coast S of Sandy Cape. See 11.69.

11.88. Prince Rupert, Vancouver or Columbia River to San Francisco and South America. The following route differs in some degree from the route recommended by the United States Naval Oceanographic Office, which will be found in 11.99 to 11.101, routes from San Francisco to South American ports.

For San Francisco, at all seasons keep as near the shore as is prudent, in order to avoid the heavy sea felt farther out.

For South American ports, from October to March SW'ly winds prevail on the coast of California as far S as about 25° N. If bound from Vancouver to Valparaiso in this season stand down the coast, keeping at about 100 miles from it until near the latitude of San Francisco, and from thence pass W of, and in sight of, Isla Guadalupe (*29° 11′ N, 118° 17′ W*), where in all probability the North-east Trade Wind will be met with; then steer to sight Clipperton Island (*10° N, 109′ W*), passing W of it; in about this latitude the North-east Trade Wind will be lost.

The belt of variable winds and calms, which at this season, on the meridian of 120° W, is 250 to 350 miles wide, will here be entered, and it may not be possible to cross the equator much to windward of 118° W. Every effort should be made not to cross farther than that to the W, as the result would be that the vessel would not weather Henderson Island or Pitcairn Island, in the vicinity of which light baffling winds from S to SE would be experienced.

In all probability at this time of year the South-east Trade Wind will be met between 5° N and 3° N; the higher latitude during the early winter (November and December), and the lower latitude towards March, when the ship should be kept full, making, as nearly as the wind will permit, a course of 180°.

In about 6° S the Trade Winds generally become more E'ly in direction, sometimes hauling N of E. Cross the parallel of 20° S in 124° W, and the parallel of 35° S on the meridian of 120° W; thence cross the meridians of 110° W in 39° S, 100° W in 40° S, 90° W in 39° S and thence proceed direct, S of Isla Robinson Crusoe to Valparaiso. From Valparaiso to Callao steer N along the coast. Calms and variable winds will be experienced in the vicinity of 30° S, settling into the NW quarter as the vessel gets more to the S. See also 11.99.

For South American ports from April to September, a course farther W may be pursued, passing the latitude of San Francisco in about 129° W. Thence keep farther from the land to avoid the calms and light variable winds experienced at this season along the coast of lower California and in the Gulf of Panama. After meeting the North-east Trade Wind in about 30° N, 127° W, stand to the S on or near the meridian of 125° W, not only to avoid the calms above mentioned, but also the hurricanes which during August and September are liable to be met with E of that meridian. Occasionally, but rarely, these storms are met with W of 125° W.

The North-east Trade Wind will be lost at this season in 11° N or 12° N, and the belt of doldrums will be found to be not so wide as during the winter. The South-east Trade Wind will, at this season, be met with in about 8° N, and if, as is most likely to be the case at first, the wind be well to the S, stand to the E in order to recover some of the ground lost by keeping farther W in the North-east Trades. Try to cross the equator in between 118° W and 120° W, and soon after crossing, the wind will haul more to the E, when stand to the S to weather Ducie Island and reach the parallel of 40° S before making easting, so as to fall in with the NW'ly winds, as calms and variable winds are met with N of that parallel. After passing the meridian of 90° W haul up for Isla Robinson Crusoe and thence for Valparaiso.

ROUTES FROM SAN FRANCISCO

11.89. San Francisco to Prince Rupert, Juan de Fuca Strait or Columbia River. From November to April, during the bad weather season, the vessel should at once be taken well out to sea. This will be easy, as the wind comes most often from NW. When far enough off to have nothing to fear from SW'ly or NW'ly winds, make as much northing as possible. To the N of the parallel of Cape Mendocino, SW'ly winds prevail, enabling vessels to finish the voyage without difficulty, but the land should be made 20 to 30 miles S of the port.

From April to November, the fine weather season, the wind almost invariably blows from between NW and NE. After leaving San Francisco run about 200 miles off-shore, and then make to the N, profiting by every shift of wind, and always standing on the most favourable tack. It would be well not to approach the land until up to the parallel of the port unless the vessel can fetch her port, or nearly so without tacking. If bound to Prince Rupert it would be well not to approach the land until nearly abreast Langara Island, at the NW extreme of Queen Charlotte Island. Hecate Strait, between Queen Charlotte island and the mainland, may also be taken.

11.90. San Francisco to Unimak pass, Aleutian Islands, and reverse. From San Francisco to Unimak Pass, the tracks for sailing vessels recommended by the United States Pilot charts for May until October are as follows:

In May and June, make W from San Francisco to 145° W, and thence proceed direct to Unimak Pass.

In July, August, and September, continue to 155° W before turning to the N. Similarly, in October continue to 158° W.

From Unimak Pass to San Francisco proceed as directly as possible.

11.91. San Francisco to Honolulu. At all times of the year the route to China and Japan passes closely S of the Hawaiian Islands, and is therefore nearly directly for Honolulu. On leaving San Francisco run to the SW for the North-east Trades; from June to December clear the coast as soon as possible, steering about 266° to avoid the calms E of 128° W. Near the Hawaiian Islands the Trades may possibly veer to E or even SE, particularly from October to May; approach the land from ENE, when all local winds will be fair. When making a landfall remember that the currents often run at the rate of 20 miles per day, and that calms and baffling winds are common to leeward of the islands.

See General remarks on winds, currents and sailing passages around the Hawaiian Islands in 11.79.

11.92. San Francisco to Yokohama. Proceed as directed in 11.91 but pass S of Hawaii. Then stand to the W between the parallels of 15° N and 20° N, being to the N in the summer, and to the S in the winter. On reaching the meridian of 160° E, proceed as follows:

From January to April, stand on to the W on the former course, until reaching the meridian of 150° E, and then curve gradually round to the WNW, NW, and finally N; pass about 60 miles to the W of Ogasawara Guntō and W of the other islands of Nanpō Shotō on a N'ly course to destination.

In May and June, make to the WNW at once, so as to cross the meridian of 150° E between 23° N and 24° N; thence proceed direct to destination, passing about 200 miles E of Ogasawara Guntō.

From July to December, leave the track across the Pacific Ocean in 163° E instead of 160° E, and set a course as directly as possible to Yokohama.

Alternatively, some navigators recommend standing for Yokohama on reaching the 180th meridian; but this is not a very usual practice.

At all times of the year, allowance must be made for Kuro Shio, setting across the track during the latter part of the voyage.

11.93. San Francisco to north part of China Sea. Follow the directions given in 11.92 as far as 160° E, and then stand slightly to the N to clear the most N'ly of the Mariana or Ladrone Islands, and then pass through Bashi Channel to destination. For an alternative route in the North-east Monsoon see 11.60.01. See also 11.95 for the passage via Manila.

11.94. San Francisco to Shang-hai or Nagasaki. Follow the directions given in 11.93 across the Pacific Ocean, but on arriving in about 135° E, make as directly as possible for either destination.

11.95. San Francisco to South China Sea. From October to March, in the North-east Monsoon, follow the directions given in 11.93 as far as Bashi Channel, and then proceed S along the W coast of Luzon if bound for Manila. For Saïgon, proceed direct across the China Sea allowing for the current which sets with the wind. For Singapore, proceed as directed in 11.67.01.

From April to September, in the South-west Monsoon, leave the W-bound track (11.92) across the Pacific Ocean in 160° E, and steer to cross the meridian of 150° E in 15° N. Thence, passing S of the Mariana or Ladrone Islands, stand directly for San Bernardino Strait or for Surigao Strait; and thence through the Philippine Islands for Manila, Iloilo, etc.

From Mindoro Strait or Verde Island Passage proceed as directed in 11.58 for Singapore, 11.59 for Saigon, or 11.60 for Hong Kong or Hsia-men.

11.96. San Francisco to Australian ports south of Brisbane. The routes usually followed are seasonal, after taking a direct course from San Francisco through the North-east Trade to about 10° N, 145° W. Thence, in June, July, and August, steer a direct course passing N of Fiji Islands and S of New Caledonia to Brisbane or, making the coast S of Sandy Cape, to Sydney. From Sydney, continue S as directed in 10.60, 11.04.01, and 11.04.02.

From September to June, steer a direct course from 10° N, 145° W to cross the equator in 152° W in December, January, and February; in 150° W from March to June; and in 152° W or 153° W in September, October, and November.

At whatever point the equator is crossed, cross the parallel of 10° S near 155° W, and thence pass S of Tonga Islands; cross the 180th meridian in 24° S to 25° S, and 160° E in 26° S to 27° S. Thence proceed to destination, passing N of Middleton Reef, if bound to Sydney making the coast S of Sandy cape. See 11.69.

Alternative seasonal routes were recommended by French authorities as follows:

From January to July, cross the parallel of 10° N in 143° W, and the equator in 148° W. In January, February and March no calms will be found between the North-east and South-east Trades. In April, May and June there will be only about 2 per cent of chances of calms in this region. From the equator steer for a position in 10° S, 155° W, and continue thence as directed above for September to June.

In July, August, and September, steer to 10° N, 148° W, and cross the equator between 150° W and 153° W. In this season, and if the precaution be taken not to follow a more E'ly route than that indicated, there will be only from 2 to 3 per cent of calms between 10° N and the equator. Thence proceed as directed above for January to July.

From October to January, steer to 10° N, 138° W, and cross the equator in 143° W. By following this route there will be only from 2 to 3 per cent chances of calms between the two Trade Wind regions. Farther to the W at this season, more calms are likely. Thence proceed as directed above for January to July.

11.97. San Francisco to Pacific islands. For the North Pacific islands, stand to the SW into the Trade Wind and the North Equatorial Current, and then run to the W in about 15° N as far as about 170° W; thence steer as directly as navigation permits to destination.

For Tahiti, steer SW on nearly the direct course to cross the equator in 140° W, or a little to the E, and then direct, allowing for the set of the South Equatorial Current.

For Samoa, Fiji, and islands to the W, steer from 10° N, 145° W as directed in 11.96 for the period September to May until arriving on the parallel of the island to which bound, and then run W on this parallel.

11.98. San Francisco to Panama. Making this passage between December and May inclusive, when the prevailing winds on the W coast of Mexico are from the N and the current is favourable, first obtain a good offing, and then stand down the coast of California, keeping about 100 miles off, and at about 150 miles off the coast of Mexico, shaping a course to make Isla Jicarita, the most S'ly of the islands S of Isla Coiba and about 55 miles W of Punta Mariato, which is a good landfall for vessels bound to Panama from the W.

Between June and November, inclusive, when calms, variable winds and oftentimes hurricanes prevail on the W coast of Mexico, stand well out to sea after passing San Francisco, and then shape a course to cross the equator in about 104° W; thence stand on to the S, until sure of reaching Panama on the other (starboard) tack.

Bound to Panama from the N, try to make Isla Jicarita (7° 13′ N, 81° 48′ W), and then try to keep under the land as far as Cabo Mala. If unable to do this, stand across for the opposite coast of the continent, when the current will be found favourable. On getting E of Cabo Mala the best plan is to shape a course for Isla Galera, and to use the passage E of Archipiélago de Las Perlas with caution, see Admiralty Sailing Directions. At the same time, if tempted up the gulf by a fair wind, try to get on the W side of Archipiélago de las Perlas, where anchorage and less current will be found if the wind should fail.

Off the coast N of Punta Guascama (2° 37′ N, 78° 25′ W), the winds become more variable and rains more frequent, and the following account by Dampier is perhaps as good as can be given:—"It is a very wet coast, and rains abundantly all the year. There are but few fair days, for there is little difference in the seasons of the year between the wet and dry; only in that season which should be dry the rains are less frequent and more moderate than in the wet season, for then it pours as out of a sieve." This kind of weather is found as far as Cabo Corrientes (5° 30′ N, 77° 33′ W), the prevailing wind being SW, but NE winds are not uncommon. Offshore in this zone, between the parallels of 2° N and 5° N, the winds are equally baffling, especially during March, April and May.

Between Cabo Corrientes and Panama, the prevailing winds are from the N and W, with frequent squalls and wet weather from the SW between June and October.

Within 60 miles of the coast there is a constant current to the N. After passing Cabo Mala (7° 28′ N, 80° 00′ W) it meets the Mexico Current from the WNW, and thus causes the numerous ripplings and short uneasy sea so often met with at the entrance of the Gulf of California. This troubled water will be found more or less to the S, according to the strength of the contending streams.

11.99. San Francisco to Callao or Iquique. Make an offing from San Francisco of about 300 miles to the SW; and then work round gradually to the S so as to cross 30° N in about 127° W. From this position make a straight course to the SSE roughly parallel with the coast, making for a position in 5° N, 110° W, about where the South-east Trades will be met. Stand through the Trades on the port tack to 20° S, 118° W.

From this position a course gradually approaching the coast may be made, as the Trade Wind is lost and the W'ly winds are felt. The most S'ly positions reached will be about 34° S, 110° W between September and November; about the parallel of 37° S from December to May; and an intermediate latitude in June, July, and August.

As the coast is neared, S'ly winds and a N-going current will be obtained, by which the destination may be reached. In any case make the port well to the S, in order to allow for the N-going current which runs the whole length of the South American coast.

11.100. San Francisco to Coquimbo, Valparaiso, and Coronel. Proceed as directed in 11.99, but do not attempt to make much easting after arriving in 20° S, 118° W until well to the S of 35° S.

Make the coast well S of destination, in order to allow for the N-going current which runs the whole length of this coast.

11.101. San Francisco to round Cabo de Hornos. Get a good offing of about 300 miles from San Francisco, and then stand nearly due S so as to cross the parallel of 5° N in about 126° W during December, January, and February; and between 120° W and 122° W during the rest of the year, being farthest E in March.

When the South-east Trades are met, stand to the S so as to cross the parallel of 30° S in about 124° W; and as soon as the Trades are lost and the W'ly winds picked up, as they will be in about 35° S, make as direct a course as possible to round Cabo de Hornos as directed in 9.66.01.

ROUTES FROM LOWER CALIFORNIA AND PANAMA

11.102. Lower California northward to North American ports. On account of the contrary S-going current, the only way to make a passage from any port of this coast to the N is to proceed W on the starboard tack until the variable winds are reached, in about 130° W, and then make northing, as directed in 11.89. From July to January vessels may have to stand on as far as 140° W.

Lumber vessels bound to Juan de Fuca Strait have found it advantageous to keep as near the land as practicable, in order to take advantage of the SE'ly storms, which work round to the SW. Rapid passages have been made in this manner.

5

10

15

20

25

30

35

40

45

50

55

60

65

70

11.103. Lower California to Pacific Ocean ports. For N-bound passages coastwise, see 11.102. For Honolulu and North Pacific islands, proceed direct when in the North-east Trades; see 11.91 and 11.97. For Sydney, steer to join the route from San Francisco (11.96) in 10° N, 145° W during June, July, and August; and at the equator at other times. For other Pacific Ocean destinations, steer SW to join the appropriate route from San Francisco in a convenient position.

11.104. Notes on passage out of Gulf of Panama. Bound in any direction from Panama, the chief difficulty is the passage out of the Gulf of Panama, for light and baffling winds or calms are met with there at all seasons.

Between October and April, the prevailing wind in the gulf is from the N; for the remainder of the year the wind hangs more to the W, and land and sea breezes are felt, varied by calms and occasional squalls from the SW. N of 5° N, between 80° W and 110° W, is a region of calms and light winds, varied by squalls of wind and rain; but S of 5° N, and W of the meridian of 80° W, between the mainland and Archipiélago de Colón, the wind is between S and W all the year round, and except between February and June, it is fairly strong. Whether bound N or S from Panama push to the S and gain the South-east Trade; by so doing the doldrums and vexatious winds will not only be avoided but there will be the additional advantage of salubrious weather.

11.105. Panama to Central America. The passage to ports along the coast of Central America is slow and troublesome to sailing vessels; advantage must be taken of every shift of wind to get to the NW. The currents will be with the ship as far as Golfo de Fonseca, but if bound for Acapulco or Mazatlan, the passage may be better made by standing off from the coast, after reaching Fonseca (*12° 54′ N, 87° 42′ W*).

If a "Norther" is blowing in Golfo de Tehuantepec, and sail can be carried, it is advisable to ease the sheets off and run well to the W, without seeking to make northing; if obliged to heave-to, from two to four days' heavy weather may be expected, with a high short sea, a clear sky overhead, and a dense red haze near the horizon. It is said that if the summits of Sierra Chimalapa are hidden about sunset by a slate-coloured vapour, a Norther will blow the following day; and if similar mists are seen on the ocean horizon at sunset, a SSW'ly wind will blow the next day.

11.106. Panama to San Francisco or Juan de Fuca Strait. From June to January, having left the Gulf of Panama (11.104), in order to gain the South-east Trade Winds, steer to pass N of Archipiélago de Colón keeping on about the parallel of 2° N until the meridian of 105° W is reached, then alter course to NW to pass W of Clipperton Island, in the neighbourhood of which the North-east Trade will be met; then stand to the NW to cross the parallel of 20° N in 120° W, and, if bound to San Francisco, stand NW as far as 35° N, 135° W; but if for Juan de Fuca Strait, keep on to the NW as far as 40° N, 138° W, then haul in for the coast as the wind allows, remembering always to make the land to windward of the desired port.

From February to May, inclusive, cross the equator between Archipiélago de Colón and the mainland, and run W until past 105° W; then alter course to NW to pass W of Clipperton Island and as for June to January.

11.107. Panama to Australia or New Zealand. Cross the equator, and pass S of Archipiélago de Colón into the South-east Trades as in 11.104 and 11.105. When in the South-east Trade, run SW to cross the meridian of 120° W in 11° S to 12° S and then W to pass S of Îles Marquises and N of Archipel des Tuamotu, and join the route from San Francisco (11.96) in 14° S or 15° S on the meridian of 160° W. (See also chart 5308).

If bound to New Zealand, leave the route to Sydney in about 170° W and proceed direct, noting that it is advisable, except when bound to Auckland, to pass down the W coast, and round the S of New Zealand, owing to the prevalence of W'ly winds.

If conditions are favourable when off Cook Strait, approach Wellington through it.

11.108. Passages from Panama to the southward are all slow and difficult for a sailing vessel, on account of the contrary coastal current, which sets N throughout the year, and the equally contrary light, but persistently S'ly winds.

The general opinion appears to be that, if bound for ports along the coast S as far as Callao, it is better to beat down the coast, but if bound to ports such as Mollendo, Iquique, Antofagasta, etc., it is better to make an offing into the Trade Winds, reach the coast by the westerlies S of 30° S, and then run N with a fair wind and current to the desired destination.

11.109. Panama to Golfo de Guayaquil. From the Gulf of Panama, make the best way S until between 5° N and the equator, and try, if possible, to keep near the meridian of 80° W; then make a SW'ly course if the winds will allow. If the wind is SW, stand to the S, but if SSW stand to the W, if a good working breeze; if the wind be light and baffling, with rain, the vessel is in the doldrums, and should get to the S as soon as possible, taking advantage of every slant of wind to Golfo de Guayaquil.

11.110. Panama to Callao. Follow the directions in 11.109 as far as Golfo de Guayaquil; then work close inshore as far as Islas Lobos de Afuera (*6° 57′ S, 80° 42′ W*). Approach these islands with care, see Admiralty Sailing Directions. Try always to be in with the land soon after the sun has set, so that advantage may be taken of the land breeze, which however light, usually begins about this time; this will frequently enable a vessel to make way nearly along shore throughout the night, and be in a good situation for the first of the sea breeze.

After having passed Islas Lobos de Afuera it would be advisable to work S until the latitude of Callao is approached; then stand in, and if it be not fetched, work S along shore, as above directed, remembering that the wind hauls to the E on leaving the coast. Some navigators attempt to make this passage by standing off for several days, hoping to fetch in well on the other tack, but this will generally be found a fruitless effort, owing to the N'ly current.

11.111. Panama to ports between Mollendo and Valparaiso. Follow the directions in 11.104 for leaving the Gulf of Panama according to season, and then, between June and January, stand to the W after crossing the parallel of 2° N, and pass N of Archipiélago de Colón, taking care to keep S of 5° N. S and SSW winds will persist as far as 85° W, but after passing that meridian the wind will haul round to the S, and vessels bound to the South Pacific may be considered fairly in the Trade.

From February to May, it is better to cross the equator between Archipiélago de Colón and the coast before proceeding to the W. This may probably take a week, which outlay of time, however, is far preferable to encountering the vexatious weather met in that season N of Archipiélago de Colón. In this route it must be remembered that S of 1° N the wind hauls to the E as the vessel leaves the coast, and in the longitude of 83° W it is frequently found E of S.

The seasonal routes from Panama, given above, passing N and S of Archipiélago de Colón, meet one another in about 20° S, 100° W; on reaching this position begin, if possible, to make southing and easting towards the coast, crossing 30° S, in about 95° W; and thence, as the W'ly winds and N-going current begin to be felt, and eventually the SW'ly and S'ly coast winds, gradually head for destination, always arranging to make the desired port to the S, on account of the current.

11.112. Panama to Cabo de Hornos. Proceed as directed in 11.111 to 20° S, 100° W, and then continue standing to the S, crossing 30° S between 102° W and 103° W; from this position or on reaching the W'ly winds, gradually curve round towards the SE, crossing the meridian of 90° W at about 50° S, being to the N from September to November and to the S from June to August. Round Cabo de Hornos as directed in 9.66.01.

ROUTES FROM SOUTH AMERICAN PORTS

11.113. Callao to Panama, Central America and Mexico. Stand N along the coast with a favourable current and a S'ly wind. See notes on winds, weather, and currents in 11.98.

To ports on the coast of Central America, N of the Gulf of Panama, follow the general directions in 11.105.

11.114. Callao to San Francisco or Juan de Fuca Strait. Stand out from the coast to pick up the South-east Trade, and then steer NW to cross the equator between the meridians of 112° W and 115° W, and the parallels of 5° N and 7° N in 115° W to 118° W, to join the route from Panama (11.106).

11.115. Callao to Australia or New Zealand. Steer W in the South-east Trade to join the route from Panama (11.107) in about 12° S, 122° W.

11.116. Callao to China, Philippine Islands, Japan, etc. Steer W in the South-east Trade to join the route from Valparaiso (11.123) in about 12° S, 122° W.

11.117. Callao to ports as far southward as 27° S. All of these ports lie within the area of the South-east Trade Wind, and it is therefore recommended normally to work along shore, from Bahía del Callao as far as Isla San Gallán, whence the coast trends more to the E, so that a long leg and a short one may be made (with the land just in sight) to Rada de Arica (*18° 29' S, 70° 21' W*) or to any of the ports between it and Bahía Pisco.

When proceeding from Callao to Bahía Pisco it is recommended to stand off the land at night, and towards it during the day until S of 13° S, when it is advisable to keep within 4 or 5 miles of the shore down to Bahía Pisco. For currents, see Admiralty Sailing Directions.

As an alternative, a very dull sailer might do better by running through the Trade and making southing in the offing, so as to return to the N along the coast, than by attempting to work to windward against a Trade Wind which never varies more than a few points.

Care is necessary when approaching Caldera in very light winds, as the current will tend to set the vessel on the rocks N of Punta Francisco.

11.118. Callao to ports south of 30° S. Bound to ports S of 30° S, there is no doubt that by standing offshore a quicker passage will be made than by working along the coast. Therefore, on leaving Bahía del Callao, stand well

5

10

15

20

25

30

35

40

45

50

55

60

65

70

out to the SW through the South-east Trade and, from January to March, cross the meridians of 90° W in 18° S, and 95° W in 30° S. From this position, as soon as the W'ly winds begin to be felt steer E for destination; making the desired port to the S on account of the current.

From April to December, a lesser offing from the coast will suffice, and on leaving Bahía del Callao, steer so as to cross the meridians of 85° W in 18° S, and 90° W in about 30° S, and thence as above described, making to the E to destination.

11.119. Callao to Cabo de Hornos. Follow the directions in 11.118, according to season, but on reaching the parallel of 30° S, continue on a S'ly course so as to cross the parallel of 50° S between 85° W and 90° W, being to the E from September to November, and to the W from June to August. Then steer to round Cabo de Hornos as directed in 11.101.

11.120. Valparaiso northward to ports in South America. Steer N along the coast. Calms and variable winds may be experienced in the vicinity of the parallel of 30° S, but S'ly winds, and a steady N-going current will be experienced throughout the remainder of the voyage.

11.121. Valparaiso to Panama, Central America, and Mexico. Stand to the NW, crossing the parallel of 30° S in about 77° W, and then standing N till on the parallel of Callao, from which position keep at a distance of about 150 miles from the land until reaching the Gulf of Panama.

If bound to ports in Central America and Mexico N of Panama proceed as directed in 11.105.

11.122. Valparaiso to San Francisco, Vancouver or Prince Rupert. The best route to pursue when making this voyage is the same at all times of the year. Leaving Valparaiso stand to the NW, passing E of Isla San Félix (*26° 19' S, 79 °54' W*), and crossing the parallel of 17° S in 90° W. With the South-east Trade Wind, steer to cross the equator in about 118° W. Continue NW into the North-east Trade Wind and cross the parallel of 20° N in 138° W, the parallel of 30° N in 142° W, and the parallel of 40° N in 140° W.

In May and June the North-east Trade Wind is often very weak to the N of 20° N, and frequently a belt of calm exists between 20° N and 30° N.

For San Francisco, after losing the North-east Trade, make to the E as soon as the W'ly winds are met with, which will be from about 33° N during the winter to 40° N in the summer up to the end of August; making allowance for the SE-going current.

Similarly, make for either Juan de Fuca Strait or Prince Rupert on reaching the parallel of 40° N at all times of the year; crossing the meridian of 130° W in 47° N before steering direct to destination. Prince Rupert may be approached either by Hecate Strait, or W of Queen Charlotte Islands. Allowance must be made for a SE-going current, setting across the track, and attention is called to the cautionary statements in 11.64.02.

11.123. Valparaiso to Philippine Islands, China or Japan. The passage may be made by using either the North-east or the South-east Trades. These two routes are described hereunder respectively as the Northerly Route and the Southerly Route.

The Northerly Route, for departures between August and February, passes through 12° S, 122° W, where vessels from Callao should join it, and continues through the South-east Trades to cross the equator in about 138° W, and the parallel of 10° N in about 143° W; the North-east Trades will be found near this parallel; thence continue as from North America, passing close S of the Hawaiian Islands, and joining the appropriate route from San Francisco to destination. References are for Philippine Islands, 11.95; Hong Kong 11.93 or 11.95; Shang-hai 11.94; Singapore 11.95; Nagasaki 11.94; Yokohama 11.92.

For the Southerly Route, which is recommended for departures between March to July, on leaving Valparaiso steer NW into the South-east Trades. Having found these, pass S of Îles Marquises, S of Gilbert Islands, and N of Caroline Islands, to a position in about 13° N, 130° E. At this point, join the "Second Eastern Passage" (10.46) from the Eastern Archipelago to China and Japan in the North-east Monsoon (October to March), E of the Philippines; and from April to September pass through San Bernardino Strait for Manila and the South China Sea. Bound to Yokohama leave the route when S of Gilbert Islands, cross the equator in about 168° E, and join the appropriate route from Sydney soon afterwards. See Chart 5308 and 11.07.

See also routes from San Francisco in 11.93, 11.94, and 11.95.

If there is a N'ly wind on leaving Valparaiso, stand W as long as it lasts and then NW into the South-east Trade. In the latitude of Valparaiso, during June, July and August, N'ly winds occasionally extend far across the Pacific.

11.124. Valparaiso to Australia or New Zealand. Steer to the NW to join the route from Panama described in 11.107, between the meridians of 120° W and 130° W, and between the parallels of 10° S and 12° S.

See note in 11.123 regarding leaving Valparaiso with a N'ly wind.

11.125. Valparaiso southward, and round Cabo de Hornos. The same rule prevails for rounding Cabo de Hornos as that from Callao (11.119) or from any port on the W coast of South America, namely, first to make an offing of between 500 and 600 miles to the SW, until the W'ly winds are steady and certain, and the strength of the NE-going current is lost.

From Valparaiso or Talcahuano the position to make for is about 40° S, 84° W. Thence stand nearly S, crossing 50° S in about 85° W. From this position, alter course gradually to the SE and E to round Cabo de Hornos, as directed in 11.101, and onward in 11.133.

5

ROUTES FROM CABO DE HORNOS

10

For directions for rounding Cabo de Hornos westbound, see 9.08.02.

11.126. Cabo de Hornos to Valparaiso. After passing the meridian of 70° W in about 57° S, as described in 9.08.02, stand NW and then N, keeping at a distance of about 150 miles from the land; begin to close the land at about 40° S. W'ly winds and a favourable current will be found from about 48° S. Make the landfall S of destination.

15

Some navigators prefer to stand farther to the NW to about 50° S, 80° W, before turning N and steering for destination.

20

11.127. Cabo de Hornos to ports in South America northward of Valparaiso. After rounding Cabo de Hornos (9.08.02), and bound to ports on the W coast of South America, and when W of the meridian of Cabo Pilar (or about 75° W), take every opportunity of making westing until the meridian of 82° W or 84° W be reached; thence steer direct, or as nearly so as is consistent with making use of the steady winds which prevail in the offing, for the intended port, being careful not to get to leeward of it on approaching the land.

25

11.128. Cabo de Hornos to Panama, Central America, and Mexico. Proceed as directed in 11.127, until reaching the meridian of 82° W or 84° W, and then steer N to close the land until it is about 60 miles distance when off, or just N of Golfo de Guayaquil. After crossing the equator steer for Isla Galera (*8° 30′ N, 79° 00′ W*), at the same time taking care, especially in the dry season, to stand inshore with the first N'ly winds. By so doing, vessels will most probably have the current in their favour along the coast, whereas by keeping in the centre, or on the W side of the gulf, a strong S'ly set will be experienced.

30

35

After making Isla Galera and clearing Banco San José, navigation towards Panama between Archipiélago de las Perlas and the mainland is clear and easy, with the advantage of being able to anchor during adverse conditions of wind and tide. As a rule the passage E of the islands should be taken, but with a strong S'ly wind the navigator is tempted to run up the gulf, in which case he should keep towards the W side of Archipiélago de la Perlas, where anchorage and less current will be found if the wind should fail, an event always to be expected in these regions.

40

Bound to ports in Central America or Mexico, N of the Gulf of Panama, proceed generally as directed in 11.105.

11.129. Cabo de Hornos to San Francisco and northward. For San Francisco, having rounded Cabo de Hornos as directed in 9.08.02, stand to the NW so as to cross the parallel of 50° S between 80° W and 85° W, and then due N to 30° N. Thence keep off to the NW, running through the South-east Trades to cross the equator between 112° W and 115° W, being to the E, throughout the whole voyage from Cabo de Hornos, from September to November; and to the W from June to August.

45

After crossing the equator, steer so as to cross the meridian of 120° W in 13° N to 15° N, where the route divides into two branches, according to season.

50

From November to February, make for 30° N, 132° W, and from that position, when the W'ly winds are met, curve gradually round towards San Francisco, making it to the N, and allowing for the current setting SE across the track.

From March to October, make for 30° N, 137° W, and turn towards the land when the W'ly winds are reached at about 35° N; again allowing for the SE-going current across the track.

55

For Columbia River, Juan de Fuca Strait, or Prince Rupert, follow the routes given above as far as 30° N; then continue to the NW, curving to the E on reaching, or nearing the parallel of 45° N, to make destination, allowing for the current as above.

60

11.130. Cabo de Hornos to Honolulu. Follow the directions given in 11.129 as far as 30° S, or, if necessary, a little farther N to enter the South-east Trade Wind; then proceed as directly as possible, crossing the equator between 120° W and 125° W.

65

11.131. Cabo de Hornos to Philippine Islands, China, Japan, Australia or New Zealand. Follow the directions given in 11.129 as far as 30° S, and then run in the South-east Trades to about 12° S, 122° W, to join the route from Valparaiso (11.123) for the Philippine Islands, China, or Japan; or the route from Panama (11.107) for Australia or New Zealand.

70

11.132. Cabo de Hornos to Pacific Islands. Follow the directions given in 11.129 as far as 30° S, 85° W, and then run WNW in the South-east Trade Wind, passing S of Pitcairn Island, thence direct to Tahiti or other destination.

For islands in the W part of the North Pacific Ocean, after crossing 30° S, run in the South-east Trade to about 12° S, 122° W, to join the most N'ly route from Valparaiso to the Philippine Islands, China, or Japan (11.123). Leave this route in about 175° E if bound to Marshall Islands, or in 160° E or 165° E if bound to Caroline Islands or farther W; and proceed direct to destination. The route to Honolulu is given in 11.130.

For islands in the W part of the South Pacific Ocean, proceed either via Tahiti as above, and thence, after reaching the parallel of destination, direct; or alternatively by the route given in 11.107 as far as about 160° W, and then to destination.

General Index

See Articles 1.12, 1.13.

References in italics are for Sailing routes, Chapters 9, 10, 11

Printed in England for HER MAJESTY'S STATIONERY OFFICE
by the Hydrographic Department, Ministry of Defence (Navy).

C.B.H. 01732 - Dd. 568880 - 10,000 - 7/76